Essential Maths 9 Higher

David Rayner

Elmwood Education

First published 2015 by
Elmwood Education
Unit 5
Mallow Park
Watchmead
Welwyn Garden City
Herts. AL7 1GX
Tel. 01707 333232

ISBN 9781 906 622 350

Numerical answers are published in a separate book
ISBN 9781 906 622 381

Typeset and illustrated by Tech-Set Ltd., Gateshead, Tyne and Wear.

PREFACE

Essential Maths Book 9 Higher has been written for pupils who are working towards the revised 2015 National Curriculum Levels 7 and 8. Level 6 work is consolidated and then developed further.

Although there is no set path through the books, the topics appear in the order suggested in the National Numeracy Strategy guide. Broadly speaking, the book is split into 6 units. Each unit of work can be used during one half-term with appropriate revision material at the end of the unit. Many topics are reviewed later in the book, in line with the NNS guide.

Puzzle activities and mental arithmetic tasks can be found between the units, to be used whenever appropriate. Investigations appear regularly throughout the book. Ideas for discussing and exploring themes from the 'history of mathematics' are included between each pair of units.

The author believes that children learn mathematics most effectively by *doing* mathematics. Many youngsters who find mathematics difficult derive much more pleasure and enjoyment from the subject when they are doing questions which help them build up their confidence. Pupils feel a greater sense of satisfaction when they work in a systematic way and when they can appreciate the purpose and the power of the mathematics they are studying.

No textbook will have the 'right' amount of material for every class. The authors believe that it is preferable to have too much material rather than too little. Opportunities for functional maths are incorporated into activities throughout the book.

Most work is broken down into two parts. 'M' exercises are aimed at all children at this level. 'E' exercises provide extension work. Pupils may move naturally onto this work after an 'M' exercise or teachers may judge that a number of students should *only* tackle 'E' exercises.

Pupil self-assessment is a very important part of assessment for learning. Regular 'check yourself' sections appear throughout the book. Answers to these parts only are provided at the back of the book for immediate feedback.

The author is indebted to Micheline and Louise for their invaluable contributions to this book.

David Rayner

CONTENTS

Unit 1 Page
1.1 Working with numbers 1
1.2 Using algebra 12
1.3 Congruent shapes and construction 23
1.4 Geometrical reasoning 26
1.5 Data handling 34
1.6 Multiplying brackets 44
Unit 1 Mixed Review 49
Puzzles and Problems 1 53

Unit 2
2.1 Using fractions 56
2.2 Working with indices 64
2.3 Standard form 71
2.4 Applying mathematics in a range of contexts 1 78
2.5 Scatter graphs 85
2.6 Trial and improvement 89
Unit 2 Mixed Review 96

Unit 3
3.1 Shape and space – mixed problems 106
3.2 Sequences – finding the rule 115
3.3 Rounding, estimating, errors and bounds 123
3.4 Drawing and visualising 3D shapes 132
3.5 Percentage change 138
Unit 3 Mixed Review 146

Unit 4 Page
4.1 Transformations, single and combined 158
4.2 Reading and interpreting charts and graphs 164
4.3 Area and volume 183
4.4 Collecting and interpreting data 198
4.5 Applying mathematics in a range of contexts 2 205
4.6 Simultaneous equations 212
4.7 Sequences 221
Unit 4 Mixed Review 231

Unit 5
5.1 Trigonometry 247
5.2 Inequalities 263
5.3 Probability 270
5.4 Gradient of a line, $y = mx + c$ 280
5.5 Mathematical reasoning, proof 285
Unit 5 Mixed Review 293

Unit 6
6.1 Drawing and using graphs 303
6.2 Compound measures – speed, distance, time, density 307
6.3 Locus 314
6.4 Changing the subject of a formula 319
6.5 Similar shapes 324
6.6 Simple interest 332
Unit 6 Mixed Review 333

UNIT 1

1.1 Working with numbers

In section 1.1 you will:

- review paper and pencil calculations
- work with prime numbers, factors and multiples
- review the correct order of operations and inverse operations
- use a calculator efficiently
- calculate with negative numbers
- practise long multiplication and division

(a) $7 \times 0.2 = 7 \times \frac{2}{10} = (7 \times 2) \div 10 = 14 \div 10 = 1.4$

(b) $21.12 \div 6$

$$6\overline{)2\,1\,.\,^{3}1\,^{1}2}\quad = 3.52$$

(c) $28 - 3.4$

$$\begin{array}{r} 2\,^{7}\not{8}.\,^{1}0 \\ -\ \ 3.\,4 \\ \hline 2\,4.\,6 \end{array}$$

(d) $8.5 \div 0.5 = 85 \div 5$
$= 17$

Multiply both numbers by 10 so that we can divide by a whole number

Exercise 1M

Work out, without a calculator

1. $6728 - 685$
2. $3800 - 175$
3. $4.18 + 29$
4. 3.24×2000
5. 8×0.3
6. 15×0.7
7. 0.2×0.8
8. 0.3×0.2
9. $485 \div 100$
10. $2003 \div 1000$
11. $49.44 \div 6$
12. $6286 + 941$
13. $48.65 \div 7$
14. $0.78 - 0.536$
15. $0.02 \times 10\,000$
16. 73×0.01
17. 4.3×0.1
18. 0.6×0.1
19. $6100 - 225$
20. $10^4 - 4321$

21 A bank is selling euros at the rate of 1.147 euros for one pound sterling. Find the cost in euros for £20 000.

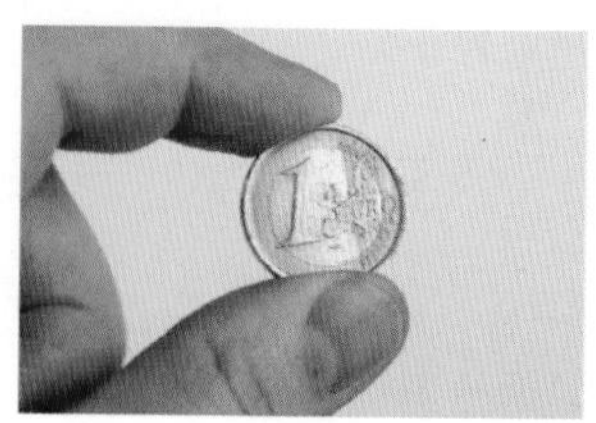

22 How many 0.3 litre cartons of apple juice are needed to give 7.2 litres in total?

23 Which is larger: 0.1×0.2 or $0.5 \div 10$?

24 Work out

(a) $14 \div 0.2$ (b) $8.4 \div 0.04$ (c) $209 \div 0.01$ (d) $0.72 \div 0.002$

Exercise 1E

Work out

1 $18 - 5 \times 2$

2 $65 - 6 \times 2$

3 $3^2 - 30 \div 5$

4 $20 \div 5 + 7$

5 $8 + 12 \div 4$

6 $20 - (4 + 11)$

7 $36 + 2^2$

8 $(8 - 5)^2 + 1$

9 $16 - 2^4$

10 $2 + 3 \times 4 + 1$

11 $(14 - 2) \div (3^2 + 3)$

12 $(7 - 6)^5 + 11$

13 $(37 + 42) \div (2^3 + 2)$

14 $(9^2 - 4^3) \div 34$

15 $\dfrac{(4^2 - 6) \times 10}{12 - 7}$

Remember:

Brackets
Indices
Divide
Multiply
Add
Subtract

Copy each question and write brackets so that each calculation gives the correct answer.

16 $6 \times 8 - 2 = 36$

17 $9 + 12 \times 5 = 105$

18 $4 + 5 \times 5 = 45$

19 $11 + 7 \times 3 = 32$

20 $22 - 10 \times 6 = 72$

21 $8 \times 6 - 4 = 16$

22 $5 \times 6 - 4 \div 2 = 13$

23 $81 \div 9 \times 12 - 4 = 104$

24 $9 + 8 \div 4 \times 0 = 0$

25 $3 + 5 \times 9 - 7 = 16$

Inverse operations

The word inverse means 'opposite'.

- The inverse of adding is subtracting
- The inverse of subtracting is adding
- The inverse of multiplying is dividing
- The inverse of dividing is multiplying

$\square\,\square \div 4 = 18$

Work out 18×4 because multiplying is the inverse of dividing.

Exercise 2M

Copy and complete.

1 (a) $\begin{array}{r} 3\;7\;5 \\ +\;\square\;4\;2 \\ \hline 6\;\square\;\square \end{array}$ (b) $\begin{array}{r} 6\;2\;\square \\ +\;\square\;5\;4 \\ \hline 7\;\square\;3 \end{array}$ (c) $\begin{array}{r} \square\;7\;6 \\ +\;3\;4\;\square \\ \hline 9\;\square\;9 \end{array}$

2 (a) $\begin{array}{r} 6\;7\;9 \\ +\;2\;\square\;5 \\ \hline \square\;3\;\square \end{array}$ (b) $\begin{array}{r} 3\;\square\;4 \\ +\;4\;8\;9 \\ \hline \square\;7\;3 \end{array}$ (c) $\begin{array}{r} 6\;8\;7 \\ +\;\square\;9\;\square \\ \hline 9\;\square\;3 \end{array}$

3 (a) $\begin{array}{r} 4\;\square \\ \times\quad 6 \\ \hline 2\;6\;4 \end{array}$ (b) $\begin{array}{r} 8\;\square \\ \times\quad 7 \\ \hline \square\;8\;1 \end{array}$ (c) $\begin{array}{r} \square\;\square\;5 \\ \times\quad 8 \\ \hline 2\;6\;0\;0 \end{array}$

4 (a) $\square\square\square \div 7 = 35$ (b) $\square\square \times 13 = 182$

(c) $15 \times \square = 120$ (d) $\square\square\square \div 9 = 108$

5 There is more than one correct answer for each of these questions. Ask a friend to check your solution.

(a) $\boxed{3}\boxed{8} - \square\square + \square\square = 37$

(b) $\boxed{4}\boxed{2} \times \square \div \square = 21$

(c) $\boxed{1}\boxed{5} \times \square\square \div \square = 45$

6 Each of these calculations has the same number missing from all three boxes. Find the missing number in each calculation.

(a) $\square \times \square - \square = 42$

(b) $\square \div \square + \square = 7$

(c) $\square \times \square + \square = 90$

7 In the circle write +, –, × or ÷ to make the calculation correct.

(a) $8 \times 7 \bigcirc 2 = 54$ (b) $6 \times 8 \bigcirc 3 = 16$

(c) $5 \bigcirc 6 + 3 = 2$ (d) $60 \div 5 \bigcirc 8 = 20$

8 (a) $\begin{array}{r} 7\;\square\;6 \\ -\;3\;8\;\square \\ \hline \square\;6\;3 \end{array}$ (b) $\begin{array}{r} 6\;\square\;4 \\ -\;\square\;4\;\square \\ \hline 2\;0\;5 \end{array}$ (c) $\begin{array}{r} \square\;6\;\square \\ -\;4\;\square\;5 \\ \hline 3\;8\;8 \end{array}$

9 (a) $\dfrac{30(7 - \square)}{8} = 17 - 6 \div 3$ (b) $(11 - 6)(\square + 2) = 6^2 + 2^3 + 1$

Factors, multiples, prime numbers

Exercise 3M

The factors of 10 are 1, 2, 5, 10
The multiples of 10 are 10, 20, 30, 40, . . .

1 Write down all the factors of:

(a) 12 (b) 15 (c) 24

2 Write down the first four multiples of:

(a) 7 (b) 20 (c) 15

3 Work out the lowest common multiple (L.C.M.) of:

(a) 4 and 6 (b) 6 and 8 (c) 5 and 8

4 Find the highest common factor (H.C.F.) of:

(a) 12 and 20 (b) 36 and 45 (c) 30 and 42

5 Answer 'true' or 'false':

(a) 'Any multiple of 6 must be a multiple of 12.'

(b) 'Any factor of 60 must be a factor of 30.'

6 Write as ordinary numbers

(a) 5^2 (b) 10^3 (c) $6^2 - 1^2$ (d) $\sqrt{144}$

(e) $\sqrt{17^2}$ (f) $\sqrt[3]{27}$ (g) $1^3 + 2^3 + 3^3$ (h) $\sqrt[3]{1000}$

7 (a) How many dots are there on one die?
(b) Express the number you obtained in part (a) as the sum of three square numbers.

8 The number x is a multiple of 7 between 50 and 60. The number y is a multiple of 8 between 100 and 110.

(a) Work out $x + y$.

(b) Write down all the factors of $x + y$.

Exercise 3E

1 Write down a list of all the prime numbers below 20.

2 Which of these numbers are prime? 39 71 41 47 91 93 81

3 As a product of primes, a number is given by $2^3 \times 5 \times 7$.
What is the number?

4 Write 42 as a product of primes.

5 Copy and complete these prime factor trees.

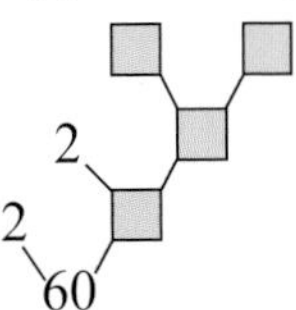

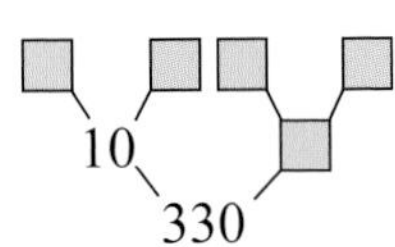

6 Consider the whole numbers from 1 to 100 inclusive. How many of these numbers are:

(a) multiples of 5

(b) factors of 5

(c) prime numbers ending in 5?

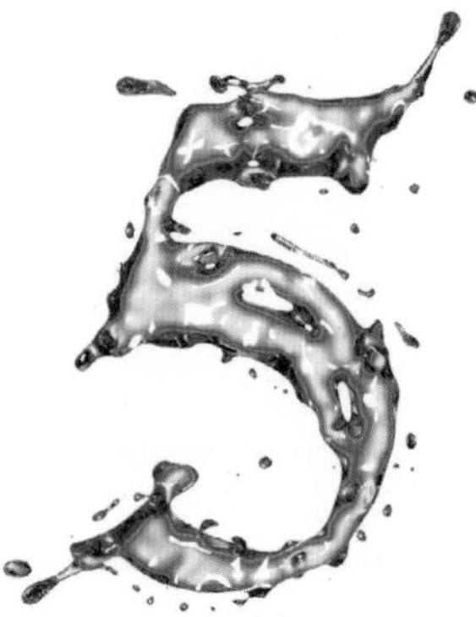

7 Make six prime numbers using the digits shown once each

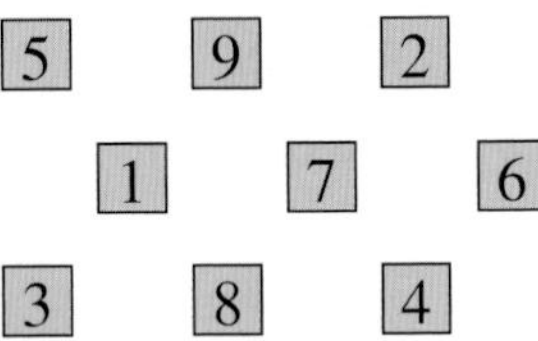

8 (a) Is 313 a prime number?

By which numbers do you need to divide 313 so that you can find out?

(b) Suppose you wanted to know whether or not 817 is a prime number. By which numbers do you need to divide 817 to find out?

(c) Is 817 prime?

Ratio and proportion

Exercise 4M

1 Write each ratio in its simplest form

(a) 4:20 (b) 12:16 (c) 18:12 (d) 20 to 30

2 Write the following ratios in their simplest form

(a) 5 cm to 55 cm (b) £39 to £13 (c) 1p to £1

(d) 50p to £5 (e) 10 cm to 1 m (f) 200g to 1 kg

3 Divide £30 between 2 people in the ratio 1:2.

4 Divide the amounts in the ratios stated

(a) £40 in the ratio 2:3

(b) £2000 in the ratio 3:7

(c) 36 kg in the ratio 1:2:3

5 What proportion of this diagram is shaded?
Give your answer as a fraction.

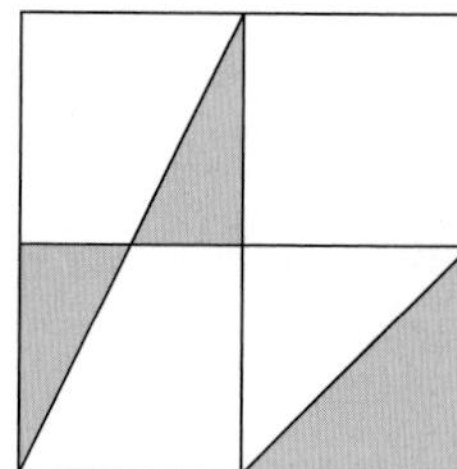

6 In a mixed class of 25 children, there are 16 girls. What proportion of the class are boys?

7 A triangle has one angle that is three times the size of another. The third angle is 92°.
Find the size of the other two angles.

Inverse proportion

Example 1

Eight men can dig a hole in four hours. How long will it take five men to dig the same size hole?

8 men take 4 hours.
1 man would take 32 hours.
5 men would take $\frac{32}{5}$ hours = 6 hours 24 minutes.

Exercise 4E

1 Three workers build a wall in 10 days. How long would it take five men?

2 A car uses 10 litres of petrol in 75 km. How far will it go on 8 litres?

3 A wire 11 cm long has a mass of 187 g. What is the mass of 7 cm of this wire?

4 A shop owner can buy 36 cans for £20.52. What will he pay for 120 cans?

5 A ship has enough food to feed 600 passengers for 3 weeks. How long would the food last for 800 people?

6 Three men can build a wall in 10 hours. How many men would be needed to build the wall in $7\frac{1}{2}$ hours?

7 A carpet in a dolls house is made to a scale of 1:12. The area of the carpet in the dolls house is 72 cm². Calculate the area of the actual carpet, giving your answer in square metres.

Inverse proportion – algebraic method

If you travel a distance of 200 m at 10 m/s, the time taken is 20 s. If you travel the same distance at 20 m/s, the time taken is 10 s. For a fixed journey, the time taken is *inversely proportional* to the speed of travel.
If s is inversely proportional to t you write $s \propto \frac{1}{t}$ or $s = k \times \frac{1}{t}$ where k is a constant (a number).

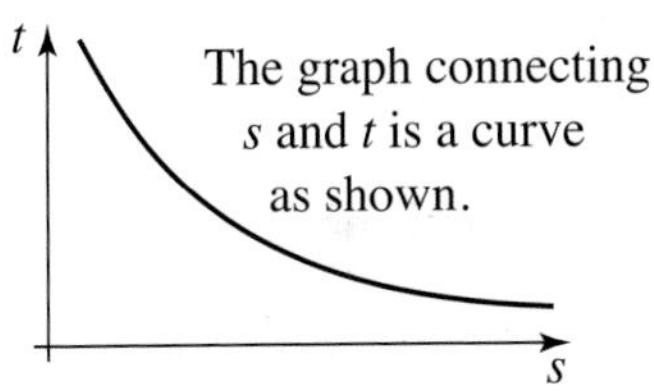

z is inversely proportional to t^2 and $z = 4$ when $t = 1$.
Calculate z when $t = 2$.

$z \propto \frac{1}{t^2}$ or $z = k \times \frac{1}{t^2}$

$z = 4$ when $t = 1$

so $4 = k \times \frac{1}{1^2}$

so $k = 4$

So $z = 4 \times \frac{1}{t^2}$ and when $t = 2$, $z = 4 \times \frac{1}{2^2} = 1$.

Exercise 5M

1 Rewrite the statements connecting the variables using a constant k.

(a) $x \propto \frac{1}{y}$ (b) $s \propto \frac{1}{t^2}$ (c) $t \propto \frac{1}{m^2}$.

2 T is inversely proportional to m. If $T = 12$ when $m = 1$, find

(a) T when $m = 2$ (b) T when $m = 24$.

3 L is inversely proportional to x. If $L = 24$ when $x = 2$, find

(a) L when $x = 8$ (b) L when $x = 32$.

4 b is inversely proportional to e. If $b = 6$ when $e = 2$, calculate

(a) the value of b when $e = 12$ (b) the value of e when $b = 3$.

Exercise 5E

Work out

1 $\frac{2}{5}+\frac{1}{3}$ 2 $\frac{5}{6}-\frac{1}{3}$ 3 $\frac{2}{9}+\frac{1}{3}$

The $a\frac{b}{c}$ key is used for fractions

4 $\frac{2}{7}-\frac{1}{4}$ 5 $\frac{3}{5}-\frac{1}{4}$ 6 $\frac{4}{9}\times\frac{11}{12}$

7 $3\frac{3}{4}+1\frac{2}{5}$ 8 $5\frac{1}{12}-3\frac{1}{4}$ 9 $3\frac{1}{2}\div\frac{3}{4}$

10 $\left(\frac{2}{5}-\frac{1}{8}\right)\times\frac{1}{4}$ 11 $\left(\frac{2}{7}+\frac{1}{2}\right)\times\frac{3}{10}$ 12 $\left(1\frac{2}{3}+\frac{1}{4}\right)^2$

13 $\left(\frac{3}{8}-\frac{1}{5}\right)\div\frac{2}{3}$ 14 $\left(\frac{2\frac{1}{5}-1\frac{1}{4}}{\frac{1}{4}-\frac{1}{5}}\right)$ 15 $\frac{5}{8}\div\left(\frac{1}{2}+\frac{1}{3}\right)$

16 Copy and complete.

(a) $\square+5\frac{2}{5}=7\frac{1}{4}$ (b) $\frac{2}{3}\div\square-\frac{1}{5}=1\frac{2}{15}$

(c) $\left(2\frac{3}{4}-\square\right)\div\frac{2}{5}=3\frac{1}{8}$ (d) $\left[\square^2+1\frac{1}{3}\right]\times\frac{3}{5}=1\frac{11}{80}$

Calculator words

On a calculator the number 4506 spells the word 'Gosh' when held upside down. You have to use your imagination with some letters. For example a zero can either be an 'O' or a 'D'. The number 0.7D reads 'Old' when held upside down. (You ignore the decimal point.)

Use a calculator to find the missing words in the story below.

When the $\left[750^2+150\,000+\sqrt{1\,452\,025}\right]$ came up,

$[50^2\times 3+15^2-7]$ took his $\left[(3.3\times 10^2+2.7\times 10^2)^2+\frac{150}{0.4}\right]$ to the $[2777^2+2889$ (two words)$]$ to collect some snow for his $[0.2^2\times 1.9025]$.

While there, he met a $[904^2+89\,621\,818]$ called $[0.4^2-0.1^2]$.

Remember: 0 can be '0' or 'D'

Now [1.5% of 10] was a rather $\left[\frac{323.6-289.5}{154.6+45.4}\right]$ animal who had just offended $[6.2\times 0.987\times 1\,000\,000-860^2+118]$ the $[(5\times 10^3+3\times 10^4)+6]$ because, without thinking, he had $\left[\sqrt{0.1369}+(1.2\times 0.03^2)\right]$ his $[5\times 58^4+48\,226$ (two words)$]$ So $[2318\times 2319+2^3\times 3\times 7^2]$ started to $\left[(6.1\times 25)\times\sqrt[3]{64}\right]$ a $[60^2+10^2+2^2]$ to $[(50\times 60)+(2\times 7)]$ in where he could $[(5^2\times 6\times 2)+(2\times 5)+6+1]$ in wait for $[\frac{1}{8}+\frac{1}{40}]$. This meant that he could take his revenge on the $[448\times 449\times 450-17^4+4155]$ by spraying him with a $[(0.6^2+0.8^2)\times 4+(5^3\times 2^2\times 7)]$. But meanwhile, $[(\frac{1}{2})^2 - (\frac{1}{2} \text{ of } \frac{1}{5})]$ had heard of the plan, and so he asked $[2 \times (2^4 + 1^7) \times 227]$ to pretend to be a $[34 \times 35 \times 36 \times 37 \times 38 + 451^2 - 407]$.

When $\left[(11 \times 12)^2 + 174 \times 175 \times 176 - \left(\frac{3}{0.5}\right)\right]$ heard $[7 \times 11 \times 10^2 + (3^2 \times 2)]$

coming, he jumped up onto a $\left[\frac{(2^2 \times 4 \times 5^2 \times 6)}{4} + 7\right]$ so quickly that $[(22\frac{3}{5} + \frac{1}{10}) \times 340]$ did not have

time to $[\frac{73}{100} + 1.45 \times 10^{-3}]$ himself from the $\left[\sqrt{(700.8 \div 0.2)^2} \times 0.5 \times 2\right]$.

However, $[0.4^2 - 0.3^2 + 2(0.2^2)]$, was already hiding on the $\left[2 \times \sqrt{\sqrt{\left(\frac{7^4}{4^2}\right)}} + (63 - \sqrt{9}) \times 5 \times 2\right]$,

and he stabbed the $\left[3.5 \times 10^4 + \frac{6 \times 5 \times 4 \times 3 \times 2}{5 \times 4 \times 3 \times 2}\right]$ with his prickles to protect his

friend. Unfortunately, $\left[15\,483 \times 300 - 1 + 89^3 + \frac{642}{0.2 \times 0.3 \times 0.4}\right]$ could not carry out his plans for

revenge, because he had all the

Never-Say-$\left[\left(\frac{1}{\left(\frac{1}{2}\right)^5} - 1\right) \div \left(\frac{0.021}{0.21}\right)\right]$ qualities of a kamikaze pilot,

so at the first $\left[\frac{10^3}{2^3} \times \left(\frac{\sqrt{2^6}}{0.331 - 0.206}\right) + 2.5\% \text{ of } 3120\right]$ of

$[13 \times 6 \div 100^2]$, he gave up and $\left[3.4 \times 10^{-4} + \left(\frac{191}{382}\right)^2 + \frac{1\frac{1}{2}}{5^2}\right]$.

Negative numbers

Exercise 6M

Work out

1. $-2 + 6$
2. $6 - 9$
3. $-4 - 3$
4. $10 - 15$
5. $-7 - 3$
6. $-10 + 13$
7. $18 - 14$
8. $-7 + 7$
9. $3 + (-4)$
10. $8 - (-2)$
11. $6 + (-6)$
12. $10 - (-3)$
13. $-4 - (-6)$
14. $7 + (-8)$
15. $8 - (-18)$
16. $-4 + (-4)$
17. $(-3) \times 4$
18. $(-5) \times (-2)$
19. $12 \times (-1)$
20. $(-8) \times (-3)$

21 $(-2) \times (-3)$ 22 $4 \times (-5)$ 23 -7×7 24 -6×0

25 $6 \div (-2)$ 26 $-8 \div 4$ 27 $10 \div (-2)$ 28 $(-8) \div (-4)$

29 $-8 + 15$ 30 $-7 - 30$ 31 $8 - (-4)$ 32 $(-7) \times (-5)$

Copy and complete these magic squares.

33

		3
	0	
−3	2	

34

		−2
	1	
4		−1

35

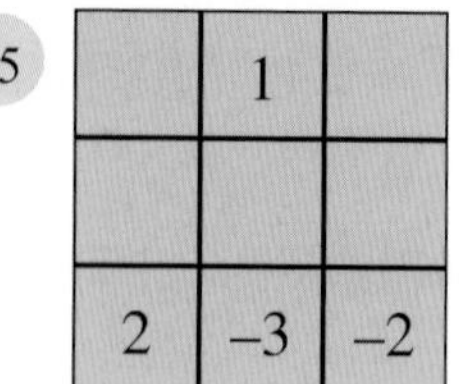

	1	
2	−3	−2

Exercise 6E

Find the letters

Perform each calculation and write down the corresponding letter from the list below, to make a sentence.

A. $5 - 8$; $-3 - 2$; $(-2)^2$; $3^2 - 20$; $6 \div (-6)$; $(-2)^2 + 3$; $-5 + (-3)$; $(-49) \div (-7)$; $-3 - (-5)$; $(-5) \times (-1)$; $-7 + 11$; $4^2 - 4$; $-1 + 13$; $(-1)^2 \times 4$; $30 \div (-10)$; $-2 + 9$; $(-3\frac{1}{2}) \times 2$; $(-8) \div (-2)$; $(-1) \div \frac{1}{10}$; $8 - 11$; $(-7)^2 + (-1)^2$; $-6 - 5$; $(-10) \times \frac{1}{2}$; $-3 + 10$; $(-2)^3 - 2$; $3 - (-5)$; $(-3) \times (-4)$; $(-16) \div (-2)$; $2 \div (-4)$? $(-6 - 2) \times (-1)$; $2 \times (-5)^2$; $(-6)^2 \div 3$; $(-2) \times (-2) \times 2$; $-5 + 13$; $-12 - (-2)$.

B. $-11 + 8$; $-3 + (-2)$; $(-2)^2$; $1 - 12$; $3 \times (-1)$; $1 - (-6)$; $-2 + 4$; $(-3) \times (-4)$; $6 \div (-6)$; $(-16) \div 2$; $(-3\frac{1}{2}) \times (-2)$; $2^2 - 2$; $1 \div (\frac{1}{2})$; $-7 - (-7)$; $(-3)^2 - 1$; $-3 - 8$; $(-14) \div (-2)$; $-3 + 8$; $-8 + 15$; $(-1)^2 + (-1)^2$; $(-5) \times 2$; $-1 - 10$; $(-2) \div (-\frac{1}{2})$; $-2 - 2 - 1$; 2^3; $4 + (-6)$; $(-1)^5$; $-3 + 10$; $(-6) \div (-1)$; $2 - (-3)$; $(-3 - 4) \times (-1)$; $19 - 22$; $(-5) \times 0$?

$(-2)^3 \div (-2)$; $-2 + 7$; $1 - (-6)$; $3 \times (-1)$; $(-50) \div (-10)$; 0.1×20; $3^2 + 2^2 - 1^2$; $(-1) \div (-\frac{1}{4})$; $(-2)^3 - 3$; $\frac{1}{7} \times 49$; $4^3 - 66$.

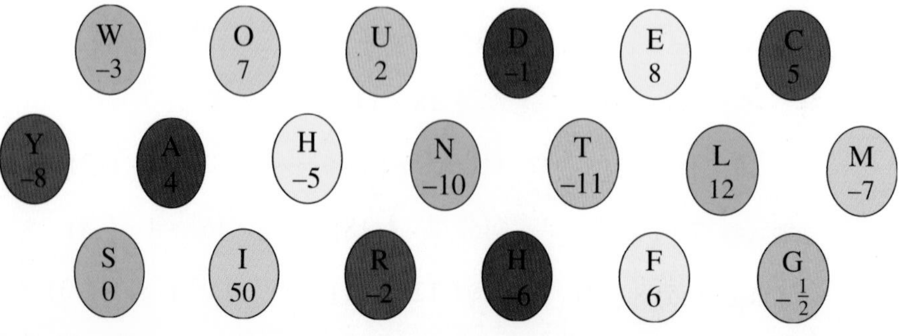

Long multiplication and division

```
   5 4
×  2 3
  1 6 2      (3 × 54)
1 0 8 0      (20 × 54)
1 2 4 2
```

```
      1 6 remainder 15
  17) 2 8 7
    − 1 7↓
      1 1 7
    − 1 0 2  ←(6 × 17)
        1 5
```

Exercise 7M (No calculators!)

Work out

1. 28 × 24
2. 53 × 27
3. 45 × 35
4. 127 × 23
5. 208 × 33
6. 248 × 43
7. 555 ÷ 15
8. 774 ÷ 43
9. 1104 ÷ 24
10. 4452 ÷ 53
11. 784 ÷ 26
12. 516 ÷ 37
13. Every day 213 slaves each had to carry 58 huge stones to build a temple. How many stones were carried altogether in 10 days?

14. A storage tank contains 5375 litres of oil. Each day 42 litres are used. After how many days will the tank be empty?
15. It cost £26 520 to lay 17 km of electric cable. Calculate the cost per km for this cable.
16. A shop keeper bought 232 melons at 58p each. How much did he spend altogether?
17. How many 42-seater coaches will be needed for a school trip for a party of 516?

Fractions, decimals, percentages

Exercise 8M

1. Change to fractions.

   (a) 80% (b) 0.15 (c) 0.05 (d) 9%

2 Change to decimals.

(a) 63% (b) $\frac{3}{4}$ (c) $\frac{5}{8}$ (d) 4%

3 Change to percentages.

(a) 0.21 (b) $\frac{2}{5}$ (c) $\frac{1}{4}$ (d) 0.99

4 Write in order, smallest first.

(a) $\frac{1}{5}$, 0.19, 22% (b) 0.035, 4%, $\frac{1}{20}$

5 What percentage of the diagram is shaded?

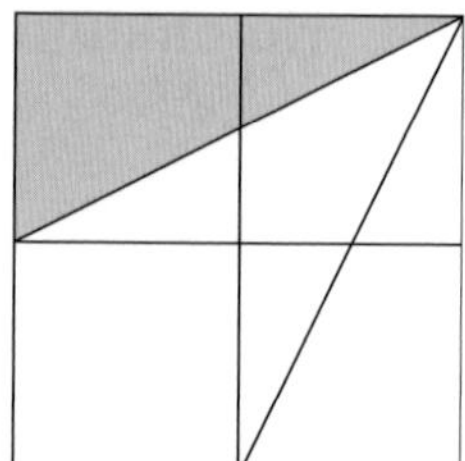

6 Work out.

(a) 7% of 2.5 kg (answer in grams)

(b) 16% of £3.50 (answer in pence)

(c) 30% of 11 cm (answer in mm)

(d) 4% of 10 hours (answer in minutes)

7 What percentage of the numbers from 1 to 100 inclusive are square numbers?

8 Work out 4% of $\frac{3}{4}$ of 22% of $\frac{2}{(0.1)^3}$.

1.2 Using algebra

In this section you will:

- revise important rules of algebra, including brackets
- solve linear equations
- solve problems using algebra
- learn how to factorise expressions

Simplifying terms

Simplify the following expressions

$5x + 3y - x = 4x + 3y$ $4n \times 3 = 12n$ $10m \div 2 = 5m$

$a \times a = a^2$ $2a \times a = 2a^2$ $5n \times 3n = 15n^2$

$8n \div 2 = 4n$ $5m^2 \div m = 5m$ $(2n)^2 = 4n^2$

Exercise 1M

Simplify the following expressions.

1 $2t \times 8$

2 $c + 4c$

3 $2x \times 5$

4 $7t + 2t$

5 $11 \times 5d$

6 $a + 3b + 4a$

7 $7n + m - n$

8 $16a \div 4$

9 $32n \div 8$

10 $7m \div 7$

11 $n \times n$

12 $b \times b$

13 $2c \times c$

14 $c^2 \times d$

15 $3c \times c$

16 $5n \times n^2$

17 $n \times n \times n^2$

18 $6a \times 3b$

19 $2n \times 5t$

20 $2m \times 2m$

21 $t \times t^2 \times t$

22 $15m^2 \div 3m$

23 $n + 2n + 30n$

24 $m^2 \times 20$

25 $(2a)^2$

26 $\frac{8mn}{n}$

27 $\frac{24a}{6}$

28 $\frac{8m - 2n}{2}$

29 $(3x)^2$

30 $\frac{xy^2}{x^2y}$

Simplify the following expressions.

$3(2n + 3) = 6n + 9$

$2(5x - 1) = 10x - 2$

$3(3n + 1) + 2n = 9n + 3 + 2n$
$= 11n + 3$

$5(a + 3) + 2(2a - 1) = 5a + 15 + 4a - 2$
$= 9a + 13$

Exercise 1E

Remove the brackets from these expressions.

1 $2(5x + 3)$

2 $5(3n - 1)$

3 $10(2y - 10)$

4 $7(2a + 9)$

5 $-3(n - 1)$

6 $-6(4 - 3a)$

7 $-6(a + h)$

8 $3(2a + b + 3)$

9 $7(7c - 10)$

10 $5(30 - 2m)$

11 $8(2x + 3y + z)$

12 $10(a^2 + a - 0.1)$

13 Write down and simplify an expression for
(a) the area of this shape and
(b) the perimeter of this shape

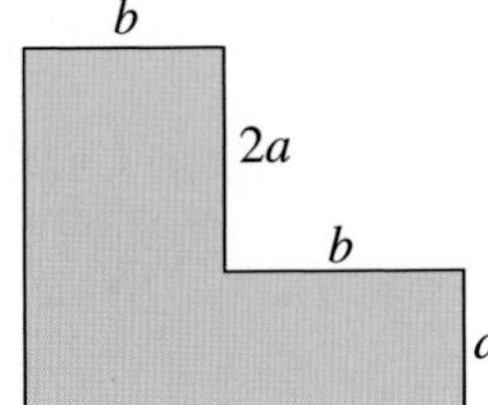

Simplify the following expressions.

14 $2(3x + 5) + 2x$

15 $5(2n - 1) - 3n$

16 $2(4t + 3) - 7$

17 $5(a + 2) + 3(2a + 1)$

18 $3(4t + 3) - 2(6t - 3)$

19 $5a + 2(3a + 4) - 2a$

20 $11k + 3 - 3(2k - 5)$

21 $2c + 5(c - 2) - 3(2c + 1)$

Copy and complete by filling in the boxes.

22 $\square(3x - 1) = 12x - 4$

23 $5(\square + \square) = 10n + 15$

24 $\square(2m + n + \square) = \square + 10n + 1$

25 $3(a + b + \square) = \square + \square + 6c$

26 $\square - (4 + 2a) = 10 + a$

27 $\square + 2(n + m - 3) = 4n + m - 6$

28 Write a number or an expression in each of the six cards so that you obtain the expression

$5a + 10b + 3n + 12m$

from $\square(\square + \square) + \square(\square + \square)$.

Exercise 2M

In questions 1 to 15 answer 'true' or 'false'.

1 $3 \times n = n \times 3$

2 $5 \times a = 5 + a$

3 $n \times n = n^2$

4 $c \times d = cd$

5 $m \times 3 = 3m$

6 $a - b = b - a$

7 $2(n + 1) = 2n + 1$

8 $t + t = t^2$

9 $2h \times h = 2h^2$

10 $m \times 3m = 3m^2$

11 $3(a - b) = 3a - 3b$

12 $n^2 + n^2 = n^4$

13 $n \div 3 = \frac{n}{3}$

14 $t \div 2 = 2t \div 4$

15 $(x + y) \div 2 = \frac{x + y}{2}$

16 In the expression $2(3n-5)$, three operations are performed in the following order:

Draw similar diagrams to show the correct order of operations for the following expressions.

(a) $6n+1$ (b) $3(5n-2)$ (c) $\dfrac{4n+5}{3}$ (d) $2(7n+3)$

(e) n^2+7 (f) $(n-7)^2$ (g) $(2n-3)^2+10$ (h) $\dfrac{(3n+1)^2+5}{7}$

17 Find the value of n in each case.

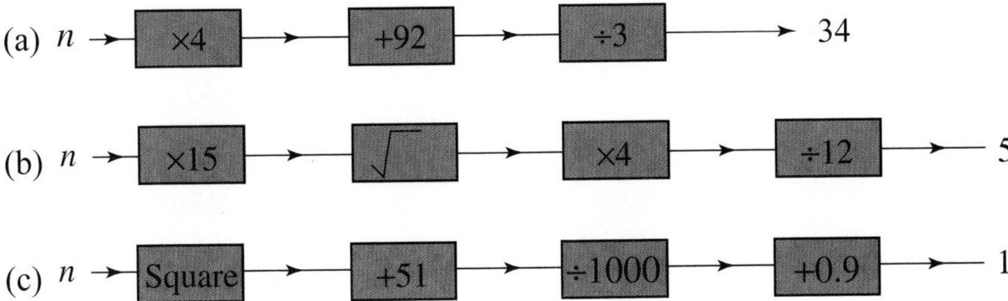

18 A large 'T' can be drawn inside the number square so that all 5 numbers in the T are inside the square.

1	2	3	4	5	6	7	8
9	10	11	12	13	14	15	16
17	18	19	20	21	22	23	24
25	26	27	28	29	30	31	32
33	34	35	36	37	38	39	40
41	42	43	44	45	46	47	48
49	50	51	52	53	54	55	56
57	58	59	60	61	62	63	64

The T can be moved around but it must stay upright.
The 'T-number' is the number in the middle of the top row. So this is T18.

17	18	19
	26	
	34	

(a) What is the smallest possible T-number?

(b) Work out the total of the numbers in T21

(c) Work out, as *quickly* as you can
(Total of numbers in T37) –
(Total of numbers in T36)

(d) Use x's to write the numbers for the following

(i) (ii) (iii)

Remove the brackets and simplify

(a) $n(n+2)$
$= n^2 + 2n$

(b) $x(2x+1)$
$= 2x^2 + x$

(c) $a(3a-2)$
$= 3a^2 - 2a$

(d) $2m(m+1)$
$= 2m^2 + 2m$

(e) $5n(2n+3)$
$= 10n^2 + 15n$

(f) $2n(3n+1)$
$= 6n^2 + 2n$

Exercise 2E

Remove the brackets and simplify.

1 $n(n+3)$

2 $n(n+7)$

3 $a(a-3)$

4 $t(t-5)$

5 $a(a-10)$

6 $m(m+11)$

7 $2a(a+1)$

8 $3n(n+2)$

9 $5t(t+1)$

10 $x(2x+1)$

11 $y(y-7)$

12 $3y(y+3)$

13 $h(h-100)$

14 $5a(a+5)$

15 $p(p+3)$

16 $2e(3e+1)$

17 $3x(3x+2)$

18 $2a(5a-1)$

Copy and complete by filling in the boxes.

19 $\square(a+7) = 2a^2 + \square$

20 $\square(n-3) = \square - 9$

21 $n(\square + 2) = 2n^2 + \square$

22 $\square(\square + \square) = n^2 + 7n$

23 $\square(3x-1) = \square - 2x$

24 $4h(\square + \square) = 8hm + 4h$

25 $\square(3n+1) + 2(\square + 5) = 11n + 13$

26 $\square(2n-1) + 3(\square + 1) = 14n - 1$

Exercise 3M

1 Four rods P, Q, R and S have lengths, in cm, as shown.

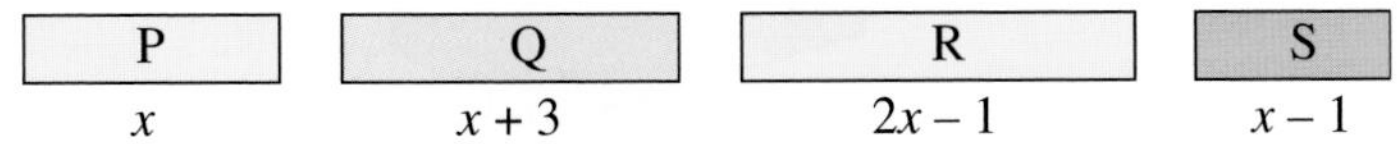

In each diagram find the length l, in terms of x. Give your answers in their simplest form.
[The diagrams are not drawn to scale.]

(a)

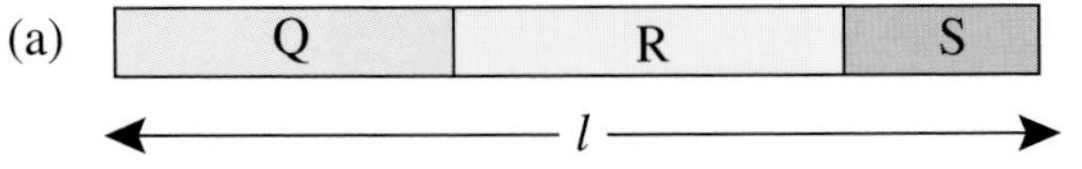

(b)

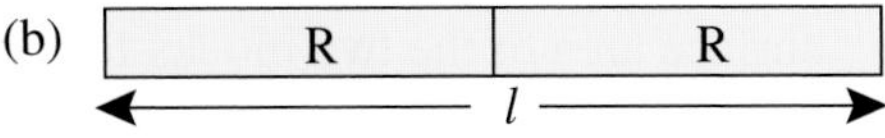

(c)

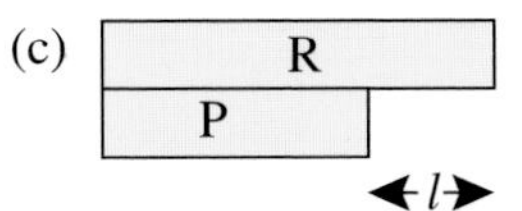

(d)

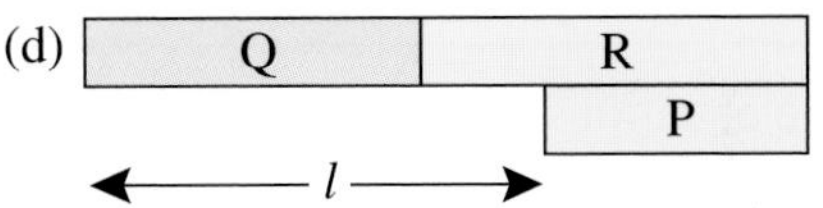

(e)

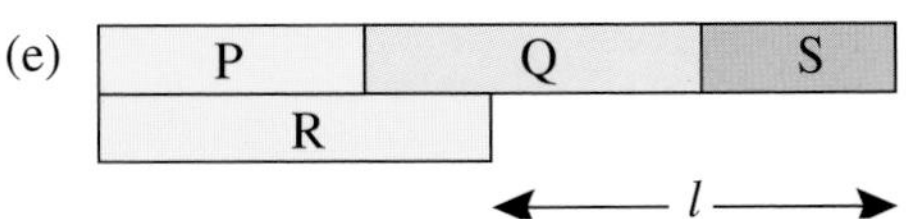

(f)

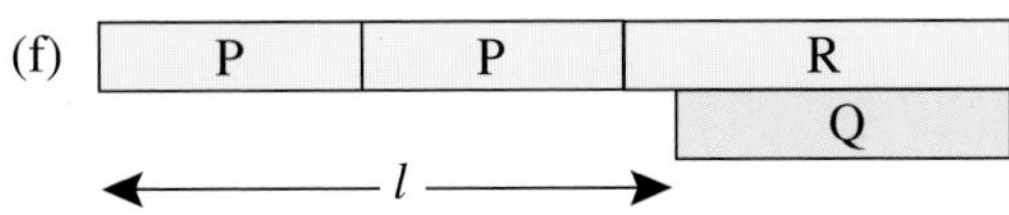

(g)

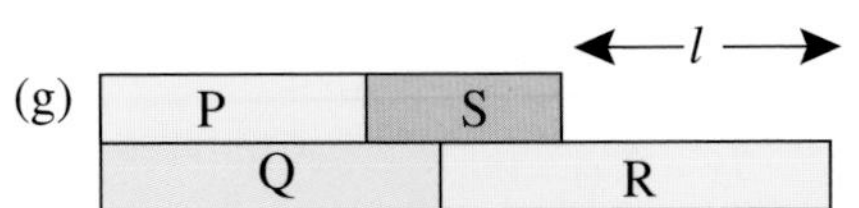

(h)

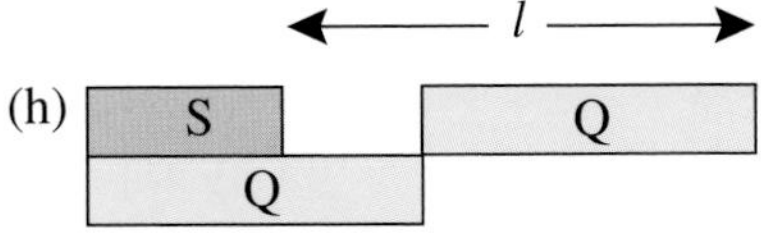

(i)

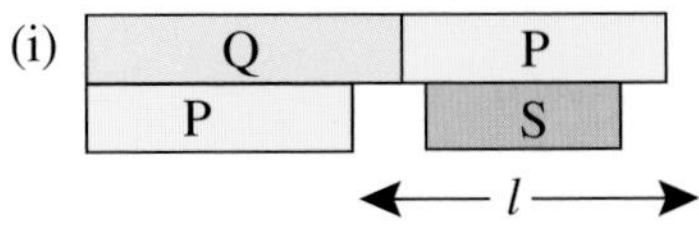

(j)

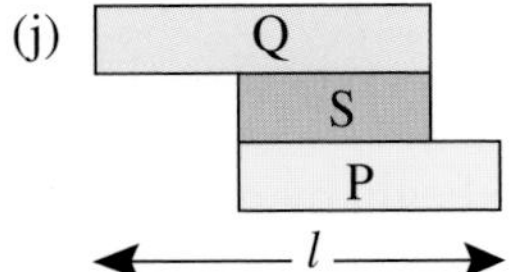

(k)

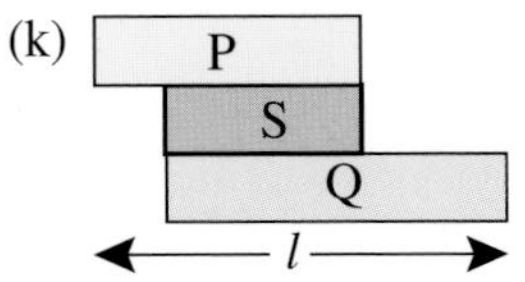

(l)

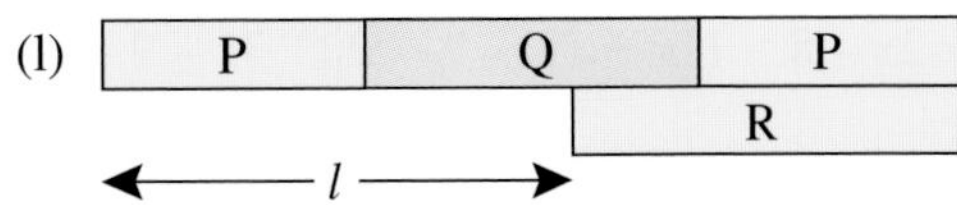

2 (a) A solid rectangular block measures x cm by x cm by $(x + 3)$ cm. Find a simplified expression for its surface area in cm^2.

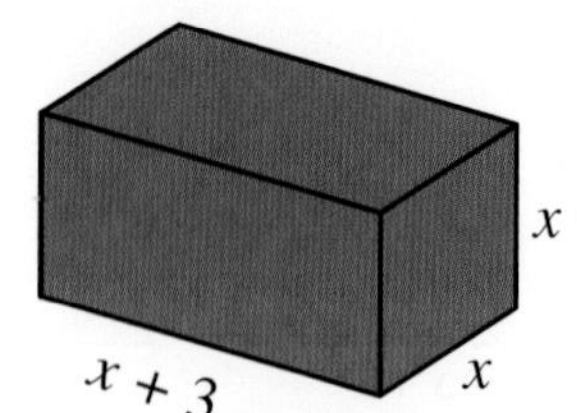

(b) The block above is divided into two rectangular blocks by cutting as shown in the diagram. Find a simplified expression for the total surface area of the two blocks formed, in cm^2.

Solving equations

Solve the equations

(a) $4n - 3 = 13$

(+3) (+3)

$4n = 16$

(÷4) (÷4)

$n = 4$

(b) $4n - 3 = 2n + 11$

(−2n) (−2n)

$2n - 3 = 11$

(+3) (+3)

$2n = 14$

$n = 7$

Exercise 4M

Solve the equations.

1 $3x - 2 = 13$

2 $4x + 1 = 25$

3 $7x - 2 = -1$

4 $5 + 2x = 6$

5 $7 + 3x = 22$

6 $3 = 4x + 1$

7 $5 = 3x - 1$

8 $7 = 15 + 2x$

9 $10 = 12 + 3x$

10 $4 = 6x + 5$

11 $7x - 1 = -8$

12 $13 + x = 10$

In questions 13 to 24, begin by putting the x terms on one side of the equation.

13 $4x + 3 = 2x - 5$

14 $7x - 5 = 2x + 8$

15 $3x + 7 = 8x + 2$

16 $6x + 1 = 2 - 3x$

17 $7x - 2 = 1 - 3x$

18 $5 - x = 2x - 7$

19 $2x - 8 = 11x + 12$

20 $3x - 9 = 4x + 4$

21 $2 + 8x = 5 - x$

22 $16x + 9 = 12x - 3$

23 $1 - 10x = 6 - 5x$

24 $4 - 5x = 4 + 7x$

Exercise 4E

1. $4(x + 1) = 2(x - 1)$
2. $5(2x + 1) = 3(x - 2)$
3. $4(3 - x) = 2(2x + 1)$
4. $5(x + 2) - (x - 2) = 0$
5. $6(1 - 2x) - 3(x + 1) = 0$
6. $5(x - 7) = 2(x + 1)$
7. $(x - 1) - (2x - 3) = 0$
8. $5(1 - x) = 4(10 + x)$
9. $3(2x - 3) = 4(5 - x)$
10. $3(3 - 2x) - 2(1 - x) = 10$
11. $6 - 3(x + 1) = 7$
12. $9 - 5(2x - 1) = 6$

Solving problems with equations

Exercise 5M

In questions 1 to 10 write an equation and solve it to find the number I am thinking of.

1. If I double the number and then add 5 the answer is 8.
2. If I subtract 5 from the number and then multiply the result by 4, the answer is 16.

3. If I double the number, add 7 and then treble the result, the answer is 22.
4. If I multiply the number by 6 and subtract 4, I get the same answer as when I add 6 to the number and then double the result.
5. If I multiply the number by 5, add 11 and then double the result, I get the same answer as when I treble the number and then add 36.
6. If I subtract 7 from the number add then multiply the result by 9, I get the same answer as when I take the number away *from* 7 and then double the result.
7. If I subtract the number *from* 11 and then multiply the result by 4, I get the same answer as when I add 1½ to the number and then multiply the result by 4.
8. If I double the number, add 7 and then divide the result by 3, I get the same answer as when I subtract the number from 12 and then divide the result by 5.

9 If I treble the number, subtract 5, multiply the result by 2 and finally divide by 4, I get the same answer as when I subtract 2 from the number.

10 If I multiply the number by 5, add 1 and then divide the result by 4, I get the same answer as when I subtract 2 from the number.

Exercise 5E

1 The angles in degrees of a quadrilateral are n, $(n + 10)$, $2n$ and $(n + 20)$. Find the angles.

2 Jacqui went to a hair stylist for a special occasion. The stylists charges were:

Cut £n

blow dry £$(n - 20)$

highlights £$(n + 25)$

make up £$(2n - 18)$

hair flowers £ 20

Jacqui paid £137 for a cut, hair flowers and make up. Find the cost of a cut.

3 Find three consecutive numbers such that three times the middle number is 12 more than the sum of the other two numbers.
[Hint. Let the three numbers be x, $x + 1$, etc.]

4 Find four consecutive *odd* numbers whose sum is 224.

5 The area of this rectangle is 20 square units.
Find x and hence find the length and width of the rectangle.

$x + 4$

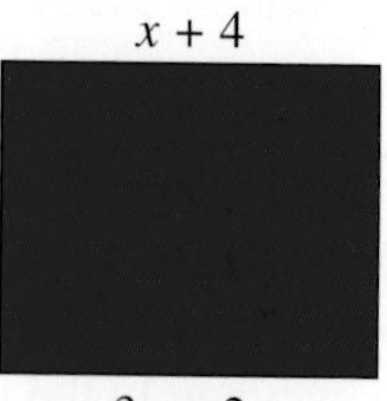

$3x + 2$

6 The length of a rectangle is three times its width. If the perimeter is 48 cm, find its width.
[Let the width be x.]

7 An equilateral triangle has sides of length $2x + 4$, $3x + 1$ and $3x + 1$. Find x.

8 Find the value of x so that the areas of the pink rectangles are equal.

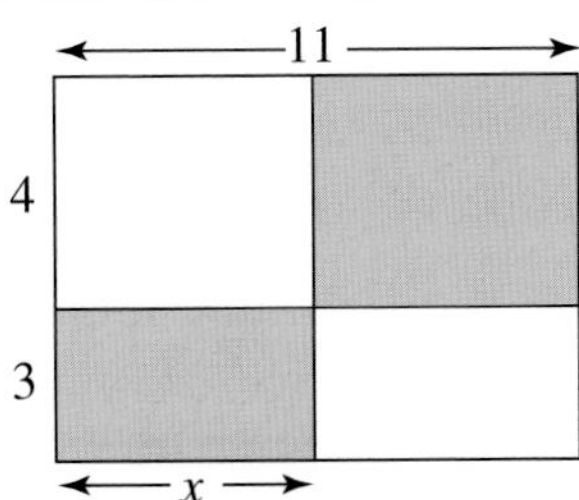

9 Two angles of an isosceles triangle are $a°$ and $(a + 10)°$. Find two possible values of a.

10 When Steve was asked how old he was, he replied: 'In 30 years I'll be twice as old as I was 8 years ago'. How old is he?

11 Neha has x 10 p coins and $(x + 3)$ 20 p coins. Find x if she has £2.70 altogether.

12 The mean height of Alan, Ben and Chris is 150 cm. Alan is $(2x - 1)$ cm tall, Ben is $3(x + 2)$ cm tall and Chris is $2(2x - 7)$ cm tall.

Find the value of x and hence find the height of Chris.

13 The diagram shows the semi-circular end of a running track.

Dave runs straight across the field from A to B at a speed of x m/s. His brother Jim runs around the track at a speed of $(x + 2)$ m/s.

Find the value of x, correct to 2 s.f., if they both take the same time to get from A to B.

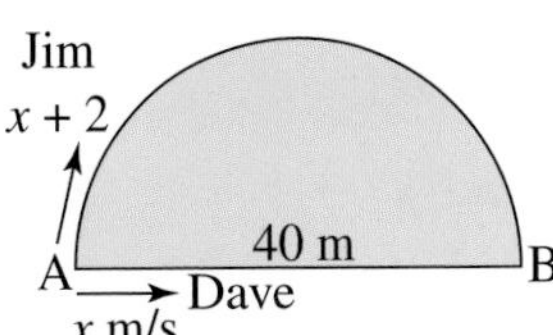

Factors

- The expression $8x + 6$ has two terms, $8x$ and 6.

  The number 2 is a factor of both terms.

  We can write $8x + 6 = 2(4x + 3)$.

  This process is called factorising.

- Here are some examples:

  $6a + 15 = 3(2a + 5)$ $\quad$ $18m + 24n = 6(3m + 4n)$

  $4x^2 + 6x = 2x(2x + 3)$ $\quad$ $7n^2 + 5n = n(7n + 5)$

Exercise 6M

Copy and complete.

1 $8a + 10 = 2(4a + \square)$

2 $6x + 3 = 3(2x + \square)$

3 $6a + 9 = 3(2a + \square)$

4 $10a + 15 = 5(\square + \square)$

5 $18x - 12 = 6(\square - \square)$

6 $18c + 24 = \square(\square + \square)$

7 $3x + 15 = \square(\square + \square)$

8 $7n - 35 = 7(\square - \square)$

9 $16m + 40 = \square(2m + \square)$

10 $45a + 36 = \square(5a + \square)$

In questions 11 to 25 factorise the expressions.

11 $4a + 10$

12 $6c + 21$

13 $10c - 5$

14 $18m + 9$

15 $9m + 12$

16 $15a + 25$

17 $14x - 21t$

18 $18x + 24t$

19 $24p - 20q$

20 $6a + 9b + 3c$

21 $10a + 15b + 25c$

22 $9x + 9y + 21t$

23 $7c + 14d - 7e$

24 $24m + 12n + 16t$

25 $18a - 27b + 36c$

Exercise 6E

Factorise the following.

1 $x^2 + 6x$

2 $3x^2 + 4x$

3 $6x^2 + x$

4 $2a^2 + a$

5 $5n^2 + n$

6 $2a^2 + 6a$

7 $3n^2 - n$

8 $5m^2 - 15m$

9 $x^3 + x^2 + x$

10 $12a^2 - 8a$

11 $6a^2 - a$

12 $mn + m^2$

13 $x^2 - xy$

14 $2x^2 + 4xy$

15 $x^3 + xy^2$

16 Copy and complete.

(a) $\square(t - \square) = t^2 - 4t$

(b) $\square(\square + 3) = 2x^2 + 6x$

(c) $a(\square + 3a + 1) = a^3 + \square + \square$

(d) $3x(\square - \square) = 6x^2 - 3x$

(e) $\square(\square + \square) = n^2 + 6n$

(f) $\square(\square + \square) = 4n^2 + 6n$

CHECK YOURSELF ON SECTIONS 1.1 AND 1.2

1 Paper and pencil calculations

(a) Work out, without a calculator

(i) 1.2×0.8

(ii) $0.834 \div 0.2$

(iii) $18.4 - 9.22$

(iv) $(11 - 3) \times (2^3 - 1)$

(v) $81 \div 9 - 3.5 \times 2$

(vi) $(10^6 \div 10^2) - 1$

(b) (i) Share £85 between 2 people in the ratio 2:3

(ii) Write 84 as a product of prime numbers.

2. Using a calculator and calculating with negative numbers

(a) Work out and give your answer correct to one decimal place where necessary.

(i) $\frac{5.61 - 1.2^2}{0.42}$ (ii) $\frac{1.92^3}{(8.01 - 7.4)}$ (iii) $\left(1\frac{3}{5} \div \frac{1}{2}\right)^2$

(b) Work out

(i) $(-7)^2 - 60$ (ii) $8 - (-7)$ (iii) $(-2) \times (-3) - 20$

(iv) $12 \div (-3)$ (v) $(-3) \times (7) \times (-0.1)$

3. Rules of algebra

(a) Simplify the following

(i) $2(5n + 1) - n$ (ii) $3(6n - 1) - 2(n + 3)$ (iii) $3n(n + 2)$

(b) Solve the equations

(i) $3x + 1 = 7x - 9$ (ii) $4(3 - x) = 2(2x + 1)$ (iii) $\frac{4}{x} = 7$

1.3 Congruent shapes and construction

In this section you will:

- learn about congruent triangles
- draw constructions using a ruler and compasses.

Congruent triangles

There are several ways in which different triangles can be described.

By convention we use: S when a side is given,
A when an angle is given,
R when a right angle is given,
H when the hypotenuse of a right angled triangle is given.

Here are five examples.

1

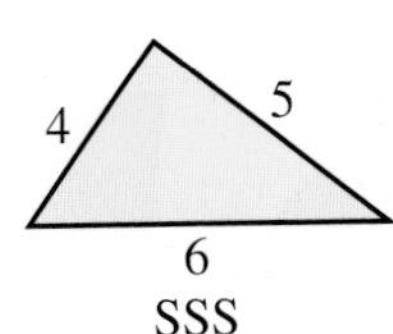

SSS

[All 3 sides]

2

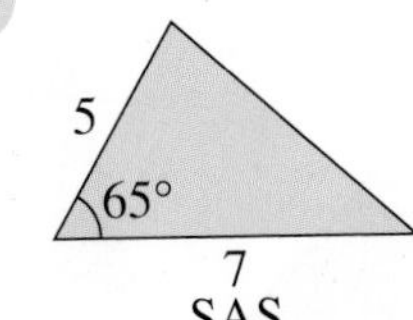

SAS

[2 sides and the included angle]

3

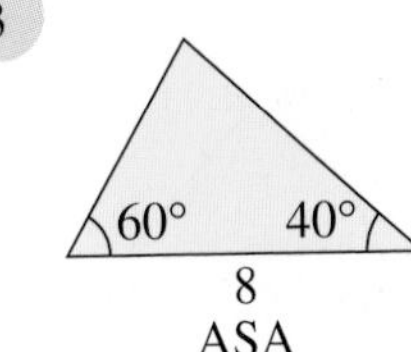

ASA

[2 angles and one side]

4 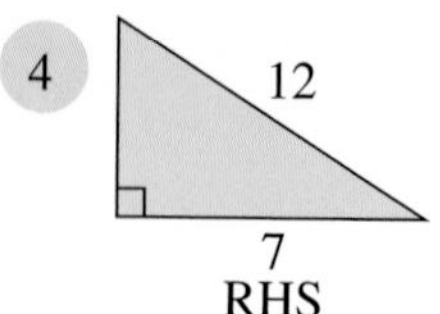

5 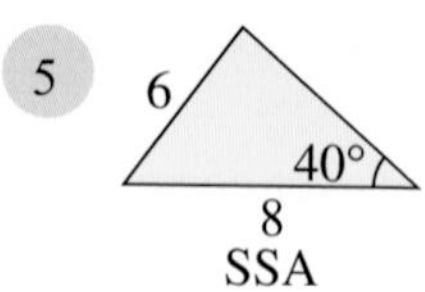

[right angle, hypotenuse and side]

[2 sides and an angle (not included)]

Exercise 1M/E

1 Using a ruler, protractor and a pair of compasses construct each of the triangles **1, 2, 3** and **4** above. Label the triangles SSS, SAS, ASA, RHS.

2 Construct triangle **5** above and, using a pair of compasses, show that it is possible to construct two different triangles with the sides and angle given.

3 Construct the triangle shown. You are given SSA. Show that you can construct two different triangles with the sides and angle given.

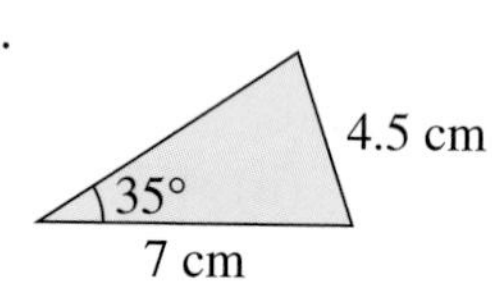

4 Copy and complete these two sentences:

'When we are given SSS, SAS, [ ] or [ ] the constructed triangle is unique.

When we are given [ ] the triangle is not unique and it is sometimes possible to construct to different triangles.'

These are the conditions for triangles to be congruent.

5 State whether each pair of triangles are congruent. Give the conditions for congruency if they are congruent.

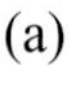
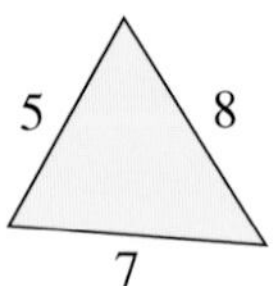

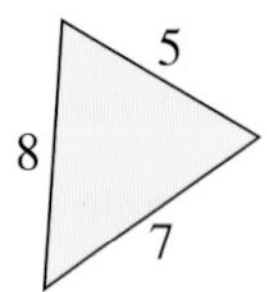

(b)
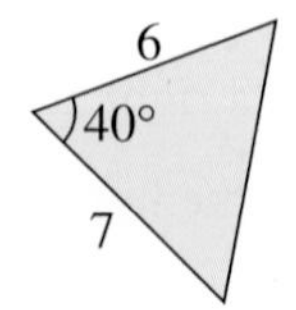

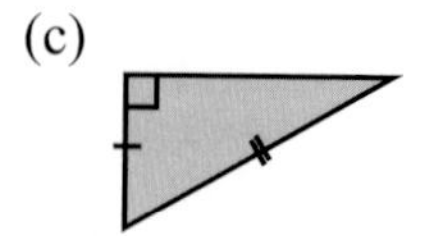

(c)

(d)
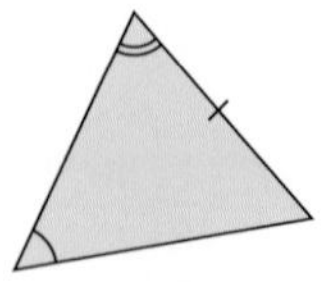
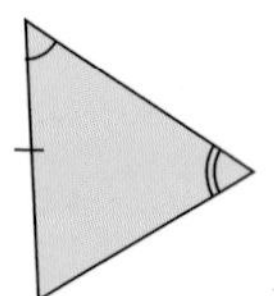
(e)

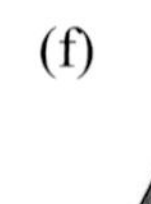
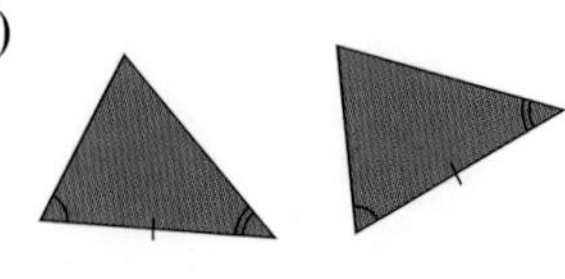

6 Suppose you are given two triangles and they each have the same three angles (say 60º, 40º, 80º). This is condition ‘AAA’. Are the two triangles always congruent?

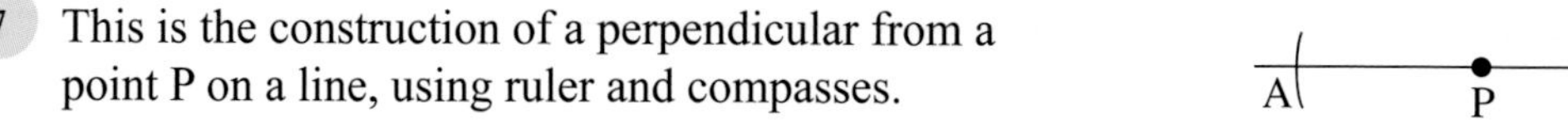

7 This is the construction of a perpendicular from a point P on a line, using ruler and compasses.

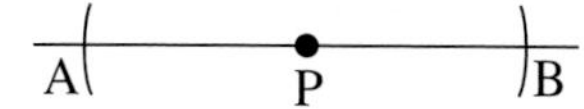

(a) With centre P, draw arcs to cut the line at A and B.

(b) Now construct the perpendicular bisector of AB.

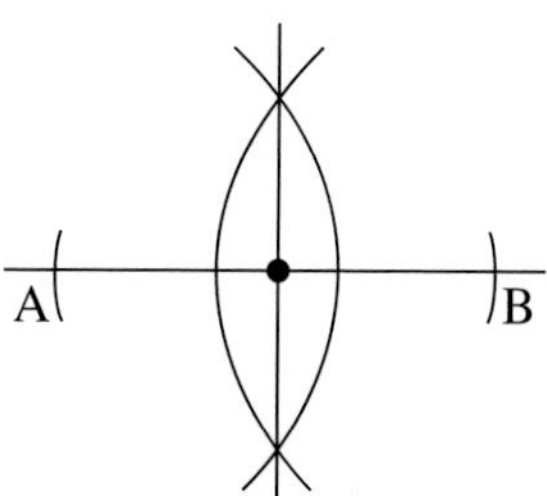

8 This is the construction of a triangle given RHS.

(a) Draw a line and construct a perpendicular at point P as in question 7.

(b) Complete the triangle, given PQ = 5 cm and RQ = 8 cm.

(c) Measure the side PR.

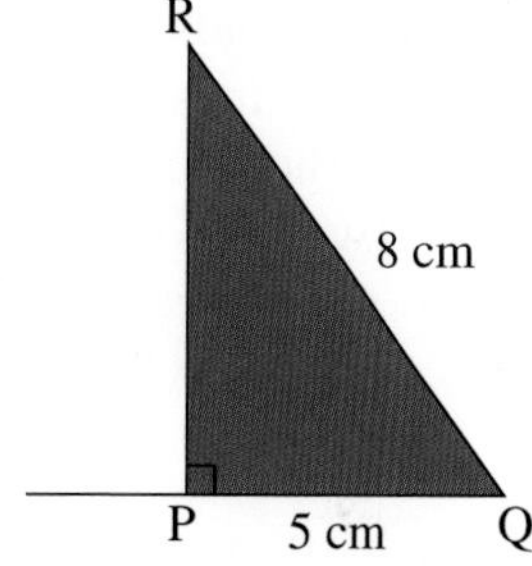

9

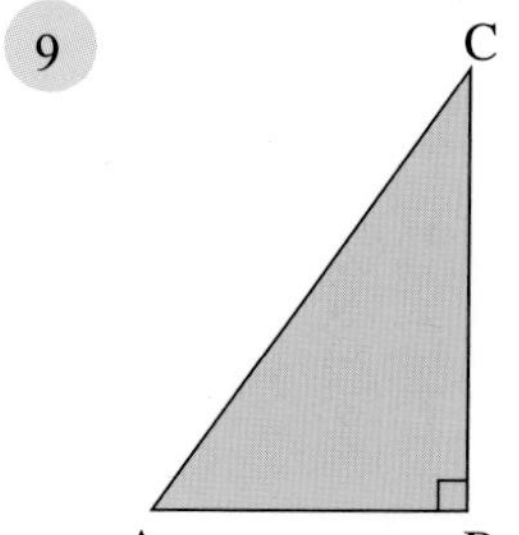

Construct the triangle shown, using ruler and compasses. BC = 7 cm and AC = 9 cm. Measure the side AB.

[*Teacher’s note*: There are more questions involving congruent triangles and proof in section 5.5].

1.4 Geometrical reasoning

In this section you will:

- review the properties of quadrilaterals and triangles
- learn about angle in polygons

Properties of quadrilaterals

Square: Four equal sides;
All angles 90°;
Four lines of symmetry.

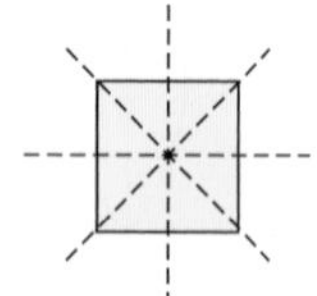

Rectangle (not square): Two pairs of equal and parallel sides;
All angles 90°;
Two lines of symmetry.

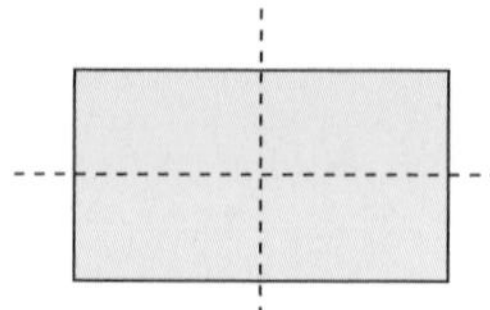

Rhombus: Four equal sides;
Opposite sides parallel;
Diagonals bisect at right angles;
Diagonals bisect angles of rhombus;
Two lines of symmetry.

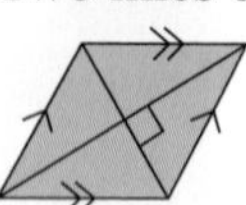

Parallelogram: Two pairs of equal and parallel sides;
Opposite angles equal;
No lines of symmetry (in general).

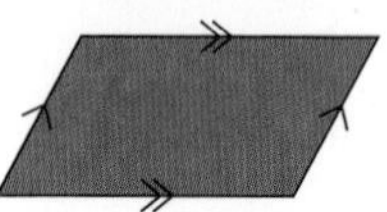

Trapezium: One pair of parallel sides.

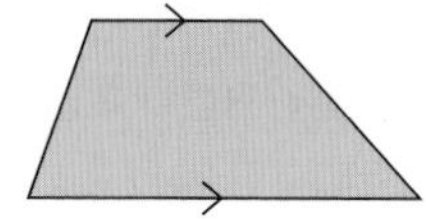

Kite: AB = AD, CB = CD; Diagonals meet at 90°; One line of symmetry.

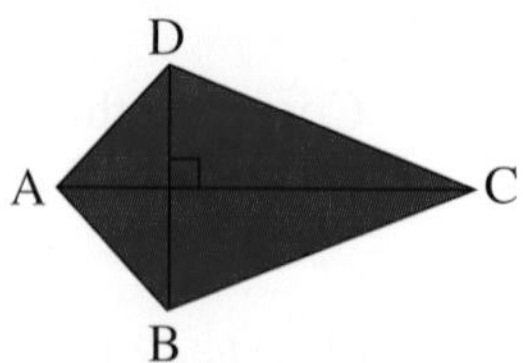

Arrowhead or **Delta:**
Two pairs of adjacent edges of equal length.
One interior angle larger than 180°.
One line of symmetry.
Diagonals cross at right angles outside the shape.

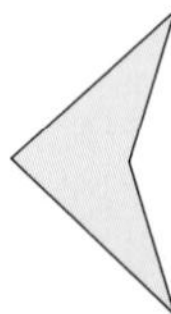

For all quadrilaterals the sum of the interior angles is 360°.

Exercise 1M

1 Name each of the following shapes:

(a) ABEH

(b) EFGH

(c) CDFE

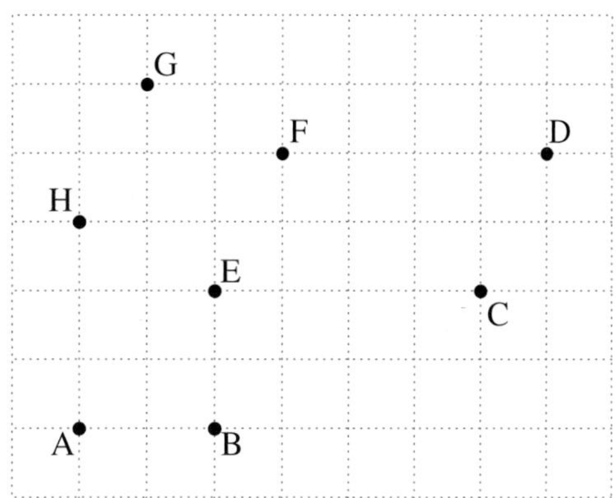

2 (a) Write down the coordinates of point D if ABCD is a kite.

(b) Write down the coordinates of point E if ABCE is a parallelogram.

(c) Write down the coordinates of point G if BCGF is an arrowhead. [There is more than one answer.]

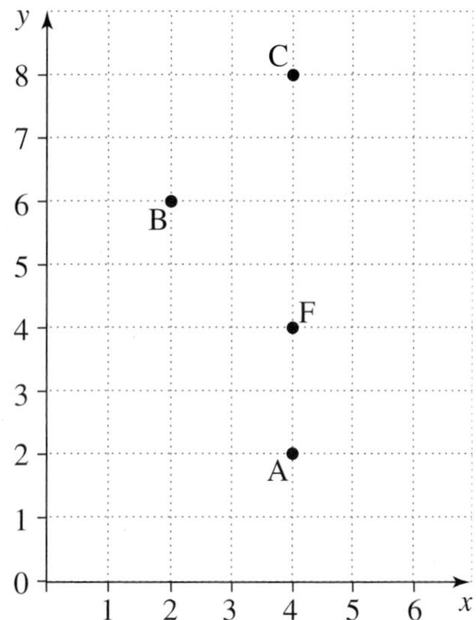

3 Copy the table and fill all the boxes with either 'Yes', 'No' or a number.

	How many lines of symmetry?	How many pairs of opposite sides are parallel?	Diagonals always equal?	Diagonals are perpendicular?
Square				
Rectangle				
Kite				
Rhombus				
Parallelogram				
Arrowhead				

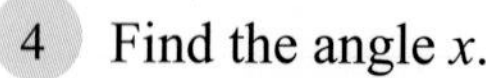

4 Find the angle x.

(a)

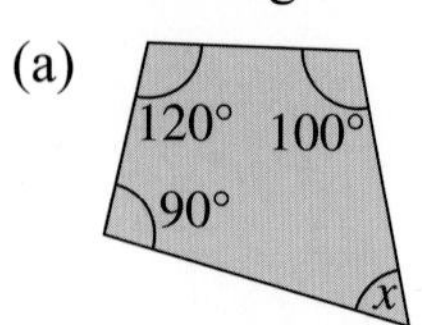

(b)

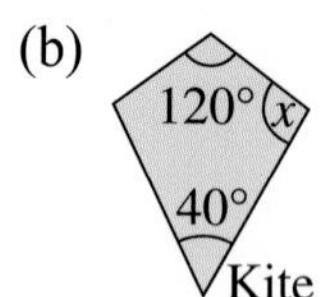

(c)

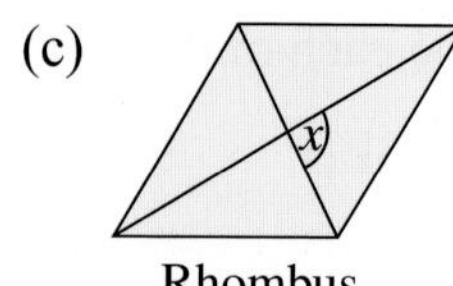

(d)

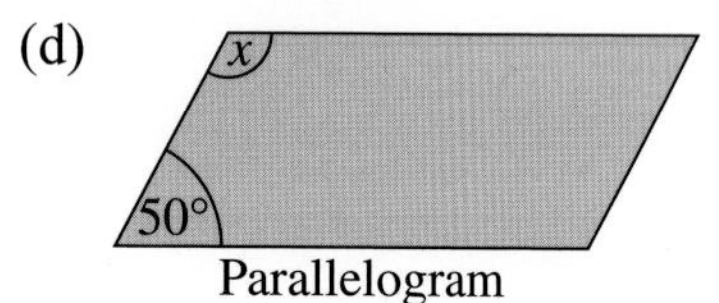

(e)

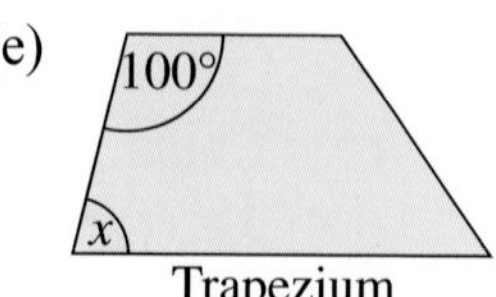

(f)

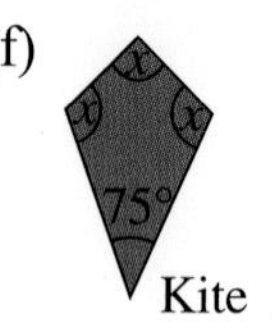

5 The diagram shows three vertices (corners) of a parallelogram. Copy the diagram and mark with crosses the *three* possible positions of the fourth vertex.

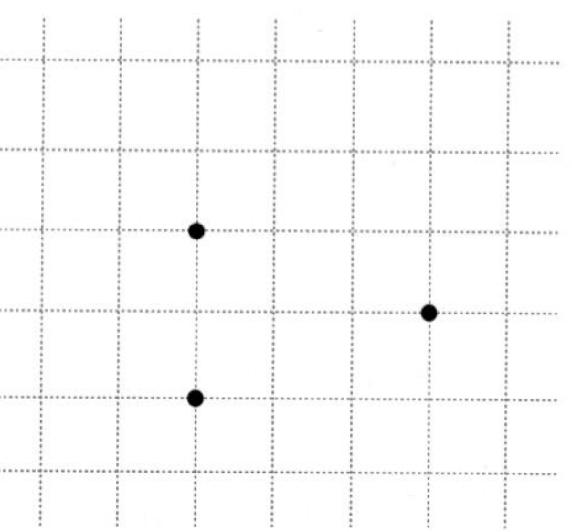

6 Line AC is one *diagonal* of a rhombus ABCD. Draw *two* possible rhombuses ABCD.

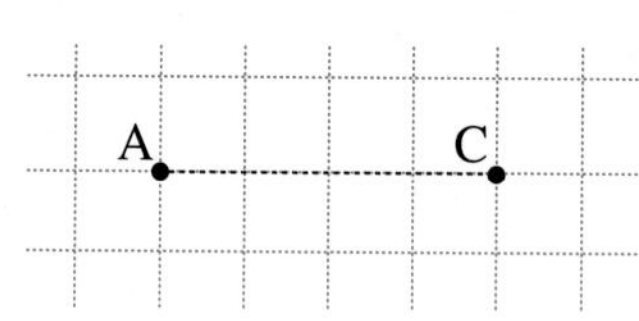

Exercise 1E

1 Find the angles marked with letters

(a)

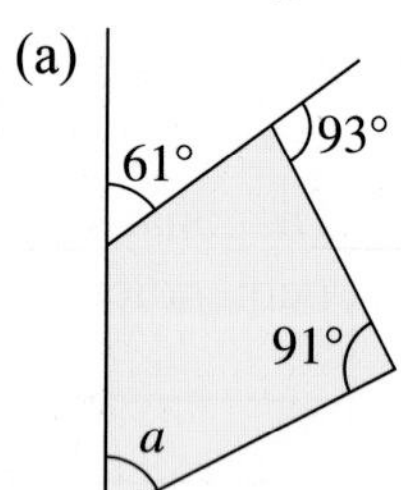

(b)

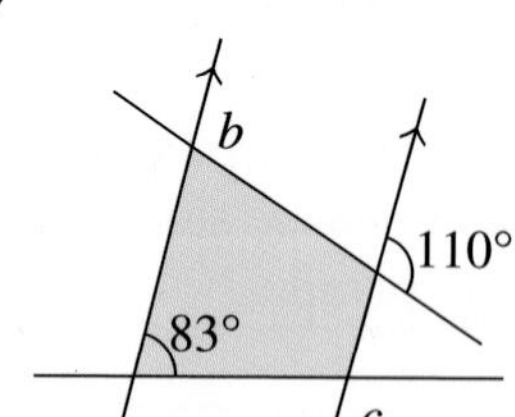

(c)

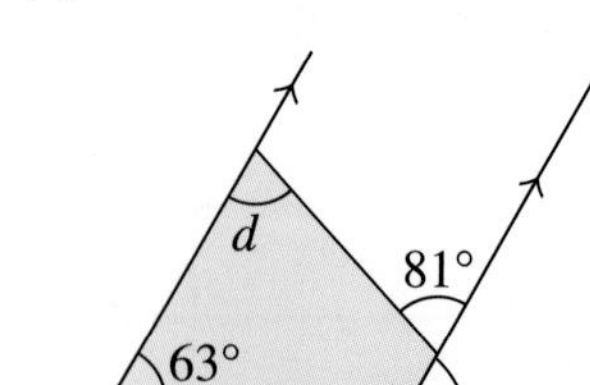

(d)

(e)

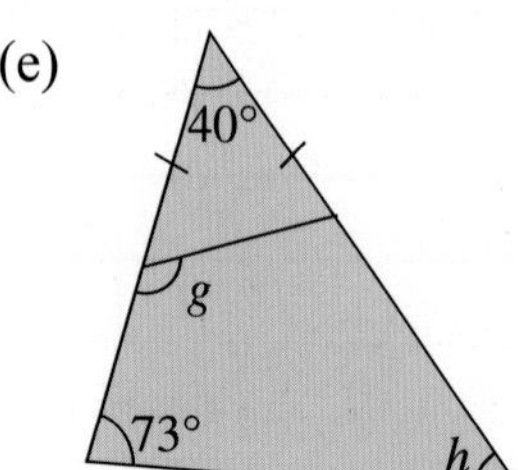

(f)

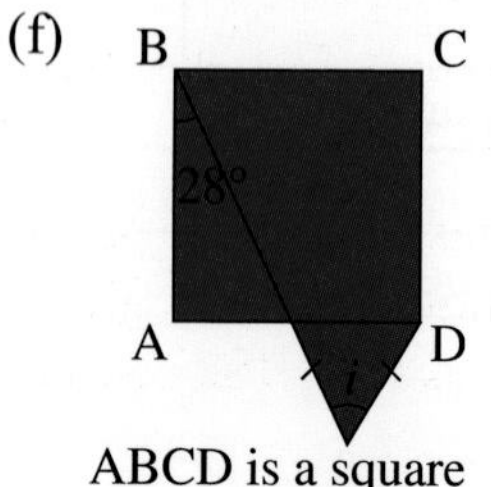

(g)

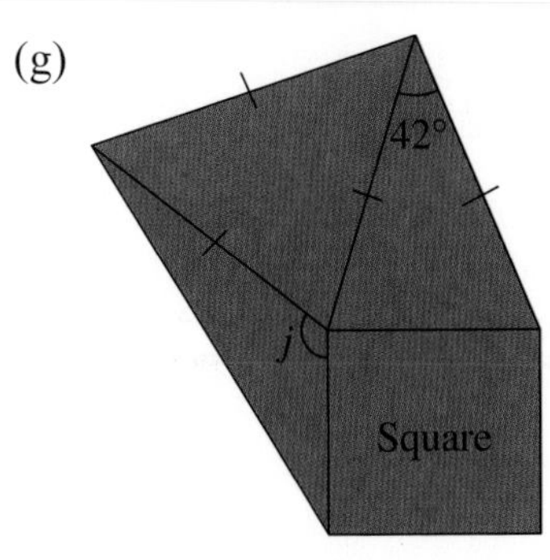

(h)

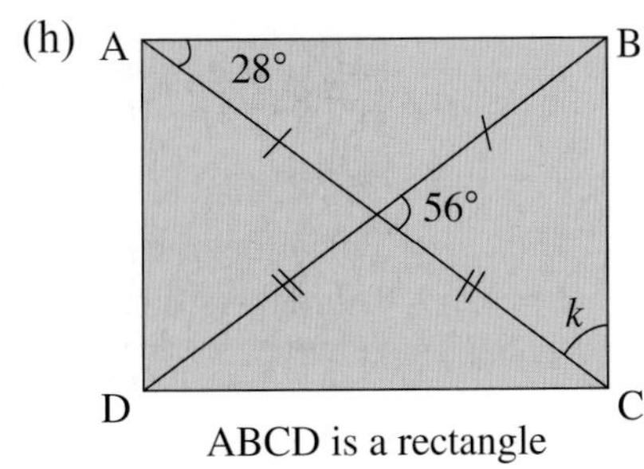

ABCD is a rectangle

2 Draw a diagram of an isosceles triangle ABC with AB = AC. Point Y lies on BC so that $A\hat{Y}B = 84°$. If $A\hat{B}C = 71°$, find the size of $C\hat{A}Y$.

3 Draw a triangle ABC with $A\hat{C}B = 54°$. Point D lies on AC so that BD bisects $A\hat{B}C$ and $A\hat{B}D = 37°$. Find the size of $A\hat{D}B$.

4 Suppose you cut along the diagonal of a rectangle to make two congruent triangles. Join the diagonals together in a different way. What shape is formed?

5 Suppose you had two identical isosceles triangles. Put the equal sides together to make as many different shapes as possible. Name the shapes formed.

6 An equilateral triangle has vertices P, Q, R.

(a) Suppose the vertex P moves perpendicular to QR. What different types of triangle can be made?
Can you make: a right-angled triangle;
an obtuse-angled triangle;
a scalene triangle?

(b) If the vertex P moves *parallel* to QR, what different types of triangle can be made?

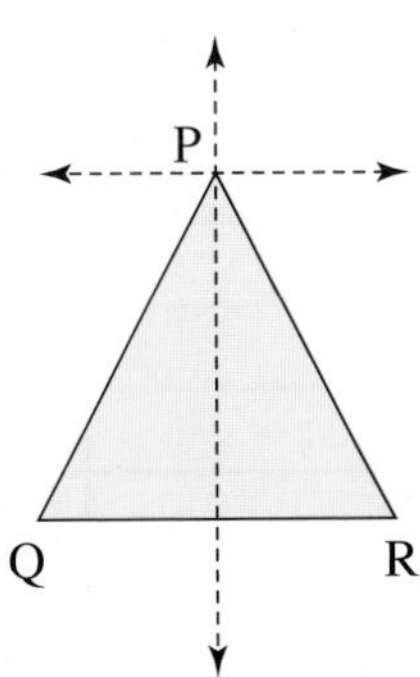

Angles in polygons

- We already know that angles in a triangle add up to 180° and angles in a quadrilateral add up to 360°.

  What happens in polygons with a greater number of sides?

- First draw any pentagon (5 sided shape).
  Choose one of the corners, A say, and join this to all the other corners. (B and E will already be joined by the sides of the pentagon).

  This divides the pentagon into 3 triangles. As we already know that the angles in each of these triangles adds up to 180° the angles in our pentagon must add up to:

  $3 \times 180° = 540°$

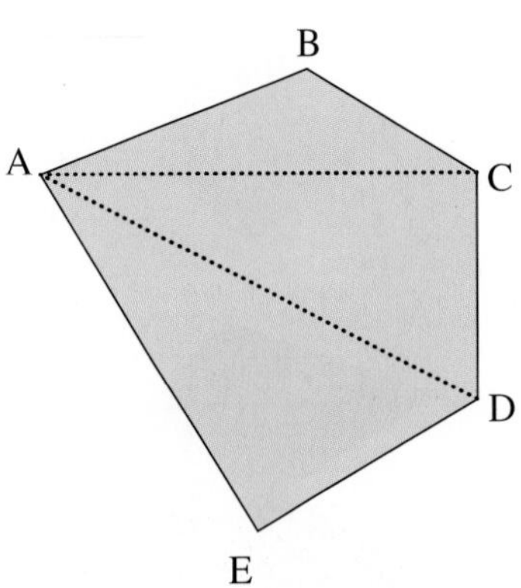

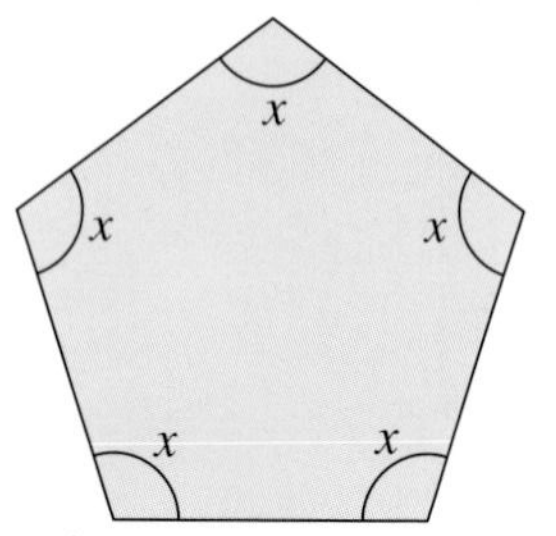

The angles in a pentagon add up to 540°

If we had started with a *regular* pentagon all the sides would have been the same length and all the angles would be the same. As there are 5 equal angles, each angle = 540 ÷ 5
= 108°

Exercise 2M

1 Copy and complete the following table. Split up polygons with 6, 8 and 10 sides into triangles as in the example above.

Look for a pattern in the numbers and try to complete the rest of the table without drawing the polygon first.

Number of sides	Number of triangles	Total of interior angles	Interior angle of regular polygon
3	1	1 × 180° = 180°	180° ÷ 3 = 60°
4	2	2 × 180° = 360°	360° ÷ 4 = 90°
5	3	3 × 180° = 540°	540° ÷ 5 = 108°
6			
8			
10			
20			
n			

Teachers note:

The result for the sum of the angles in a polygon with *n* sides obtained from the bottom row is needed in subsequent questions.

2 Find the angles marked with letters.

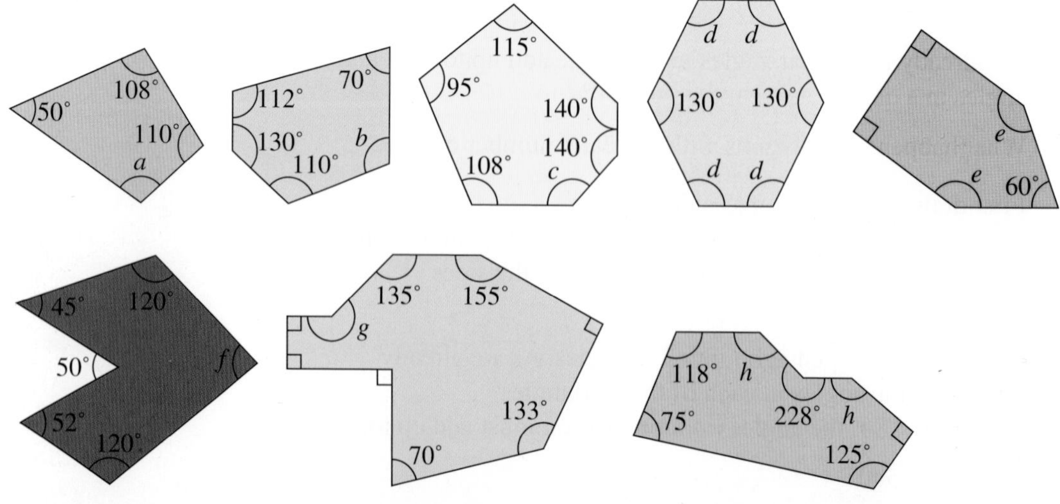

3 ABCDEF is a regular hexagon. AE and DF intersect at point X. Find the size of angle DXE.

4 ABCD is a square. Equilateral triangles ABE and ADF are drawn with points E and F either inside or outside the square.
Find angle AEF if,

(a) E and F are both outside the square,

(b) E is outside and F is inside the square,

(c) E and F are both inside the square.

Exterior angles of a polygon

The exterior angle of a polygon is the angle between a produced side and the adjacent side of the polygon. The word 'produced' in this context means 'extended'.

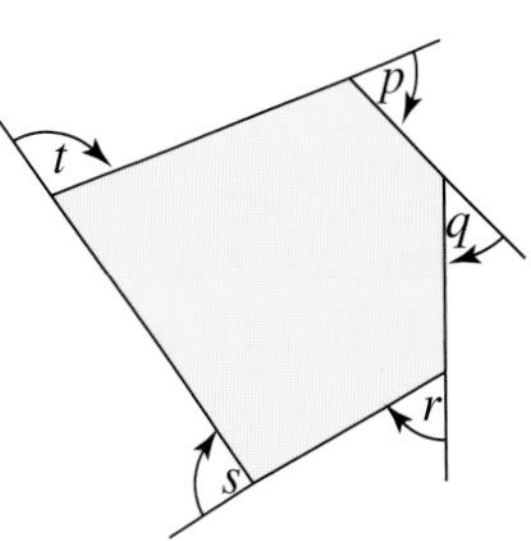

If we put all the exterior angles together we can see that the sum of the angles is 360°. This is true for any polygon.

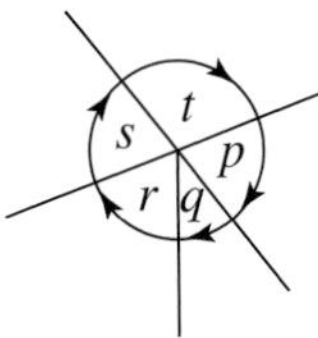

The sum of the exterior angles of a polygon = 360°

Note:

(a) In a regular polygon all exterior angles are equal.

(b) For a regular polygon with n sides, each exterior angle $= \dfrac{360°}{n}$.

Exercise 2E

1 Find the angles marked with letters.

2 Find (a) the exterior (b) the interior angles of regular polygons with

(i) 9 sides (ii) 18 sides (iii) 45 sides (iv) 60 sides

3 Below are two sets of tiling patterns used for flooring. Each set consists of two regular polygons. Describe the polygons that are used.

(a)

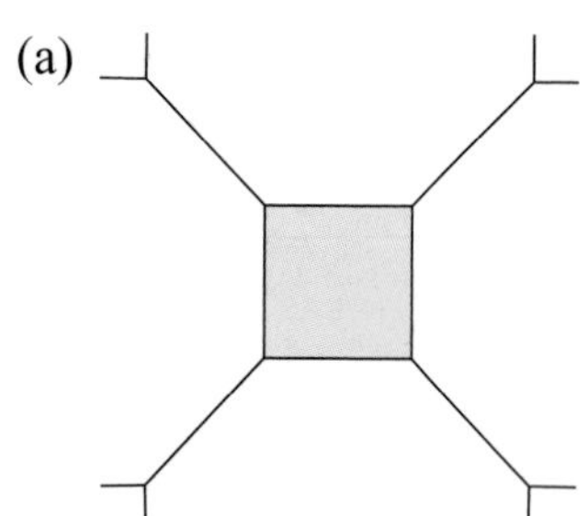

(b)

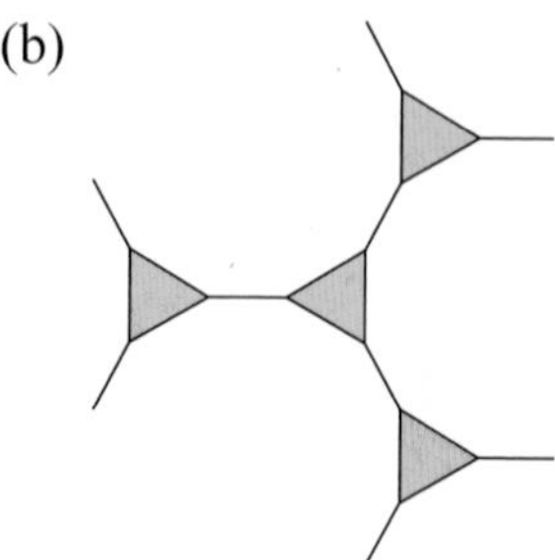

4 Find the labelled angles in this regular 9-sided polygon. Point O is the centre of the polygon.

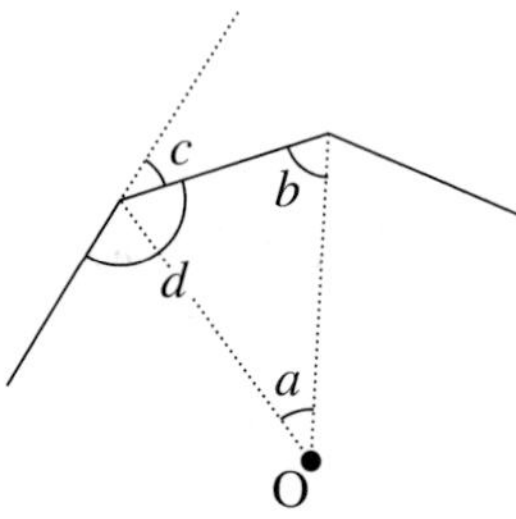

Questions 5 to 14 are more difficult.

5 Each interior angle of a regular polygon is 140°. How many sides has the polygon?

6 Each exterior angle of a regular polygon is 18°. How many sides has the polygon?

7 The sum of the interior angles in a polygon is 3780°. How many sides has the polygon?

8 The sides of a regular polygon subtend angles of 18° at the centre of the polygon. How many sides has the polygon?

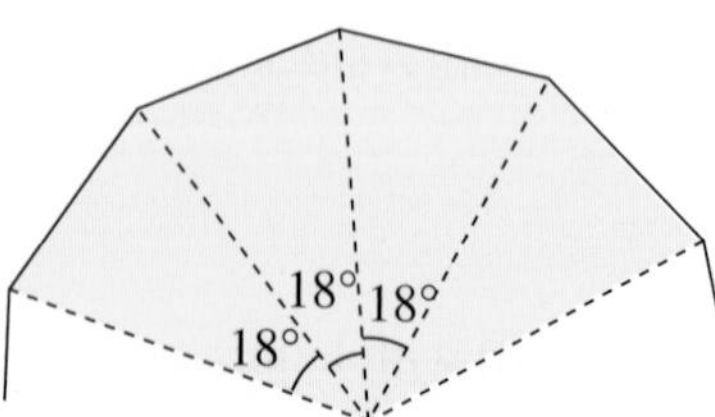

9 In a regular polygon each interior angle is 135° greater than each exterior angle. How many sides has the polygon?

10 A polygon with 7 sides (a heptagon) has 6 equal angles x and one angle $2x$. Find the value of x and draw a sketch of the polygon.

11 Which of the following could be the interior angle of a regular polygon: 144°, 160°, 163°, 172°?

12 The diagram shown is formed by joining regular pentagons. Find the angles x and y.

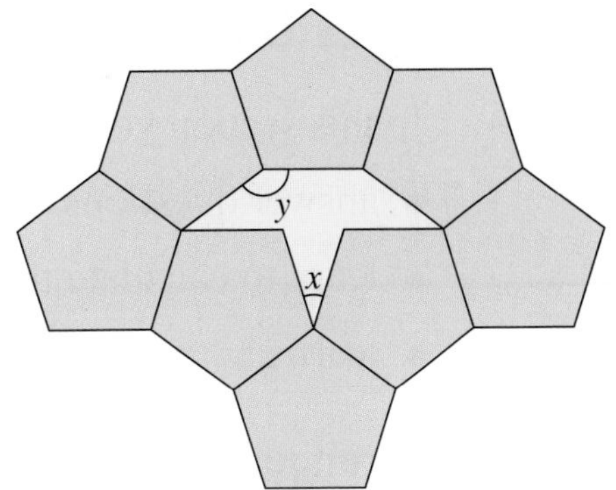

13 PQ is one side of a regular polygon with centre O.
If $y = 4\frac{1}{2}x$ find the number of sides in the polygon.

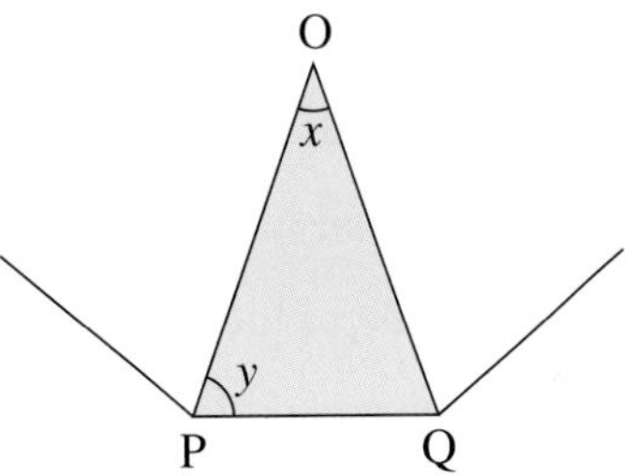

14 Half of the exterior angles of a polygon are 8° and the other exterior angles are each 12°. How many sides has the polygon?

CHECK YOURSELF ON SECTIONS 1.3 AND 1.4

1 Congruent shapes and construction

(a) Using a ruler and compasses, construct triangle ABC.

(b) Measure the length of side AC.

(c) Construct the bisector of angle ABC.

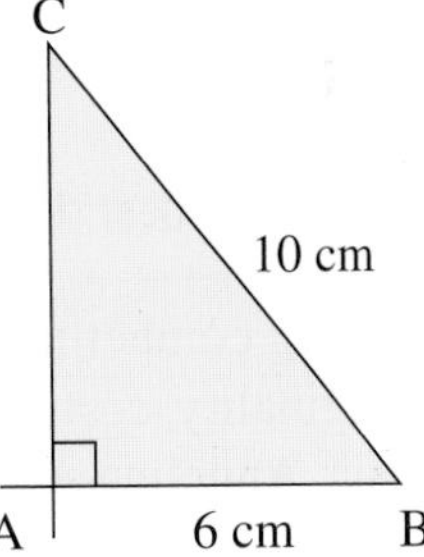

2 Geometrical reasoning

Find the angles marked with letters.

(a)

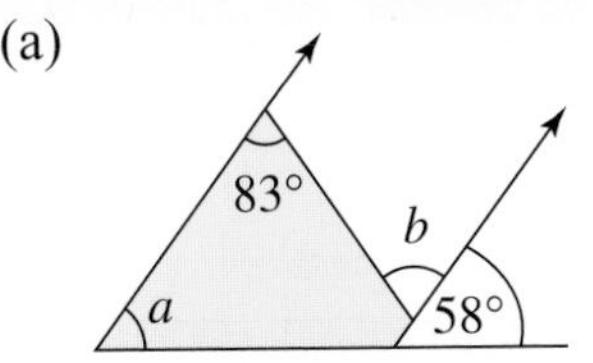

(b)

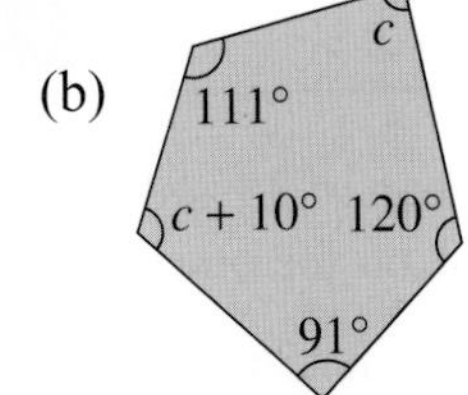

(c)

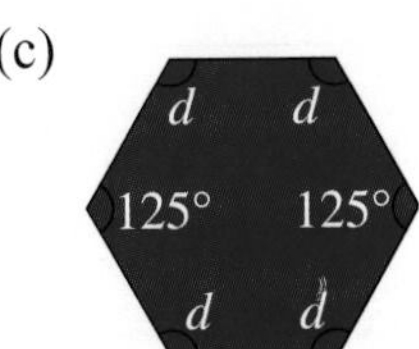

(d) Each interior angle of a regular polygon is 162°. How many sides has the polygon?

1.5 Data handling

In this section you will:

- answer questions about averages and range of data
- learn to calculate the mean of data presented in groups
- learn about frequency polygons

Averages and range

Exercise 1M

1 (a) Find the mean of the numbers 3, 2, 7, 8, 11

(b) Find the median of the numbers 8, 5, 3, 1, 4, 3, 9

(c) Find the mode of the numbers 4, 3, 4, 4, 3, 2, 4, 3

2 Write a sentence which describes how you would find the median of a set of nine numbers.

3 Find the range of each set of numbers

(a) 5, 2, 11, 25, 7, 10

(b) 2, 2, 2, 2, 2, 2, 2

(c) 8, 0, –3, 6, 15, 7

4 For the set of numbers below, find the mean and the median.

0, 0, 1, 1, 1, 2, 51

Which average best describes this set of numbers? Explain why.

5 In a dancing competition marks were awarded for style, originality, costume and interpretation of the music. Angelina scored marks of 4, 2, 1, 5 and 3.
What was her mean score?

6 Duncan has three test results with a mean of 25 and a range of 20.
His first result was 21. What did he get on the other two tests?

7 Prini has 5 cards. The 5 cards have a mean of 11 and a range of 8. What are the numbers on the last two cards?

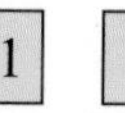

?

8 Oliver has three dart scores with a median score of 36 and a mean score of 32. The range of the three scores is 20. What are the three scores?

9 The mean height of 10 people is 150 cm. One person of height 141 cm leaves the group. Find the mean height of the remaining nine people.

Exercise 1E

1 The masses of 20 stones are given in the table.

mass	5 g	8 g	9 g	10 g
number of stones	7	4	7	2

Find the mean mass of the stones.

2 The marks achieved by 30 grandmothers in a football quiz were as follows:

mark	1	2	3	4	5
frequency	4	7	7	9	3

Find (a) the mean mark
(b) the median mark
(c) the modal mark

3 Here is the stem and leaf diagram showing the weights, in pounds, of animals in a pet shop.

(a) Write down the range of the masses.

(b) How many animals were in the shop?

(c) What is the median weight?

Stem (tens)	Leaf (units)			
1	2	5	8	
2	1	3		
3	2	7	8	8
4	5	6		

1|2 means 12

4 Here are two stem and leaf diagrams showing the marks of children in two tests, Maths and Science.

Maths:

Stem	Leaf				
2	8				
3	3	4	5	8	
4	2	4	7	7	9
5	1				

2|8 means 28

Science:

Stem	Leaf		
2	1	2	5
3	6	7	
4	5	6	
5	5	7	
6	3	8	

(a) What was the median mark for each test?

(b) What was the range for each test?

(c) In which test were the marks spread out more widely?

5 Here are five cards, written in terms of n, which is a whole number.

$n+2$ | $n-2$ | $2n+4$ | $5n+7$ | $n+4$

(a) Find, in terms of n,

(i) the range of the five cards

(ii) the median of the five cards

(iii) the mean of the five cards

(b) The mean is 3 greater than the median. Find the value of n.

Frequency distributions

Parcelforce weighed the parcels carried by one of their delivery vans in a day.

The parcels weighed up to 25 kg. The range from 0 to 25 is divided into equal intervals. The interval 5–10 kg includes weights from 5 kg up to just less than 10 kg.

A parcel weighing 10 kg goes in the 10–15 kg interval. Similarly a parcel weighing 20 kg goes in the 20–25 kg interval.

The diagram is called a frequency chart.

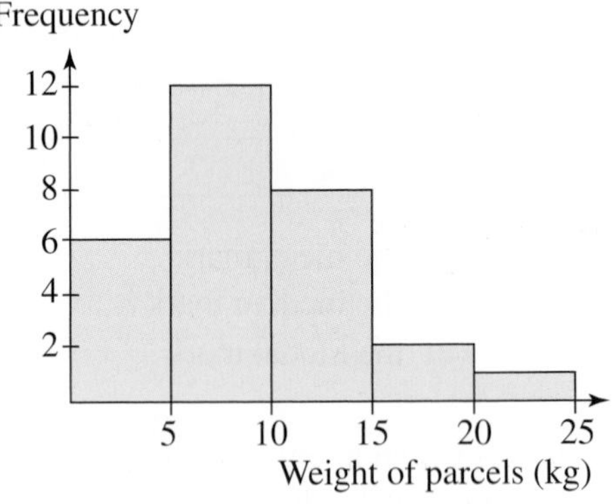

The information displayed on the chart can be written in a table, as shown on the right. This table is a *frequency distribution*.

Notice that the table does not tell us the actual weight of each parcel. For example, all we know is that there is one parcel in the interval 20–25 kg.

Weight of parcel (kg)	Number of parcels [Frequency]
0–5	6
5–10	12
10–15	8
15–20	2
20–25	1

Calculating the mean

We can obtain an *estimate* for the mean weight of the parcels by *assuming* that all the parcels in each interval have the weight at the mid-point of the interval. So we are assuming that we have 6 parcels weighing 2.5 kg, 12 parcels weighing 7.5 kg, 8 parcels weighing 12.5 kg and so on.

Weight (kg)	Mid-point	Frequency
0–5	2.5	6
5–10	7.5	12
10–15	12.5	8
15–20	17.5	2
20–25	22.5	1

$$\text{The mean weight} = \frac{\text{Total weight of parcels}}{\text{Number of parcels}}$$

$$= \frac{(2.5 \times 6) + (7.5 \times 12) + (12.5 \times 8) + (17.5 \times 2) + (22.5 \times 1)}{29}$$

$$= 9.05 \text{ kg (to 3 s.f.)}$$

Realistically, we can *estimate* the mean weight of the parcels to be about 9 kg.

Notice that the mid-point of the 0–5 interval is $\frac{0+5}{2} = 2.5$,

and that the mid-point of the 5–10 interval is $\frac{5+10}{2} = 7.5$ etc.

Exercise 2M/E

1 The heights of 30 children were measured and are shown in the table.

(a) Calculate an estimate of the mean height of the children.

(b) Why is your answer only an *estimate* of the mean height?

Height (cm)	Mid-point	Frequency
110–120	115	6
120–130		10
130–140		8
140–150		4
150–160		2

2 Fruit pickers weighed each berry they picked. The weights of the berries are shown in the table. Calculate an estimate for the mean weight of the berries.

Weight (g)	Mid-point	Frequency
4–7		5
7–10		10
10–13		15
13–16		7
16–19		4
19–22		2
22–25		2

3 Calculate an estimate for the mean for each frequency distribution.

(a)

Length (cm)	Frequency
0–10	5
10–20	11
20–40	7
40–50	7

(b)

Mass (kg)	Frequency
20–25	1
25–30	5
30–35	9
35–40	3
40–80	2

(c)

Times (s)	Frequency
20–40	5
40–60	21
60–70	15
70–90	9

4 Students were timed as they attempted to perform a simple test of dexterity. The incomplete table of results is shown. Find x, if the mean time taken was 16 seconds.

Time taken (s)	Frequency
0–10	20
10–20	50
20–30	x

5 A biologist measured the lengths of 20 worms as they slid across a special 'worm-meter' board. Find the value of x if the mean length of the worms was 15.5 cm.

Length of worm (cm)	Frequency
0–x	5
x–20	10
20–40	5

Frequency polygons

A frequency polygon can be drawn by joining the mid-points of the tops of the bars on a frequency chart.
Frequency polygons are used mainly to compare data.

- Here is a frequency chart showing the heights (or lengths!) of the babies treated at a hospital one day.

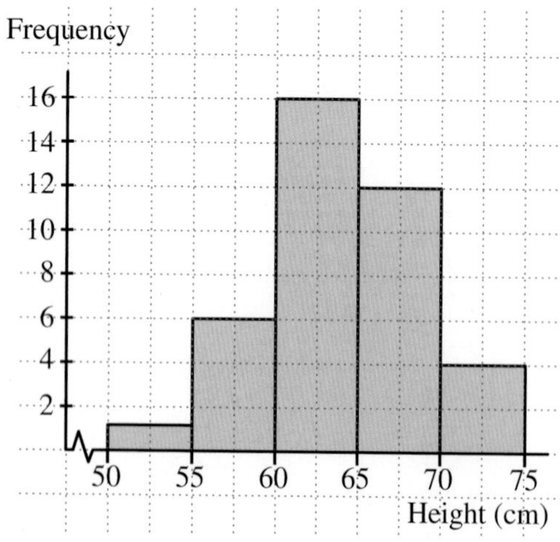

- Here is the corresponding frequency polygon, drawn by joining the mid-points of the tops of the bars.

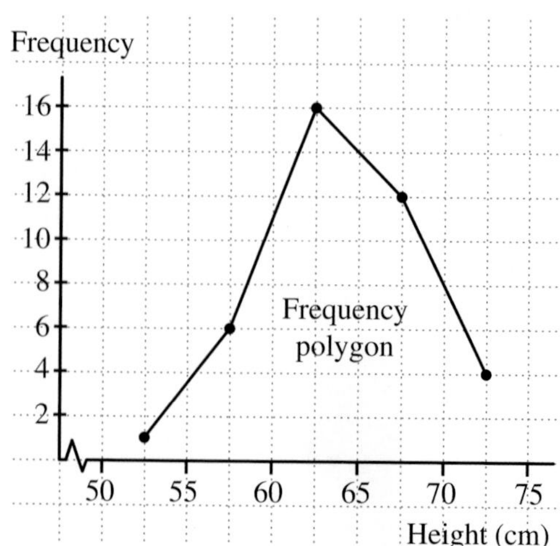

It is not necessary to draw the bars if you require only the frequency polygon.

The diagram on the right shows the frequency polygons for the exam results of 34 pupils in two subjects, Maths and French.

Two main differences are apparent:

(a) The marks obtained in the Maths exam were significantly lower for most pupils.

(b) The marks obtained in the French exam were more spread out than the Maths marks. The French marks were distributed fairly evenly over the range from 0 to 100% whereas the Maths marks were mostly between 0 and 40%.

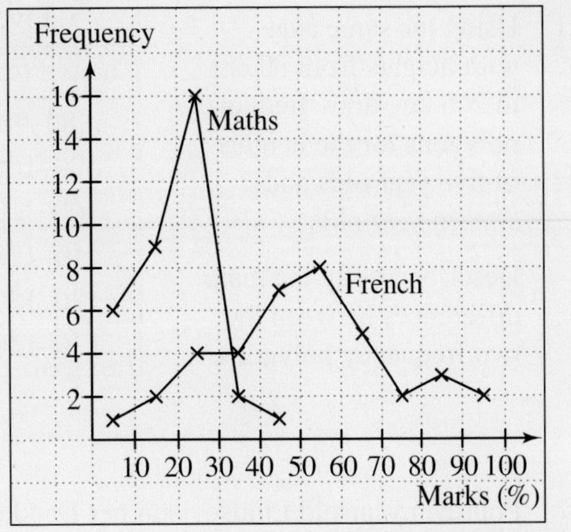

Exercise 3M

1 Draw a frequency polygon for the distribution of weights of children shown in the diagram.

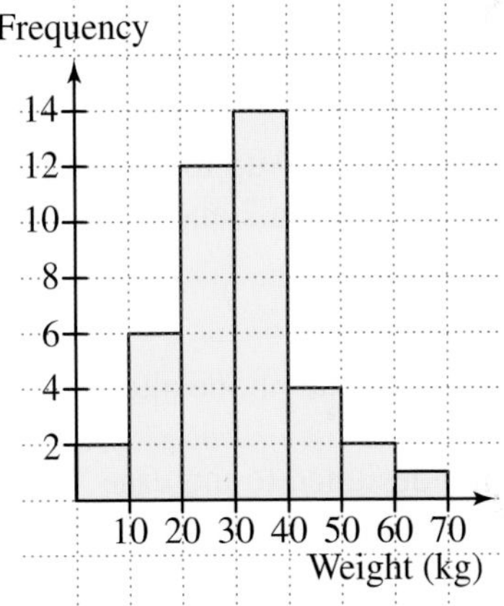

2 Here is a frequency polygon showing the weights of the people on a coach trip.

(a) How many people weighed between 50 kg and 70 kg?

(b) How many people were weighed altogether?

(c) What percentage of the people weighed less than 50 kg?

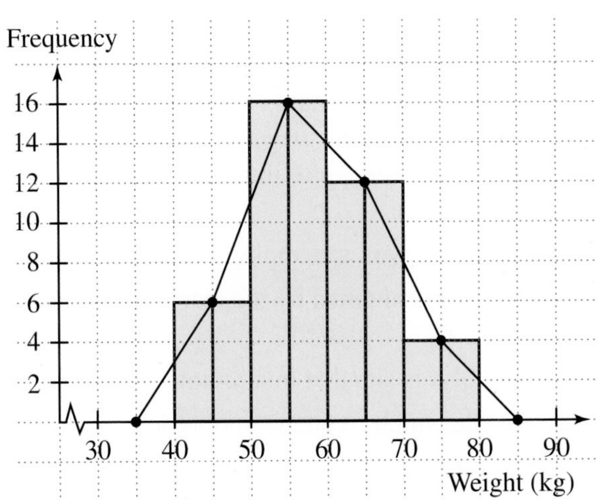

3 Using the same axes, with heights from 80 cm to 200 cm, draw frequency polygons for the heights of five year olds and sixteen year olds.

Describe briefly the main differences between the two frequency polygons.

Five year olds	
height (cm)	frequency
80–90	0
90–100	6
100–110	15
110–120	3
120–130	1
130–140	0

Sixteen year olds	
height (cm)	frequency
120–130	0
130–140	2
140–150	3
150–160	4
160–170	7
170–180	6
180–190	3
190–200	0

4 Fourteen year-old Lindsey and her Dad kept a record of the length of their telephone calls for a week. Draw frequency polygons for both Lindsey and Dad on the same set of axes.

	–2	–4	–6	–8	–10	–12	–14	–16	–18	–20	–22	–24	–26	–28	–30
Dad	10	12	14	8	0	4	0	1	0	0	0	0	0	0	0
Lindsey	0	0	0	0	0	0	0	2	6	0	2	4	8	10	6

Note: The interval '–2' mean 0 up to and including 2 min, similarly '–4' means more than 2 and up to 4 min and so on.

(a) Comment on the differences between the two polygons.
(b) Who made the most calls?
(c) Who spent longest on the phone altogether?

5 As part of a program designed to increase understanding between different generations, teachers in two schools were given a comprehension test in which they had to interpret expressions commonly used by 14/15 year olds.

For example, the teachers were asked to describe briefly what is meant by words like '*fit*', '*sorted*', '*tragic*', '*mega*' and '*chill*' and to give an approximate translation of the sentence.

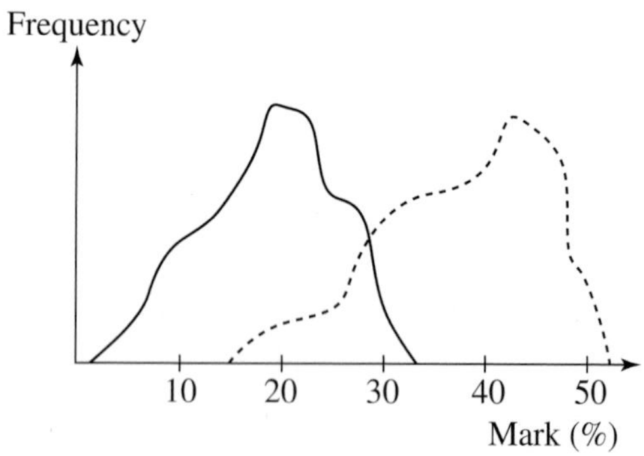

'Get a life, you sad apology for a well out of order dog!'

The marks attained by the teachers from schools A and B are shown on the frequency polygons.

School A is situated in a remote part of Scotland and school B is an inner-city school.

Decide which frequency polygon corresponds to each school.

Give reasons for your choice.

6 In a supermarket survey, shoppers were asked two questions as they left:

(a) How much have you just spent?

(b) How far away do you live?

The results were separated into two groups: shoppers who lived less than 2 miles from the supermarket and shoppers who lived further away. The frequency polygons show how much shoppers in each group had spent.

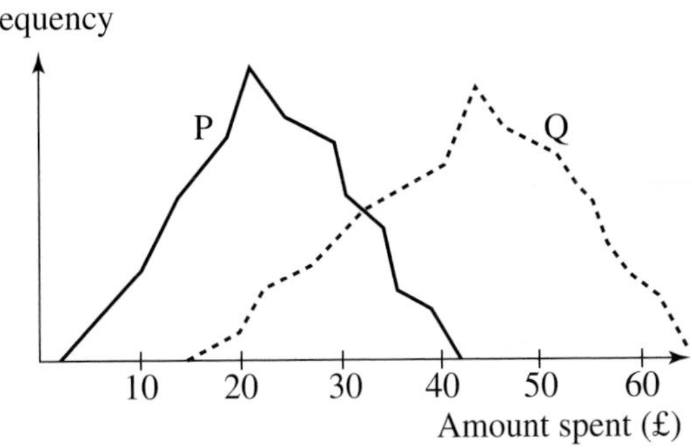

Decide which polygon, P or Q, is most likely to represent shoppers who lived less than 2 miles from the supermarket. Give your reasons.

7 Scientists doing research in genetic engineering altered the genes of a certain kind of spider. Over a period of several years, measurements were made of the adult weight of the spiders and their lifespans. The frequency polygons below show the results.

What can you deduce from the two frequency polygons? Write one sentence about weight and one sentence about lifespan.

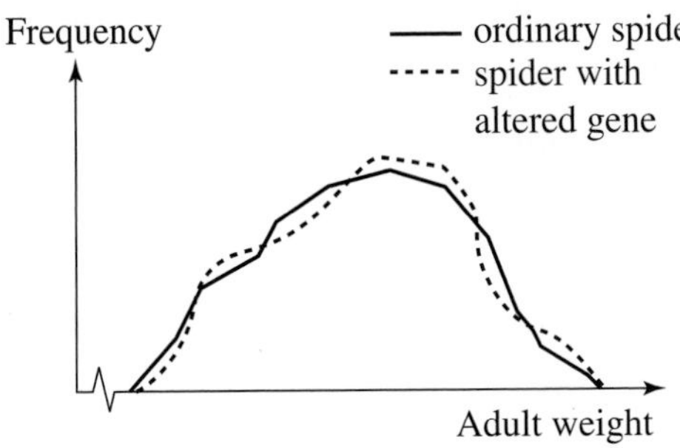

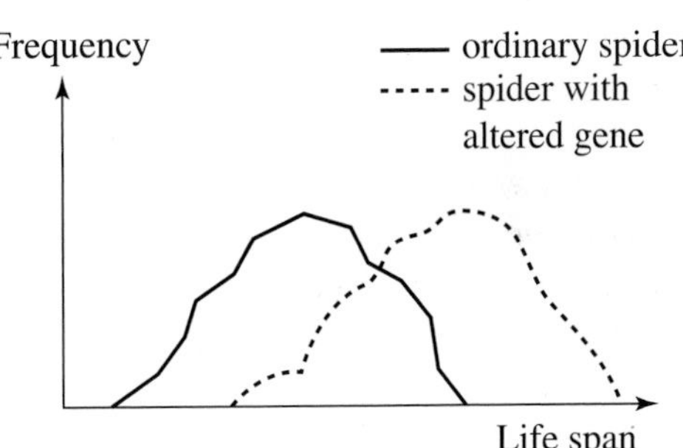

8 A large number of children were asked to state the approximate price of two items:

(a) a Mars bar; (b) a large cauliflower.

Which frequency polygon, X or Y, do you think shows the approximate prices they gave for a Mars bar? Give your reasons.

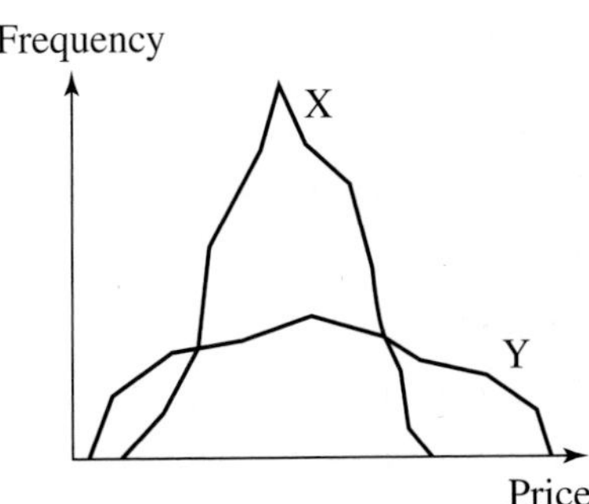

Cumulative frequency diagrams

A large set of grouped data can be displayed effectively on a *cumulative frequency* diagram.

Here is a cumulative frequency diagram which shows the marks obtained by 100 people in a test.

Point A shows that 80 people got a mark of 40 or less.

Point B shows that 30 people got a mark of 20 or less.

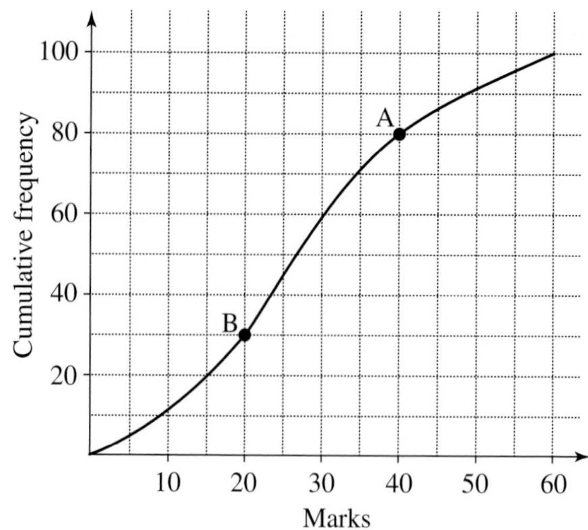

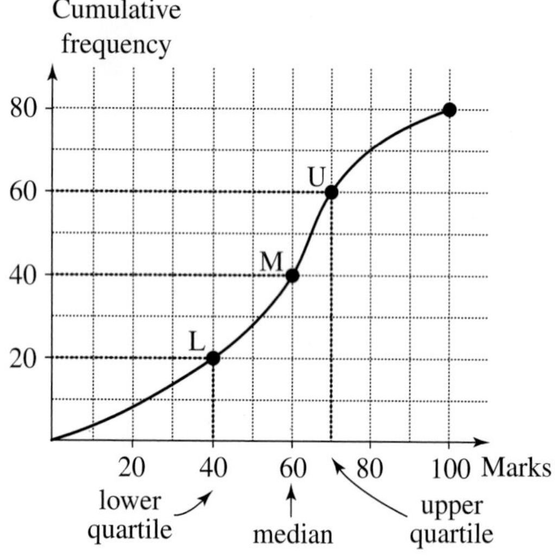

Here is another cumulative frequency diagram showing marks obtained by 80 people in a different test.

Point M is at the *median* value (half-way up the C.F. scale). We see that the median value is 60 marks.

The lower *quartile*, L, is one quarter up the C.F. axis. Here the lower quartile mark is 40.

The upper *quartile*, U, is three quarters up the C.F. axis. The upper quartile mark is 70.

The *interquartile range* is the difference between the upper and lower quartiles, in this case it is equal to $70 - 40 = 30$.

The interquartile range is an important measure of spread. It shows how widely or closely the data is spread.

Exercise 4M

1 The two graphs below show the marks obtained in two tests.

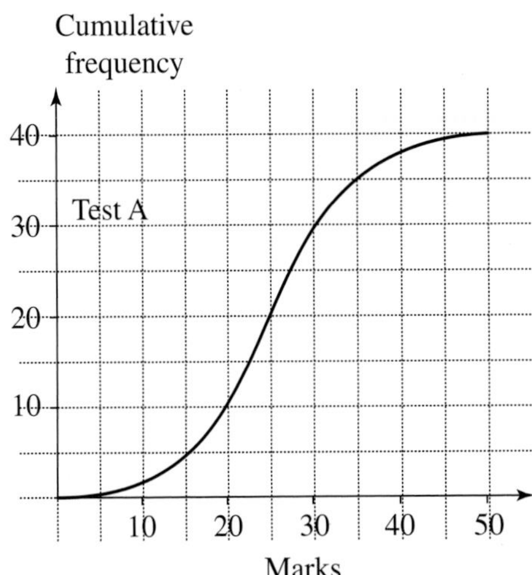

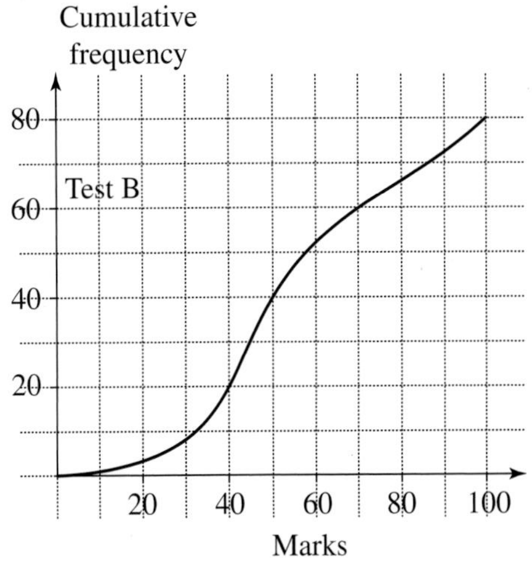

(a) How many people took test A and how many took test B?

(b) Find the median mark for each test.

(c) Find the upper and lower quartiles for each test.

(d) Find the interquartile range for each test.

2 The diagram shows the times taken by 60 pupils to solve a problem.

(a) What was the median time taken?

(b) Find the upper and lower quartiles.

(c) Find the interquartile range.

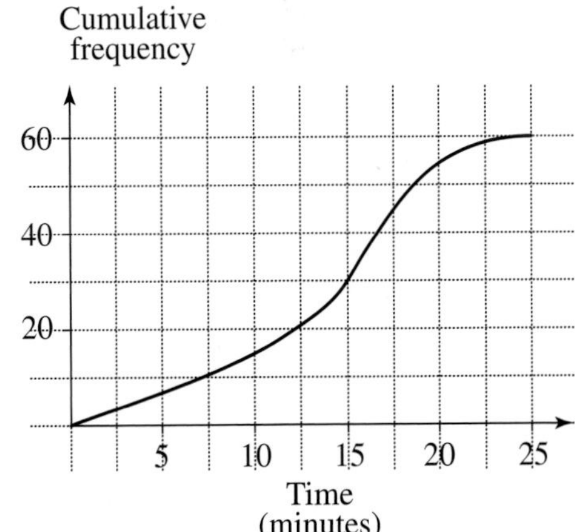

1.6 Multiplying brackets

In this section you will:

- learn how to multiply pairs of expressions in brackets
- solve a variety of problems using algebra

- The rectangle shown has length $(x + 5)$ and width $(x + 2)$. The area of the rectangle is, therefore, $(x + 5)(x + 2)$.

  The large rectangle can be split into four smaller rectangles.

  Total area of 4 smaller rectangles

  $= x^2 + 2x + 5x + 10$

  We see that $(x + 5)(x + 2) = x^2 + 2x + 5x + 10$.

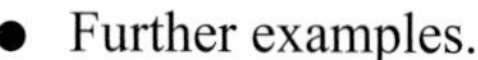

- Further examples.

(a) $(x + 7)(x + 3) = x(x + 3) + 7(x + 3)$
$= x^2 + 3x + 7x + 21$
$= x^2 + 10x + 21$

(b) $(2x + 1)(x - 3) = 2x(x - 3) + 1(x - 3)$
$= 2x^2 - 6x + x - 3$
$= 2x^2 - 5x - 3$

(c) $(x - 3)^2 = (x - 3)(x - 3)$
$= x(x - 3) - 3(x - 3)$
$= x^2 - 3x - 3x + 9$
$= x^2 - 6x + 9$

(d) $(3x + 1)^2 = (3x + 1)(3x + 1)$
$= 3x(3x + 1) + 1(3x + 1)$
$= 9x^2 + 3x + 3x + 1$
$= 9x^2 + 6x + 1$

- The ability to multiply pairs of brackets enables us to solve a wide range of problems in mathematics. Here is a proof of Pythagoras' theorem in which we require the product $(x - y)^2$.

  The square ABCD is drawn on the hypotenuse of the right-angled triangle ABE. The square ABCD is then split into four equal triangles and a square in the middle, as shown.

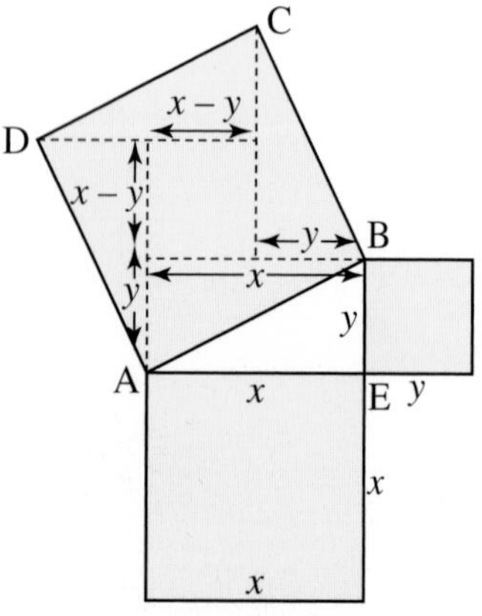

Area of square ABCD

$= 4 \times (\frac{1}{2}xy) + (x - y)^2$

$= 2\cancel{x}y + x^2 - 2\cancel{x}y + y^2$

$= x^2 + y^2$

So the square on the hypotenuse is equal to the sum of the squares on the other two sides.

Exercise 1M

Remove the brackets and simplify.

1 $(x + 3)(x + 5)$
2 $(x + 7)(x + 2)$
3 $(x + 9)(x + 1)$
4 $(x + 3)(x - 3)$
5 $(x + 3)(x - 5)$
6 $(x + 11)(x + 4)$
7 $(x + 4)(x + 2)$
8 $(x + 3)(x - 1)$
9 $(x + 3)^2$
10 $(x + 1)^2$
11 $(x + 5)^2$
12 $(x - 2)(x + 7)$
13 $(x + 5)(x + 7)$
14 $(x + 3)(x - 2)$
15 $(x - 4)(x + 1)$
16 $(x - 4)(x - 2)$
17 $(x - 3)(x - 1)$
18 $(x - 1)^2$

Exercise 1E

Remove both sets of brackets and simplify.

1 $(x - 3)(x + 1) + (x + 2)(x + 5)$
2 $(x - 7)(x - 1) + (x + 3)(x + 2)$
3 $(x + 1)^2 + (x - 3)(x - 5)$
4 $(2x + 1)(x + 1) + (x - 4)(x + 3)$
5 $(2x + 1)(x - 3) + x(x + 5)$
6 $(x - 3)(3x + 1) + 3x(x + 1)$
7 $(2x + 1)^2 + (x + 4)^2$
8 $(x + 2)^2 - x(x + 3)$
9 $(3x + 1)(2x + 3) + 3x(x - 2)$
10 $(3x + 1)(x - 5) - 3x(x - 5)$

11 Find pairs of expressions from the yellow loop that multiply to give

(a) $n^2 + 7n + 10$
(b) $n^2 + 5n + 6$
(c) $n^2 + 4n - 5$
(d) $2n^2 - 5n - 3$

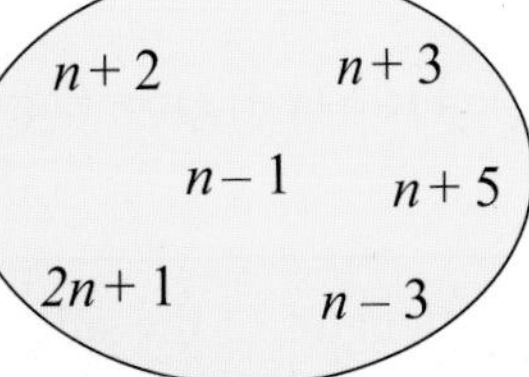

12 The area of each rectangle is inside. Find expressions for the unknown sides.

(a)

(b)

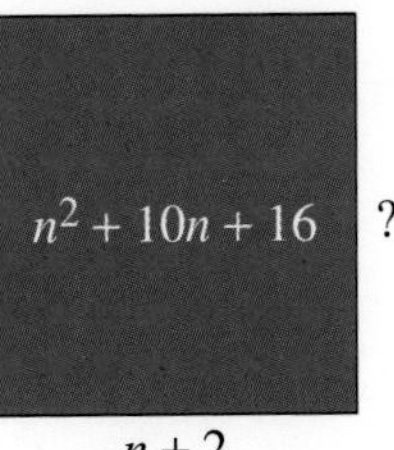

13 Copy and complete.

(a) $(x + 3)(\quad) = x^2 + 9x + 18$

(b) $(\quad)(x + 2) = x^2 - 4$

(c) $(\quad)(\quad) = n^2 + 8n + 15$

(d) $(\quad)(\quad) = a^2 + a - 6$

(e) $(\quad)(\quad) = n^2 + n - 12$

(f) $(\quad)(\quad) = m^2 - m - 20$

Solving equations

Solve the equation $(x - 1)(x + 2) = (x + 3)^2$

$$x(x + 2) - 1(x + 2) = (x + 3)(x + 3)$$

$$\cancel{x^2} + 2x - x - 2 = \cancel{x^2} + 3x + 3x + 9$$

[Subtract x^2 from both sides.] $-2 - 9 = 3x + 3x - 2x + x$

$$-11 = 5x$$

$$-2\tfrac{1}{5} = x$$

Exercise 2M

Solve the equations.

1 $(x + 3)(x - 1) = (x + 4)(x - 3)$

2 $x(x + 7) = (x - 3)(x - 1)$

3 $(x + 5)^2 = (x + 6)(x + 3)$

4 $(3x + 1)(x - 1) = 3x(x - 2)$

5 $(2x + 1)(x + 3) = x(2x - 5)$

6 $(x + 3)^2 = (x - 2)^2$

7 $(2x + 1)^2 = (4x - 1)(x + 1)$

8 $(x - 3)(x + 3) = x^2 - 18x$

9 $(x + 1)^2 + (x + 2)^2 = (2x + 1)(x + 1)$

10 $(x + 2)^2 + (2x - 1)^2 = 5x(x + 1)$

Find the lengths of the sides of the right angled triangle.

By Pythagoras' theorem:

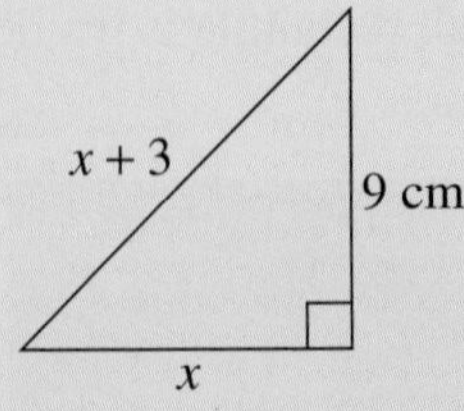

$$(x + 3)^2 = x^2 + 9^2$$

$$\cancel{x^2} + 3x + 3x + 9 = \cancel{x^2} + 81$$

$$6x = 72$$

$$x = 12$$

The sides of the triangle are of length 9 cm, 12 cm, 15 cm

Exercise 2E

In each question form an equation involving x and then solve it.

1 Use Pythagoras' theorem to form an equation. Solve the equation to find x.

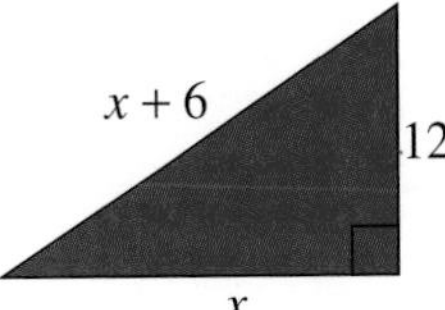

2 Find x, and hence the three sides of the triangles shown.

(a)

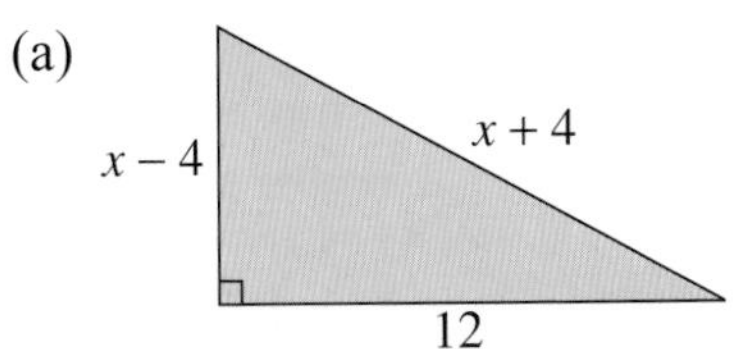

(b)

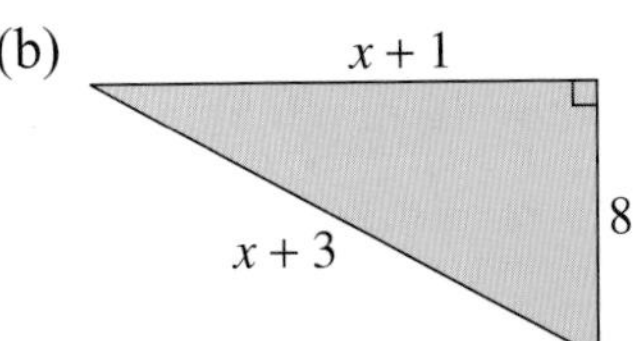

3 The two pictures have the same area. Find x.

4 A rectangle measures x by 10. The length of a diagonal of the rectangle is 2 cm greater than the longer side x. Find x.

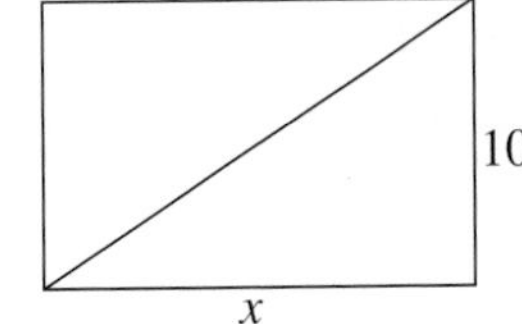

5 The sum of the areas of the two rectangles is equal to the area of the square. Find x.

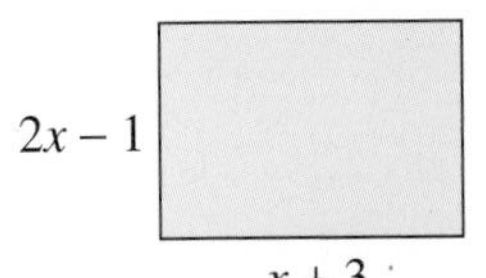

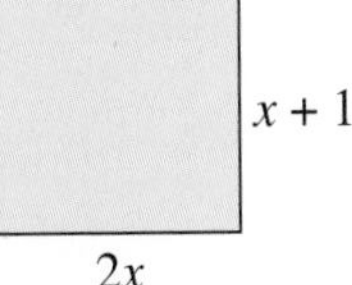

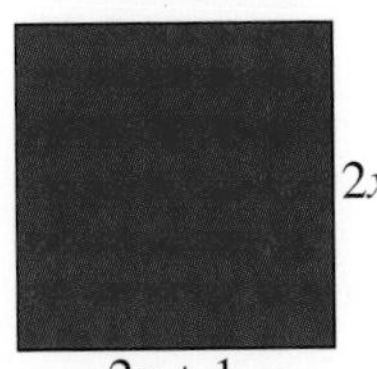

6 The rectangle and the triangle have the same area. Find x.

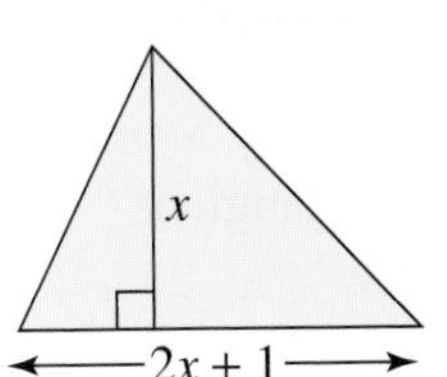

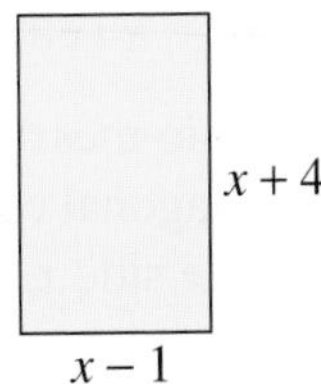

7 If the radius of a circle is increased by 3 cm the area is increased by 99π cm^2. Find the radius of the original circle.

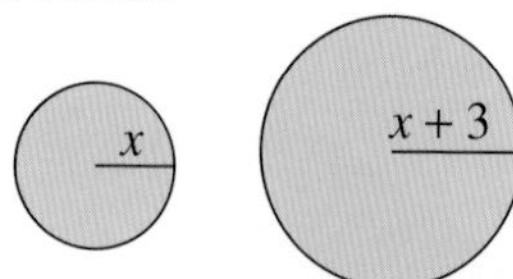

8 An approximate formula for the stopping distances when travelling in a car is given by

$d = \frac{v(v+20)}{60}$ $\quad d$ = distance in metres, $\quad v$ = speed in m.p.h.

If a driver increases his speed by 10 m.p.h. it takes him 15 metres extra to stop. What is his initial speed?

CHECK YOURSELF ON SECTIONS 1.5 AND 1.6

1 Averages and range

(a) The leading five cyclists in the Tour de France have weights 63 kg, 68 kg, 59 kg, 61.5 kg and 60 kg.

By how much does the mean weight of these cyclists exceed the median weight?

(b) The heights of the leading 30 riders are shown in the table. Calculate an estimate of the mean height of the riders.

Height (cm)	Frequency
140–150	5
150–160	6
160–170	11
170–180	8

2 Multiplying brackets

(a) Remove the brackets and simplify

(i) $(n + 2)(n + 10)$ (ii) $(a - 1)^2$ (iii) $(x - 3)(x + 6) + (2x + 1)(x + 2)$

(b) Solve the equation $x(x + 4) = (x - 2)^2$

(c) The rectangular photo measures x cm by 5 cm. The length of the diagonal of the rectangle is 1 cm greater than the side x. Find x.

UNIT 1 MIXED REVIEW

Part 1

1 ABCD is a square. Find angle ADE.

D C E 266° A B

2 (a) Work out (i) $9 + 15 \div 3$ (ii) $(7 - 5)^5 \div 10^2$

(b) Copy each question and write brackets so that you obtain the correct answer.

(i) $6 + 7 \times 4 = 52$ (ii) $5 \times 6 - 4 \div 2 = 13$

(iii) $72 \div 8 + 4 + 5 = 11$ (iv) $8 \times 5 - 8 \div 4 = 8$

3 Sales of a computer were worth £26 540 000. After a 'Help' button was fitted sales increased by 21.2%. Find the value of the increased sales.

4 (a) Write down all the factors of

(i) 16 (ii) 30

(b) Write 3080 as the product of its prime factors.

5 Work out and give your answer correct to 1 decimal place.

(a) $\left[\dfrac{3.7}{0.84 + 1.113}\right] \times (11.5 \div 4.2)$ (b) $\dfrac{3.5 + 8.027}{8.4 - 1.7^3}$

6 The diagonal of a square is 7 cm long. Work out the area of the square.

7 Multiply out and simplify these expressions.

(a) $2(3x - 1) - 3(x + 1)$ (b) $x(3x + 5) - 2x(x + 1)$

(c) $(x + 2)(x + 5)$ (d) $(2x + 1)^2$

8 Look at the diagram.

(a) Name a triangle that is congruent to TQS.

(b) Name a triangle that is similar to TQS.

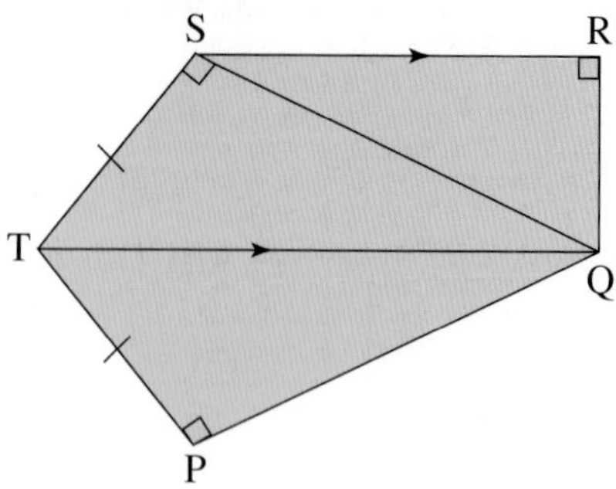

9 When Grace is in an argument, she wins 8 out of 25 disputes when she does not scream.

When she screams she wins 6 out of 20. Which is the better strategy?

10 Work out, without a calculator:

(a) 2.7×5.3 (b) $10\,795 \div 17$

11 On a map of scale 1:10000 the length of a car park is 8 cm.

What is the actual length of the car park?

12 Find the value of n in each case.

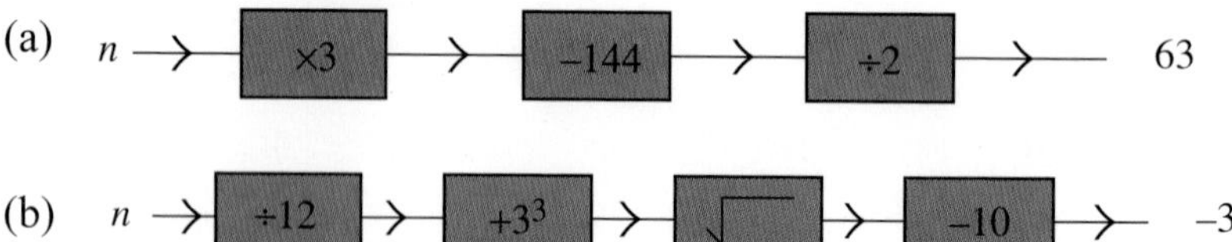

13 Copy and complete by filling in the boxes

(a) $\square(n + 5) = 2n^2 + \square$

(b) $\square(n - 2) = \square - 10$

(c) $\square(\square + \square) = n^2 + 5n$

14 A regular polygon has n sides. Each interior angle of the polygon is 176°. Work out the value of n.

15 An angry rooster runs 32 metres in 8 secs.

Work out his speed in km/h.

Part 2

1 Solve the equation $(n + 5)(n - 1) = (n + 3)(n + 2)$

2 Work out 4% of $\frac{3}{4}$ of 25% of $(1 \div 0.0001)$

3 Fill in the boxes so that $\square(\square + \square) + \square(\square + \square) = 5a + 10b + 3n + 12m$

4 What is the angle between adjacent wires at the centre of this umbrella?

5 (a) For the set of numbers below, work out the mean, the median and the mode.

−1, 2, 2, 3, 4, 11, 84

(b) Which average best describes this set of numbers? Explain why.

6 Find the angle x.

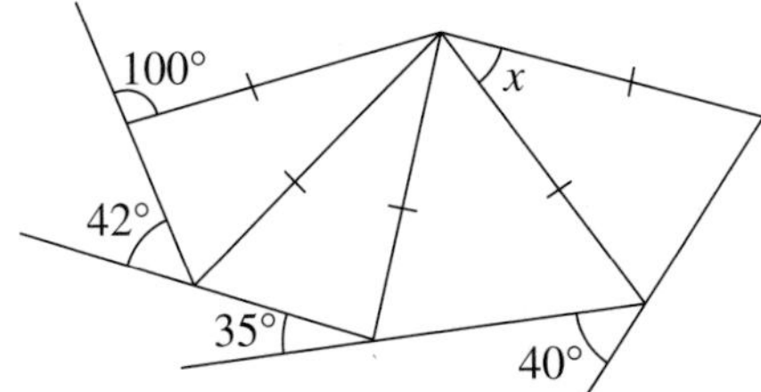

7 The stem and leaf diagram shows the ages in years of people on a bus.

Stem	leaf
1	0 3 7
2	6 8
3	2 2 6 9
4	1 4

(a) Find the range of the ages.

(b) Find the median age.

1|0 means 10

8 

The sides of the photo are in the ratio 3:2. Its perimeter is 60 cm. Calculate the area of the photo.

9 Solve the equation $\frac{n}{4} + 7 = 6$

10 The table shows the marks of 30 footballers in a spelling test.

mark	0	1	2	3	4	5
frequency	1	3	11	8	5	2

Find (a) the mean mark

(b) the median mark

11 On a map of scale 1:20 000 the area of a forest is 5 cm^2. Calculate the actual area of the forest in hectares.

12 The cross section of this wire 'cylinder' is a regular polygon with 20 sides. Work out the size of the interior angles of the polygon.

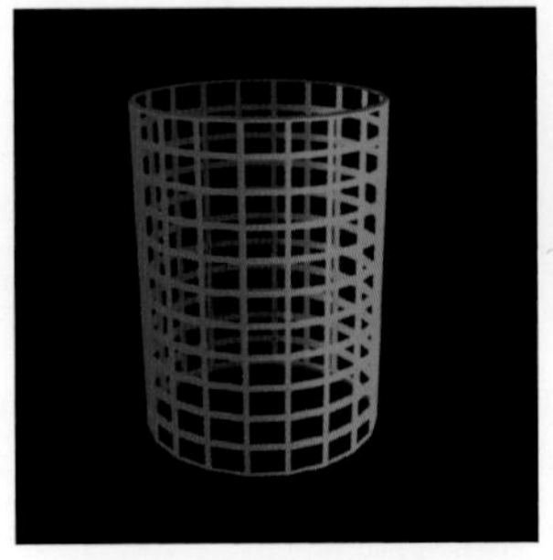

13 What fraction of the area of a circle of radius 5 cm is more than 3 cm from the centre?

3 cm

5 cm

14 The diagram shows a rectangle. Form an equation and solve it to find the value of x.

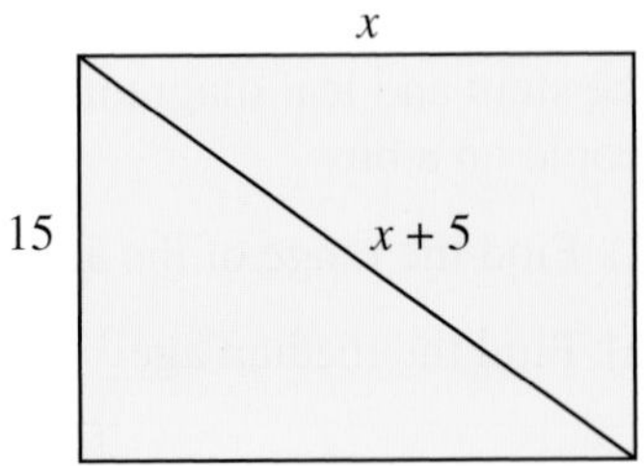

15 ABCDE is a regular pentagon, and ABFGHI is a regular hexagon.

(a) Calculate the size of

(i) $E\hat{D}C$ (ii) $B\hat{C}F$

(b) Is it possible that E, A and I are successive vertices of a regular polygon? Explain your answer.

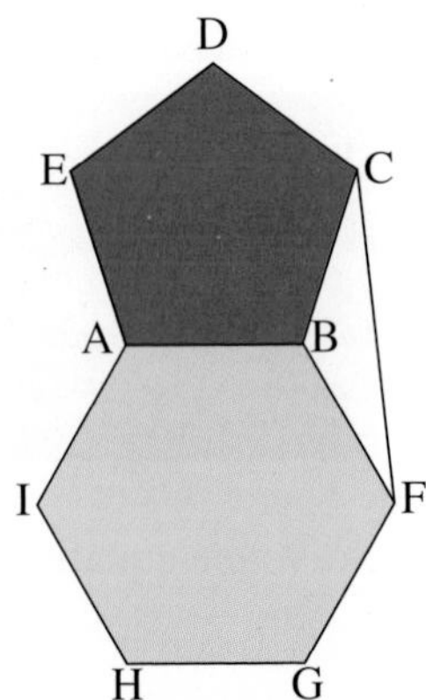

Puzzles and Problems 1

Find the letters

The totals for the rows and columns are given. Find the values of the letters.

1

A	A	A	A	24
A	B	C	A	23
A	C	D	B	26
D	B	B	B	
	20	26	18	

2

P	Q	Q	P	34
P	P	Q	Q	34
P	Q	P	Q	34
Q	Q	P	Q	37
31	37	34	37	

3

P	Q	P	Q	Q	19
Q	Q	T	R	S	13
P	Q	Q	P	Q	19
R	Q	R	Q	R	12
T	Q	S	T	S	13
16	15	15	14	16	

4

D	C	E	B	D	25
B	A	B	B	A	19
C	C	B	A	D	18
A	E	D	A	B	27
B	B	C	A	E	21
19	20	22	21	28	

5

B	A	E	B	C	23
A	C	D	E	D	21
B	7	B	B	E	30
A	D	D	E	A	20
C	B	A	B	B	28
24	27	24	25	22	

6 The letters A, B, C, D, E, F, G, H, I, J stand for the numbers 0, 1, 2, 3, 4, 5, 6, 7, 8, 9 but not in that order. Use the clues below to find the number for each letter.

(a) $A \times B = B$

(b) $J + D = J$

(c) $J + A = H$

(d) $C - B = E$

(e) $G \times G \times G = F$

(f) $C - A = H$

(g) $B \times B = I$

(h) $E \times G = A \times F$

7 Now we have twelve letters for the digits 0, 1, 2, ... 11 but not in that order. Find the number for each letter.

(a) $B + C = L$
(b) $H = I \times I \times I$
(c) $C \times I = J$
(d) $E + E = E$
(e) $D - K = K + B$
(f) $A \times A = D$
(g) $B \times B = B$
(h) $I + A = C$
(i) $L + B = F$

A long time ago! 1

Islamic patterns – Girih tiles

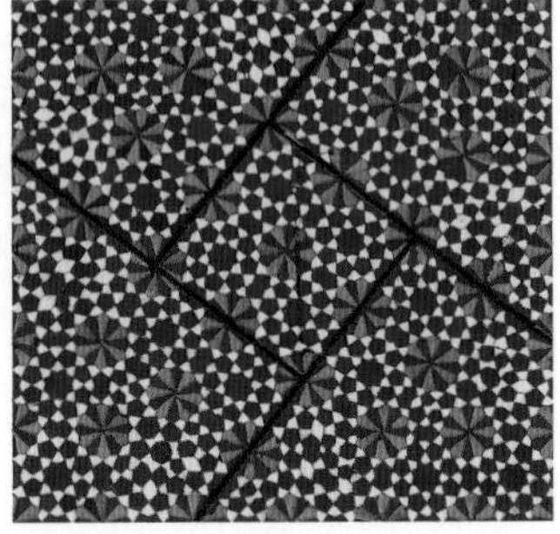

Islamic mosques and palaces are often decorated with ornate stars and polygons.

They were decorated like this hundreds of years ago. While Europe was in the Dark Ages, Islamic culture flourished.

'Girih' designs use tessellating polygons and are often overlaid with a zigzag network of lines.

'Girih' tiles are a set of five tiles: a regular decagon (10 sides), a rhombus, a regular pentagon, a bow tie and an elongated hexagon as shown below:

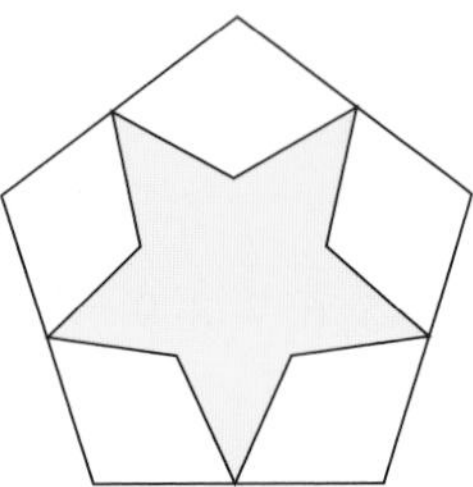

pentagon (all interior angles are 108°)

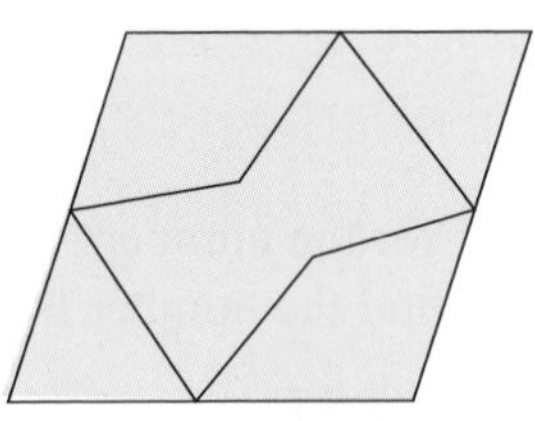

rhombus (interior angles are 72°, 108°, 72°, 108°)

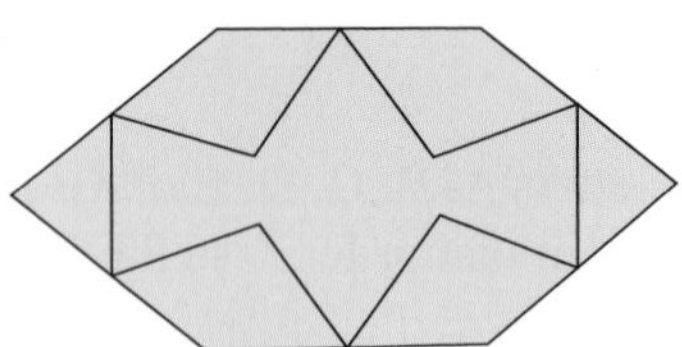

hexagon (interior angles are 72°, 14°, 144°, 72°, 144°, 14°)

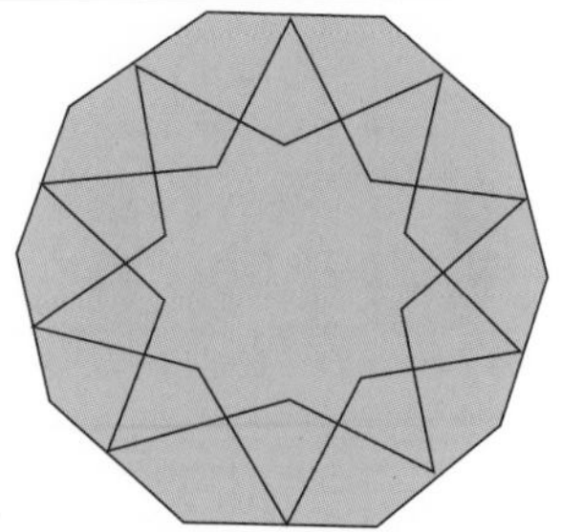

decagon (all interior angles are 144°)

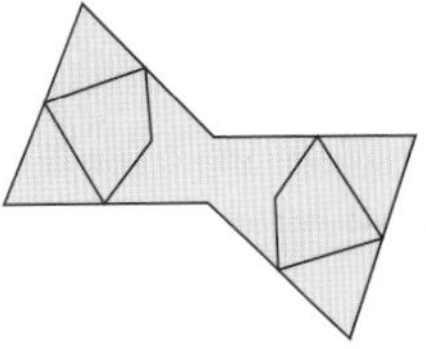

bow tie (interior angles are 72°, 72°, 216°, 72°, 72°, 216°)

Teacher's note: Accurate drawings of these five tiles are in the answer book where they can be photocopied.

Exercise 1M

1 Draw each of the five 'girih' tiles onto tracing paper or your teacher may choose to provide you with several photocopies of the tiles. In a small group try to arrange the tiles to make your own pattern. Part of a design is shown below. There must be no gaps.

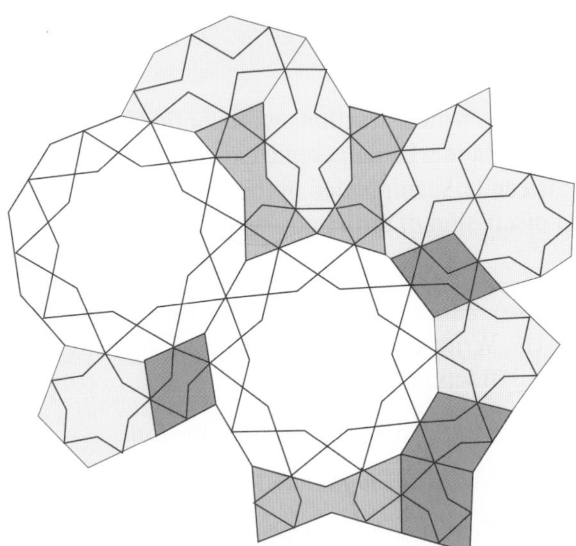

Draw all the zigzag network of lines in the same colour. Colour in the remaining part of your design as you wish.

In many designs, only the zigzag lines would be left visible.

2 **RESEARCH:**

(a) Islamic designs feature quasicrystalline geometry.
Find out what 'quasicrystalline' means.

(b) Look out examples of Islamic art, particularly mosaics.
Can you spot any use of 'girih' tiles? Write a short description about what you find and whether you like it.

UNIT 2

2.1 Using fractions

In this section you will:

- multiply, divide, add and subtract fractions
- solve problems involving fractions
- learn about recurring decimals
- learn about algebraic fractions

Arithmetic with fractions

As you progress further in mathematics, the ability to handle fractions with confidence becomes more and more important. Mistakes are frequently made when algebraic expressions contain fractions. Fractions involving algebraic symbols can be manipulated in the same way as ordinary numerical fractions. This section begins with a discussion of arithmetic with fractions.

Multiplying

(a) $\frac{3}{4}$ of $12 = \frac{3}{4} \times \frac{12}{1}$
$= \frac{36}{4}$
$= 9$

(b) $\frac{2}{3} \times \frac{5}{7} = \frac{10}{21}$

(c) $2\frac{1}{2} \times \frac{1}{4} = \frac{5}{2} \times \frac{1}{4}$
$= \frac{5}{8}$

(i) Write any mixed fractions as top heavy fractions.

(ii) Multiply the numbers on the top

(iii) Multiply the numbers on the bottom.

(iv) Cancel down if necessary. This can be done either before or after multiplying.

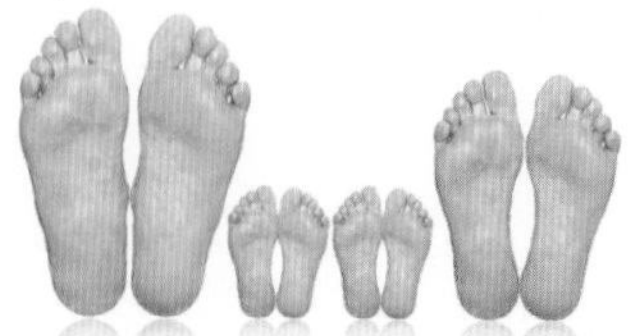

In this photo 4 out of 8 feet are those of small children.
4 out of 8 = one half.

Dividing

Method: (i) Invert the fraction you are dividing by and then multiply the two fractions.

(ii) Write any mixed fractions as top heavy fractions.

Examples: $\frac{3}{5} \div \frac{2}{3}$ $\quad$ $2\frac{1}{3} \div \frac{3}{4}$

$= \frac{3}{5} \times \frac{3}{2}$ $\quad$ $= \frac{7}{3} \times \frac{4}{3}$

$= \frac{9}{10}$ $\quad$ $= \frac{28}{9}$

$= 3\frac{1}{9}$

Addition and subtraction

Method: (i) The fractions to be added must be written as fractions with the same denominator.

(ii) Mixed fractions should be written as top heavy fractions.

(a) $\frac{1}{5} + \frac{1}{3}$

$= \frac{3}{15} + \frac{5}{15}$

$= \frac{8}{15}$

(b) $\frac{3}{4} + \frac{1}{5}$

$= \frac{15}{20} + \frac{4}{20}$

$= \frac{19}{20}$

(c) $3\frac{1}{5} - 2\frac{1}{2}$

$= \frac{16}{5} - \frac{5}{2}$

$= \frac{32}{10} - \frac{25}{10}$

$= \frac{7}{10}$

Exercise 1M

Work out without a calculator and give the answer in its simplest form.

1 $\frac{1}{4} + \frac{3}{8}$

2 $\frac{3}{5} + \frac{1}{10}$

3 $\frac{2}{3} + \frac{1}{6}$

4 $\frac{5}{12} + \frac{1}{4}$

5 $\frac{7}{8} - \frac{1}{2}$

6 $\frac{1}{3} + \frac{1}{2}$

7 $\frac{3}{5} - \frac{1}{4}$

8 $\frac{4}{7} - \frac{1}{2}$

9 $\frac{2}{3} + \frac{1}{4}$

10 $\frac{2}{5} + \frac{1}{3}$

11 $\frac{1}{7} + \frac{1}{2}$

12 $\frac{1}{5} - \frac{1}{6}$

13 $\frac{2}{3} - \frac{5}{12}$

14 $\frac{7}{9} - \frac{1}{6}$

15 $\frac{4}{5} - \frac{2}{7}$

16 $\frac{7}{10} - \frac{1}{3}$

17 $1\frac{1}{4} - \frac{2}{5}$

18 $1\frac{3}{4} - \frac{2}{3}$

19 $3\frac{1}{4} + 1\frac{3}{5}$

20 $2\frac{5}{6} + 1\frac{1}{4}$

Questions 21 to 40 involve either multiplying or dividing.

21 $\frac{2}{3} \times \frac{1}{5}$

22 $\frac{3}{5} \times \frac{3}{4}$

23 $\frac{5}{9} \times \frac{3}{4}$

24 $1\frac{3}{4} \times \frac{1}{5}$

25 $\frac{3}{8} \times \frac{4}{5}$

26 $\frac{2}{9} \times \frac{6}{7}$

27 $\frac{5}{12} \times \frac{3}{10}$

28 $\frac{5}{8} \times \frac{6}{15}$

29 $\frac{5}{6} \div \frac{1}{2}$

30 $\frac{7}{8} \div \frac{2}{3}$

31 $\frac{5}{9} \div \frac{3}{4}$

32 $2\frac{1}{2} \div \frac{1}{5}$

33 $3\frac{1}{4} \times 2\frac{1}{2}$

34 $\frac{5}{8} \div 1\frac{1}{2}$

35 $\frac{5}{9} \div \frac{1}{3}$

36 $\frac{3}{5} \div \frac{9}{100}$

37 $\frac{3}{5} \div 2$

38 $\frac{4}{7} \div 3$

39 $1\frac{1}{4} \div 4$

40 $5\frac{1}{2} \div 3$

41 $\left(\frac{3}{5} \div \frac{1}{3}\right) + \left(1\frac{1}{4} \times \frac{1}{10}\right)$

42 $\left(\frac{1}{2} + \frac{1}{3} + \frac{1}{9}\right) \div \left(\frac{1}{4} - \frac{1}{9}\right)$

Exercise 1E

Copy each square and fill in the missing numbers or symbols (+, –, ×, ÷). The arrows act as equals signs.

1

	÷	2	→	$1\frac{1}{2}$
÷		÷		
	×		→	2
↓		↓		
	×	8	→	

2

$\frac{1}{4}$	–	$\frac{1}{16}$	→	
		+		
$\frac{1}{8}$	÷		→	1
↓		↓		
$\frac{1}{8}$			→	$\frac{5}{16}$

3

	–	$\frac{1}{5}$	→	$\frac{7}{15}$
–		×		
	÷		→	$1\frac{1}{2}$
↓		↓		
	÷	$\frac{1}{20}$	→	

4

	–	$\frac{1}{5}$	→	$\frac{1}{20}$
×		÷		
2	÷		→	
↓		↓		
	×	$\frac{4}{5}$	→	

5

$\frac{2}{3}$	$\times$	4	$\rightarrow$	
		$\div$		
$\frac{1}{2}$	$\div$		$\rightarrow$	$\frac{1}{16}$
$\downarrow$		$\downarrow$		
$\frac{1}{3}$			$\rightarrow$	$\frac{5}{6}$

6

	$\times$	$\frac{1}{3}$	$\rightarrow$	$\frac{1}{8}$
		$\div$		
$\frac{1}{4}$			$\rightarrow$	$\frac{11}{12}$
$\downarrow$		$\downarrow$		
$\frac{5}{8}$	$-$		$\rightarrow$	$\frac{1}{8}$

Solving Problems

After 45 ml is poured from a full bottle of wine, the bottle is $\frac{5}{8}$ full.
How many ml are there in a full bottle?

The difference between a full bottle and $\frac{5}{8}$ of a bottle is $\frac{3}{8}$ of a bottle.

So $\frac{3}{8}$ of a bottle = 45 ml

$\therefore \frac{1}{8}$ of a bottle $= \frac{45}{3} = 15$ ml

$\therefore \frac{8}{8}$ of a bottle $= 15 \times 8$

$= 120$ ml

A full bottle contains 120 ml of wine.

Exercise 2M

1. Of the 495 pupils at Cantonna College, $\frac{1}{3}$ travel by bus, $\frac{1}{5}$ travel by car and the rest cycle.

   How many pupils cycle to the college?

2. Of his weekly income, Gary spends $\frac{1}{4}$ on food and $\frac{1}{3}$ on rent. What fraction of his income is left for other things?

3. (a) Mrs. Beaton has $3\frac{1}{4}$ pounds of flour. The recipe for a cake calls for $\frac{1}{4}$ of a pound of flour.
   How many cakes can be made?

   (b) Suppose she has $4\frac{2}{3}$ pounds and the recipe calls for $\frac{2}{5}$ pound per cake. How many complete cakes can be made now?

4. The number of magazines sold by a newsagent is $2\frac{1}{4}$ times the number of books sold. If 549 magazines are sold, how many books are sold?

5 The reciprocal of 3 is $\frac{1}{3}$. The reciprocal of 8 is $\frac{1}{8}$. The reciprocal of x is $\frac{1}{x}$.

(a) Find the reciprocal of [the reciprocal of 3 + the reciprocal of 4].

(b) Find the reciprocal of the reciprocal of the reciprocal of $\frac{3}{4}$.

6 Find the square root of the reciprocal of $\left(\frac{71}{121} - \frac{2}{11}\right)$.

7 A bottle is $\frac{9}{10}$ full of coke. After 800 ml is drunk, the bottle is $\frac{1}{2}$ full. How many ml are there in a full bottle?

Exercise 2E

1 At midday Wembley Stadium is $\frac{1}{5}$ full. By 2.00 p.m. a further 39 200 people have arrived for a concert and the stadium is $\frac{2}{3}$ full. What is the capacity of the stadium?

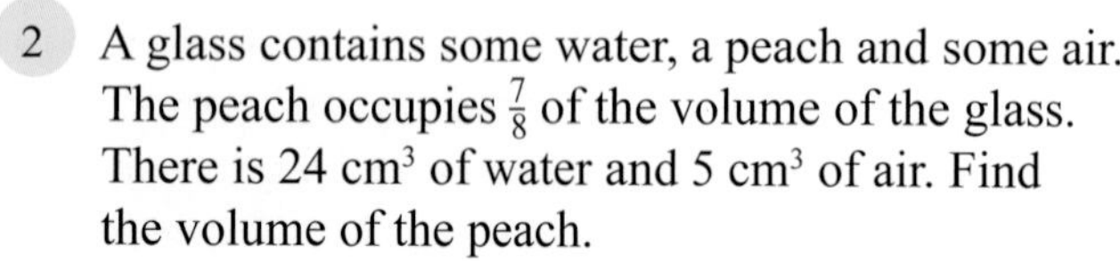

2 A glass contains some water, a peach and some air. The peach occupies $\frac{7}{8}$ of the volume of the glass. There is 24 cm^3 of water and 5 cm^3 of air. Find the volume of the peach.

3 Work out

(a) $\left[\frac{1}{2} \text{ of } \left(\frac{1}{3} + \frac{1}{4}\right)\right] \div \frac{1}{5}$ (b) $\dfrac{\frac{1}{2} + \frac{1}{3} + \frac{1}{4}}{\frac{1}{2} \times \frac{1}{3} \times \frac{1}{4}}$ (c) $\sqrt{\left(\frac{2}{3} \times \frac{3}{4} \times \frac{4}{5} \times \ldots \times \frac{99}{100}\right) \times \left(\frac{9}{50}\right)}$

4 Copy and complete

$\left(\frac{4}{7} - \frac{1}{2}\right) \times \dfrac{\square}{\square} + \frac{1}{9} = \frac{1}{6}$

5 Two whole numbers a and b are chosen such that $a < b$ and $b < 7$. How many *different* fractions are there of the form $\frac{a}{b}$?

6 If three fifths of a number is 45, what is two thirds of it?

7 Find two whole numbers, x and y, such that $\frac{x}{y}$ is equal to π, correct to 3 decimal places. You are not allowed $\frac{22}{7}$ or multiples of these numbers.

Recurring decimals

We have seen that fractions can be converted into decimals by dividing the numerator by the denominator. [E.g. $\frac{3}{4} = 3 \div 4 = 0.75$]

Sometimes the division gives a decimal which recurs, for example $\frac{1}{3} = 1 \div 3 = 0.33333\ldots$

It is important to realise that all recurring decimals can be written as exact fractions. Here is a method for converting recurring decimals to fractions.

(a) Change 0.7777 … to a fraction.

Let $r = 0.7777\ldots$

$10r = 7.7777 \ldots$ (multiply by 10)

$9r = 7$ (subtract)

$r = \frac{7}{9}$

So $0.7777 \ldots = \frac{7}{9}$

(b) Change 0.373737… to a fraction.

Let $r = 0.373737\ldots$

$100r = 37.373737\ldots$

$99r = 37$

$r = \frac{37}{99}$

so $0.\dot{3}\dot{7} = \frac{37}{99}$

Exercise 3E

1 Copy and complete to change 0.4444… to a fraction.

Let $r = 0.4444\ldots$

$10r = \square$ (multiply both sides by 10)

$9r = \square$ (subtract)

$r = \square$

2 Copy and complete to change 0.28282828… to a fraction.

Let $r = 0.28282828\ldots$

$100r = \square$

$99r = \square$

$r = \square$

In questions 3 to 10 change the recurring decimals to fractions.

3 0.2222…

4 0.737373...

5 $0.\dot{5}\dot{1}$ (= 0.515151…)

6 $0.\dot{2}\dot{9}$

7 0.245245245…

8 $0.\dot{3}2\dot{6}$

9 $0.\dot{4}1\dot{7}$

10 $0.\dot{8}\dot{2}$

11 Change these fractions to recurring decimals.

(a) $\frac{1}{6}$ (b) $\frac{8}{9}$ (c) $\frac{2}{7}$ (d) $\frac{5}{13}$

Algebraic fractions

Rewrite the following as single fractions:

(a) $\frac{x}{3}+\frac{x}{3}=\frac{2x}{3}$

(b) $\frac{1}{2}y-\frac{1}{9}y=\frac{y}{2}-\frac{y}{9}$

$=\frac{9y}{18}-\frac{2y}{18}=\frac{7y}{18}$

(c) $\frac{3}{5}\times\frac{t}{4}=\frac{3t}{20}$

(d) $\frac{x}{5}\div\frac{x}{4}=\frac{x}{5}\times\frac{4}{x}$

$=\frac{4x}{5x}=\frac{4}{5}.$

In part (b) $\frac{1}{2}y$ is written as $\frac{y}{2}$ and $\frac{1}{9}y$ is written as $\frac{y}{9}$.

The fractions $\frac{y}{2}$ and $\frac{y}{9}$ are easier to work with.

Exercise 4M

Rewrite the following as single fractions.

1 $\frac{x}{5}+\frac{x}{5}$

2 $\frac{2}{7}x+\frac{1}{7}x$

3 $\frac{1}{2}z+\frac{1}{4}z$

4 $\frac{x}{5}+\frac{x}{10}$

5 $\frac{3}{4}x-\frac{1}{8}x$

6 $\frac{2}{3}x-\frac{1}{4}x$

7 $\frac{x}{5}+\frac{x}{4}$

8 $\frac{2}{5}x-\frac{1}{4}x$

9 $\frac{x}{4}\times\frac{x}{3}$

10 $\frac{2}{5}t\times\frac{1}{2}$

11 $\frac{1}{4}a\times\frac{1}{2}b$

12 $\left(\frac{3}{4}x\right)^2$

13 $\left(\frac{y}{3}\right)^2$

14 $\frac{4t}{5}\div\frac{1}{2}$

15 $\frac{5y}{3}\div\frac{y}{2}$

16 $2\frac{1}{2}x\times 1\frac{1}{2}x$

17 $\frac{3}{x}+\frac{5}{x}$

18 $\frac{9}{t}-\frac{3}{t}$

19 $\frac{11}{P}+\frac{10}{P}$

20 $\frac{4}{x}\times\frac{3}{x}$

Exercise 4E

Write as a single fraction.

1 (a) $\frac{3}{5}+\frac{1}{2}$ (b) $\frac{3}{5}x+\frac{1}{2}x$ (c) $\frac{3}{5}\times\frac{1}{2}$ (d) $\frac{3}{5}\div\frac{1}{2}$

2 (a) $\frac{1}{3}-\frac{1}{4}$ (b) $\frac{m}{3}-\frac{m}{4}$ (c) $\frac{m}{3}\times\frac{m}{4}$ (d) $\frac{m}{3}\div\frac{m}{4}$

3 (a) $\frac{3}{8}+\frac{1}{3}$ (b) $\frac{3s}{8}+\frac{s}{3}$ (c) $\frac{3s}{8}\times\frac{1}{3}$ (d) $\frac{3s}{8}\div\frac{s}{8}$

4 (a) $\frac{5}{7}-\frac{1}{2}$ (b) $\frac{5t}{7}-\frac{t}{2}$ (c) $\frac{5t}{7}\times\frac{t}{2}$ (d) $\frac{5t}{7}\div\frac{t}{2}$

5 Here are some cards

$\boxed{\frac{n}{2}}$ $\boxed{\frac{2}{n}}$ $\boxed{\left(\frac{n}{2}\right)^2}$ $\boxed{\frac{n}{2}+\frac{2}{n}}$ $\boxed{\frac{n}{2}-\frac{n}{4}}$ $\boxed{2 \div n}$

$\boxed{n^2 \div 2}$ $\boxed{\frac{1}{2}n}$ $\boxed{\frac{n+2}{2n}}$ $\boxed{\frac{4}{n}-\frac{2}{n}}$ $\boxed{\frac{n}{2} \times \frac{n}{2}}$

(a) Which cards will always be the same as $\boxed{n \div 2}$?

(b) Which cards will always be the same as $\boxed{\frac{n^2}{4}}$?

(c) Which card will always be the same as $\boxed{\frac{n}{4}}$?

(d) Draw a new card which will always be the same as $\boxed{\frac{n^2}{2} \div \frac{n}{4}}$

The last twelve questions are more difficult. Rewrite as a single fraction and simplify the final answer as far as possible.

6 $\frac{3}{x}+\frac{2}{y}$

7 $\frac{x}{t}\times\frac{3}{x}$

8 $\frac{4}{p}-\frac{5}{q}$

9 $\frac{\pi r^2}{h}\div\frac{\pi}{h}$

10 $\frac{p}{x}+\frac{q}{x}$

11 $\frac{5}{x}+\frac{1}{2x}$

12 $\frac{m}{n}\times\frac{n^2}{m^2}$

13 $\frac{3pq}{x}\div\frac{p^2}{x}$

14 $\frac{x}{a^2}\div\frac{ax}{y}$

15 $\frac{x}{2\frac{1}{2}}+\frac{x}{1\frac{1}{2}}$

16 $\frac{1}{2}$ of $a - \frac{1}{5}$ of b

17 $\frac{3}{4}$ of $t + \frac{1}{3}$ of z

18 (a) Work out $\left(1+\frac{1}{2}\right)\left(1+\frac{1}{3}\right)\left(1+\frac{1}{4}\right)\ldots\ldots \left(1+\frac{1}{100}\right)$

(b) Simplify $\left(1+\frac{1}{2}\right)\left(1+\frac{1}{3}\right)\left(1+\frac{1}{4}\right)\ldots\ldots \left(1+\frac{1}{n}\right)$

Equations with fractions

(a) $\frac{2x}{3} = 5$

$2x = 15$ [Multiply by 3]

$x = \frac{15}{2}$ [Divide by 2]

$x = 7\frac{1}{2}$

(b) $\frac{4}{x} = -2$

$4 = -2x$ [Multiply by x]

$\frac{4}{-2} = x$ [Divide by –2]

$-2 = x$

(c) $\frac{x}{2} + 3 = 7$

$\frac{x}{2} = 4$ [Subtract 3 from both sides.]

$\cancel{2} \times \frac{x}{\cancel{2}} = 4 \times 2$ [Multiply both sides by 2.]

$x = 8$

(d) $\frac{4}{x} - 1 = 14$

$\frac{4}{x} = 15$ [Add 1 to both sides.]

$\cancel{x}\frac{4}{\cancel{x}} = 15x$ [Multiply both sides by x.]

$4 = 15x$

$\frac{4}{15} = x$

Exercise 5M

Solve the equations.

1 $\frac{x}{3} = 4$ 2 $\frac{x}{5} = 2$ 3 $5 = \frac{x}{4}$ 4 $\frac{x}{7} = -2$

5 $\frac{x}{5} = -5$ 6 $\frac{2x}{3} = 1$ 7 $\frac{3x}{4} = 2$ 8 $\frac{5x}{2} = 2$

9 $\frac{6}{x} = 7$ 10 $\frac{4}{x} = 9$ 11 $\frac{2}{x} = 1$ 12 $\frac{3}{x} = \frac{1}{4}$

13 $3 = \frac{8}{x}$ 14 $\frac{2}{3} = \frac{10}{x}$ 15 $\frac{8}{x} = -11$ 16 $-2 = \frac{100}{x}$

Exercise 5E

1 $\frac{x}{3} + 1 = 5$ 2 $\frac{x}{2} - 1 = 8$ 3 $\frac{x}{5} + 9 = 8$ 4 $6 + \frac{x}{3} = 10$

5 $\frac{1}{2}x + 9 = 20$ 6 $\frac{1}{3}x - 6 = 11$ 7 $\frac{2}{3}x + 8 = 10$ 8 $\frac{4}{5}x - 1 = 0$

Questions 9 to 17 are more difficult.

9 $\frac{3}{2x+1} = 2$ 10 $\frac{3}{x} = \frac{2}{x-1}$ 11 $\frac{9}{x+2} = \frac{7}{2x+1}$

12 $\frac{x-3}{5} = \frac{2x+1}{3}$ 13 $\frac{1-x}{2} = \frac{1}{4}$ 14 $\frac{3x}{5} = 2(x+1)$

15 $\frac{3}{x+1} + 3 = 0$ 16 $\frac{8}{1-x} = 16$ 17 $\frac{5(x-3)}{2} = \frac{2(x-1)}{5}$

2.2 Working with indices

In this section you will:

- learn about the rules for multiplying and dividing using indices
- learn about raising to a further power and the zero index
- solve equations involving indices
- solve a variety of problems

Index laws

Indices are used as a convenient way of writing products.

For example $4^3 = 4 \times 4 \times 4$ and $7^5 = 7 \times 7 \times 7 \times 7 \times 7$.

For 7^5 we say '7 to the power 5' or just '7 to the 5'.

Multiplying Consider the product $(3^2) \times (3^4)$.
We have $(3 \times 3) \times (3 \times 3 \times 3 \times 3) = 3^6$.
Similarly $8^4 \times 8^3 = 8^7$.
We observe that

To multiply : Add the indices.

Dividing Consider the division $\frac{6^5}{6^2} = \frac{\not{6} \times \not{6} \times 6 \times 6 \times 6}{\not{6} \times \not{6}} = 6^3$

Similarly $\frac{7^9}{7^4} = 7^5$

We observe that

To divide : Subtract the indices.

Note that you cannot use either of the above rules if different numbers are raised to powers. So $3^4 \times 5^2$ or $7^5 \div 8^3$ *cannot* be found using the rules.

Exercise 1M

In questions 1 to 30 write the answer in index form.

1 $2 \times 2 \times 2 \times 2$

2 $7 \times 7 \times 7 \times 7 \times 7 \times 7$

3 $3 \times 3 \times 2 \times 2 \times 2 \times 2 \times 2$

4 $a \times a \times a \times a \times a$

5 $p \times p \times p$

6 $5 \times 5 \times 5 \times 5 \times 8 \times 8$

7 $3^4 \times 3^6$

8 $4^2 \times 4^3$

9 $8^6 \times 8^2$

10 $7^4 \times 7^{40}$

11 $9^2 \times 9^{22}$

12 $n^3 \times n^2$

13 $a^7 \times a^3$

14 $n^5 \times n^5$

15 $y^7 \times y$

16 $8^6 \div 8^2$

17 $7^5 \div 7^2$

18 $3^{10} \div 3^3$

19 $11^7 \div 11^2$

20 $6^9 \div 6$

21 $5^{11} \div 5^4$

22 $n^7 \div n^2$

23 $a^{10} \div a^3$

24 $x^{11} \div x$

25 $(3^5 \times 3^2) \div 3^4$

26 $(2^3 \times 2^4) \div 2^2$

27 $(4^7 \times 4^2) \div 4^3$

28 $2^3 \times (2 \times 2 \times 2)$

29 $4^5 \times 4 \times 4$

30 $n^5 \times n^2 \times n$

In questions 31 to 39 copy and complete.

31 $5^3 \times 5^2 = \square$

32 $7^5 \div \square = 7^2$

33 $\square \times 3^{10} = 3^{12}$

34 $\square \div 7^{10} = 7^3$

35 $n^3 \times n^3 = \square$

36 $3^{100} \div \square = 3^{20}$

37 $3^6 \div 3 = \square$

38 $10^{10} \div \square = 10$

39 Half of $2^5 = \square$

In questions 40 to 48 give the answer as an ordinary number.

40 $5^4 \div 5^2$

41 $2^5 \div 2^3$

42 $10^3 \div 10$

43 $3^5 \div 3^2$

44 $1^{11} \times 1^{10}$

45 $4^{12} \div 4^{10}$

46 2×2^3

47 $10^6 \div 10^3$

48 $(\frac{1}{2})^2 \times 4$

Negative indices Consider $\frac{5^2}{5^6} = \frac{\cancel{5} \times \cancel{5}}{\cancel{5} \times \cancel{5} \times 5 \times 5 \times 5 \times 5} = \frac{1}{5^4}$

Using the subtraction rule: $5^2 \div 5^6 = 5^{-4}$

We see that $5^{-4} = \frac{1}{5^4}$

Similarly we can show that $7^{-2} = \frac{1}{7^2}$ and $10^{-3} = \frac{1}{10^3}$

In general: $x^{-n} = \frac{1}{x^n}$

Exercise 1E

Write the answer as an ordinary number.

1 2^{-1}

2 3^{-1}

3 10^{-1}

4 4^{-1}

5 8^{-1}

6 n^{-1}

7 2^{-2}

8 3^{-2}

9 10^{-2}

10 10^{-3}

11 2^{-3}

12 5^{-2}

13 $10^3 \times 10^{-1}$

14 $4^3 \times 4^{-1}$

15 $5^4 \times 10^{-2}$

16 $3^{-3} \times 3^1$

17 $2^{-4} \times 2^2$

18 $10^3 \times 10^{-4}$

reminder
$4^{-2} = \frac{1}{4^2} = \frac{1}{16}$

In questions 19 to 30, answer 'True' or 'False'.

19 $3^2 \times 3^{-1} = 3^1$

20 $4^3 \times 4^{-1} = 4^2$

21 $6^5 \times 6^{-2} = 6^2$

22 $5^1 \times 5^{-2} = 5^{-1}$

23 $6^5 \times 6^5 = 6^{25}$

24 $3^{-2} \times 3^{-2} = 3^4$

25 $7^{-1} \times 7^{-1} = 7^{-2}$

26 $10^{-1} \times 10^2 = 10$

27 $n^5 \times n = n^5$

28 $8^7 \div 8^2 = 8^{\frac{7}{2}}$

29 $7^5 \div 7^3 = 7^2$

30 $5^2 \div 5^3 = 5^{-1}$

In questions 31 to 36 copy and complete.

31 $4^{-5} \times \square = 1$

32 $\square \times 3^7 = 1$

33 $5 \div \square = 5^{-2}$

34 $(\frac{1}{2})^{-1} \times \square = 4$

35 $10^{-3} \times 10^6 = \square$

36 $7^3 \times \square = 0$

Raising to a power

Consider $(3^2)^3$, which means '3 squared all cubed'.

$(3^2)^3 = (3 \times 3) \times (3 \times 3) \times (3 \times 3)$

$(3^2)^3 = 3^6$

In general: $(x^n)^m = x^{nm}$

To the power zero

By division $\frac{7^3}{7^3} = 7^0 = 1$ and $\frac{3^{11}}{3^{11}} = 3^0 = 1$

$x^0 = 1$ for any non-zero value of x

Calculator

To work out 3.5^3, press [3.5] [^] [3] [=] [= 10.5]

To work out 5^{-4}, press [5] [^] [–] [4] [=] [= 0.0016]

[You could use the [x^y] button.]

Exercise 2M

Write the answer in index form.

1 $(2^3)^2$

2 $(3^4)^2$

3 $(10^2)^3$

4 $(4^3)^5$

5 $(6^2)^2$

6 $(7^3)^6$

7 $(n^2)^3$

8 $(a^4)^5$

9 $(5^{-1})^2$

10 $(2^2)^3 \times 2^4$

11 $(3^2)^4 \times 3^3$

12 $(5^3)^2 \times 5$

13 $(5^3)^{10} \div 5^{20}$

14 $(7^2)^3 \div 7^5$

15 $(a^2)^4 \times a^3$

16 Write as an ordinary number.

(a) 3^0 (b) 7^0 (c) 111^0

(d) $(-6)^0$ (e) $3^2 \times (5^0)$ (f) $2^3 \div (17^0)$

In questions 17 to 28 answer 'True' or 'False'.

17 $\frac{1}{3} = 3^{-1}$

18 $(3^2)^{10} = 3^{20}$

19 $1^{15} = 15$

20 $5^{-2} = 2^{-5}$

21 $3^2 > 2^3$

22 $10^{-1} = -10$

23 $2^2 \times 3^2 = 6^4$

24 $7^{-2} > 7^{-3}$

25 $(-\frac{1}{4})^0 = 1$

26 $(5^2)^5 = 5^7$

27 $(10^{-2})^3 = 10^{-6}$

28 $2^{-1} > 3^{-1}$

Solve the equations

(a) $3^x = 81$ We know that $3^4 = 81$, so $x = 4$.

(b) $5^x = \frac{1}{25}$ We know that $5^{-2} = \frac{1}{5^2} = \frac{1}{25}$, so $x = -2$.

Exercise 2E

Solve the equations for n.

1 $n^2 = 9$

2 $n^3 = 8$

3 $n^3 = 1000$

4 $2^n = 16$

5 $3^n = 27$

6 $5^n = 25$

7 $10^n = 100$

8 $3^n = \frac{1}{3}$

9 $4^n = \frac{1}{4}$

10 $n^4 = 0$

11 $8^n = 1$

12 $17^n = 1$

Use a calculator to evaluate the following

13 5^3

14 6^3

15 3^4

16 7^3

17 3^5

18 $144^{0.5}$

19 $289^{0.5}$

20 1^{17}

21 2.35^0

22 $10\,000^{0.5}$

23 $16^{0.25}$

24 $625^{0.25}$

In questions 25 to 30 answer 'True or 'False'.

25 $n^0 = 1$

26 $2n^0 = 1$

27 $2^{2^2} = (2^2)^2$

28 $a^{-2} = \frac{1}{a^2}$

29 $0.1^{-2} = 100$

30 $n^{-3} = \frac{3}{n}$

31 A white cell splits into two new cells every hour. So after one hour there are 2 cells, after two hours there are 4 cells and so on.

The number of cells, N, is given by the equation $N = 2^h$, where h is the number of hours after the start of the process.

(a) How many cells are there after 10 hours?

(b) After how many hours will there be more than one billion cells for the first time?

(c) After how many hours will there be more than two billion cells?

Exercise 3M

In questions 1 to 6 give your answer in index form.

1 The number of grains of sand in a bucket is 2^{20}. The contents of the bucket are divided into two equal piles. How many grains of sand are there in each pile?

2 There are 6^5 small cubes in a large model skyscraper and each cube has 6 faces. How many faces are there on all the cubes in the model?

3 The distance of the sun from the Earth is about 10^8 miles. A spacecraft is about 10^5 miles from the Earth. How many times further from the Earth is the Sun than the spacecraft?

4 An imaginary cube of side 10^7 metres is drawn around the Moon. Calculate the volume of the cube in cubic metres.

5 A scientist estimates that there are 10^{11} bacteria in a specimen dish. After an antibiotic is added, the number is reduced to one millionth of the original. How many bacteria are left?

6 A spacecraft is moving at a steady speed of 10^4 m/s towards a planet which is 100 million km away. How long will it take the spacecraft to reach the planet? Give your answer in seconds and state whether the time required is more or less than one year.

7 Fractional powers of numbers can be found using the $\boxed{x^y}$ or the $\boxed{\wedge}$ button on a calculator.

For example to work out $25^{\frac{1}{2}}$ press: $\boxed{25}$ $\boxed{\wedge}$ $\boxed{0.5}$ $\boxed{=}$.

(a) Use a calculator to work out the following:

(i) $9^{\frac{1}{2}}$ (ii) $16^{\frac{1}{2}}$ (iii) $100^{\frac{1}{2}}$ (iv) $144^{\frac{1}{2}}$

(v) $8^{\frac{1}{3}}$ (vi) $27^{\frac{1}{3}}$ (vii) $1000^{\frac{1}{3}}$ (viii) $16^{\frac{1}{4}}$

(P.T.O.)

(b) Copy and complete the sentences below.

(i) $x^{\frac{1}{2}}$ means the same as ____________

(ii) $x^{\frac{1}{3}}$ means the same as ____________

8 Write in order of size, smallest first.

4^{2^2} $\quad 2^5$ $\quad 2^{5^2}$ $\quad 5^2$ $\quad 2^{3^4}$ $\quad 3^{2^{2^2}}$

Exercise 3E

1 The graph shows the curve $y = 3^x$.
Use the graph to give an estimate for the value of x which satisfies the equation $3^x = 15$.

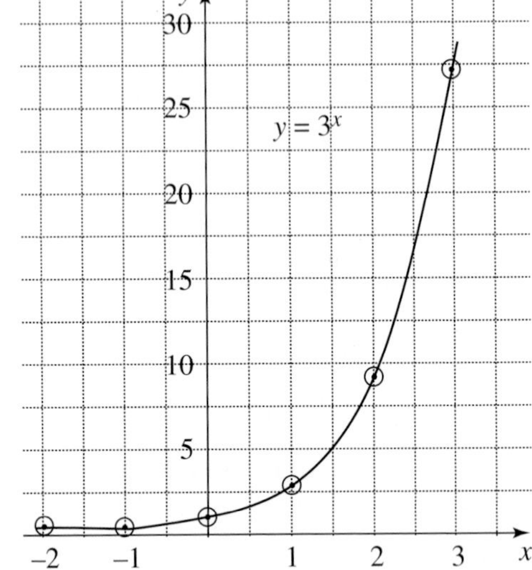

2 Draw the graph of $y = 2^x$ for values of x from -2 to $+4$.
Use a scale of 2 cm to 1 unit for x and 1 cm to 2 units for y.

3 Draw the graph of $y = \frac{x^2}{2^x}$ for values of x from 0 to 8.
Use a scale of 2 cm to 1 unit for x and 1 cm to 0.1 unit for y.

(a) For what value of x is the value of y maximum?

(b) Use your graph to give you two approximate solutions to the equation $\frac{x^2}{2^x} = 0.8$, correct to 2 decimal places.

4 The cube root of 2 is written $\sqrt[3]{2}$. [In index form $\sqrt[3]{2} = 2^{\frac{1}{3}}$.]

The fourth root of 2 is written $\sqrt[4]{2}$. [In index form $\sqrt[4]{2} = 2^{\frac{1}{4}}$.]

The nth root of 2 is written $\sqrt[n]{2}$. [In index form $\sqrt[n]{2} = 2^{\frac{1}{n}}$.]

(a) Use a calculator to work out $\sqrt[n]{2}$ for $n = 4, 5, 10, 100, 1000$.
Copy and complete the following sentence: 'As n becomes larger and larger, $\sqrt[n]{n}$ gets closer and closer to ____________.'

(b) Use a calculator to work out $\sqrt[n]{n}$ for $n = 4, 5, 10, 100, 1000$ and write a sentence similar to the one above.

5 Solve the equations for x

(a) $2^x + 3^x = 35$

(b) $x^x = 2000$ (give your answer correct to three significant figures)

2.3 Standard form

In this section you will:

- learn to write numbers in standard form
- solve problems involving numbers in standard form
- learn how to use standard form on a calculator

Writing numbers in standard form

- (a) Using a calculator, work out 3 000 000 multiplied by 2 000 000.
  The answer is 6 000 000 000 000 but most calculators will give the answer as [6.¹²].

  The calculator cannot show the answer in full because there are too many zeros. The display [6.¹²] is short for 6×10^{12}, which is 'six times 10 to the power 12'.

  (b) Similarly for the division 0.006 ÷ 2 000 000 the calculator will give the answer as [3.⁻⁰⁹]. This is how the calculator shows 3×10^{-9}.

  (c) The numbers 6×10^{12} and 3×10^{-9} are written in *standard form*.
  Standard form is used to represent very large numbers or very small numbers.

Here are some examples of changing numbers into standard form.

(a) Numbers greater than 1.

$2000 = 2 \times 1000 = 2 \times 10 \times 10 \times 10 = \mathbf{2 \times 10^3}$

$140\,000 = 1.4 \times 100\,000 = 1.4 \times 10 \times 10 \times 10 \times 10 \times 10 = \mathbf{1.4 \times 10^5}$

$25\,000\,000 = 2.5 \times 10\,000\,000 = \mathbf{2.5 \times 10^7}$

(b) Numbers less than 1

$0.005 = \frac{5}{1000} = 5 \times \frac{1}{10^3} = \mathbf{5 \times 10^{-3}}$

$0.00087 = \frac{8.7}{10\,000} = 8.7 \times \frac{1}{10^4} = \mathbf{8.7 \times 10^{-4}}$

- The numbers in bold type above are all in standard form. A number is in standard form when it has the form $a \times 10^n$, where a is a number between 1 and 10 [strictly $1 \leq a < 10$] and n is a positive or negative integer [whole number].

  So 5.2×10^7 *is* standard form but 52×10^6 is *not*.

- Quick method

  (a) 800 000.0 = 8.0×10^5. The decimal point moves 5 places from A to B
  (B: after the 8; A: the decimal point before the final 0)

  (b) 1 600. = 1.6×10^3. The decimal point moves 3 places from A to B.
  (B: after the 1; A: after 600)

  (c) 0.000 032 = 3.2×10^{-5}. The decimal point moves 5 places from A to B.
  (A: after the 0; B: after the 3)

  (d) 0.002 87 = 2.87×10^{-3}. The decimal point moves 3 places from A to B.
  (A: after the 0; B: after the 2)

Notice: In large numbers the power of 10 is positive.
In small numbers the power of 10 is negative.

Exercise 1M

Write the numbers in standard form.

1 5000   2 70 000   3 3 million   4 7500

5 26 000   6 14 million   7 542 000   8 5 billion

9 61 million   10 240   11 1000   12 165 million

Write the following small numbers in standard form.

13 0.0002   14 0.000 007   15 0.005   16 0.000 041

17 0.000 000 82   18 0.012   19 0.000 072 3   20 0.2

Write the following as decimal numbers.

21 6×10^4 22 5.2×10^3 23 6×10^{-3} 24 5×10^{-1}

25 3.2×10^6 26 1.7×10^{-4} 27 3.25×10^4 28 5.8×10^{-3}

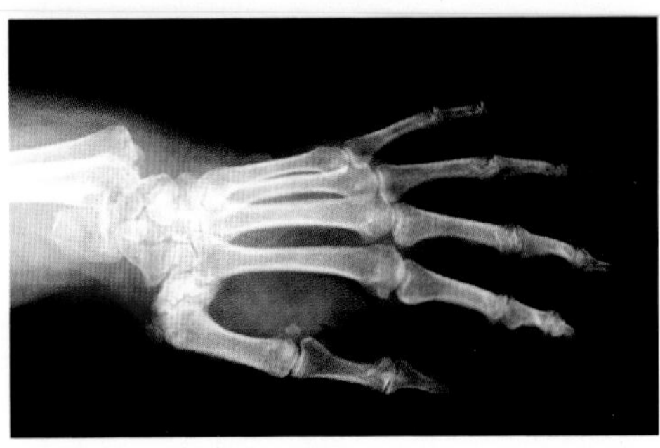

29 Every year the U.K. Government spends almost 200 thousand million pounds on defence, hospitals, schools etc. Write this number in standard form.

30 The thickness of very thin gold plate is 0.000 000 24 m. Write this in standard form.

31 The mass of the Earth is about 6 000 000 000 000 000 000 000 tonnes. Write this mass in standard form.

32 The population of Mexico City is about 1.8×10^7. Write this in decimal form.

33 The hairs on the knee of the common flea are of length 0.000 007 m. Write this in standard form.

34 A swarm of locusts is estimated to contain 5×10^9 locust. Write this in decimal form.

35 The wavelength of a radio signal is 6.2×10^{-6} cm. Write this in decimal form (a) in cm (b) in m.

In 2010 the U.S. defence budget was 2 trillion dollars.

[1 trillion = 1000 billion, 1 billion = 1000 million]

(a) Write the 2010 budget in standard form.

(b) In 2011 the new President decides to reduce the budget to $\frac{1}{10}$ of its previous size. Write down the reduced budget in standard form.

(c) \$2 trillion $= \$2\,000\,000\,000\,000$

$= \$2 \times 10^{12}$

(d) Reduced budget $= (\$2 \times 10^{12}) \div 10^1$

$= \$2 \times 10^{11}$

[Remember: To divide, subtract the indices]

Exercise 1E

1 A pile of 10 000 sheets of the paper used in this book is one metre high. Work out the thickness of one sheet of paper in metres, writing your answer in standard form.

2 If the number 3.52×10^{11} is written out in full, how many zeros follow the 2?

3 If the number 6.2×10^{-7} is written out in full, how many zeros would there be between the decimal point and the 6?

4 Write in order of size, smallest first: $p = 5 \times 10^5$

$q = 6 \times 10^4$

$r = 8 \times 10^{-6}$

$s = 25\ 000$

5 Which of the following has the largest value if $x = 2 \times 10^4$ and $y = 2 \times 10^{-2}$

(a) xy (b) x^2 (c) $\frac{x}{y}$ (d) $\frac{1}{y^3}$?

6 The diagram shows a cube of side one metre.
Complete the following statement:
'$1\ \text{m}^3 =$ _______ mm^3'

Write the missing number in standard form.

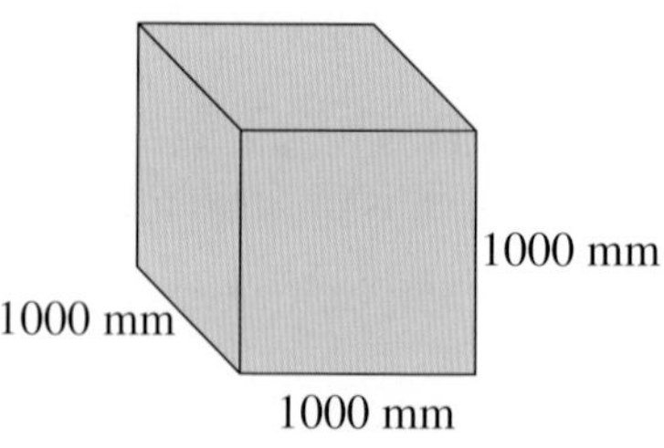

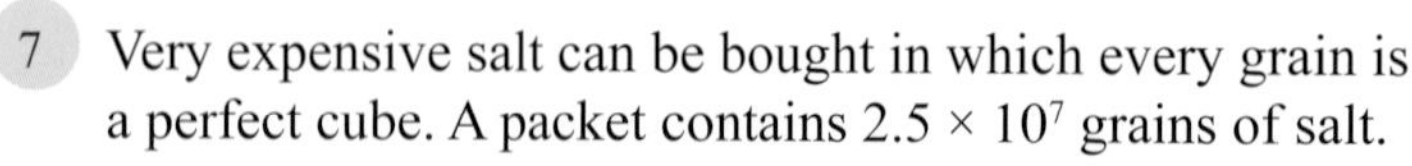

7 Very expensive salt can be bought in which every grain is a perfect cube. A packet contains 2.5×10^7 grains of salt.

(a) How many vertices are there altogether on the grains?

(b) How many edges are there altogether on the grains?

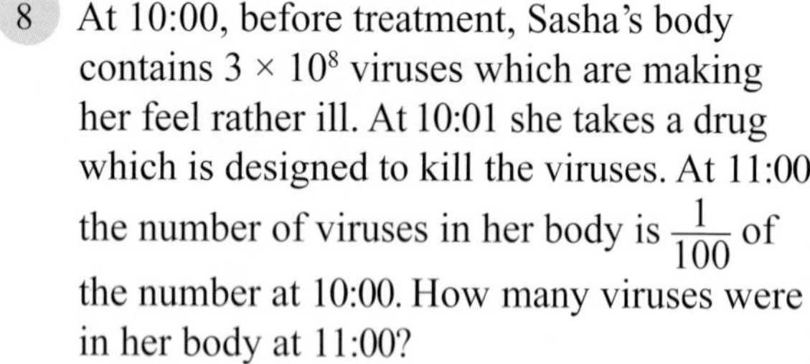

8 At 10:00, before treatment, Sasha's body contains 3×10^8 viruses which are making her feel rather ill. At 10:01 she takes a drug which is designed to kill the viruses. At 11:00 the number of viruses in her body is $\frac{1}{100}$ of the number at 10:00. How many viruses were in her body at 11:00?

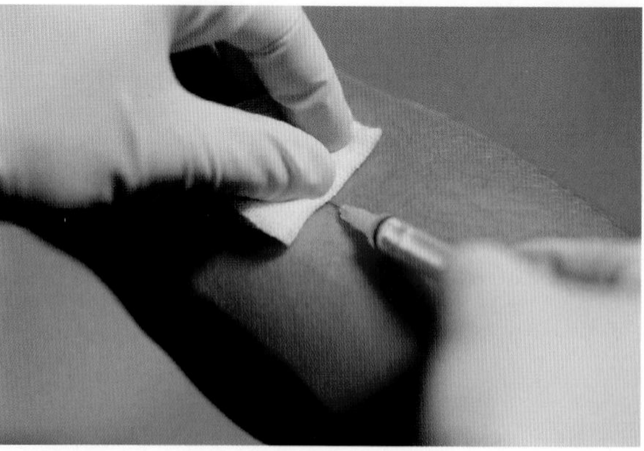

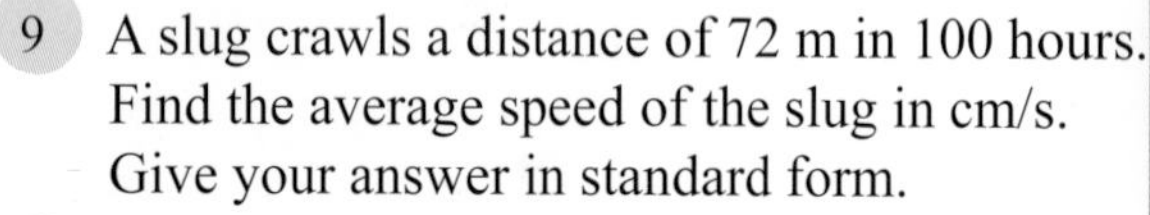

9 A slug crawls a distance of 72 m in 100 hours. Find the average speed of the slug in cm/s. Give your answer in standard form.

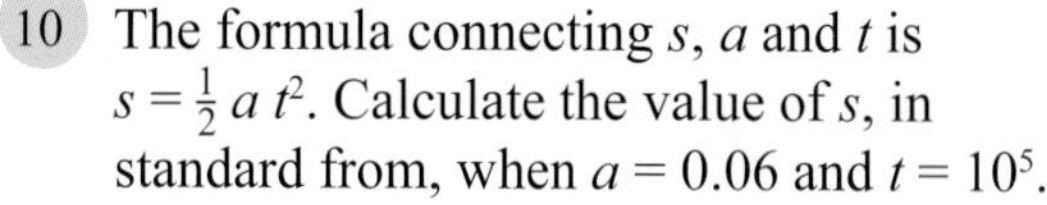

10 The formula connecting s, a and t is $s = \frac{1}{2}at^2$. Calculate the value of s, in standard from, when $a = 0.06$ and $t = 10^5$.

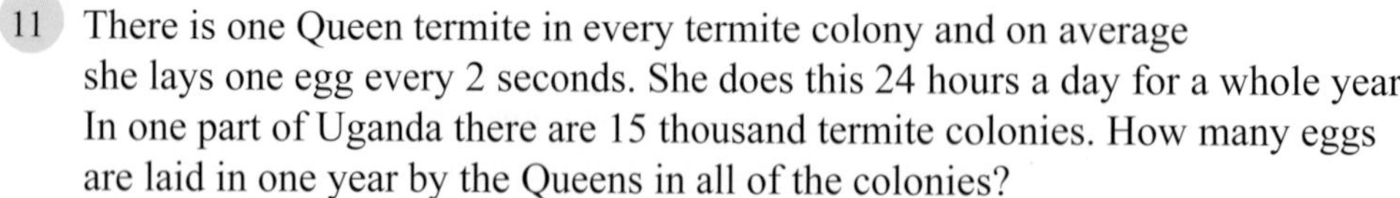

11 There is one Queen termite in every termite colony and on average she lays one egg every 2 seconds. She does this 24 hours a day for a whole year. In one part of Uganda there are 15 thousand termite colonies. How many eggs are laid in one year by the Queens in all of the colonies?

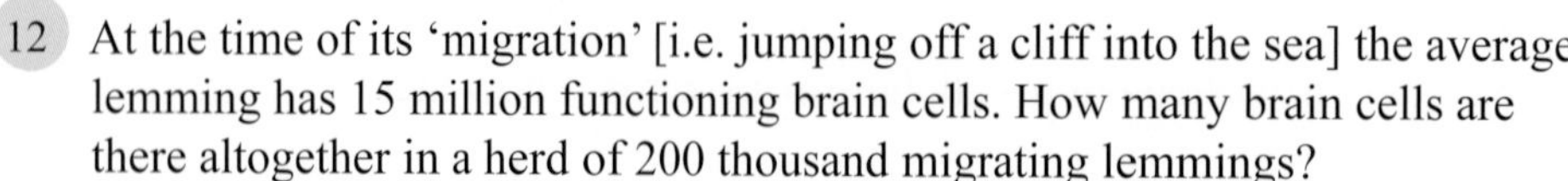

12 At the time of its 'migration' [i.e. jumping off a cliff into the sea] the average lemming has 15 million functioning brain cells. How many brain cells are there altogether in a herd of 200 thousand migrating lemmings?

13 Write down, in standard form, the next two numbers in each sequence.

(a) 5×10^2, 1.5×10^3, 4.5×10^3, $\square$, $\square$

(b) 1.6×10^5, 8×10^4, 4×10^4, $\square$, $\square$

(c) 4×10^{-3}, 1.6×10^{-2}, 6.4×10^{-2}, $\square$, $\square$

(d) 3×10^2, 6×10^3, 1.2×10^5, $\square$, $\square$

Using a calculator

(a) Work out $(5 \times 10^7) \times (3 \times 10^{12})$

Use the [EXP] button as follows:

[5] [EXP] [7] [×] [3] [EXP] [12] [=] Answer = 1.5×10^{20}.

Notice that you do NOT press the [×] button after the [EXP] button!

(b) Work out $(3.2 \times 10^3) \div (8 \times 10^{-7})$

[3.2] [EXP] [3] [÷] [8] [EXP] [−] [7] [=] Answer = 4×10^9

(c) $(5 \times 10^{-8})^2$

[5] [EXP] [−] [8] [x^2] Answer = 2.5×10^{-15}

Exercise 2M

Use a calculator to work out the following and write the answer in standard form.

1 $2000 \times 30\,000$

2 $40\,000 \times 500$

3 $25\,000 \times 600\,000$

4 3500×2 million

5 $600\,000 \times 1500$

6 $(40\,000)^2$

7 $18\,000 \div 400$

8 $(4 \times 10^5) \times (3 \times 10^8)$

9 $(6.2 \times 10^4) \times (3 \times 10^6)$

10 $(5 \times 10^{-4}) \times (4 \times 10^{-7})$

11 $(3 \times 10^8) \times (2.5 \times 10^{-20})$

12 $(5 \times 10^7) \div (2 \times 10^{-2})$

13 $(3 \times 10^5)^3$

14 $(7 \times 10^{-2}) \div (2 \times 10^4)$

15 $(9 \times 10^{-11})^2$

16 $(4.2 \times 10^8) \times (1.5 \times 10^5)$

17 $(3 \times 10^{-4}) \div (2 \times 10^{-20})$

18 $(4 \times 10^5) \times (2 \times 10^{-2})$

19 $(1.4 \times 10^{-1}) \times (2 \times 10^{17})$

20 $(2 \times 10^5)^2 \times (4 \times 10^{-8})$

21 $(8 \times 10^{-5}) \div (2 \times 10^{-3})^2$

22 $(2 \times 10^{-4}) \div (1.6 \times 10^8)$

23 $10^5 \div (2 \times 10^8)$

24 $(3 \times 10^{-7}) \times 10^{-4}$

Exercise 2E

Give answers in standard form correct to 3 significant figures, where necessary.

1 The dimensions of a rectangular component in a computer are shown.

4×10^{-4} m

2×10^{-5} m

(a) Calculate the area of one component.

(b) How many of these components can be fitted into an area of 2×10^{-3} m^2?

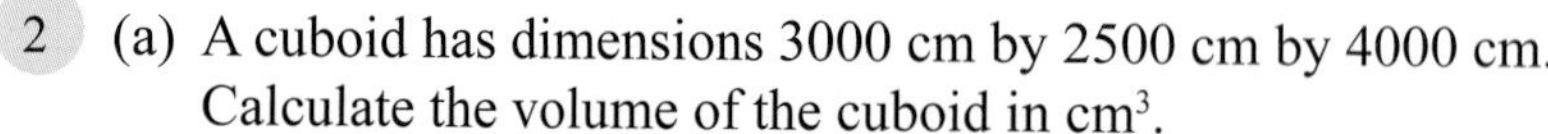

2 (a) A cuboid has dimensions 3000 cm by 2500 cm by 4000 cm. Calculate the volume of the cuboid in cm^3.

(b) A cylinder has radius 500 mm and height 10 m. Calculate the volume of the cylinder in cm^3. [$V = \pi r^2 h$].

3 Water flows from a hose at the rate of 200 cm^3 per second. How long will it take to fill a tank of capacity 1.2×10^7 cm^3?

4 A smallpox virus is approximately 2.8×10^{-7} m across. If these viruses were placed next to each other in a straight line across this page (0.186 m), how many viruses would there be?

5

The mass of the Earth is 5.97×10^{21} tonnes and the mass of the Moon is 7.35×10^{19} tonnes.

(a) Calculate the mass of the Sun, given that it is 333 000 times that of the Earth.

(b) How many times heavier is the Sun than the Moon?

6 A light year is the distance travelled by light in one year (365.24 days). The speed of light is 2.998×10^5 km/s. Calculate the length of a light year in km.

7 As the Earth moves in its elliptical orbit around the Sun, its average distance from the Sun is 1.5×10^8 km. How many minutes does it take light to travel from the Sun to Earth?

8 The light reaching Earth from the star 'Betelgeux', a *very* distant star of Orion, left Betelgeux in AD 1470. In the year 2000 how far away from Earth was Betelgeux in km?

9 The Sun uses up 4×10^9 kg of hydrogen every second.

(a) Calculate how many tonnes of hydrogen are used up every year.

(b) This might seem rather alarming since life on Earth depends entirely on heat and light from the Sun. Work out what percentage of the mass of the Sun is used up every year. Refer to question 5 for the mass of the Sun.

10 The most massive living thing on Earth is a tree (Sequoiadendron giganteum) in the U.S.A. It stands over 85 m tall and its weight is estimated at 2040 tonnes. The seed which produced this tree weighed approximately 4.5 mg. By what factor has the weight of the seed increased as the tree has grown to its present size?

CHECK YOURSELF ON SECTIONS 2.1, 2.2 AND 2.3

1. Using fractions

(a) Work out

(i) $\frac{1}{4}-\frac{1}{7}$ (ii) $\frac{3}{5}\div\frac{9}{100}$ (iii) $\left(\frac{2}{3}\div\frac{1}{5}\right)^2$

(b) A barrel of water is initially $\frac{7}{10}$ full. After 243 litres of water are removed, the barrel is $\frac{1}{4}$ full. How many litres does the barrel hold when it is full?

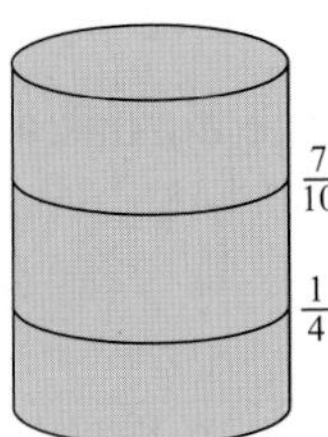

2. Working with indices

(a) Work out or simplify

(i) $5^3 \div 5^7$ (ii) $(3^2)^4$ (iii) $(n^7 \times n^4) \div n^{-2}$

(b) Solve the equations for x

(i) $5^x = 125$ (ii) $4^x = \frac{1}{16}$ (iii) $13^x = 1$

(c) On the putting greens at St Andrews golf course, there are 30 blades of grass per square centimetre. How many blades of grass are there on a circular green of radius 20 metres? Give your answer in standard form, correct to 2 significant figures.

3. Standard form

(a) Write the following numbers in standard form:

(i) 56 000 (ii) 0.000 002 (iii) 250 million.

(b) Give the answers to the following in standard form.

(i) $(4.3 \times 10^4) \times (6.5 \times 10^{12})$

(ii) $(3.6 \times 10^7) \div (2 \times 10^{11})$

(iii) $(4.8 \times 10^{-3}) \times (2 \times 10^{-8})$

(c) Given $x = 4 \times 10^3$ and $y = 5 \times 10^{-2}$ evaluate:

(i) xy (ii) $x + y$ (iii) x^3 (iv) $\frac{1}{y^2}$

2.4 Applying mathematics in a range of contexts 1

In this section you will:

- solve problems by applying mathematical knowledge across a range of topics

Exercise 1

1 Thirty articles cost £48. How many of these articles could be bought for £88?

2 Work out, without using a calculator.

(a) 0.021×100 (b) 4% of £450 (c) $8.6 \div 0.2$

(d) Half of 4×10^5 (e) $0.1^3 \times 10^6$ (f) $\sqrt{(27.28 + 8.72)}$

3 Write down *two* possible answers for the missing digits. Ask a friend to check your solutions.

$\boxed{3}\boxed{0} \times \square\square \div \square = 120$

4 (a) Increase £60 by 10%.

(b) Decrease £900 by 20%.

(c) Increase £2000 by 2%.

5

A chicken can run at a speed of 2.5 metres per second. How far can it run in 2 minutes?

6 Write 350 billion pounds in pence. Give your answer in standard form.

7 Copy and complete.

(a) $6n - 15 = 3(2n - \square)$ (b) $7n - 28 = 7(\square - \square)$ (c) $5x + 30 = \square(\square + \square)$

(d) $\square(y - \square) = y^2 - 4y$ (e) $\square(\square + \square) = n^2 + 8n$ (f) $\square(\square + \square) = 4x^2 + 6x$

8 A man starts work each day at 07.30 and works until 16.00. He stops working for one hour at lunchtime. How many hours does he work in a 5-day week?

9 Copy each pattern and write down the next line

(a)
$$2^2 = 1^2 + 3$$
$$3^2 = 2^2 + 5$$
$$4^2 = 3^2 + 7$$
$$5^2 = 4^2 + 9$$

(b)
$$1 + 9 \times 0 = 1$$
$$2 + 9 \times 1 = 11$$
$$3 + 9 \times 12 = 111$$
$$4 + 9 \times 123 = 1111$$

10 A 20p coin is 1.2 mm thick. What is the value of a pile of 20p coins which is 21.6 cm high?

Exercise 2

1 Copy each calculation and find the missing numbers

(a)
$$\begin{array}{r} 3\ 5\ \square \\ 4\ \square\ 3 \\ +\ \square\ 0\ 9 \\ \hline \square\ 4\ 4\ 0 \\ \hline \end{array}$$

(b)
$$\begin{array}{r} \square\ 9\ 4\ 3 \\ 5\ \square\ 7\ 1 \\ +\ 1\ 4\ \square\ 6 \\ \hline 9\ 6\ 4\ \square \\ \hline \end{array}$$

2 A jar with 8 chocolates in it weighs 160 g. The same jar with 20 chocolates in it weighs 304 g. How much does the jar weigh on its own?

3 Use the clues to find the mystery number

- the sum of the digits is 18
- the number reads the same forwards as backwards
- the number is less than 2000
- the number has four digits

4 Chloe has the same number of 20p and 50p coins. The total value of the coins is £17.50. How many of each coin does she have?

5 

A ship's voyage started at 20.30 on Monday and finished at 07.00 on the following Wednesday. How long was the journey in hours and minutes?

6 Work out (a) $\frac{1}{8} \times \frac{8}{9} \times \frac{9}{10} \times \frac{10}{21}$

(b) $(5 \times 10^4) \times (3 \times 10^7)$

(c) $1^6 + 2^5 + 3^4 + 4^3 + 5^2 + 6^1$

7 At a party there are 116 people and there are 6 more boys than girls. How many boys are there?

8 The sum of the ages of a mother and her daughter is 39. The product of their ages is 224. How old are they?

9 Amrik uses 14 screws in each of the model aircraft which he makes.

How many *complete* aircraft can he make using a box of 360 screws?

10 Three consecutive whole numbers can be expressed as x, $x + 1$ and $x + 2$. If four times the largest number is added to twice the middle number the answer is seven times the smallest number. Find the three numbers.

Exercise 3

1 Answer 'true' or 'false'

(a) $(-2)^3 > 3^2$ (b) $\frac{1}{16} = 6.25\%$ (c) $\frac{1}{3} + \frac{1}{6} = \frac{1}{2}$

(d) $\frac{1}{7} > 0.15$ (e) $(2-5)^4 = 81$ (f) $10^3 - 10^2 = 10^1$

2 The bullet from a rifle travels at a speed of 3×10^4 cm/s. Work out the length of time in seconds taken for the bullet to hit a target 54 m away.

3 A sewing machine cost £162.40 after a price increase of 16%. Find the price before the increase.

4 Draw a pair of axes on squared paper.

(a) Plot the points A (1, 2) and B (5, 5)

(b) Draw a circle with AB as a diameter

(c) Write down the coordinates of two points, with whole number coordinates, which lie on the circle (apart from A and B!).

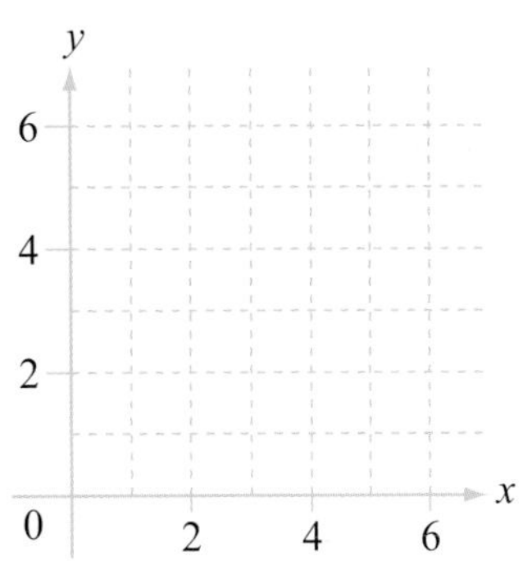

5 A shooting target consists of four rings of radii 3 cm, 6 cm, 9 cm and 12 cm.
Find the percentage of the target that is shaded.

6 North

P

Draw a small sketch showing the possible position of points Q and R given that:

(a) the bearing of point Q from P is 200°.

(b) the bearing of point P from R is 300°.

7 (a) Calculate the total surface area of a solid cuboid with dimensions 6 cm × 8.5 cm × 4 cm.

(b) How many of these cuboids could be painted on all faces, using a tin with enough paint to cover an area of 6m^2?

8 A code uses 1 for A, 2 for B, 3 for C and so on up to 26 for Z. Coded words are written without spaces to confuse the enemy, so 18 could be AH or R. Decode the following message.

208919 919 1 2251825 199121225 31545.

9 Use a calculator to work out 11^2, 111^2 and 1111^2. Use your answers to predict the values of $11\,111^2$ and $111\,111^2$.

10

Dinky's high price

A Dinky Toy model of a Bentalls Kingston-on-Thames delivery van which cost 6d ($2\frac{1}{2}$p) in 1936, fetched a record £12,650 at a Christie's auction.

Calculate the percentage profit made on the sale of the toy in the newspaper cutting. Give your answer correct to 3 significant figures.

Exercise 4

1 The numbers 1 to 12 are arranged on the star so that the sum of the numbers along each line is the same.

Copy and complete the star.

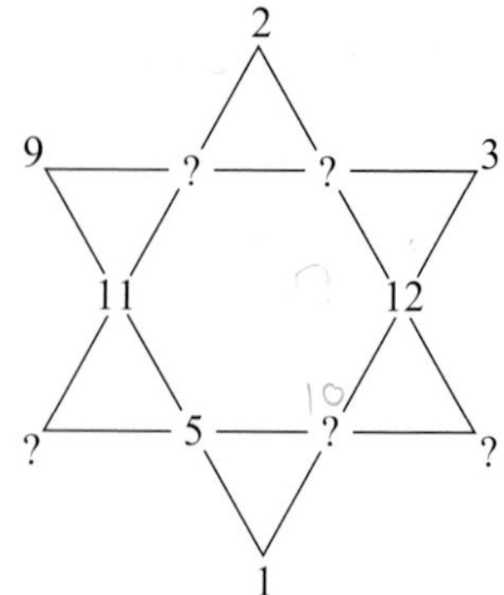

2 If $x = 3$, $y = -4$ and $z = -5$, work out

(a) $x + z$ (b) $3y + x$ (c) $yz + x$

3 Use a calculator to evaluate the following, correct to 3 s.f.

(a) $\frac{(3.2^2 - 7)}{7(6.5^2 + 1)}$ (b) $\frac{8.2 + 5.9}{\sqrt{(7.1 - 1.3^2)}}$ (c) $\frac{7.3}{1.5} - \frac{3.6}{1.31^2}$

4 Four touching circles of radius 4 cm are shown.

Calculate the area of the region shaded pink.

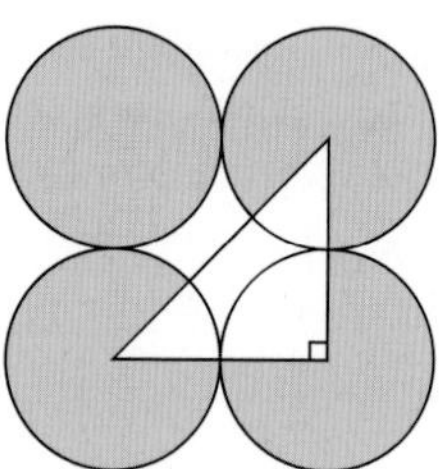

5 To get the next number in a sequence you double the previous number and subtract two. The fifth number in the sequence is 50. Find the first number.

6 A woman hires a car from a car hire firm which charges £15 per day plus 7p per km travelled.

£15 per day
7p per km

(a) How much does it cost to hire a car for four days and drive 200 km?

(b) A woman hired a car for two days and had to pay £65. How far did she drive?

7 A wall measuring 3 m by 4.5 m is covered with square tiles of side 10 cm. The tiles cost £8.45 for ten. How much will the tiles cost for this wall?

8 Find the missing digits

(a)
```
  □4□
+ 1□8
  ---
  414
```

(b)
```
  □□9
 ×  4
 ----
 139□
```

(c) □4 × 2□ = 1512

9 **That's the way the money goes: used banknotes, chopped up and compressed, are dumped for the Bank of England at a landfill site near Tilbury. The bank has to dispose of seven tonnes a day. To avoid pollution they are no longer burned, but selling them as novelty firelighters is among proposals being investigated.**

Estimate the value of the banknotes which are dumped each day. Make the following assumptions:

(a) All the notes dumped are £10 notes.

(b) Each note weighs 0.87 grams. [1 tonne = 1000 kg]

10 The diagram shows a rectangle.

Work out x and then find the area of the rectangle.

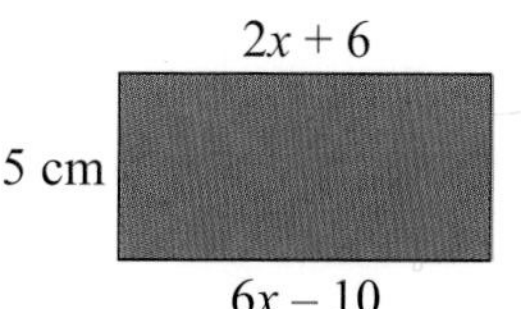

Exercise 5

1 Work out a half of ninety-nine and a half.

2 On a calculator $\frac{1}{9} = 0.1111111....$ *Without* using a calculator, write down $\frac{1}{900}$ as a decimal.

3 The diagrams shows a point O where three regular polygons meet. How many sides does the third regular polygon have?

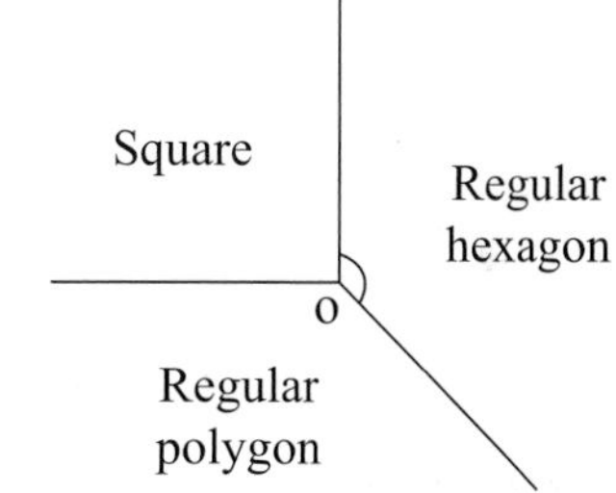

4

Q:	"Doctor, before you performed the autopsy did you check for a pulse?"
A:	"No."
Q:	"Did you check for blood pressure?"
A:	"No."
Q:	"Did you check for breathing?"
A:	"No."
Q:	"So then it is possible that the patient was alive when you began the autopsy?"
A:	"No."
Q:	"How can you be so sure, Doctor?"
A:	"Because his brain was sitting on my desk in a jar."
Q:	"But could the patient have been alive, nevertheless?"
A:	"It is possible that he could have been alive and practising law somewhere."

Here are the questions asked by a barrister and the answers given during a recent trial. This is a true story.
In your opinion which of the two persons in this exchange would be more likely to solve question 3 above?

5 The nth term of the sequence 1, 3, 6, 10, ... is given by the expression $\frac{n(n+1)}{2}$.

(a) Use the expression above to write down

(i) the 10th term of the sequence

(ii) the nth term of the sequence 10, 30, 60, 100, ……..

(b) Write down an expression for the $(n-1)$th term of the sequence.

(c) Find an expression for the sum of the nth term and the $(n-1)$th term of the sequence. Simplify your answer.

6 A stone wall was built by 15 people in ten hours.

How long would it take 4 people to build the wall if they worked at the same speed?

7 Find the distance travelled by light in 1 hour, given that the speed of light is 300 000 kilometres per second. Give the answer in km in standard form.

8 A solid block of chocolate measuring 1.5 cm by 15 cm by 8 cm is melted down and spread out to make a square layer of chocolate 2 mm thick. How long is the side of the square?

9 The number n has nine factors, including 1 and n. Two of its factors are 2 and 12. What is n?

10 

One hundred and twenty girls we asked to name their favourite lipstick. The results were:

Mac 36   Bobbi Brown 15   Rimmel 30   Estee Lauder 12
Max Factor 27

Display this information on a pie chart, showing the angles for each sector.

2.5 Scatter graphs

In this section you will:

- draw and interpret scatter graphs
- draw and use a line of best fit

Correlation

Scatter graphs can be drawn to investigate if there is a connection, or *correlation*, between sets of data.

When the height and armspan of a group of people are recorded, we would expect a scatter graph like the one shown. This scatter graph shows *strong positive* correlation. You would expect a tall person to have a long armspan.

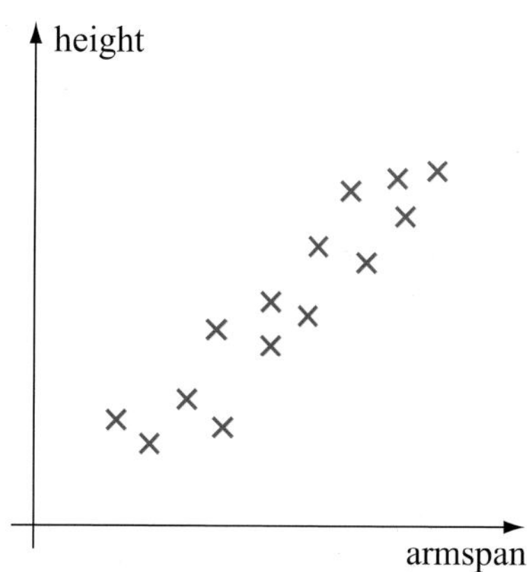

The correlation between two sets of data can be positive or negative and it can be strong or weak as indicated by the scatter graphs below. Sometimes there is *no* correlation.

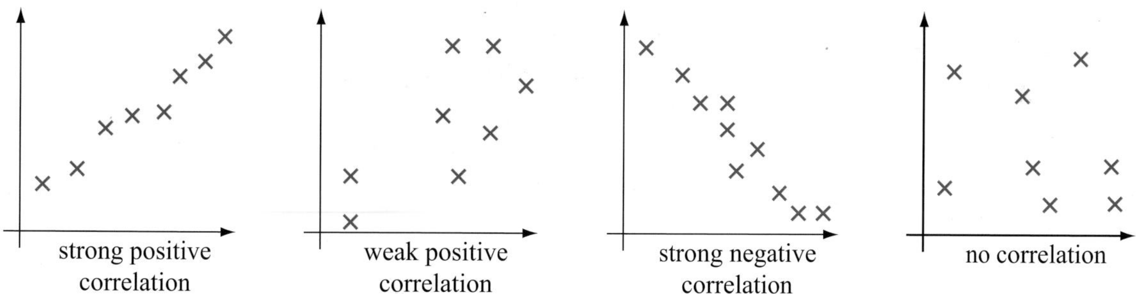

Exercise 1M

Plot the points given on a scatter graph, with x across the page and y up the page. Draw axes with values from 0 to 20.

Describe the correlation, if any, between the values of x and y.

[i.e. 'strong negative', 'weak positive' etc.]

1

x	8	14	4	12	19	6	20	4	10	12
y	7	13	6	12	18	9	18	7	10	13

2

x	2	9	12	15	17	5	6	17	8
y	3	3	10	17	6	10	17	11	15

3

x	12	2	16	7	3	19	8	4	13	19
y	6	13	7	14	17	1	11	8	11	4

4

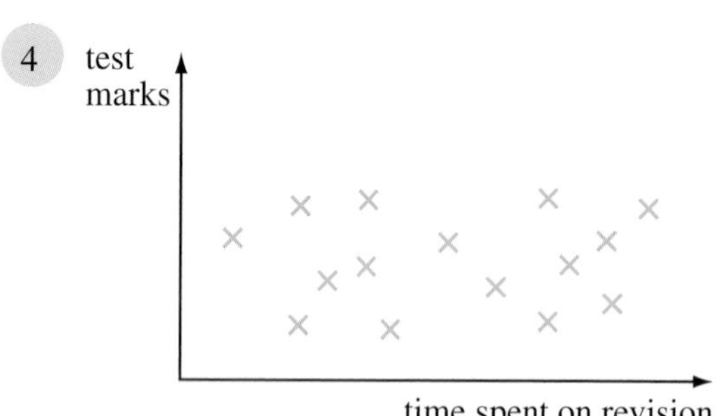

This is a scatter graph of the marks of 15 pupils in a history test and the length of time they spent revising for the test.

What can you deduce from the graph?

5 Describe the correlation you would expect if you drew a scatter graph for each pair of variables below:

(a) age of person; time to run 1 mile

(b) annual income; person's height

(c) value of a house; age of house

Line of best fit

When a scatter graph shows either positive or negative correlation, a *line of best fit* can be drawn. The sums of the distances to points on either side of the line are equal and there should be an equal number of points on each side of the line. The line is easier to draw when a transparent ruler is used.

Here are the marks obtained in two tests by 9 students.

Student	A	B	C	D	E	F	G	H	I
Maths mark	28	22	9	40	37	35	30	23	?
Physics mark	48	45	34	57	50	55	53	45	52

A line of best fit can be drawn as there is strong positive correlation between the two sets of marks.

The line of best fit can be used to estimate the maths result of student I, who missed the maths test but scored 52 in the physics test.

We can *estimate* that student I would have scored *about* 33 in the maths test. It is not possible to be *very* accurate using scatter graphs. It is reasonable to state that student I 'might have scored between 30 and 36' in the maths test.

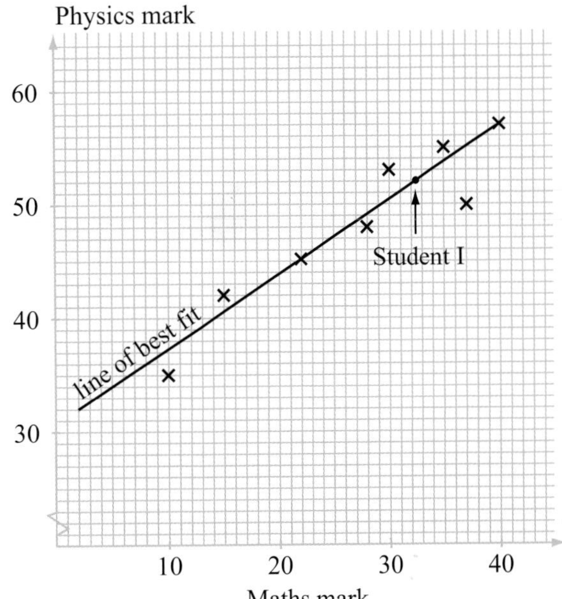

Here is a scatter graph in which the heights of boys of different ages is recorded. A line of best fit is drawn.

(a) We can estimate that the height of an 8 year old boy might be about 123 cm [say between 120 and 126 cm].

(b) We can only predict a height within the range of values plotted. We could not extend the line of best fit and use it to predict the height of a 30 year old! Why not?

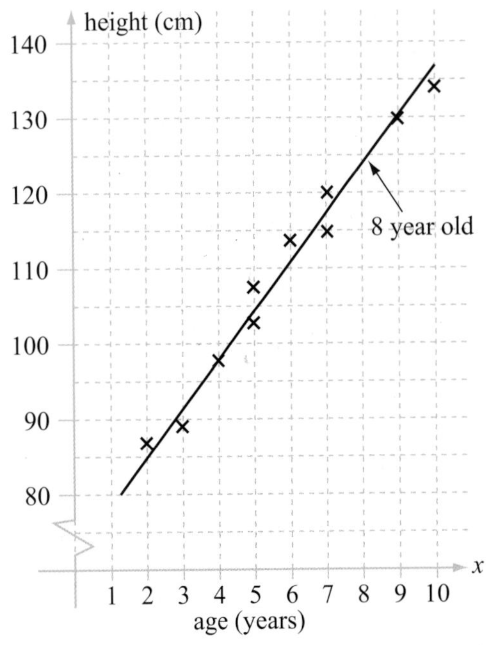

Exercise 1E

In questions 1, 2 and 3 plot the points given on a scatter graph, with s across the page and p up the page.

Draw axes with values from 0 to 20.

If possible draw a line of best fit on the graph.

Where possible estimate the value of p on the line of best fit where $s = 10$.

1

s	2	14	14	4	12	18	12	6
p	5	15	16	6	12	18	13	7

2

s	2	15	17	3	20	3	6
p	13	7	5	12	4	13	11

3

s	4	10	15	18	19	4	19	5
p	19	16	11	19	15	3	1	9

4 The following data gives the marks of 11 students in a French test and in a German test.

French	15	36	36	22	23	27	43	22	43	40	26
German	6	28	35	18	28	28	37	9	41	45	17

(a) Plot this data on a scatter graph, with the French marks on the horizontal axis.

(b) Draw the line of best fit.

(c) Estimate the German mark of a student who got 30 in French.

(d) Estimate the French mark of a student who got 45 in German.

5 The data below gives the petrol consumption figures of cars, with the same size engine, when driven at different speeds.

Speed (m.p.h.)	30	62	40	80	70	55	75
Petrol consumption (m.p.g)	38	25	35	20	26	34	22

(a) Plot a scatter graph and draw a line of best fit.

(b) Estimate the petrol consumption of a car travelling at 45 m.p.h.

(c) Estimate the speed of a car whose petrol consumption is 27 m.p.g.

6 For a medical survey 12 children had the span of their right hand and the length of their right foot measured. These are the results:

handspan (cm)	16.5	15	14	12.5	12	11	24	24	21	21	20
length of foot (cm)	20	23	18	19	17	14	28	24.5	27.5	23	25

(a) Draw a scatter graph, plotting handspan on the horizontal axis and length of foot on the vertical axis. Take values from 10 to 28 on both axes.

(b) Describe the results in one sentence.

(c) One girl had her leg in plaster so her foot length could not be measured. Her handspan was 17.5 cm. Draw a line of best fit on your scatter graph and use it to estimate the likely length of her foot.

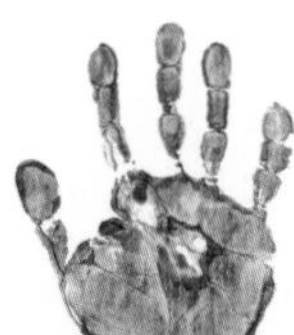

2.6 Trial and improvement

In this section you will:

- learn about the method of trial and improvement
- learn how to solve equations and problems of increasing difficulty

Trial and improvement

Many problems and equations are more difficult than those you have met so far. Equations such as $x^2 = 7 - x$, $2x = x^3$ or $3^x = 19$ are impossible to solve using methods you have learned before.

We begin by solving problems involving areas.

Exercise 1M

Find the answers to these questions by trying different numbers until you find the dimensions that give the required area.

1 In the 3 rectangles below, the length is *twice* the width.
Find the dimensions of each rectangle.

(a)

area = 98 cm^2

(b)

area = 12.5 cm^2

(c)

area = 9.68 cm^2

2 In these rectangles, the length is *three* times the width. Find the dimensions of each rectangle.

(a)

area = 48 cm^2

(b)

area = 36.75 cm^2

(c)

area = 3.63 cm^2

3 In the rectangles below, the length is 1 cm greater than the width. Find the dimensions of each rectangle.

(a)

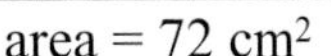

area = 72 cm^2

(b)

area = 210 cm^2

(c)

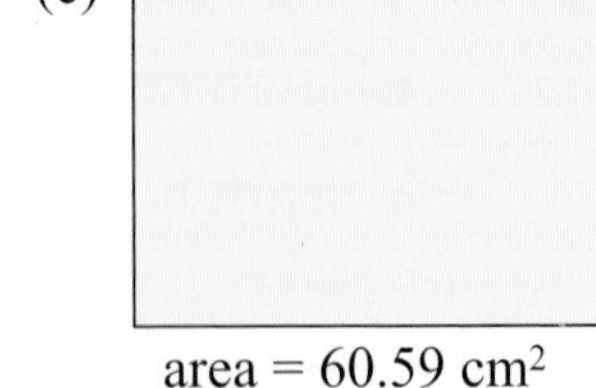

area = 60.59 cm^2

4 The volume of the box is given by the formula $n(n-1)(n+1)$.
The box has a volume of 10 626 cm^3.
Find the dimensions of the box.

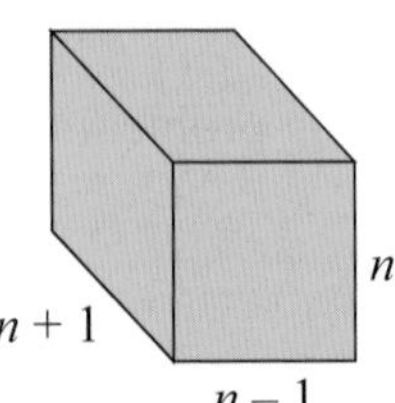

In the questions in the last exercise, we could always find dimensions which gave the *exact* answer required. In many problems this is not the case and we have to give the answer as an approximate value. This is not a major drawback because the solution can generally be found correct to as many decimal places as are required, especially when a computer is used.

The rectangle shown has width h cm, length $(h+5)$ and area 525 cm^2.
Find the value of h, giving your answer in the form:

'h is between ________ and ________'.

(h by $h+5$ rectangle)

The two numbers to be found differ by 0.01 [e.g. 3.61 and 3.62]

The equation to be solved is $h(h+5) = 525$.

Try $h = 15$:	$15 \times 20 = 300$,	$h = 15$ is too small.
Try $h = 25$:	$25 \times 30 = 750$,	$h = 25$ is too large.
Try $h = 20$:	$20 \times 25 = 500$,	$h = 20$ is too small.
Try $h = 21$:	$21 \times 26 = 546$,	$h = 21$ is too large.
Try $h = 20.5$:	$20.5 \times 25.5 = 522.75$,	$h = 20.5$ is too small.
Try $h = 20.6$:	$20.6 \times 25.6 = 527.36$,	$h = 20.6$ is too large.
Try $h = 20.55$:	$20.55 \times 25.55 = 525.0525$,	$h = 20.55$ is too large.
Try $h = 20.54$:	$20.54 \times 25.54 = 524.5916$,	$h = 20.54$ is too small.

When $h = 20.55$, the area of the rectangle is greater than 525 cm^2 and when $h = 20.54$, the area of the rectangle is less than 525 cm^2.

Answer: The value of h is between 20.54 and 20.55.

Exercise 2E

1. The picture shown has height h cm, length $(h + 1)$ cm and area 200 cm^2.
   You need to find h so that $h(h + 1) = 200$.
   Between which *one decimal place* numbers does h lie?
   Write your answer as 'h is between ________ and ________'.
   Here is the start of the solution:

   Try $h = 10$: $10 \times 11 = 110$ too small

   Try $h = 20$: $20 \times 21 = 420$ too large

   Try $h = 15$: $15 \times 16 = 240$ too large

   Try $h = 14$: etc

   h

   $h + 1$

2. Find the value of h for each rectangle. Give your answer in the form:
   'h is between _______ and _____', where the two numbers to be found differ by 0.1

   (a)
   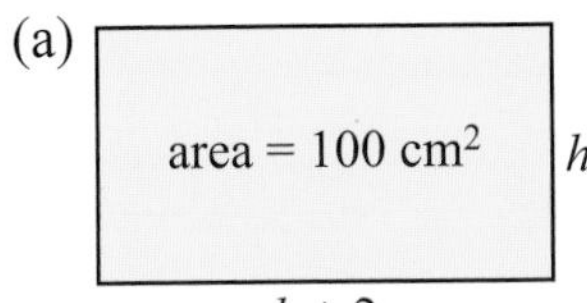

   $h + 2$

   (b)
   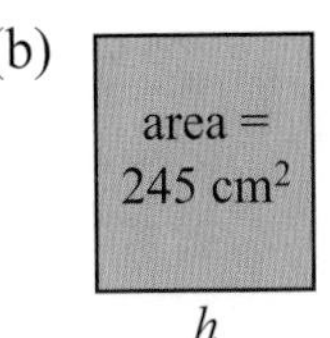

   h

3. Solve the equations below. Give your answers in the form
   'x is between ________ and _____', where the two numbers to be found differ by 0.1

   (a) $x(x + 10) = 210$ (b) $x^2 + x = 300$ (c) $x(x - 1) = 100$

Accuracy

In the last exercise the answers were given in the form 'h is between 20.54 and 20.55'.

Sometimes it is more convenient to give a solution which is correct to a specific degree of accuracy, like 2 decimal places or 3 significant figures.

In the example below, the answer is found correct to 2 decimal places.

Solve the equation $z(z - 2) = 50$, giving the answer correct to 2 decimal places.

(a) Try different values for z.

$z = 10$: $10(10 - 2) = 80$ Too large

$z = 8$: $8(8 - 2) = 48$ Too small

$z = 8.1$: $8.1(8.1 - 2) = 49.41$ Too small

$z = 8.2$: $8.2 \times 6.2 = 50.84$ Too large

$z = 8.13$: $8.13 \times 6.13 = 49.83$ Too small

$z = 8.14$: $8.14 \times 6.14 = 49.996$ Too small

$z = 8.15$: $8.15 \times 6.15 = 50.1225$ Too large

(b) At this stage we know that the answer is between 8.14 and 8.15.
We also note that the value of $z = 8.14$ gave the value closest to 50. [i.e. 49.996]

(c) We can take the solution to be $x = 8.14$, correct to 2 decimal places.

(d) Notes: (i) We have tried values of x just above and just below 8.14 [namely 8.15 and 8.13].

(ii) Strictly speaking, to ensure that our answer *is* correct to 2 decimal places, we should try $x = 8.145$. This degree of complexity is unnecessary at this stage.

Solve the equation $x^3 + 10x = 100$, giving the answer correct to one decimal place.

Try $x = 3$:	$3^3 + (10 \times 3) = 57$	$x = 3$ is too small.
Try $x = 4$:	$4^3 + (10 \times 4) = 104$	$x = 4$ is too large.
Try $x = 3.9$:	$3.9^3 + (10 \times 3.9) = 98.318$	$x = 3.9$ is too small.

Now 98.318 is closer to 100 than 104.

$\therefore$ The solution is $x = 3.9$, correct to 1 decimal place.

Exercise 3M

1 Find the value of h, correct to 1 decimal place.

(a)

area = 738 cm²

h

$h + 10$

(b)

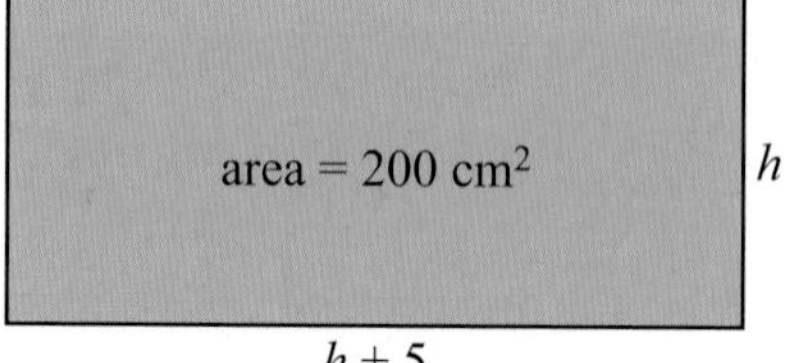

2 Solve the equations, correct to 1 decimal place.

(a) $x^2 + x = 13$ (b) $x^2 - x = 80$ (c) $x^3 - x = 70$

3 Use trial and improvement to find the cube root of 60, correct to 2 decimal places.

The cube root of 60 is written $\sqrt[3]{60}$.

Here is the start of the method:

Try 3:	$3 \times 3 \times 3 = 27$	too small
Try 4:	$4 \times 4 \times 4 = 64$	too big
Try 3.5:	etc	

4 Use trial and improvement to find these roots, correct to 2 d.p.

(a) $\sqrt[3]{150}$ (b) $\sqrt[3]{58}$ (c) $\sqrt[3]{84}$ (d) $\sqrt{90}$ [square root not cube root]

5 A cuboid has a square base of side x cm, height $(x + 1)$ cm and volume 2000 cm^3. Find the value of x, correct to 2 d.p.

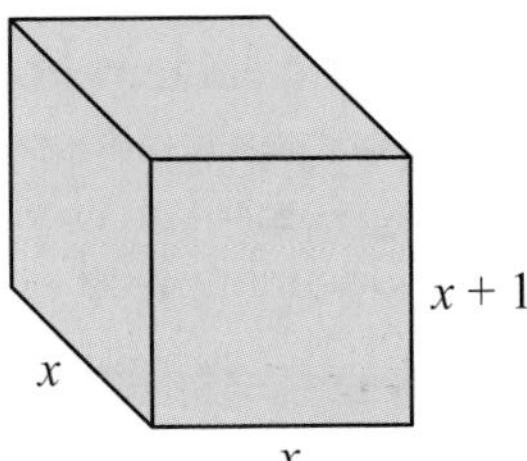

6 Find a solution to the equation $4x + 1 = x^2$. Try values of x between $x = 1$ and $x = 6$.
Give your answer correct to 2 d.p.

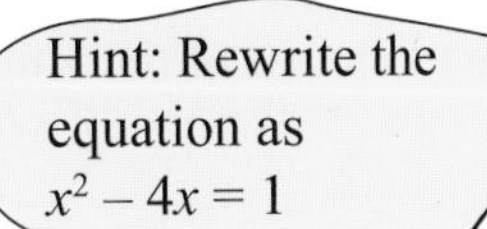

7 In this question we require much greater accuracy.
The area of the picture is 40 cm^2.
Find the value of h correct to *five* decimal places.

8 A cube has a volume of 751 cm^3. Use trial and improvement to find the length of a side to *2 decimal places*.

9 Solve the equation $x^3 + 3x = 200$.
Give your answer correct to 1 decimal place.

10 The 'L' shaped card shown has an area of 45 cm^2.
Find the value of x, correct to 2 decimal places.

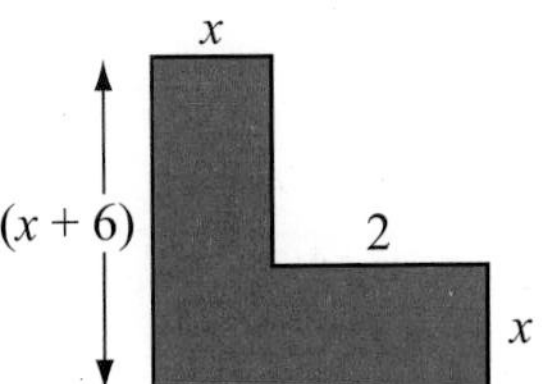

Exercise 3E

1 A rectangle has length $(x + 2)$ cm, perimeter $(4x + 6)$ cm and area 52 cm^2.

(a) Using the perimeter, find an expression for the width of the rectangle.

(b) Form an equation and solve it to find the value of x, correct to 3 significant figures.

2 The large triangle is an enlargement of the small triangle. Form an equation in x and solve it, giving your answer correct to 1 decimal place.

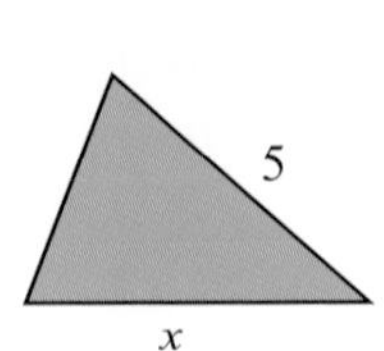

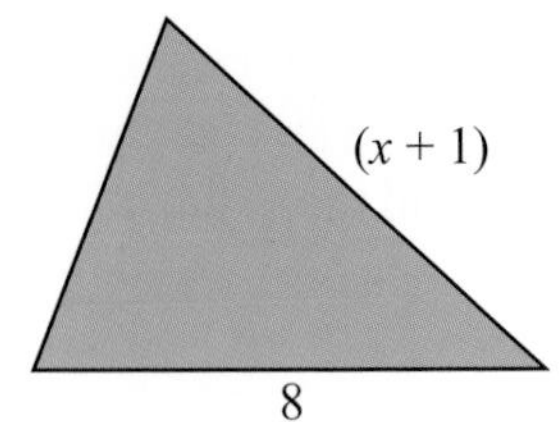

3 A window is in the shape of a semicircle joined to a rectangle. Find the radius of the semicircle, correct to 1 decimal place, if the total area of the window is 12 m^2.

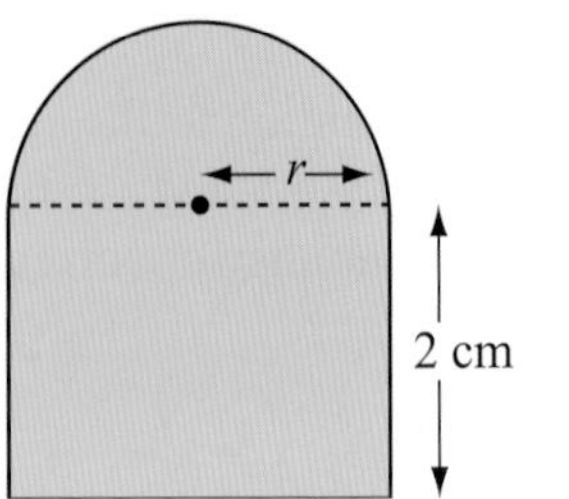

4

x

$(x + 1)$

The length of a diagonal of the photo shown is 19 cm. Find the value of x, correct to 1 decimal place.

5 Find the number whose square is ten times as large as its square root. Give your answer correct to 2 decimal places.

$\square^2 = 10\sqrt{\square}$

6 The area of circle D is equal to the sum of the areas of circles A, B and C. Find the radius of circle D correct to 2 decimal places.

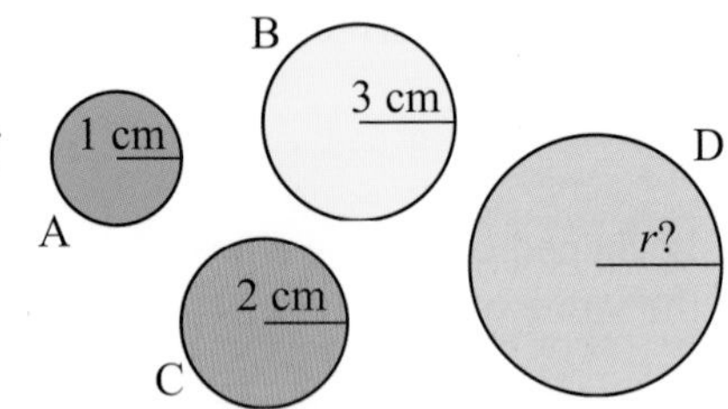

7 In the early stages of its growth, the height of an Elmer plant increases as shown.

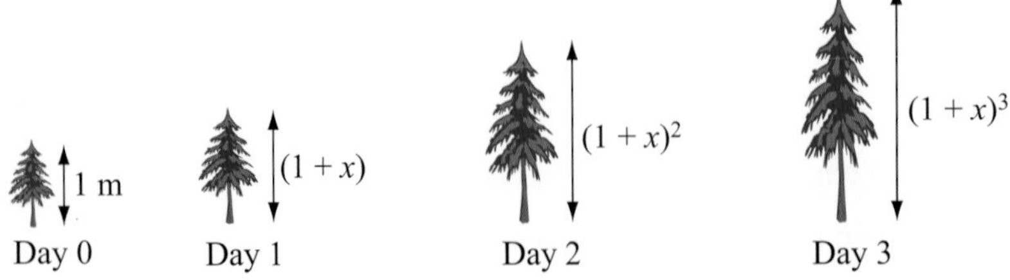

After 10 days the height of the plant is 2 m so we have the equation

$$(1 + x)^{10} = 2.$$

Find the value of x, correct to 2 *decimal* places.

8 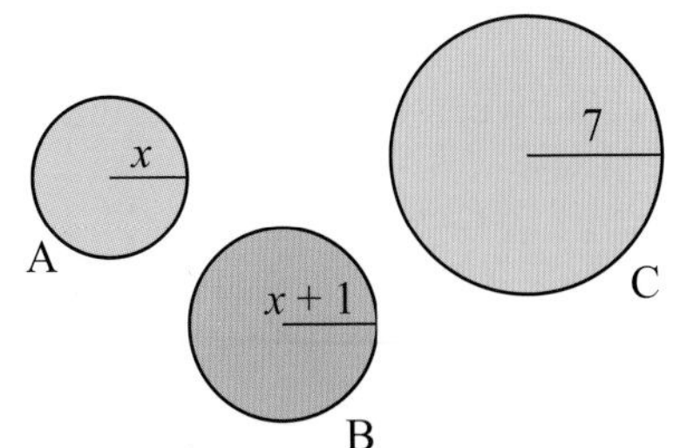

The area of circle A plus the area of circle B is equal to the area of circle C. Find the value of x, correct to 1 decimal place.

9 So far, you have solved equations involving powers of x like x^2 or x^3. Solve the equations below where numbers are raised to the power x. Give your answers correct to 1 decimal place.

(a) $3^x = 10$ (b) $12^x = 100$ (c) $7^x = 0.1$

10 This time a number x is raised to the power x. Solve the equation $x^x = 150$. Give your answer correct to 1 d.p.

11 Solve the equation $x^{x^2} = 1300$, correct to 1 d.p.

12 This question requires a knowledge of trigonometry (Unit 6)

In triangle ABC, angle BAC = x°, BC = x cm and AC = $(x + 10)$ cm.

Find the value of x, correct to the nearest whole number.

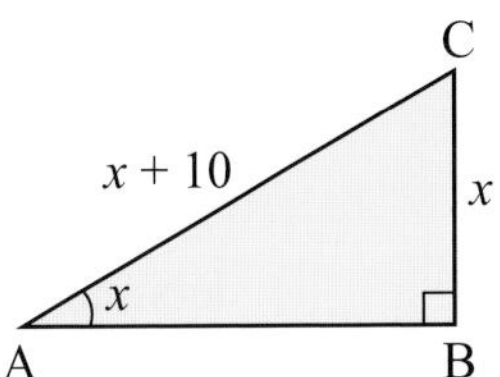

CHECK YOURSELF ON SECTIONS 2.5 AND 2.6

1 Scatter graphs

(a) Describe the correlation in these scatter graphs

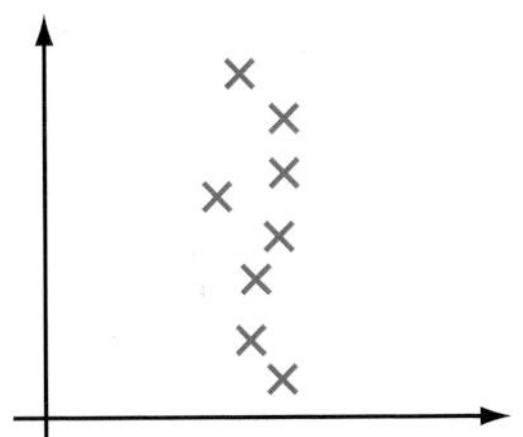

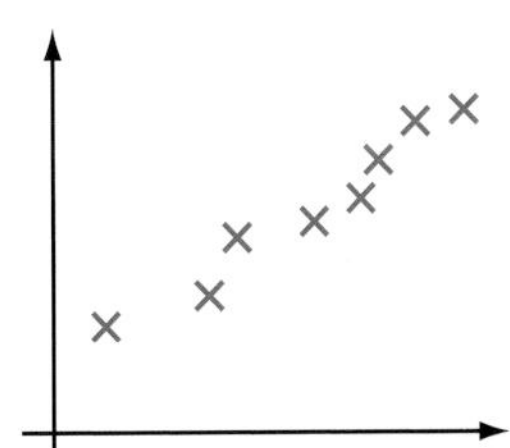

(b) Eight customers of a holiday firm were asked to give a score to their holiday. They were asked to rate the holiday on a scale of 1 to 10. (1 = awful, 10 = outstanding)
The table shows their replies and the cost of each holiday.

Rating	2	5	6	7	7	8	8	9
Cost (£)	210	250	265	270	300	290	315	329

(i) Plot a scatter graph for these data.

(ii) What does this graph tell you about the connection between the rating and the cost?

(c) On the graph, draw the line of best fit.

Another customer gave a score of 4 for her holiday.

(i) Use your scatter graph to estimate the cost of her holiday.

(ii) Give one reason why your answer may not be a very good estimate.

2 Trial and improvement

(a) Use trial and improvement to find a solution to the equations below, giving your answers correct to 1 decimal place.

(i) $x(x-3) = 100$ (ii) $x(x+8) = 95$

x

(b) The length of the rectangle shown is 3 cm more than the width x cm.

(i) Write down the length of the rectangle in terms of x.

(ii) The area of the rectangle is 80 cm^2. Form an equation involving x.

(iii) Use trial and improvement to solve the equation, giving your answer correct to 1 decimal place.

UNIT 2 MIXED REVIEW

Part one

1 When I think of a number, multiply it by 6 and subtract 120, my answer is –18. What was my original number?

2 There are 1.5×10^{26} atoms in one kilogram of helium. How many atoms are there in 32 kg of helium?

3 A circular tin of diameter 9 cm rolls along the floor for a distance of 3 m. How many times does it rotate completely?

4 Work out

(a) $\left(\frac{3}{4} - \frac{1}{8}\right) \times \frac{3}{5}$ (b) $\left(\frac{3}{7} \div \frac{3}{5}\right) - \frac{1}{3}$

5 The mean of five positive whole numbers is 6. The mode is 10 and the median is 7. Write down the five numbers.

6 Use a calculator to work out $\frac{(2 \times 4.2 \times 10^{11}) \times (3 \times 10^4)}{(3.5 \times 10^7 - 1.2 \times 10^6)}$

Give your answer correct to 2 significant figures.

7 L'Oreal 'Plenitude' face cream was advertised on television. According to the advert: 'Tests show that skin treated with L'Oreal Plenitude is 71% more radiant'.

After 2 months treatment with the above face cream, Georgina's skin is measured at 215.3 on the S.R.U. scale (Skin Radiance Units). If the claims in the advert are true what was Georgina's S.R.U. scale reading before being treated? Give your answer correct to one decimal place.

8 In a diving competition divers A, B, C, … H each perform one dive. The dives are given a mark by three different judges. Here are the results:

Diver	A	B	C	D	E	F	G	H
Judge 1	9	4	2	2	6.5	5	8	6
Judge 2	7	6	8	3.5	7	2.5	3	4
Judge 3	7	4.5	2.5	3	6	4	7	5.5

(a) Draw two scatter graphs for the marks.

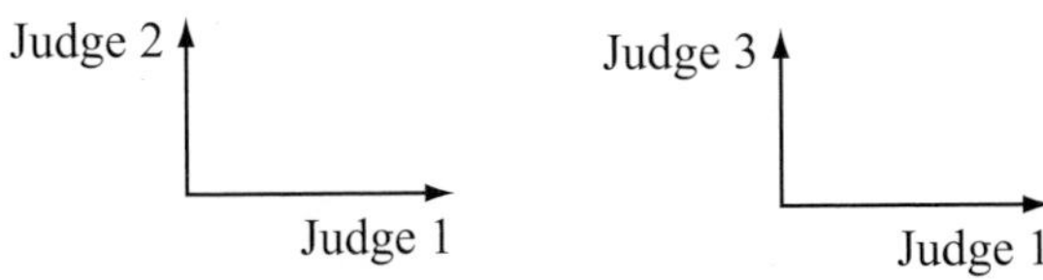

(b) Comment on the results. Can you draw a line of best fit in each case?

What correlation (if any) is there between the marks of judges 1 and 2? What about judges 1 and 3?

(c) Another diver was given 3 marks by judge 1. Estimate, if possible, the mark which might have been awarded by: (i) judge 2; (ii) judge 3.

9 Solve the equations

(a) $3(x + 6) = 2(6 - 3x)$ (b) $\frac{x + 6}{4} = \frac{3x - 3}{7}$

10 A cylinder is $\frac{1}{2}$ full of water

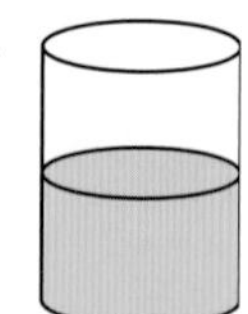

After 40 ml of water is added the cylinder is $\frac{2}{3}$ full.

Calculate the volume of the cylinder when full.

11 As a publicity stunt the organisers of the National Lottery decide to make a huge pile of £10 notes to the value of £20 million. A £10 note measures 14 cm by 7.5 cm and a wad of ten £10 notes is 1 mm thick. The pile of notes is made into a cuboid whose base is a rectangle measuring 140 cm by 75 cm. How high will the pile be?

12 The rectangle shown has length $(2x + 1)$ cm and perimeter $(6x + 8)$ cm.

(a) Find an expression, in terms of x, for the width of the rectangle.

(b) Given that the area of the rectangle is 103 cm^2, use trial and improvement to find the value of x correct to 1 decimal place.

$2x + 1$cm

13 Work out, correct to 3 significant figures.

(a) $\dfrac{(3 \times 10^{12}) \times (3.8 \times 10^{4})}{(7 \times 10^{-2})}$ (b) $\dfrac{9.74}{1.3} - \sqrt{\dfrac{5.1}{7.2 - 3.47}}$

(c) $\dfrac{1}{7.3} + \dfrac{3}{5.2} - \dfrac{5}{9.7}$ (d) $\dfrac{3.9}{1.7 - 0.821} - \left(\dfrac{1.4}{7.3}\right)^2$

14 PQRS is a rectangle. Lengths PQ and SA are shown and the perimeter of the rectangle is $6x + 20$.

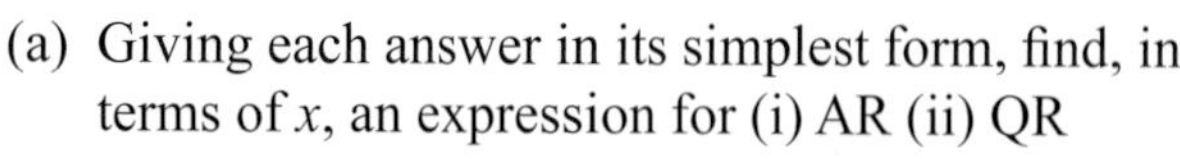

(a) Giving each answer in its simplest form, find, in terms of x, an expression for (i) AR (ii) QR

(b) If QR = $6\frac{1}{2}$ cm, find the area of triangle AQR.

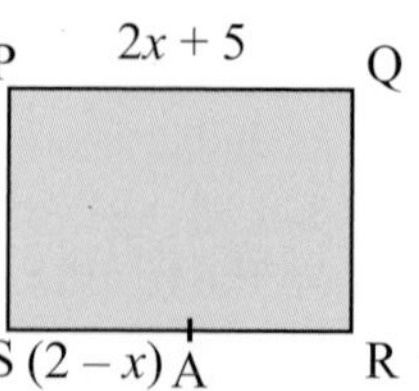

Part two

1 (a) $81 = 9^n = 3^a$. Find the values of n and a.

(b) If $3^{10} = 59049$, work out 3^9. Show your working.

(c) Work out $(200)^2 \times 100\,000$ and write the answer in standard form.

2 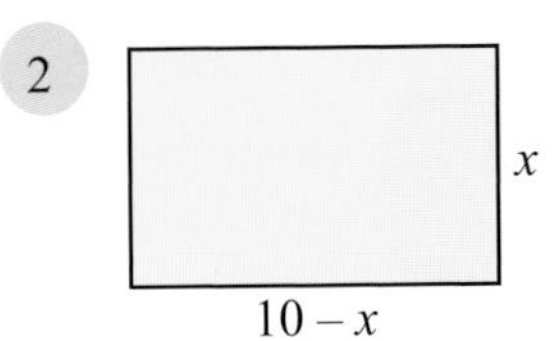

Lisa draws a rectangle with sides x cm and $(10 - x)$ cm.

Work out the perimeter of the rectangle.

The *area* of the rectangle is 20 cm^2. She wants to find x so that $x(10 - x) = 20$.

Between which *one decimal place* numbers does x lie? Write your answer as 'x is between ________ and ________'.

3 The Isle of Wight has a land area of 380 km^2. In a violent storm 6 cm of rain fell over the entire island. Calculate the volume (in m^3) of water which fell in the storm.

4 Find the smallest whole number value of x which satisfies the inequality $3^x > 300$.

5 The rule for the number sequences below is '*double and add 1*'. Write down each sequence and fill in the missing numbers or expressions.

(a) $2 \rightarrow 5 \rightarrow 11 \rightarrow \square$ (b) $\square \rightarrow \square \rightarrow 15 \rightarrow \square$ (c) $n \rightarrow \square \rightarrow \square$

6 One link of a chain is 2 cm long. When two links are joined together the maximum length is 3.4 cm. Work out the maximum total length when

(a) 3 links are joined together

(b) 300 links are joined together

(c) n links are joined together.

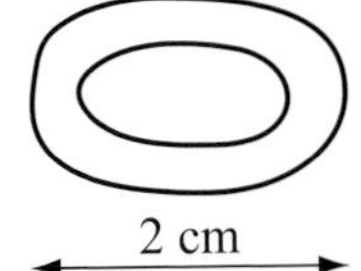

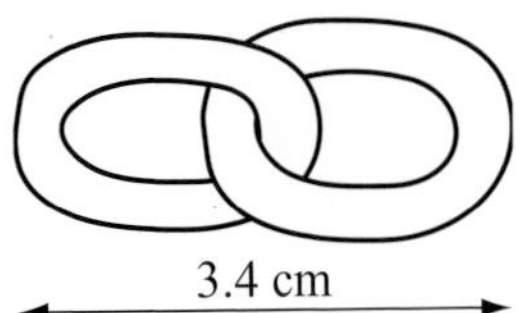

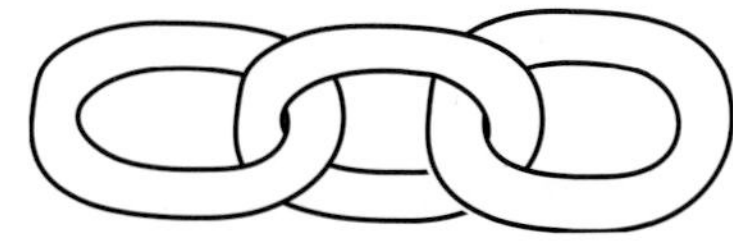

7 Copy each calculation and find the missing numbers.

(a) $\frac{1}{8} = \square\,\%$ (b) $\frac{1}{5} + \frac{\square}{\square} = \frac{1}{2}$ (c) $4 \div \square = 80$

(d) $(2 - \square)^2 = 9$ (e) $\frac{20}{\square - 4} = 40$ (f) $\square^4 = 10^{-4}$

8 A human brain has about 10 billion brain cells. [1 billion = 1000 million] Doctors estimate that a person loses 55 brains cells every time they sneeze. Michelle suffers from hay fever and on average she sneezes 100 times every day of the year.

(a) How many brain cells, correct to one significant figure, will Michelle lose in a year?

(b) How many of the original 10 billion brain cells are left after a year of sneezing?

9 Use the method of trial and improvement to find a solution to the following equation, giving your answer correct to one decimal place.

$$x^x = 3\ 600\ 000$$

10 Water flows from a full cubical tank of side 50 cm into a cylindrical tank of diameter 70 cm. What is the depth, *d*, of water in the cylindrical tank when all the water has been transferred?

11 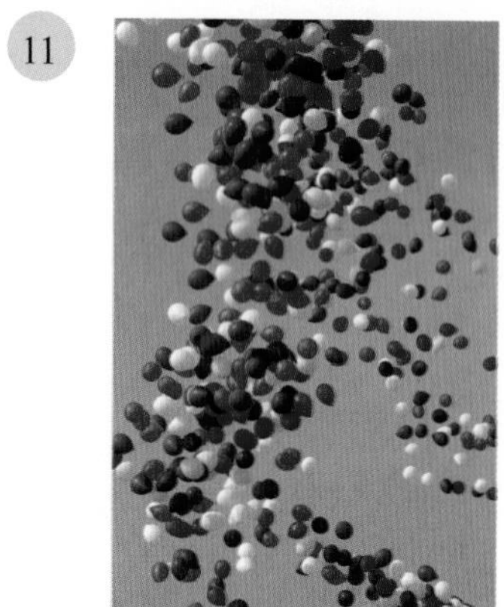

To celebrate the anticipated victory of England in the soccer World Cup, British embassies throughout the world ordered lots and lots of balloons (420,000 for *each* embassy). The balloons were to be released when Peter Gibson, the England captain, received the cup.

There are 127 British embassies in the world. How many balloons were ordered?

12 (a) A solid metal cylinder of radius 5 cm and height 8 cm is melted down and recast as a solid cube. Find the length of each side of the cube.

(b) The cube is then melted down and made into a cylinder of height 1 cm.
Calculate the radius of the cylinder.

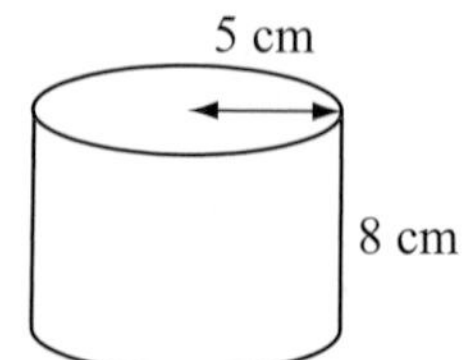

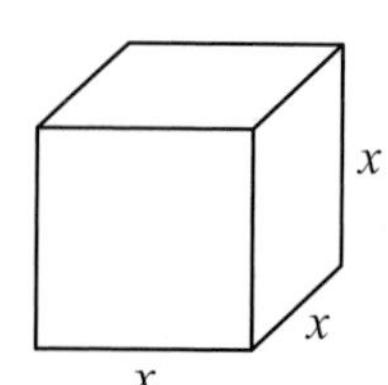

13 A reservoir, when full, contained 2×10^9 litres of water.

(a) During a dry summer, the volume of water in the reservoir was reduced by 5×10^7 litres each day until it was empty. How many days supply did the reservoir hold when full?

(b) Find the volume of water in the reservoir when it was half full, giving your answer in standard form.

14 It is given that

(area of square A) + (area of square B)
= (area of square C)

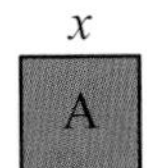

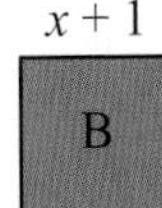

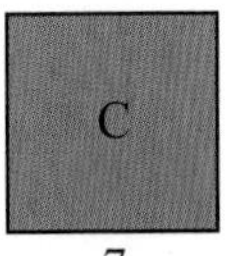

(a) Form an equation involving x.

(b) Use trial and improvement to find x, correct to 1 decimal place.

15 The table gives approximate stopping distances for cars at different speeds.

Speed (km/h)	40	60	80	100
Stopping distance (m)	18	33	50	74

Assume that cars are 4 m long and that they are driven at a steady speed, leaving a gap between cars equal to the stopping distance for that speed.

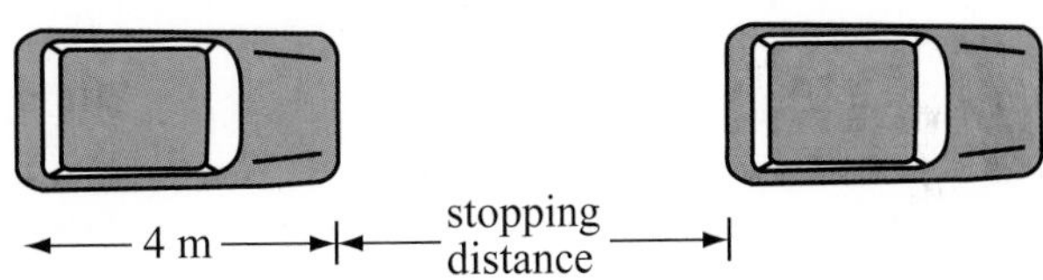

(a) How many cars, all travelling at 60 km/h, will there be on each kilometre of a single lane road?

(b) How many cars, travelling at 60 km/h, will pass a fixed point in one hour?

(c) On a 3 lane motorway, cars travel in the inside lane at 60 km/h, in the middle lane at 80 km/h and in the outside lane at 100 km/h. How many cars altogether will pass a fixed point in one hour?

Puzzles and Problems 2

Crossnumbers

(a) Copy out the crossnumber pattern.

(b) Fit all the given numbers into the correct spaces.
Tick off the numbers from the lists as you write them in the square.

1

2 digits	*3 digits*	*4 digits*	*5 digits*	*6 digits*
14	173	1615	14798	443205
16	202	1624	23641	533245
19	222	1824	31241	815713
21	227	3112	43641	885724
30	235	4076	46015	961723
32	302	4271	60111	
44	377	4284	60318	
47	378	4289	62078	
55	456	4875	71341	
56	532	5381		*7 digits*
57	628	5623		1402224
58	732	5673		6133335
58	770			
63	828			
73	853			
80				

2

2 digits		*3 digits*	*4 digits*	*5 digits*	*6 digits*
11	53	111	2905	10752	523416
12	63	134	3072	12282	538222
17	66	499	3141	15216	762214
25	70	525	3333	18253	
28	73	571	4951	25837	
29	74	576	7364	26275	
30	78	611	9362	31785	
32	81	773	9591	43567	
35	82	817		47907	*7 digits*
38	83			50078	2308712
41	85			69073	4284173
44	91			77527	
47	99			83114	
				95392	

Problems

The questions below are taken from past School Mathematics Challenge Papers. They are reproduced here with the kind permission of Dr Tony Gardiner of the U.K. Mathematics Foundation, Birmingham.

1 Weighing the baby at the clinic was a problem. The baby would not keep still and caused the scales to wobble. So I held the baby and stood on the scales while the nurse read off 78 kg. Then the nurse held the baby while I read off 69 kg. Finally I held the nurse while the baby read off 137 kg. What would the combined weight of nurse, baby and me be (in kilograms)?

A 142 **B** 147 **C** 206 **D** 215 **E** 284

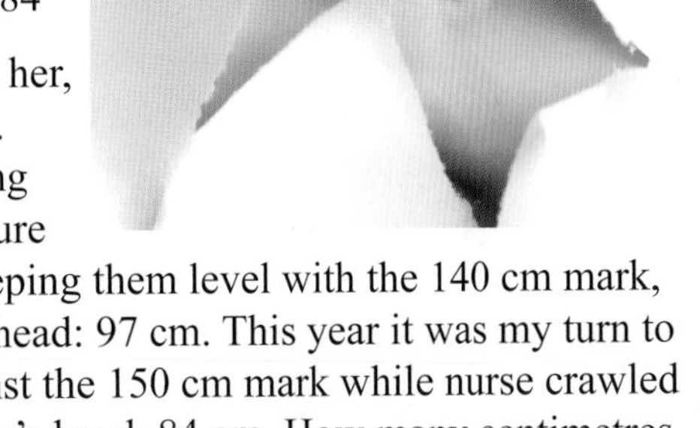

2 Baby's nearly 1 now. We've worked out how to weigh her, but nurse and I still have trouble measuring her height. She just *will* not stand up straight against our measuring chart. In fact she can't stand up at all yet! So we measure her upside down. Last year nurse held Baby's feet, keeping them level with the 140 cm mark, while I read off the mark level with the top of Baby's head: 97 cm. This year it was my turn to hold the feet. Being taller than nurse I held them against the 150 cm mark while nurse crawled on the floor to read the mark level with the top of Baby's head: 84 cm. How many centimetres has Baby grown in her first year?

A 13 **B** 237 **C** 53 **D** 23 **E** 66

3 Baby's 2 now and drinks milk by the quarter pint, so we have decided to call her GILL. Getting her to recognize her name proved difficult, so we put the four letters G, I, L, L on separate building blocks. She loves arranging them, but rarely gets them in the right order. One day she managed to produce every possible four-letter 'word' (L I L G is one such). How many different four-letter words did she produce that day?

A 3 **B** 4 **C** 12 **D** 16 **E** 24

4 Gill's back! This year, was her fourth birthday. The highlight of her party was a game of musical chairs. The game got down to herself, nurse, and me. Only two chairs were left – the hard chair and the comfy chair, with a big gap between them. The music stopped and we all piled onto the nearest chair, some on top of one another. If Gill's bottom was firmly in contact with one of the two chairs, in how many different ways could this have happened?

A 4 **B** 6 **C** 8 **D** 10 **E** 12

5 Gill has now started primary skool and is learning to spell. We got her to help by writing out this queschun for us. We gave her a score of 100 to start with, and deducted 10% of her running total each time we found a word spelt rong. What was her final score?

A 70 **B** 72.9 **C** 80 **D** 81 **E** 90

6 Gill is just six and boasts that she can count up to 100. However, she often mixes up nineteen and ninety, and so jumps straight from nineteen to ninety one. How many numbers does she miss out when she does this?

A 70 **B** 71 **C** 72 **D** 78 **E** 89

7 Gill arranges the fingers of her right hand so that her thumb points upwards, her first finger points north and her second finger points west: we write this for short as "TU, 1N, 2W". She then keeps her fingers fixed like this, but can twist her arm and her wrist if she likes. Which of the following arrangements can she *not* achieve? (D = down, S = south, E = east.)

A TD, 1N, 2E **B** TN, 1D, 2W **C** TS, 1E, 2U

D TE, 1U, 2S **E** TW, 1S, 2D

8 Last year's carnival procession was $1\frac{1}{2}$ km long. The last float set off, and finished, three quarters of an hour after the first float. Just as the first float reached us, young Gill escaped. She trotted off to the other end of the procession and back in the time it took for half the procession to pass us. Assuming Gill trotted at a constant speed, how fast did she go?

A 3 km/h **B** 4 km/h **C** 5 km/h **D** 6 km/h **E** 7 km/h

A long time ago! 2

The Möbius Strip

You will need a piece of A4 paper, scissors and some glue or sellotape.

Cut the paper lengthways into strips about one inch (2.5 cm) wide.

1 Take one strip of paper. Make a loop by bringing the ends of the strip together. Before sticking the ends together, twist one end of the paper over then attach the two ends together. You now have a Möbius strip, a piece of paper with a half-twist in it.

Now starting anywhere on the strip, draw a line following the length of the strip. Do not take the pencil off the paper. You will end up back where you started having gone around the loop twice. How many sides does your möbius strip have? Discuss.

What about the edge of the strip? Mark a point near the edge of your strip. Move your finger along the edge. What happens when you have gone around the loop twice? Discuss.

History:

The strip was discovered independently by German mathematicians August Ferdinand Möbius and Johan Benedict Listing in 1858. An ant walking in a straight line on a Möbius strip would never stop because there is no edge in the direction of their movement.

2 Cut your Möbius strip in half, dividing it down the middle all along its length. What do you expect to get? What do you actually get? Discuss.

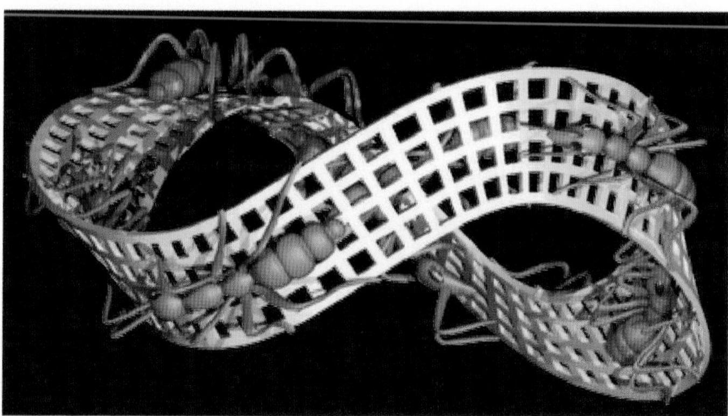

3 What do you expect to get if you cut the new strip down the middle all along its length? Now do this. What do you actually get? Discuss.

4 Make a brand new Möbius strip. Make a small cut about a third of the way in from the edge. Using this as your starting point, make a cut along the strip. Go around the loop twice. Try to describe what you get now. Discuss.

5 Make another new strip but this time twist one end of the paper over twice before attaching the two ends together. This strip has two half-twists in it. Cut right down the middle, all along its length. Describe what you get now. Discuss.

6 Make strips with different numbers of half-twists. Make cuts down the middle and explore the results.

Applications

Möbius strips occur in many aspects of Science. They inspire artists. They have been used as conveyor belts because they last longer (the whole surface area of the belt gets the same amount of wear).

7 **Valentine's Special!**

Make a Möbius strip with one clockwise half-twist. Make another Möbius strip with one anticlockwise half-twist.
Draw a small arrow on each strip parallel to the edge.
Stick the two strips together so that the arrow on one strip is at right angles to the arrow on the other strip.
Carefully cut each strip down the middle, completely along the length.
You should get a pair of hearts linked together. How sweet?
(If this does not work, you probably did not have a clockwise and anticlockwise twist for one each of the strips at the start).

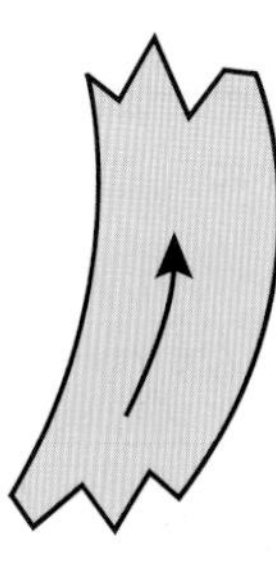

UNIT 3

3.1 Shape and space, mixed problems

In this section you will:

- find angles in a variety of shapes
- answer questions involving bearings
- use Pythagoras' theorem to solve problems
- review reflection, rotation, enlargement and translation

Finding angles

Exercise 1M

Find the angles marked with letters

1 107° 57° a

2 b c 65°

3 100° d 85° 65°

4 $2f$ $2f$ f

5

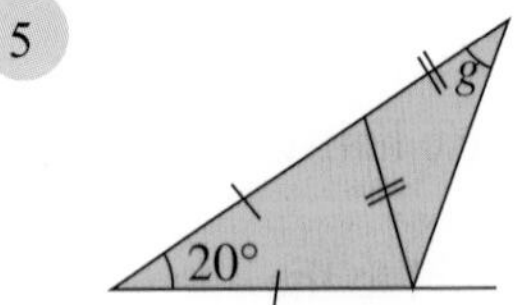

6 h 15°

7

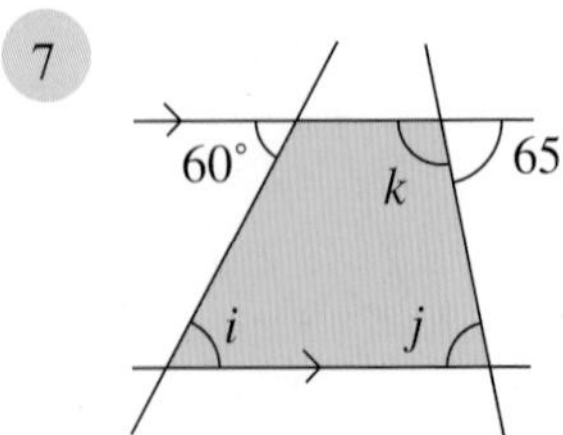

8

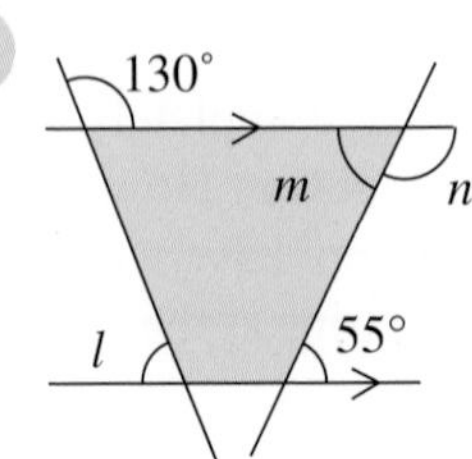

9

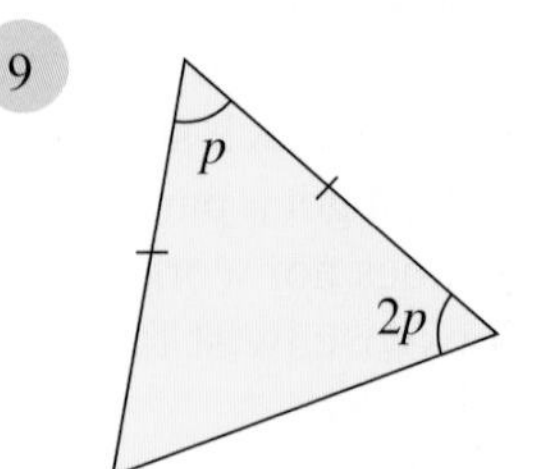

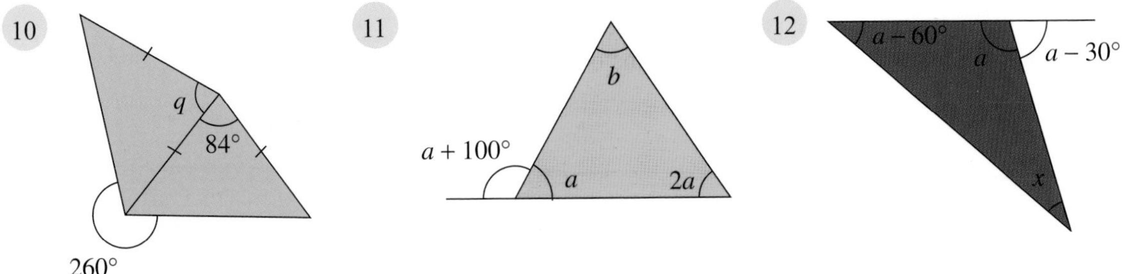

13

Find the angle between adjacent spokes of this wagon wheel. State any assumptions that you make.

Exercise 1E

1. Draw a triangle ABC with AB = AC. Point D lies on AC so that BD bisects angle ABC. Given that angle ACB = 76°, find the size of angle BDC.
2. Draw a square PQRS with an equilateral triangle PQT inside the square. Calculate the size of the angle STR.
3. Draw triangle LMN with point K on LN so that KN = KM and LK = LM. Given that angle NLM = 32°, find the size of angle LNM.

In 4 to 9 use the fact that the tangent at any point on a circle is perpendicular to the radius at that point.

tangent

4 O j i 35°

5 O 63° k

6 O 50° m k 20°

7 $2n$ n

8 42° p

9 q 26°

10 The diagram shows two equal squares and a triangle. Find the size of angle x, in terms of a

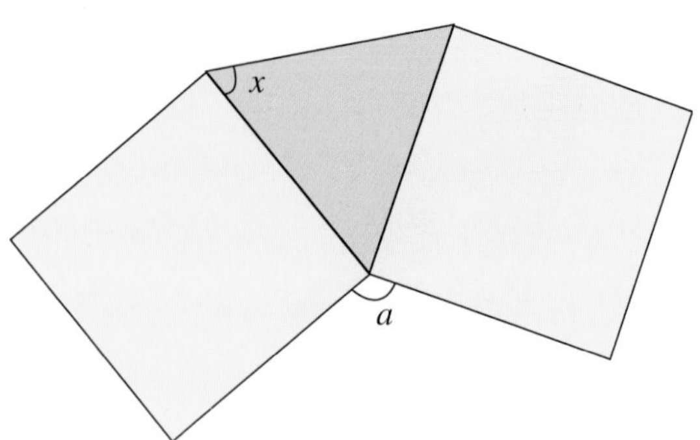

Bearings

Exercise 2M

1 Using a protractor measure the bearings on which ships A, B, C, D and E are sailing.

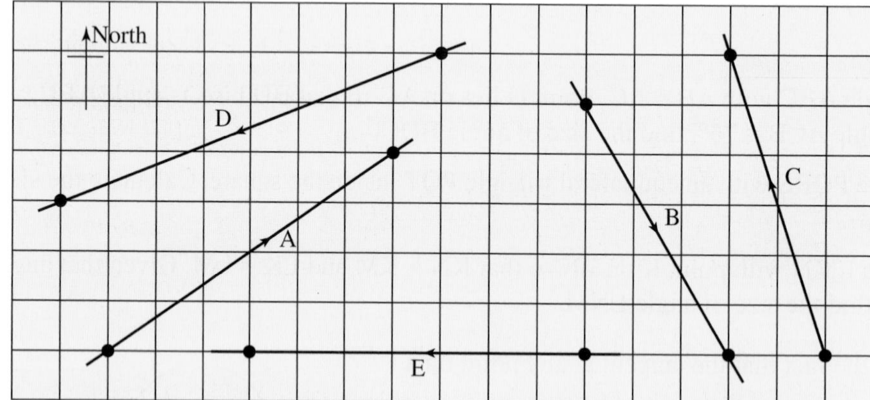

Remember: Bearings are measured clockwise from North.

2 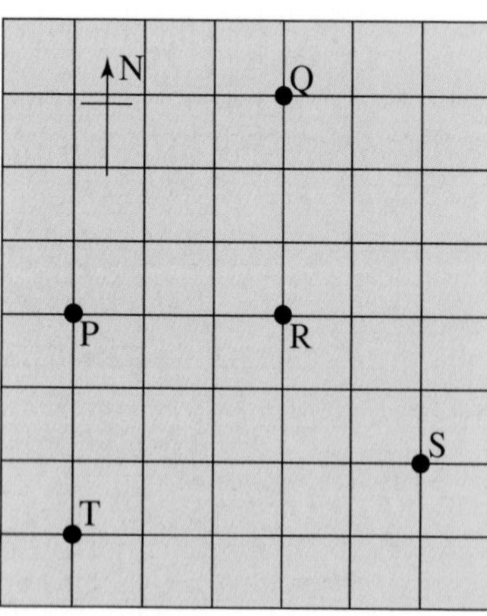

State the bearings of (a) Q from P

(b) R from P

(c) S from R

(d) R from Q

(e) T from R

(f) P from R

3 A ship sails 8 km on a bearing 041° and then a further 6 km on a bearing 090°. Make a scale drawing (1 km = 1 cm) and find how far the ship is from its starting point.

4 A ship sails 9 km on a bearing of 072° and then a further 7 km on a bearing of 130°. How far is the ship from its starting point?

5 Copy the diagram on squared paper. Mark a point P such that

(a) the bearing of P from A is 038°

(b) the bearing of P from B is 300°.

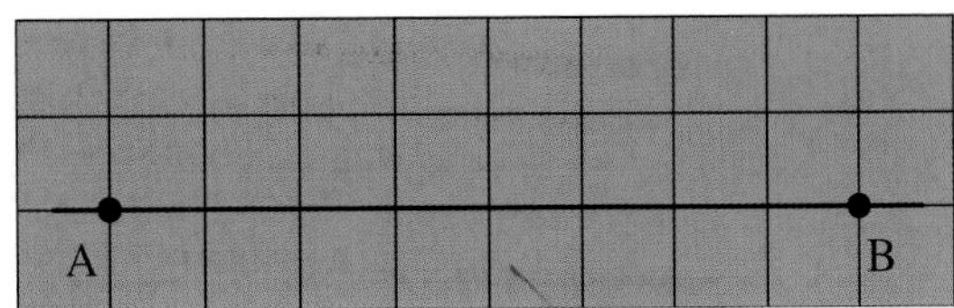

6 Write down the coordinates of the point which is:

(a) on a bearing 090° from A and 180° from B

(b) on a bearing 045° from A and 180° from C

(c) on a bearing 135° from A and 270° from D

(d) on a bearing 315° from B and 045° from A

(e) on a bearing 045° from A and 315° from D

(f) on a bearing 180° from C and 270° from B

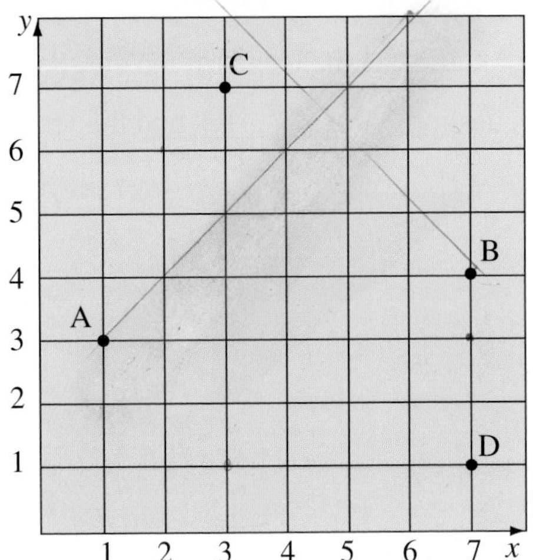

Pythagoras' theorem

Exercise 3M

Find the side marked x. All lengths are in cm. Give answers correct to one decimal place.

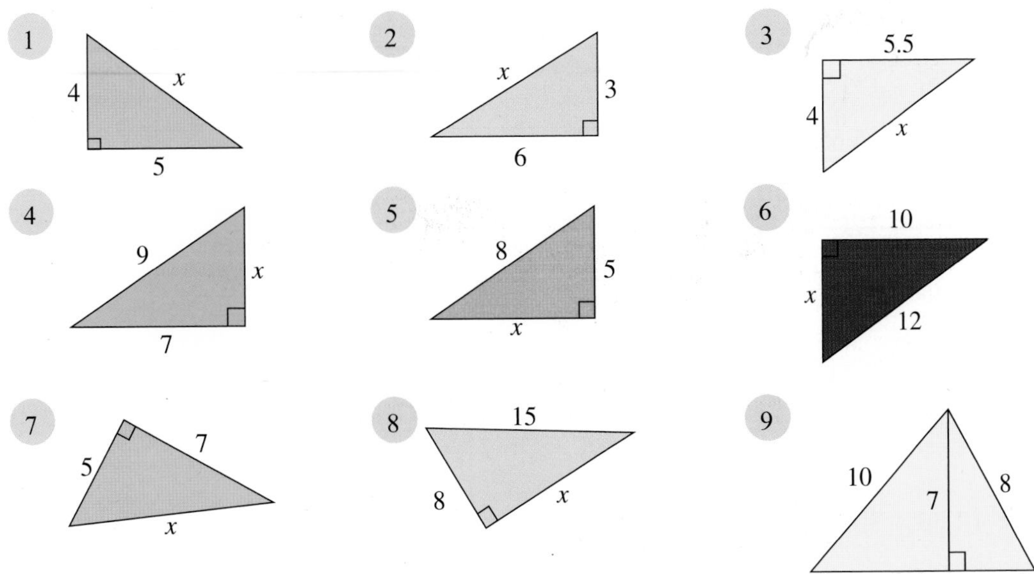

10

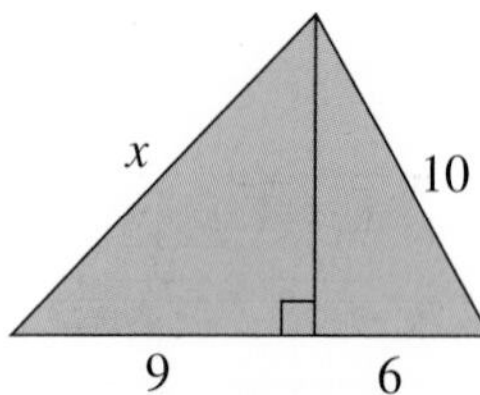

11

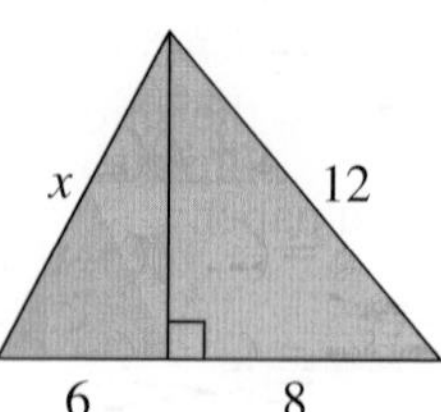

12 A ladder of length 4 m rests against a vertical wall, with its foot 2.2 m from the wall. How far up the wall does the ladder reach?

13 Calculate the length of the diagonal of a rectangle measuring 9 cm by 12 cm.

In questions 14, 15, 16 find the length x, correct to 2 decimal places. All lengths are in cm.

14

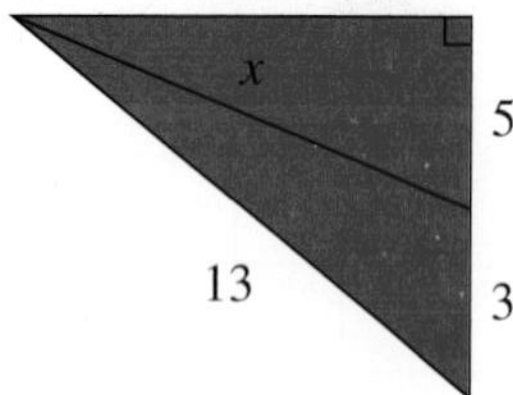

15

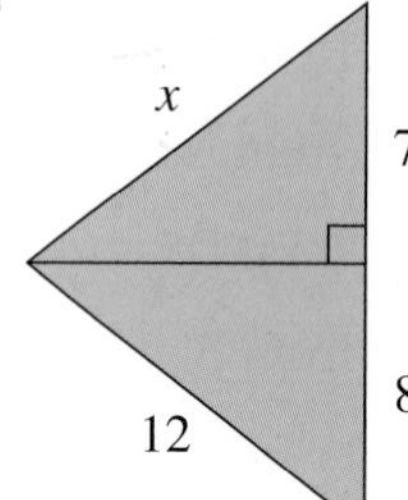

16

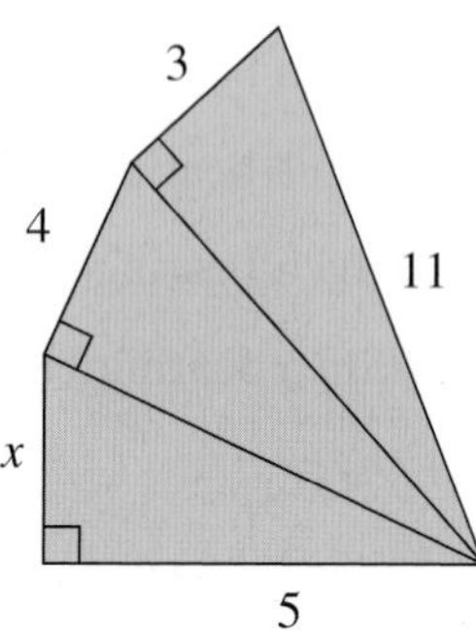

Pythagoras' theorem in circles

A circle is drawn through the corners of a square of side 8 cm. Find the yellow shaded area.

Let the length of the diameter be x cm.

By Pythagoras', $x^2 = 8^2 + 8^2$

$x = 11.313\,708$

$\therefore$ radius $= 5.656\,854\,2$

area of circle $= \pi \times 5.656\,854\,2^2$

$= 100.530\,96$ cm^2

area of square $= 64$ cm^2

shaded area $= 36.5$ cm^2 (3 s.f)

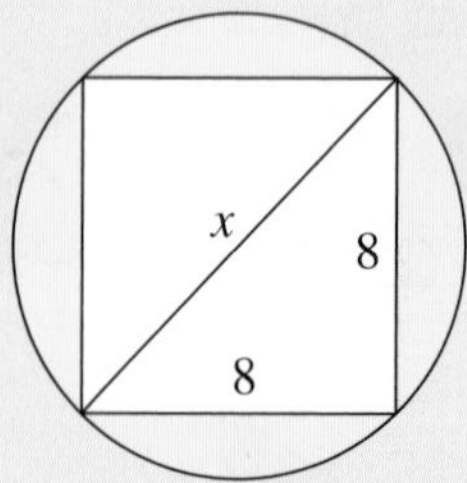

Notice that we have approximated to 3 s.f. only at the very end of the calculation.

Exercise 3E

In questions 1 and 2 find the shaded area. Lengths are in cm. In questions 3, 4, 5 all arcs are either semicircles or quarter circles. You do not *always* have to use Pythagoras' theorem.

1

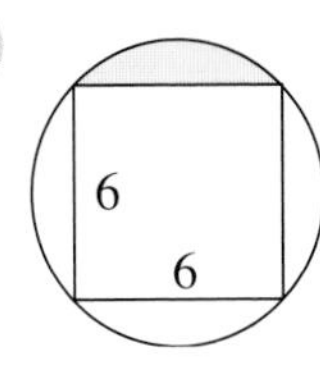

2

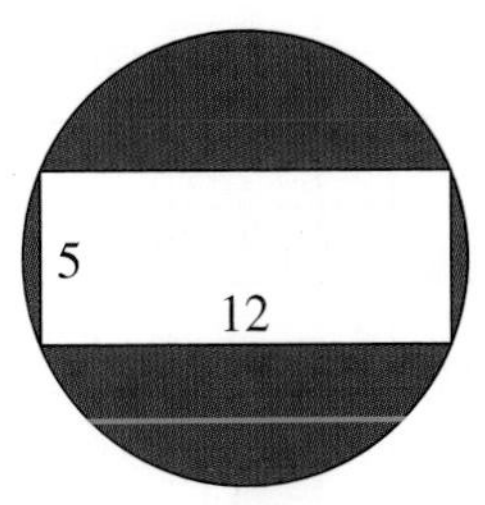

3 All arcs are semicircles. Find the total area.

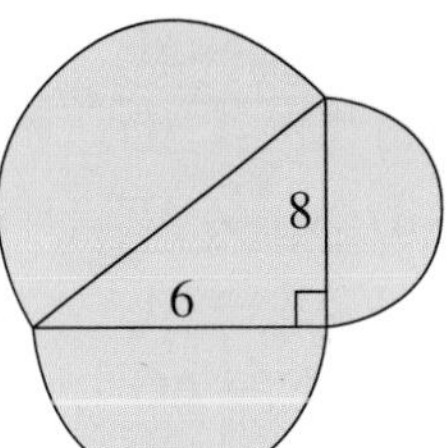

4 This diagram contains two semicircles. Calculate the shaded area, given that the diameter of the larger semicircle is 12 cm.

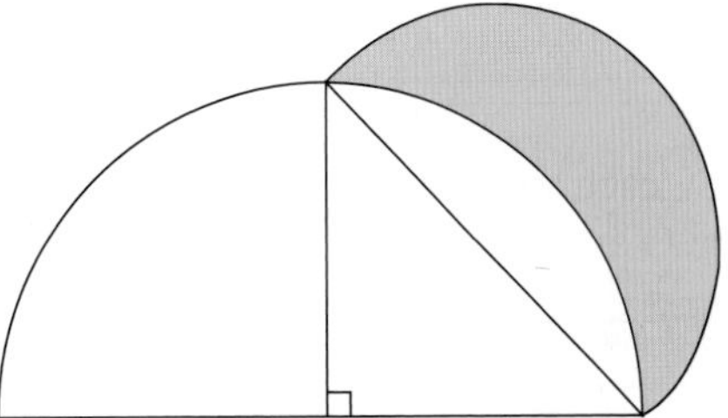

5 This diagram has one quarter circle and two semicircles. Calculate the shaded area.

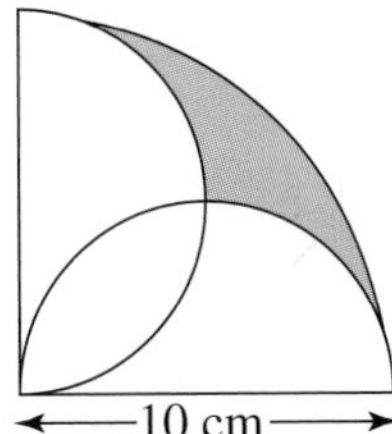

Transformations

Exercise 4M

1 Draw each shape on a squared paper and then draw its reflection.

(a)

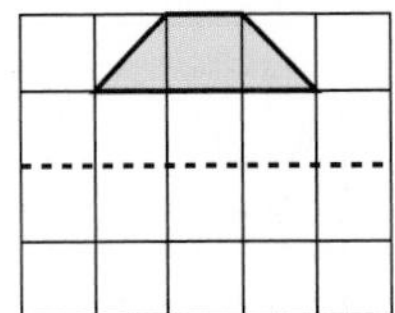

(b)

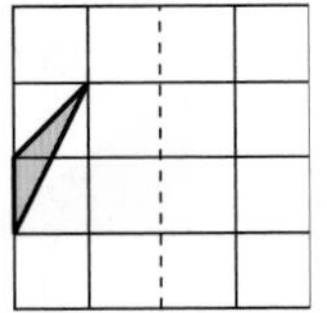

(c)

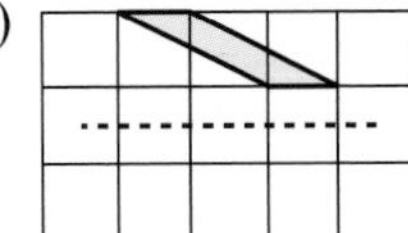

(d)

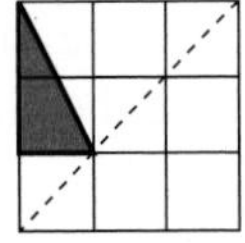

(e)

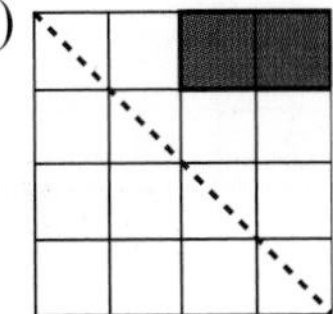

(f)

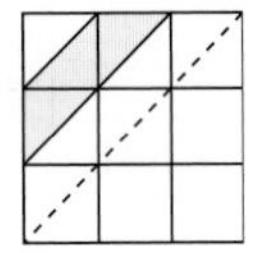

(g)

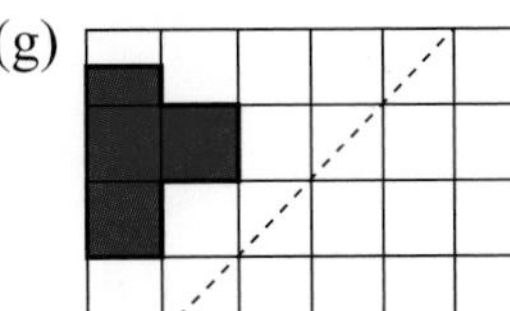

2 Write down the equation of the mirror line for each reflection.

(a) ΔA → ΔB
(b) ΔA → ΔF
(c) ΔE → ΔD
(d) ΔB → ΔC
(e) ΔE → ΔF
(f) ΔF → ΔG

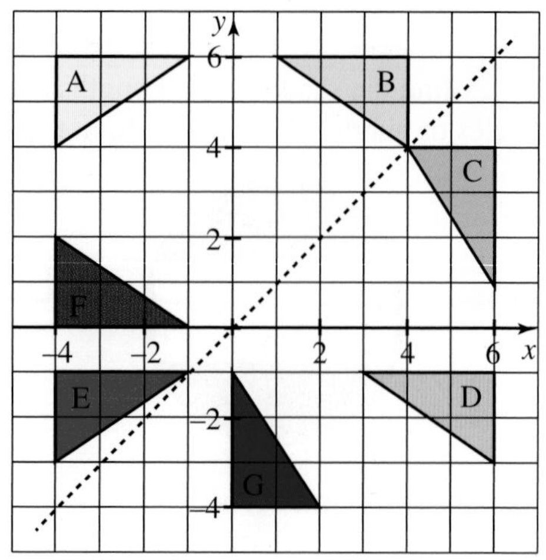

3 Draw each shape and its image under the rotation given.
Take O as the center of rotation in each case.

(a)
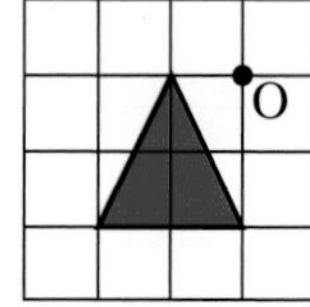
90° anticlockwise

(b)
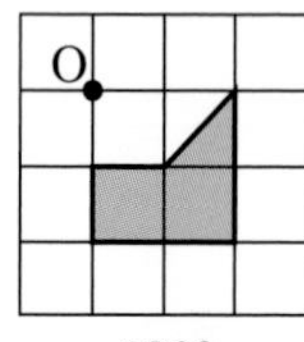
180°

(c)
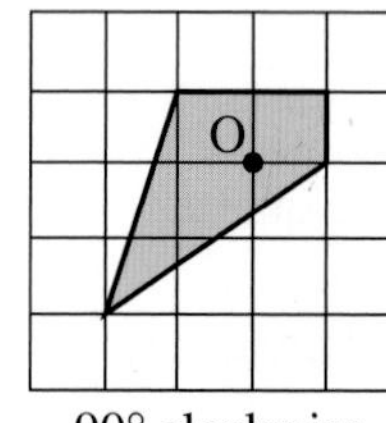
90° clockwise

(d)
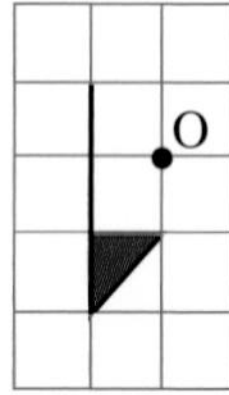
90° clockwise

(e)
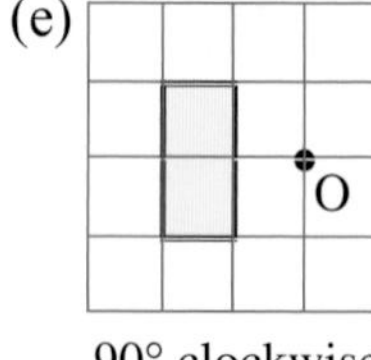

90° clockwise

(f)
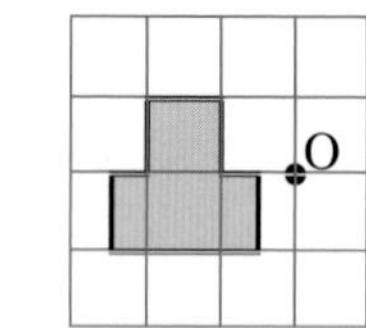
90° anticlockwise

4 Describe fully the rotations.
(give the angle, direction and centre)

(a) ΔA → ΔB
(b) ΔA → ΔC
(c) ΔA → ΔD
(d) ΔE → ΔD
(e) ΔC → ΔE
(f) ΔD → ΔF

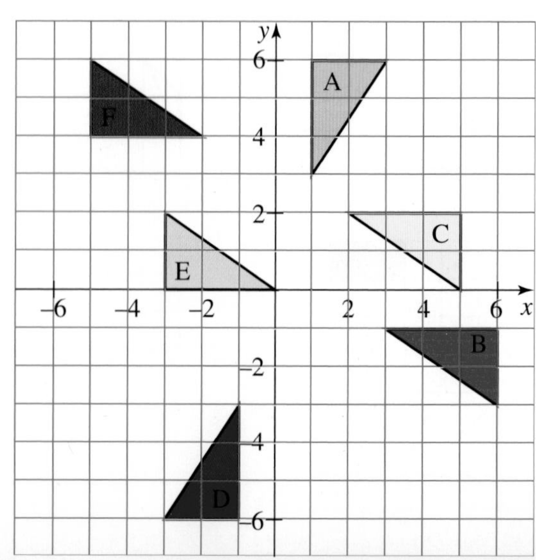

5 Copy each shape with its centre of enlargement. Then enlarge the shape by the scale factor given.

(a)

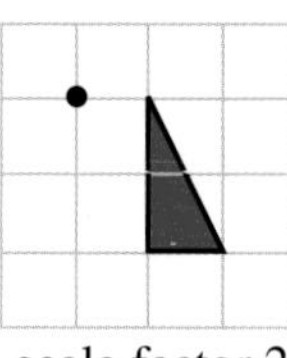

scale factor 2

(b)

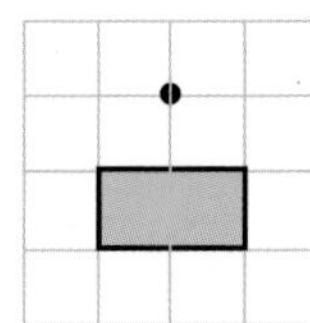

scale factor 2

(c)

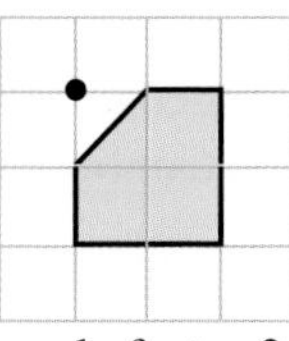

scale factor 3

(d)

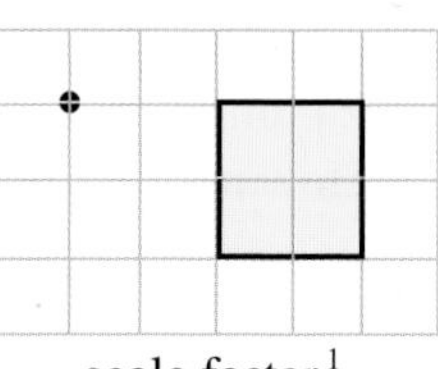

scale factor $\frac{1}{2}$

(e)

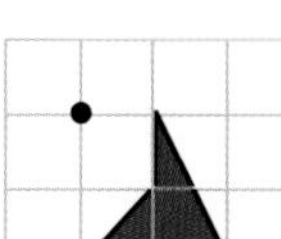

scale factor 3

(f)

scale factor 4

(g)

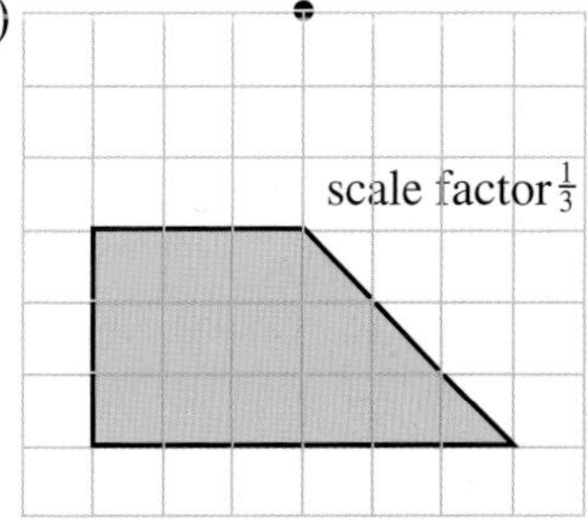

scale factor $\frac{1}{3}$

6 Describe fully each of the following enlargements

(a) $\Delta D \rightarrow \Delta C$

(b) $\Delta A \rightarrow \Delta B$

(c) $\Delta F \rightarrow \Delta E$

(d) $\Delta D \rightarrow \Delta E$

(e) $\Delta B \rightarrow \Delta D$

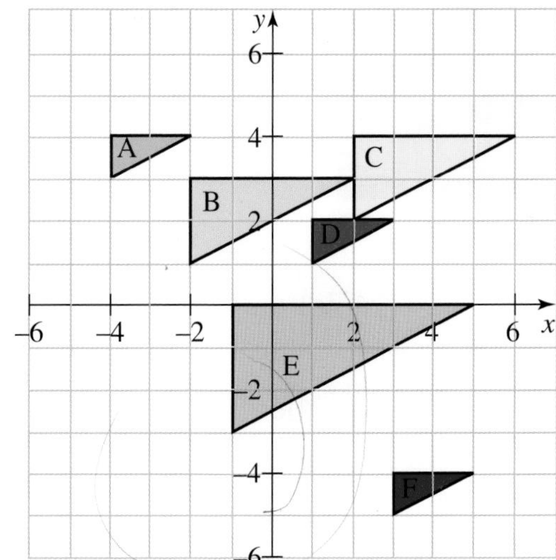

Exercise 4E (Miscellaneous)

1

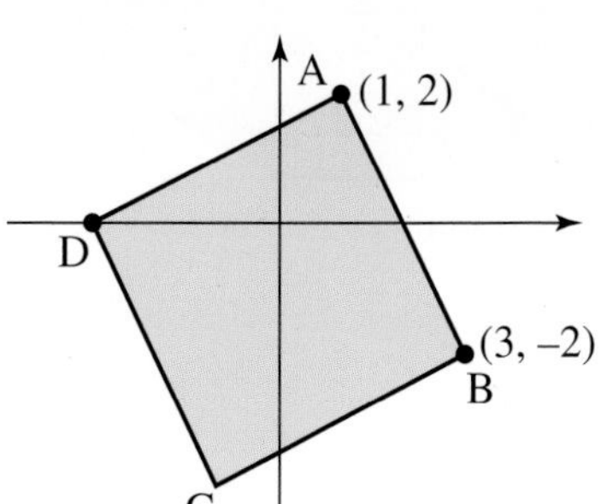

The diagram shows a square ABCD. Find the coordinates of C.

2 Many small cubes of side 1.2 cm are stuck together to make a large cube of volume 216 cm^3.
How many cubes are needed?

3 (a) 24 unit cubes can be stuck together to make cuboids of different shapes. How many *different* cuboids can be made?

(b) How many different cuboids can be made with (i) 56 cubes?
(ii) 100 cubes?

4 Copy and complete

(a) 10 gallons ≈ □ litres (b) 3kg ≈ □ pounds

(c) 8 km ≈ □ miles (d) 6 feet ≈ □ cm

(e) 9 litres ≈ □ gallons (f) 44 pounds ≈ □ kg

(g) 100 cm ≈ □ feet (h) 1.1 pounds ≈ □ kg

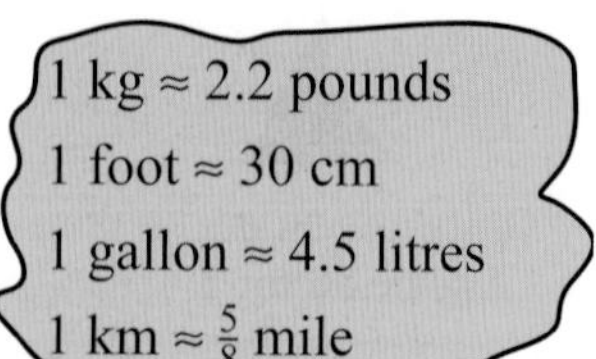

5 

Some elephants are looking for water. They start from point A and walk 80 km on a bearing 240°. They then change direction and walk a further 100 km on a bearing 315° and find water. How far is the water from point A?

6 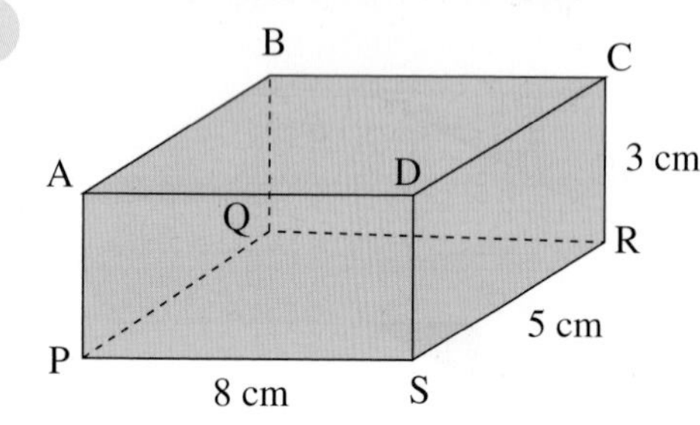

The diagram shows a cuboid.
(a) Use triangle PQS to find the length of QS.
(b) Use triangle BSQ to find the length of BS.

7 Find the length of the diagonal MN in the cuboid opposite.

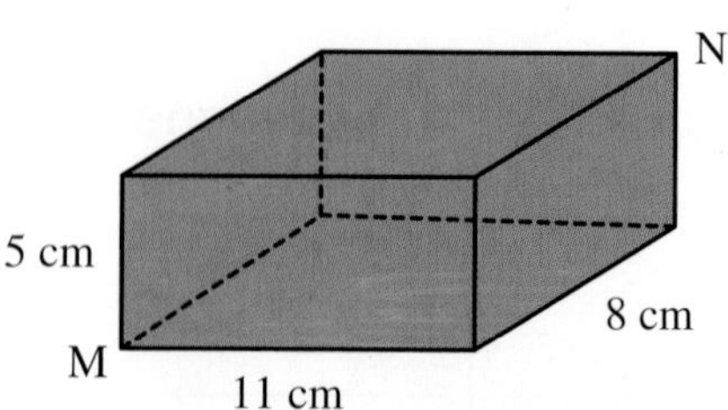

8 The bearing of E from F is 133°. What is the bearing of F from E?

9 Use a ruler, pencil and compasses *only* to construct a triangle with angles 30°, 60° and 90°. Show your construction marks.

3.2 Sequences – finding a rule

In this section you will:

- learn how to find the nth term of an arithmetic progression
- learn about geometric sequences
- learn about quadratic sequences (optional)

Arithmetic progression (or 'arithmetic sequence')

In an arithmetic progression (A.P.) the difference between successive terms is constant.

For the arithmetic progression (A.P.) 3, 8, 13, 18, … the rule is 'add 5'. We draw a mapping diagram with a column for 5 times the term number (i.e. $5n$).

n	$5n$	term
1	5	3
2	10	8
3	15	13
4	20	18

We see that each term is 2 less than $5n$.

So, the 10th term is $(5 \times 10) - 2 = 48$

the 20th term is $(5 \times 20) - 2 = 98$

the nth term is $5 \times n - 2 = 5n - 2$

The nth term of the arithmetic progression is $5n - 2$

Exercise 1M

1 Look at the arithmetic progression 5, 8, 11, 14, …
The difference between terms is 3.
Copy the table, which has a column for $3n$.
Copy and complete: 'The nth term of the sequence is $3n + \square$.'

n	$3n$	term
1	3	5
2	6	8
3	9	11
4	12	14

2 Look at the arithmetic progression and the table underneath. Find the nth term in each case.

(a) 5, 9, 13, 17, …

n	$4n$	term
1	4	5
2	8	9
3	12	13
4	16	17

nth term = $\square$

(b) 2, 8, 14, 20, …

n	$6n$	term
1	6	2
2	12	8
3	18	14
4	24	20

nth term = $\square$

3 In the arithmetic progression 6, 11, 16, 21, …
the difference between terms is 5.
Copy and complete the table and write an expression for the nth term of the sequence.

n	☐	term
1	☐	6
2	☐	11
3	☐	16
4	☐	21

4 Look at the sequence 6, 10, 14, 18, …
Write down the difference between terms.

Make a table like the one in question 3 and use it to find an expression for the nth term.

5 Write down each sequence in a table and then find the nth term.

(a) 5, 7, 9, 11, …

(b) 3, 7, 11, 15, …

(c) 2, 8, 14, 20, …

6 Make a table for each sequence and write the nth term.

(a) 2, 10, 18, 26, …

(b) 7, 10, 13, 16, …

(c) 21, 30, 39, 48, …

7 Here is a sequence of triangles made from a number of matches m.

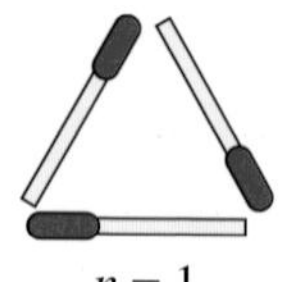

$n = 1$
$m = 3$

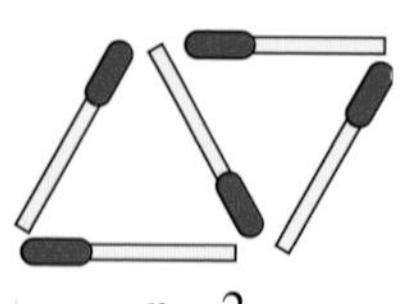

$n = 2$
$m = 5$

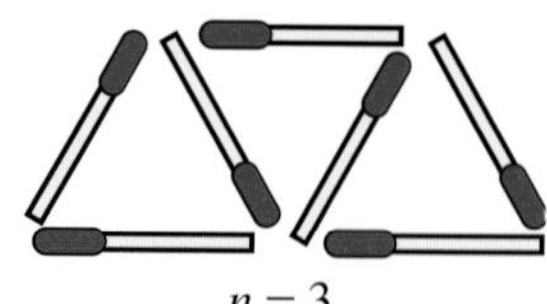

$n = 3$
$m = 7$

n	m
1	3
2	5
3	7
4	

Draw the next diagram in the sequence and write the values for n and m in a table.
How many matches are in the nth term?

8 Crosses are drawn on rectangular 'dotty' paper. The diagram number of the cross is recorded together with the total number of dots d on each cross.

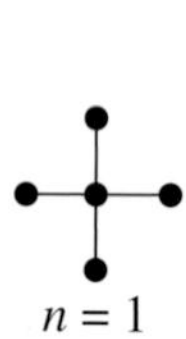

$n = 1$

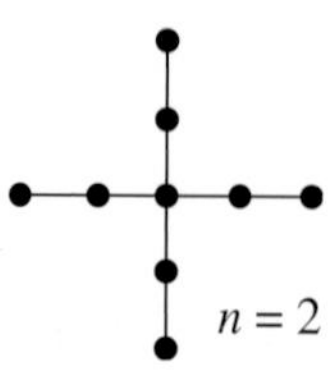

$n = 2$

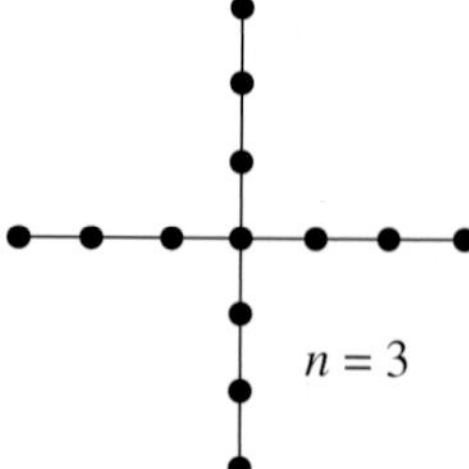

$n = 3$

n	d
1	5
2	9
3	13

Find a formula connecting n and d.
Write it as '$d = …$'

9 Look at the tables below. In each case, find a formula connecting the two letters.

(a)

n	h
2	10
3	13
4	16
5	19

write '$h =$

(b)

n	p
3	12
4	17
5	22
6	27

write '$p =$

(c)

n	s
2	4
3	$4\frac{1}{2}$
4	5
5	$5\frac{1}{2}$

write '$s = \ldots$'

10 

Many films described as 'romantic comedies' have a common sequence of events. Write the events listed below in a sensible order. You may add a few events of your own invention to liven up the story. You may or may not choose to make use of the banana with the 'valentine heart'.

Get married | get back together | get engaged | fall in love

Live happily ever after | have massive argument | meet for the first time

Break up, throw ring away | meet parents | pass maths GCSE

Exercise 1E

1 In each diagram below, a number of white squares w surrounds a rectangle of blue squares. The length of each rectangle is one unit more than the height h.

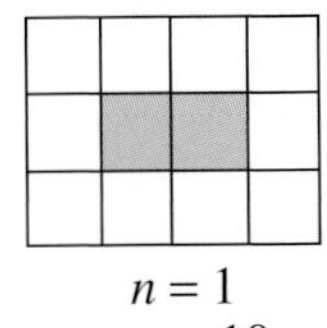

$n = 1$
$w = 10$

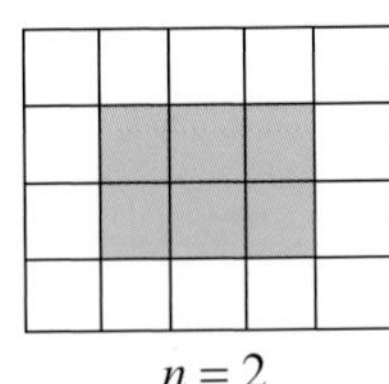

$n = 2$

$n = 3$

n	w
1	10

Make a table of values of n and w. Use it to find a formula connecting n and w. Write it as '$w = \ldots$'

2 In a sequence of diagrams similar to the one in question 1, white squares surround a rectangle but this time the length of the red rectangle is twice the height. The diagram with $n = 2$ is shown.

Draw the sequence of diagrams and make a table of values of n and w.

Write the formula connecting n and w in the form '$w = \ldots$'

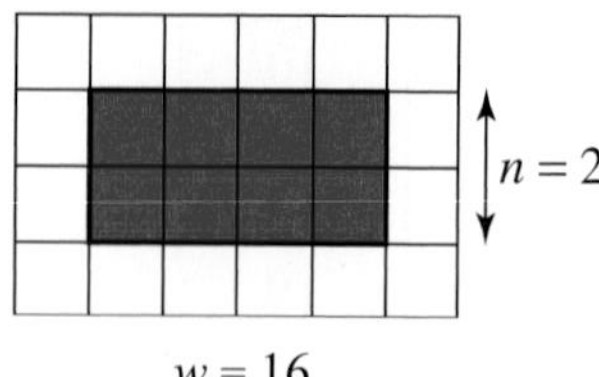

3 Open 'boxes' are drawn on rectangular dotty paper.

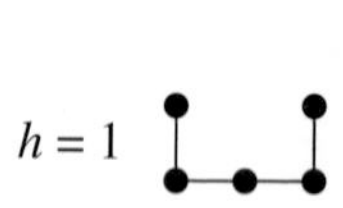

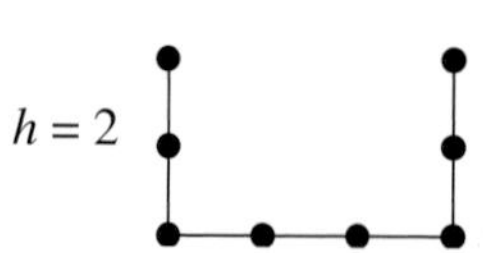

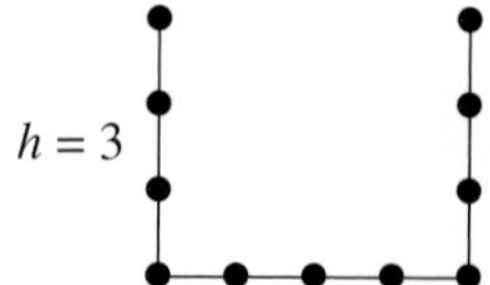

Count the number of dots d in each diagram and find a formula for d in terms of h (the height of the box).

4 Look at the tables below and in each case find a formula for z in terms of n. Write the formula as '$z = \ldots$'

Notice that in part (a) the values of n are not consecutive.

(a)

n	z
2	7
3	13
5	25
6	31

(b)

n	z
0	15
1	12
2	9
3	6

5 In these diagrams 4 triangles are joined either at a vertex or along a whole side. We are counting the number of common edges c [shown bold] and the perimeter of the shape p.

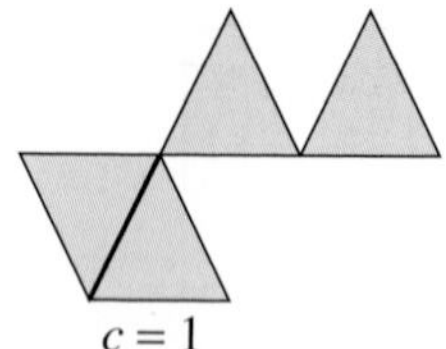

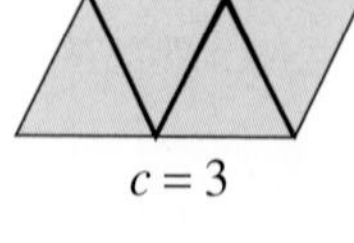

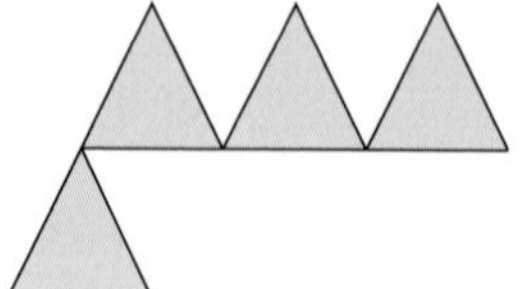

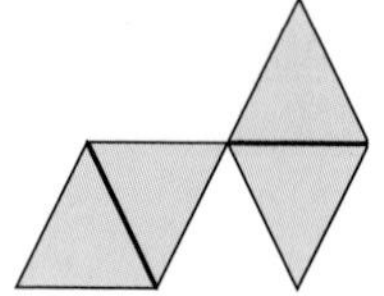

Make a table of values of p and c and find a formula for p in terms of c [i.e. '$p = \ldots$']

6 In each diagram below a 'V' is formed by shading squares inside a rectangle of height h and width w.

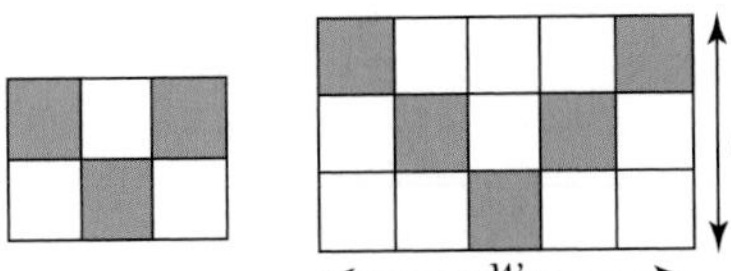

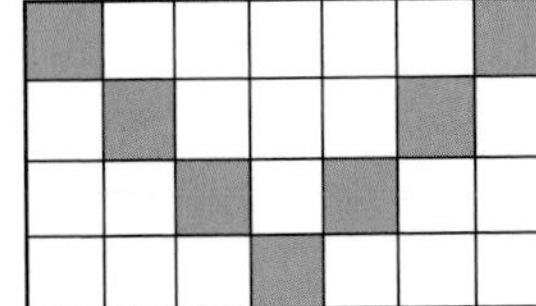

(a) Record the number of shaded squares s and the height h of each rectangle. Find a formula for s in terms of h [i.e. '$s = \ldots$']

(b) Find the width w for each value of h and hence find the number of *unshaded* squares in a rectangle with $h = 10$.

7 A chain of pentagons can be made from matches, as shown.

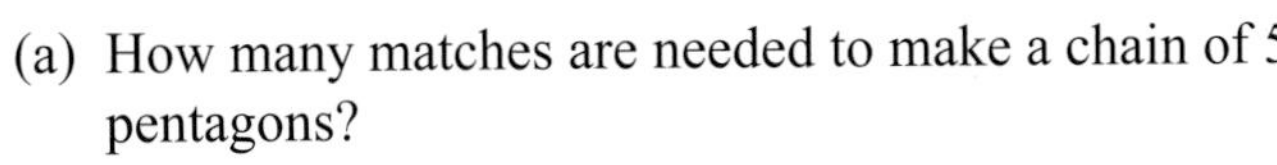

(a) How many matches are needed to make a chain of 5 pentagons?

(b) How many matches are needed to make a chain of n pentagons?

8 The nth term of a sequence is $\frac{3}{n^2 + 1}$.

The first term is $\frac{3}{2}$

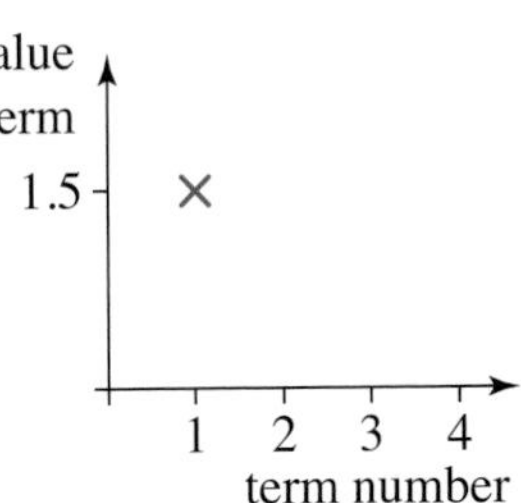

(a) Write down the next three terms.

(b) The sequence goes on and on for ever. Draw a sketch graph to show how the sequence continues.

9 The lace edge of a table cloth consists of a number of hexagons joined together as shown.

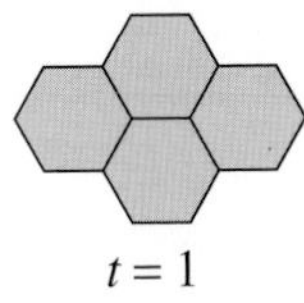

$t = 1$
$h = 4$

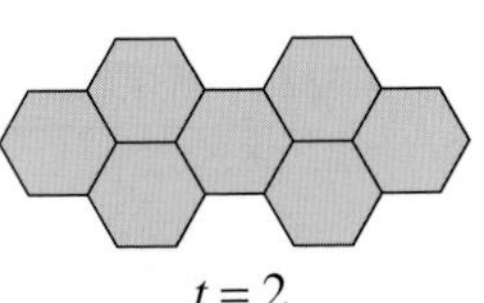

$t = 2$
$h = 7$

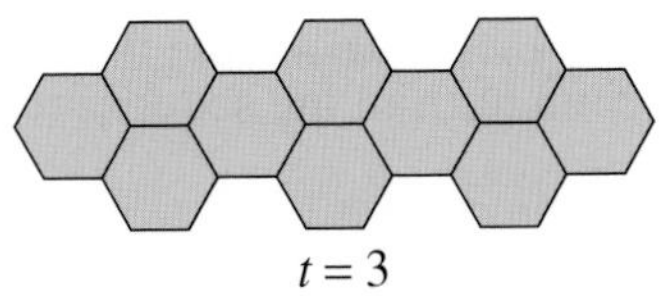

$t = 3$
$h = 10$

(a) How many hexagons will be needed when $t = 7$?

(b) How many hexagons will be needed when $t = 1000$?

(c) How many hexagons will be needed for the nth pattern?

10 Matching place mats are made up of hexagons as shown.

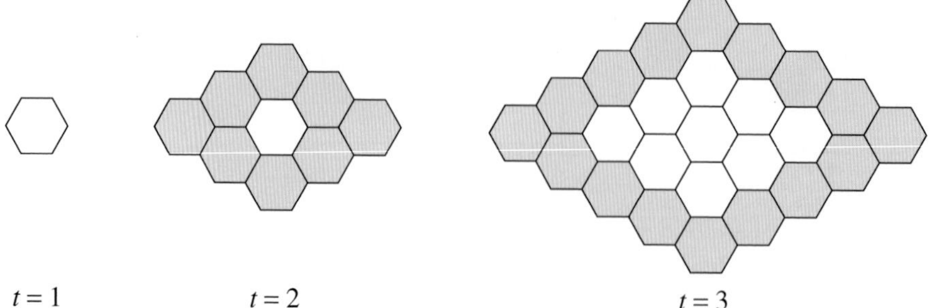

$t = 1$ $t = 2$ $t = 3$

Copy and complete the table.

t	hexagons on outer edge	total number of hexagons
1	0	1
2	8	9
3	16	25
4	–	–
5	–	–
n	–	–

Quadratic sequences* (Optional)

- In the sequence below we have written the first and second differences.

Sequence →	9		15		25		39		57
First difference		6		10		14		18	
Second difference			4		4		4		

- If the second difference is constant it tells us about terms involving n^2.

  +2 tells us it is n^2

  +4 tells us it is $2n^2$

  +6 tells us it is $3n^2$

- Make a table

n	$2n^2$	Sequence
1	2	9
2	8	15
3	18	25
4	32	39

We see that the nth term of the sequence is $2n^2 + 7$.

Exercise 2M

Use differences to help you find the nth term of these sequences.

1 3, 9, 19, 33, 51, …

2 4, 7, 12, 19, 28, …

3 1, 7, 17, 31, 49,…

4 7, 16, 31, 52, 79, …

5 4, 16, 36, 64, 100, …

6 7, 13, 23, 37, 55

In the sequence below we have written the first and second differences

Sequence	11		21		33		47		63
First difference		10		12		14		16	
Second difference			2		2		2		

For *any* quadratic sequence, nth term $= an^2 + bn + c$

The second difference above is 2, so we know that $a = 1$

So the nth term is now $n^2 + bn + c$

when $n = 1$, $\quad 1 + b + c = 11$

when $n = 2$, $\quad 4 + 2b + c = 21$

Solving the simultaneous equations, we obtain $b = 7$, $c = 3$

The nth term of the sequence is $n^2 + 7n + 3$

Exercise 2E

Use the method above to find the nth term of each sequence.

1 2, 7, 14, 23, 34 …

2 5, 11, 19, 29, 41 …

3 2, 3, 6, 11, 18 …

4 4, 11, 22, 37 …

5 7, 16, 31, 52 …

6 2, 10, 20, 32, 46 …

7 1, 3, 6, 10, 15 …

8 4, 5, 8, 13, 20 …

9 In these diagrams 'steps' are made from sticks.

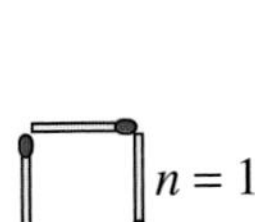

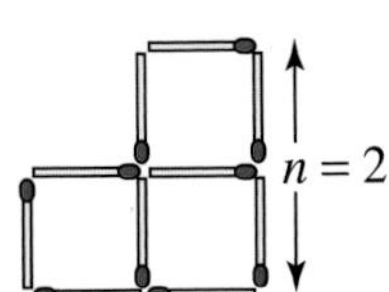

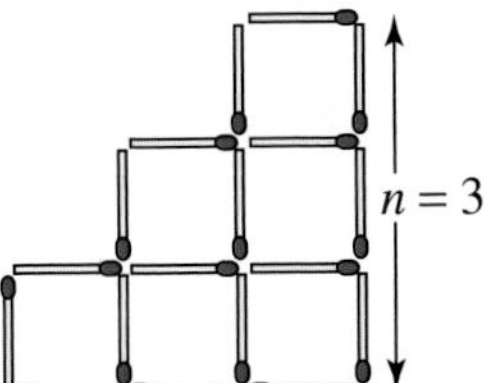

(a) Draw the next diagram in the sequence.

(b) Count the number of sticks s for each value of n, the height of the steps.

(c) Find the number of sticks in the nth term of the sequence.

10 In the pyramid shown there is

1 ball on layer 1

4 balls on layer 2

9 balls on layer 3 and so on.

The total number of balls in the first n layers is given by the formula

$$1^2 + 2^2 + 3^2 + \ldots\ldots + n^2 = \frac{n}{6}(n+1)(2n+1)$$

(a) Show that this formula works with $n = 3$.

(b) Use the formula to find the total number of balls in a pyramid with 20 layers.

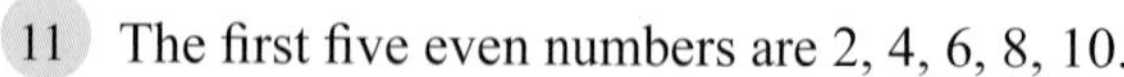

11 The first five even numbers are 2, 4, 6, 8, 10.

(a) Write down, in terms of n, an expression for the nth even number.

(b) Write an expression for the next even number after the nth.

12 In the Fibonacci sequence below each term is found by adding the two previous terms.

3, 4, 7, 11, 18, 29, ….

Consider the Fibonacci sequence which starts a, b, $a + b$, ….

(a) Show that the 7th term of this sequence is $5a + 8b$.

(b) Use algebra to show that the sum of the first six terms is four times the fifth term.

CHECK YOURSELF ON SECTIONS 3.1 AND 3.2

1. Shape and space problems

(a) In the diagram triangle ABC is drawn inside a semicircle. AB = 8 cm, BC = 6 cm and $A\hat{B}C = 90°$

Find the length AC and hence or otherwise find the total area of the regions shaded pink.

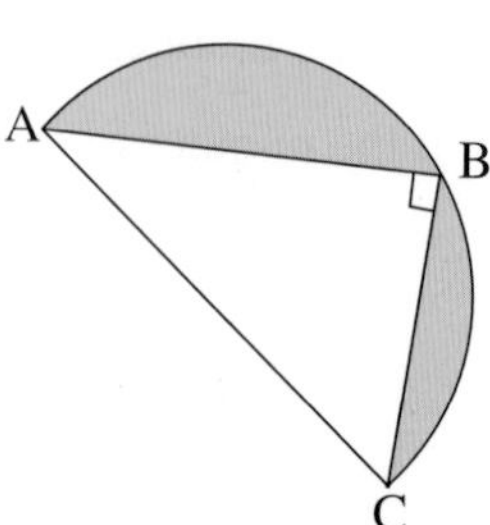

(b) Draw a pair of axes for x and y from –8 to 8

Plot and label the following triangles:

Δ1: (–2, 1) (–6, 1) (–6, 3).

Shade this triangle.

Δ2:	(4, 1)	(8, 1)	(8, 3)
Δ3:	(8, 6)	(4, 6)	(4, 8)
Δ4:	(2, –1)	(6, –1)	(6, –3)
Δ5:	(4, –4)	(–4, –4)	(–4, 0)
Δ6:	(–2, 1)	(–2, 5)	(0, 5)
Δ7:	(–2, –5)	(–6, –5)	(–6, –7)

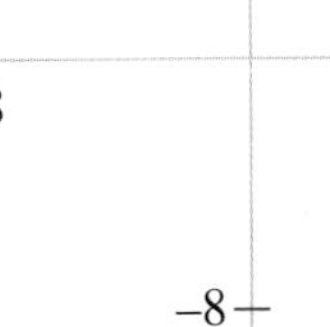

Describe fully the following transformations:

(i) Δ1→ Δ2 (ii) Δ1 → Δ3

(iii) Δ1 → Δ4 (iv) Δ1 → Δ5

(v) Δ1→ Δ6 (vi) Δ1 → Δ7

2. Sequences

(a) Write each sequence in a table and find an expression for the nth term.

(i) 7, 9, 11, 13, …. (ii) 11, 21, 31, 41, 51, …

(iii) 1, 9, 17, 25, … (iv) $\frac{1}{2}, \frac{2}{3}, \frac{3}{4}, \frac{4}{5} \ldots$

(v) 4, 9, 16, 25,…

(b) You are given an expression for the nth term of a sequence. Find the first 4 terms.

(i) nth term = $50 - 2n$ (ii) nth term = 3^n (iii) nth term = $n^2 + 3n$

3.3 Rounding, estimating, errors and bounds

In this section you will:

- round off numbers
- learn how to estimate the answer to a calculation
- learn about errors in measurement
- learn about bounds of accuracy

Significant figures, decimal places

We have already seen how we can round off a number to one decimal place or to two decimal places.

Reminder: 4.281 = 4.3 to one decimal place.
↑
0.2354 = 0.24 to two decimal places.
↑
We look at the digit arrowed to see if it is '5 or more'.

Sometimes numbers are rounded off to a certain number of *significant figures* rather than decimal places.

For decimal places we started counting from the decimal point.

For significant figures we approach from the left and start counting as soon as we come to the first figure which is not zero. Once we have started counting we count any figure, zeros included.

(a) 52.7211 = 52.7 to 3 significant figures. (3 s.f.)
↑
[Count 3 figures. The 'next' figure is 2, which is less than 5].

(b) 7.0264 = 7.03 to 3 significant figures.
↑

(c) 0.0237538 = 0.0238 to 3 significant figures.
↑

(d) 2475.6 = 2500 to 2 significant figures.
↑
Notice that we need the two noughts after the '5' as the original number is approximately 2500.

Exercise 1M

1 Write the following numbers correct to 3 significant figures

(a) 1.0765 (b) 24.897 (c) 195.12 (d) 0.7648

(e) 17.482 (f) 0.07666 (g) 28 774 (h) 2391.2

(i) 0.8555 (j) 4258 (k) 0.01128 (l) 675899

2 Write the following numbers to the degree of accuracy indicated

(a) 19.72 (2 s.f.) (b) 8.314 (1 s.f.) (c) 0.71551 (3 s.f.)

(d) 1824.7 (3 s.f.) (e) 23 666 (2 s.f.) (f) 0.03476 (2 s.f.)

3 Work out the following on a calculator and write the answer correct to 3 significant figures.

(a) $17 \div 3.1$ (b) 0.13×0.11 (c) $2 \div 0.11$ (d) $87 \div 19$

(e) 1.7×8.32 (f) $5 \div 0.753$ (g) $19 \div 0.021$ (h) $1 \div 0.7$

4 Which of the numbers below round off to 5.27 correct to two decimal places

5.275	5.270	5.277	5.2739	5.265	5.259

5 Round off these numbers to one decimal place

(a) 8.67 (b) 27.45 (c) 11.072 (d) 0.747

(e) 180.77 (f) 3.046 (g) 0.072 (h) 0.046

6 Work out the following on a calculator and write the answers correct to two decimal places.

(a) $\frac{5.67}{0.46}$ (b) $\frac{8.3^2}{9.9}$ (c) $\frac{\sqrt{11.6}}{1.45}$ (d) $\frac{6.25 - 1.272}{0.87}$

(e) $\frac{6.9}{1.8} - 0.783$ (f) $\frac{4.2}{8.6 - 0.947}$ (g) $\frac{4.7^3}{1.1}$ (h) $1.7^4 - 0.9^5$

Estimating

- In some situations an estimate of a quantity is more helpful than the actual number. For example we may know that on January 1st 2011 the population of France is 61 278 514 and the population of Greece is 9 815 972. For purposes of comparison we could use 60 million for France and 10 million for Greece so that the population of France is *about* six times that of Greece.

- Find an estimate for the radius of a circular pond of area 150 m^2.

We know that $\pi \times (\text{radius})^2 = 150$

The value of π is about 3, so $3 \times (\text{radius})^2 \approx 150$

$(\text{radius})^2 \approx 50$

The square root of 50 is about 7.

The radius of the pool is about 7 m.

- Estimate, correct to one significant figure

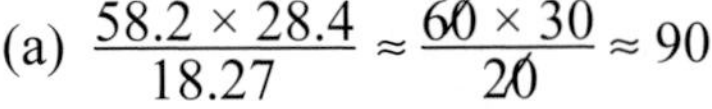

(a) $\frac{58.2 \times 28.4}{18.27} \approx \frac{60 \times 30}{20} \approx 90$

(b) $\frac{\sqrt{11213} \times 0.0974}{52.7} \approx \frac{100 \times 0.1}{50} \approx 0.2$

(c) 48% of £22 615 $\approx \frac{50}{100} \times 20\,000 \approx$ £10 000

Exercise 2M

Write down each calculation and decide (by estimating) which answer is closest to the exact answer. Do not do the calculation exactly.

	Question	Answer A	Answer B	Answer C
1	78.4×3.15	150	400	240
2	$603 \div 3.89$	100	150	200
3	6.73×9.58	60	120	90
4	956×982	90 000	600 000	1 million
5	23.8% of 611	150	200	250
6	0.2×211	30	40	50
7	$1251.6 \div 6.1$	21	200	2000
8	$(19.4 - 8.9) \times 19.7$	200	2000	400
9	5.6% of 19 468	120 000	700	1000
10	$\sqrt{145.2} \times 0.983$	100	9	12
11	$98 \times 97 \times 9$	100 000	10 000	50 000
12	$71 \div 0.483$	100	150	1500
13	$269 \div 0.097$	1000	270	2700
14	$87.9 + 97 + 541$	500	600	700
15	$\sqrt{10632.6}$	50	100	140
16	$(289 - 47.2) \times 62$	150	1500	15 000
17	$\frac{2}{5}$ of (21.3×18.75)	80	120	160
18	76.2% of $10^4 \times 0.207$	1000	1500	15 000
19	$\sqrt{0.985} \div \sqrt{27.1}$	0.01	0.1	0.2
20	$\frac{1}{3}$ of $\frac{1}{4}$ of $\frac{1}{10}$ of 11.3×10^4	10^3	2×10^3	4×10^3

Exercise 2E

In questions 1 to 9 give your answer correct to one significant figure.
Do not use a calculator.

1 A doctor is paid a salary of £49 450 per year. Work out a rough estimate for her weekly pay.

2 Estimate the mean weight of articles with the following weights:

4.9 kg, 0.21 kg, 0.72 kg, 25.1 kg, 0.11 kg.

3 

Look at the photo and estimate the circumference and diameter of the circle formed.
Show how you obtained your estimates.

4 In 2011 Kirsty's pay was £19 380 per year. In 2012 she receives a pay increase of 19.2%. Estimate the *monthly increase* in her pay.

5 Estimate the length of the diagonals of a square of side 7.2 cm.

6 A lorry can carry a maximum load of 30 tonnes. A copy of Peter Gibson's autobiography weighs 475 g. The manager of the delivery firm estimates that each lorry can take about 6000 copies of the book. Is this a reasonable estimate? If not, suggest a better estimate. [1 tonne = 1000 kg]

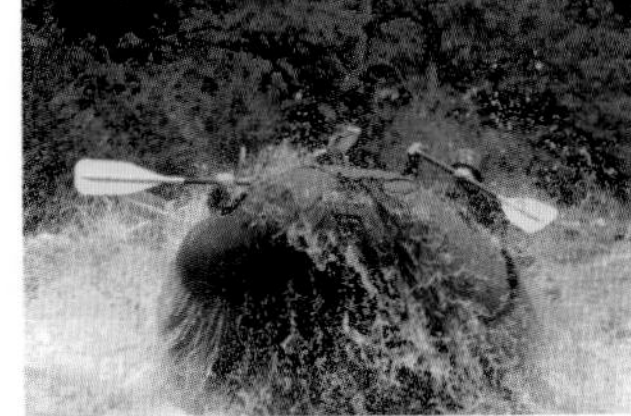

7 Four people on a river raft travel at an average speed of 18.7 km/h from 0810 until 1217. Roughly how far do they go?

8 In the grounds of his palace, the Sultan of Brunei has a circular pond with a surface area of $\frac{3}{4}$ hectare.
Estimate the diameter of the pond in metres.
[1 hectare = 10 000 m^2]

9 Estimate the mean weight, in kg, of two wrestlers weighing 131 kg and 10 stones 4 pounds respectively.

[1 pound ≈ 0.45 kg, 1 stone = 14 pounds].

10 Give an estimate for each of the following calculations. Show your working.

(a) $\dfrac{82.4 \times \sqrt{907.4}}{2.824}$ (b) $\dfrac{2848.7 - 1.94}{0.32 + 39.83}$ (c) 52% of 0.394 kg

(d) $\dfrac{3.15^2 + 30.63^2}{0.104^2}$ (e) $\dfrac{7}{15}$ of £3918.25 (f) $\dfrac{207.5 + 4.21 + 0.63}{109.4 + 293.2}$

(g) $\dfrac{5.13 \times 18.777}{0.952}$ (h) $\pi \times 9.73^2$ (i) $\dfrac{17}{31}$ of 12% of £2057

11 Decide whether or not the following are reasonable estimates.

Write 'yes' or 'no' for each part.

(a) The total weight of thirty 14 year-olds = 1500 kg.

(b) The time taken by an international athlete to run 1 mile = 240 s.

(c) The total weight of 10 £1 coins = 1 kg.

(d) The top speed of your maths teacher's car = 150 km/h.

(e) The height of a four storey office building = 80 m.

12 The population of the Earth is about 6 billion. Estimate how many people share the same birthday as you.

13 When you multiply by a number greater than 1, you make it bigger.

When you multiply by a number less than 1, you make it smaller.

When you divide by a number greater than 1, you make it smaller.

When you divide by a number less than 1, you make it bigger.

E.g. $5.7 \times 1.2 > 5.7$, $16.8 \div 1.2 < 16.8$.

$5.7 \times 0.8 < 5.7$, $16.8 \div 0.8 > 16.8$

Copy and complete the following with the correct sign ($>$ or $<$) instead of the box.

(a) $3.58 \times 1.3 \square 3.58$ (b) $19 \times 0.92 \square 19$ (c) $5.5 \times 1.04 \square 5.5$

(d) $9.2 \div 1.5 \square 9.2$ (e) $11.2 \div 0.87 \square 11.2$ (f) $67 \div 1.34 \square 67$

(g) $59 \times 0.89 \square 59$ (h) $0.42 \times 0.73 \square 0.42$ (i) $17 \div 0.99 \square 17$

(j) $0.2^2 \square 0.2$ (k) $0.061 \div 0.41 \square 0.061$ (l) $(0.85)^3 \square 0.85$

14

It is estimated that the cost per inch of widening a 51-mile stretch of the M6 motorway is £989.

Find an estimate for widening this motorway.

Errors in measurement

Whenever a quantity is measured the measurement is never *exact*. If you measure the thickness of a wire with a ruler, you might read the thickness as 2 mm. If you use a more accurate device for measuring you might read the thickness as 2.3 mm. An even more accurate device might give the thickness as 2.31 mm. None of these figures is precise.

They are all approximations to the actual thickness. This means that there is always an error in making any kind of measurement such as length, weight, time, temperature and so on. An error of this kind is not the same as making a mistake in a calculation!

Bounds of accuracy

(a) Suppose the length of a book is measured at 22 cm to the nearest cm. The actual length could be from 21.5 to *almost* 22.5. We say 'almost' 22.5 because a length of 22.499 999 9 .... would be rounded off to 22 cm. The number 22.499 999.... is effectively 22.5 and we take 22.5 as the *upper bound*.
So in this case the *bounds of accuracy* are 21.5 cm and 22.5 cm.
The maximum possible error is 0.5 cm.

$21.5 \le \text{length} < 22.5$

(b) Using a ruler, the length of the nail shown is measured at 3.8 cm to the nearest 0.1 cm. In this case the bounds of accuracy are 3.75 cm and 3.85 cm.

$3.75 \le \text{length} < 3.85$

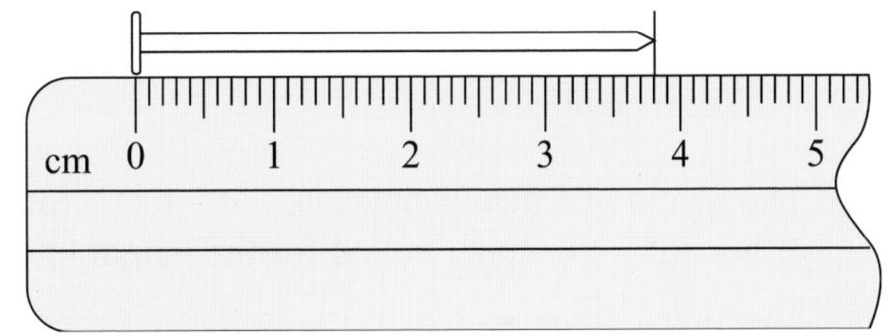

(c) Sometimes measurements are given 'to the nearest 10, 100, etc.'
Suppose the length of a lake is measured at 4200 m to the nearest 100 m.
The bounds of accuracy are 4150 m and 4250 m.

(d) Summary. In (a), (b) and (c) above the maximum possible error is always half of the level of accuracy.
In part (b) the level of accuracy is the nearest 0.1 cm.
The maximum possible error is 0.05 cm.

(e) Here are some further examples:

	lower bound	upper bound
(i) The weight of an apple is 43 g to the nearest gram	42.5 g	43.5 g
(ii) The temperature of a room is 22.9°C to one decimal place	22.85°C	22.95°C
(iii) The length of a road is 780 m to the nearest 10 m	775 m	785 m
(iv) The capacity of a mug is 115 ml to the nearest 5 ml	112.5 ml	117.5 ml
(v) The weight of a lorry is 23 000 kg to 2 s.f.	22 500 kg	23 500 kg

Exercise 3M

1 Copy and complete each statement. Part (a) is done as an example.

(a) A length d is 42 m, to the nearest m, so $41.5 \leq d < 42.5$

(b) A volume V is 8 m^3, to the nearest m^3, so $7.5 \leq V < \square$

(c) A mass m is 72 kg, to the nearest kg, so $\square \leq m < \square$

(d) A time t is 3.2 h, to the nearest 0.1 h, so $\square \leq t < 3.25$

(e) A radius r is 5.8 cm, to the nearest 0.1 cm, so $\square \leq r < \square$

2 The height of a table is measured at 84 cm to the nearest cm.
Write down the lower bound for the height of the table.

3 A postmaster weighs a parcel at 5.2 kg to the nearest 0.1 kg.
Write down the upper bound for the weight of the parcel.

4 The length and width of a rectangle are measured to the nearest 0.1 cm, as shown.

(a) Write down the upper bound for the length of the rectangle.

(b) Write down the lower bound for the width of the rectangle.

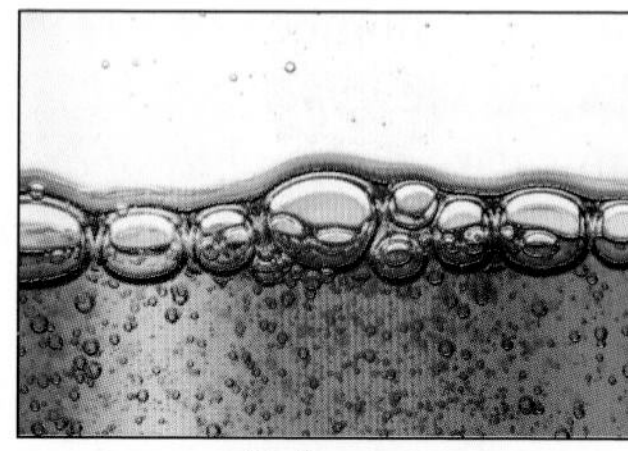

5 The height of a man is measured at 5 feet 8 inches, to the nearest inch.
Write down the upper bound for the height of the man.

6 A scientist weighs a fossil sea shell at 3.7g, correct to one decimal place. What is the least possible weight of the fossil?

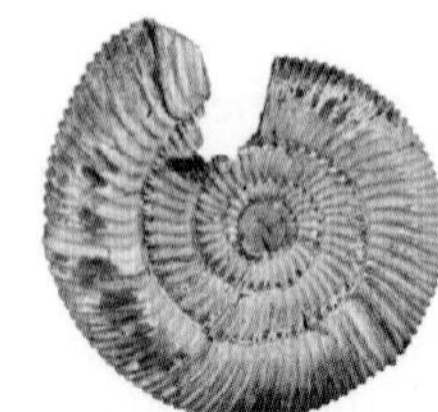

7 A book states that the distance from the Earth to the Sun is 93 million miles correct to two significant figures. What is the shortest possible distance?

8 In a 200 m race a sprinter is timed at 20.63 seconds to the nearest 0.01 seconds. Write down the least possible time.

Exercise 3E

1 The weight of an egg is 17.8 g, correct to one decimal place.
What is the greatest possible weight of the egg?

2 Copy and complete the table:

	lower bound	upper bound
(a) length of nail = 5.6 cm, to nearest mm		
(b) height of lighthouse = 37 m, to nearest m		
(c) weight of insect = 0.27 mg, to 2 d.p.		
(d) temperature in oven = 230°C, to nearest 10°C		
(e) length of oil pipeline = 315 km, to nearest km		

3 The painting shown measures 12 cm by 8 cm to the nearest centimetre.

(a) Write down the greatest possible length and width of the painting.

(b) Work out the greatest possible area of the painting.

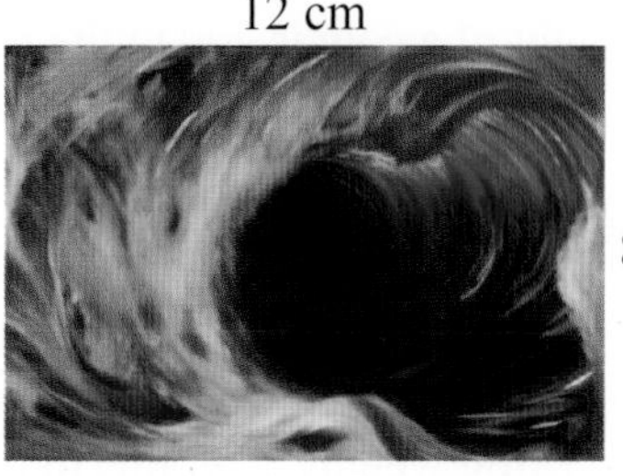

4 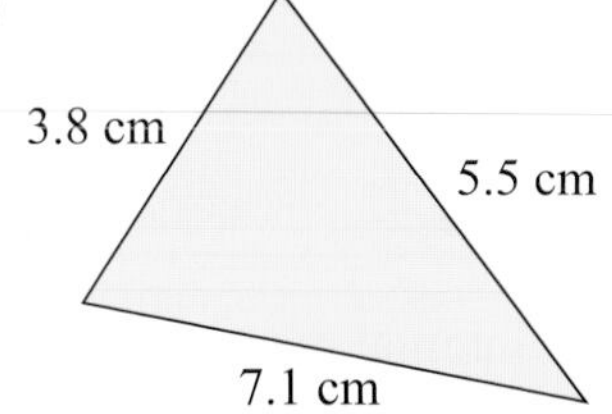

The lengths of the sides of this triangle have been measured to the nearest 0.1 cm.
Find the lower bound for the perimeter of the triangle.

5 If $a = 5.7$, $b = 6.2$ and $c = 10.2$, all measured correct to one decimal place, calculate:

(a) the greatest possible value of $a + b$

(b) the greatest possible value of ac

(c) the least possible value of $c + b$

(d) the least possible value of $c - b$

6 You are given $p = 3.8$, $q = 0.9$, $r = 5.7$, measured correct to one decimal place, calculate:

(a) the least possible value of $p + q + r$

(b) the greatest possible value of pq.

(c) the greatest possible value of $r - p$

(d) the least possible value of $r - p$

7 A cherry is weighed at 6.7 grams to the nearest 0.1 gram.
What is the greatest possible weight of ten similar cherries?

8 The weight of a coin is 7 g, to the nearest gram. The weight lies between:

A	B	C
6 g and 8 g	6.9 g and 7.1 g	6.5 g and 7.5 g

9 Chuck and Dave each weigh a different frog and they both say that their frog weighs 27 grams to the nearest gram. What is the greatest possible difference in the actual weights of the two frogs?

10 

A painting is 72.5 cm by 42 cm, correct to the nearest millimetre.
A carrying case has internal measurements of 70 cm by 45 cm, correct to the nearest 5 cm.
Is it possible that the painting will fit inside the carrying case?
Show your working.

3.4 Drawing and visualising 3D shapes

In this section you will:

- draw 3D objects using isometric dot paper
- draw different views of an object
- solve puzzles involving 3D objects
- learn about planes of symmetry

Exercise 1M

1 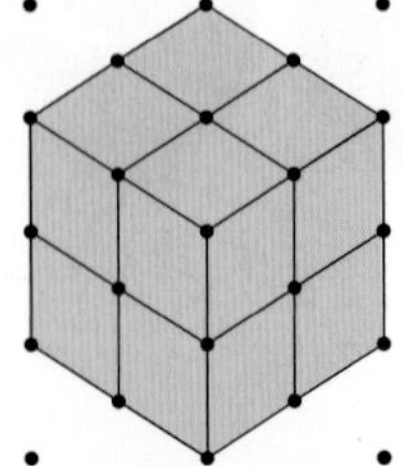

Here is a cube made from eight 1 cm cubes.
Draw a cuboid with a volume of 12 cm^3.

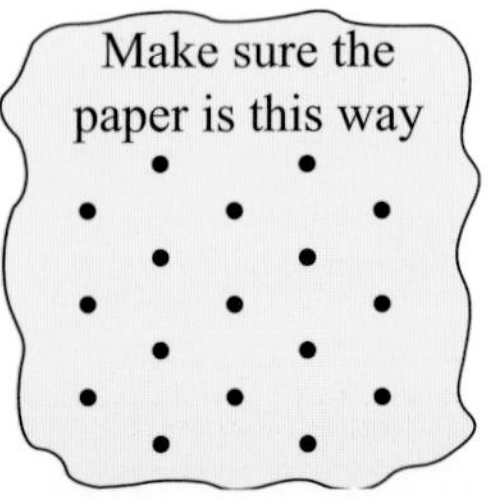

2 (a) Make this shape using cubes.

(b) Draw two other isometric views of the shape.

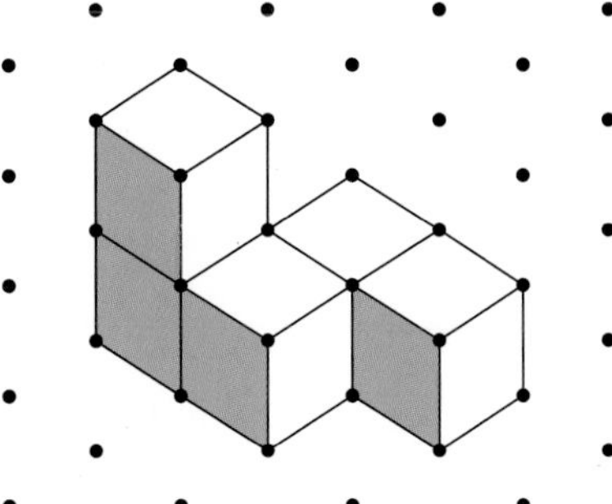

3 The S-shape falls over onto the blue shaded face. Draw the shape after it has fallen over.

4 You need 16 cubes. Make the two shapes shown and then arrange them into a $4 \times 4 \times 1$ cuboid by adding a third shape, which you have to find. Draw the third shape on isometric paper. There are *two* possible shapes.

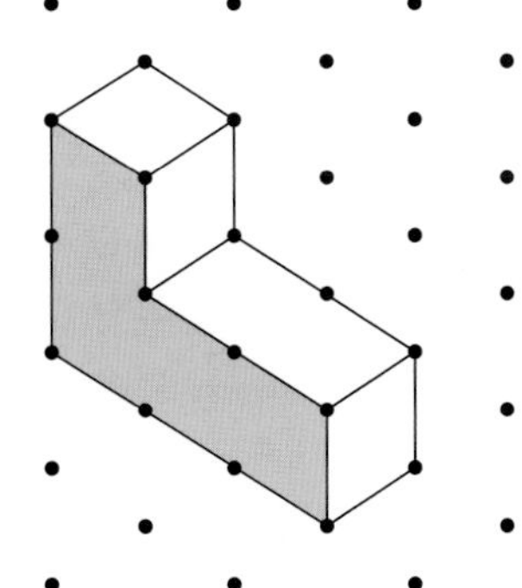

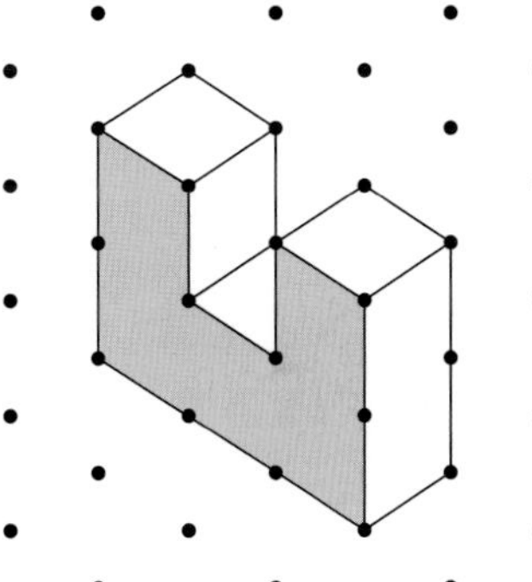

5 (a) Make the S-shape from question 3 and the two shapes from question 4

(b) Join the three shapes together and add a fourth shape to make a $4 \times 4 \times 1$ cuboid. Describe the fourth shape.

6 Here are two possible nets to make a cube. For each net decide which face is opposite the red face in the cube.

(a)

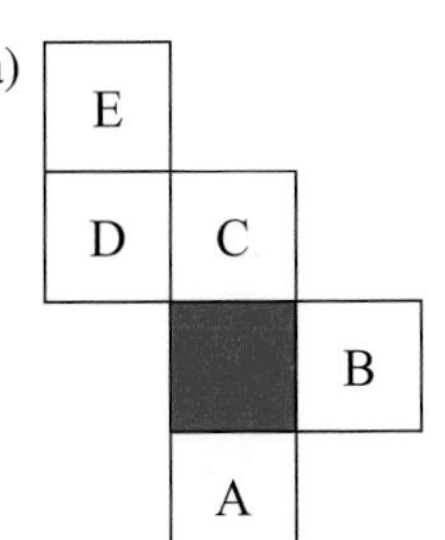

(b)

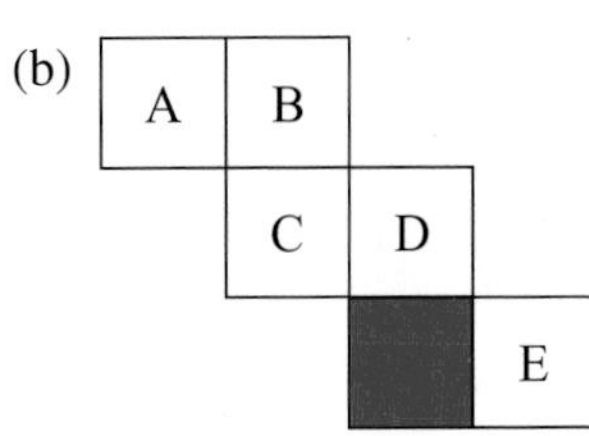

7 The net for a tetrahedron consists of four equilateral triangles. On isometric paper draw two possible nets for a tetrahedron.

8 Draw an accurate net for a square-based pyramid where the vertex is directly above the centre of the base.

9 The diagrams below show four side-views of the model.

Which side-view does each diagram show?

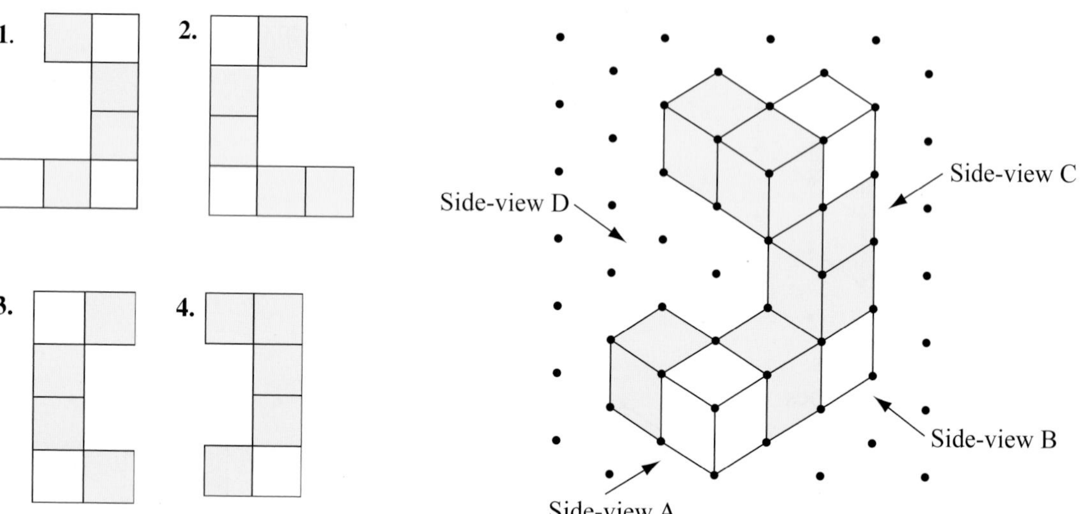

10 The diagram shows a model made with 9 cubes, 5 blue and 4 white.

Draw 5 diagrams to show the side-views A, B, C and D and also the plan view.

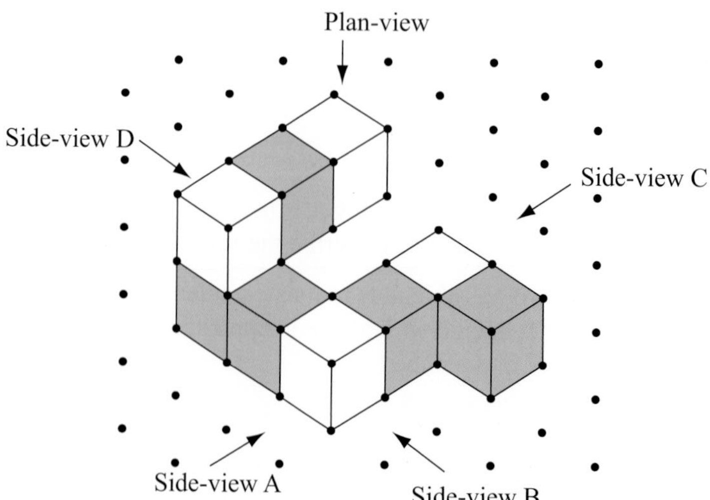

Exercise 1E

You need 27 small cubes for questions 1, 2, 3. Make the four shapes below and arrange them into a $3 \times 3 \times 3$ cube by adding a fifth shape, which you have to find. Draw the fifth shape on isometric paper. (The number next to each shape indicates the number of small cubes in that shape).

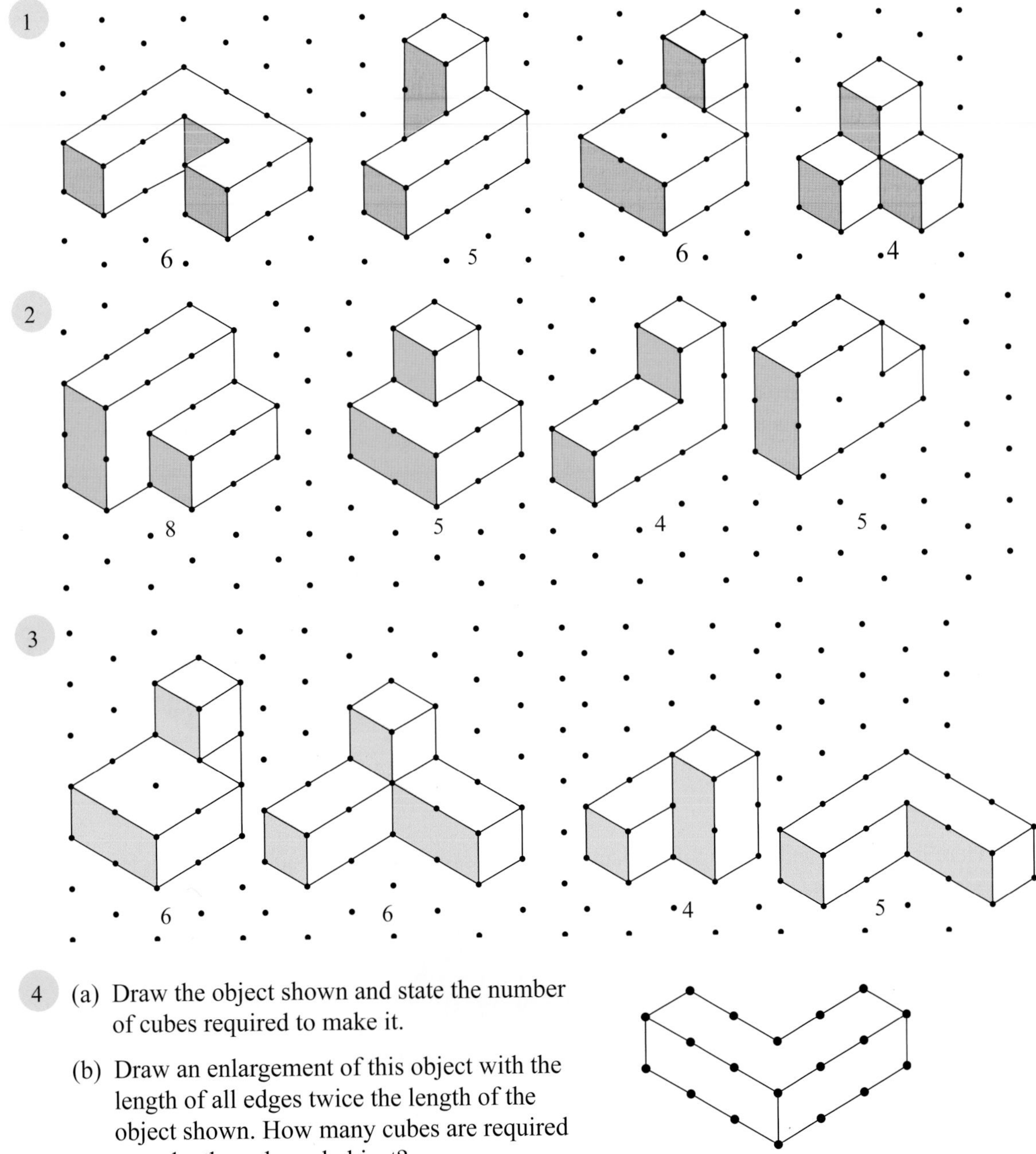

4 (a) Draw the object shown and state the number of cubes required to make it.

(b) Draw an enlargement of this object with the length of all edges twice the length of the object shown. How many cubes are required to make the enlarged object?

5 Repeat parts (a) and (b) from question 4 for this object.

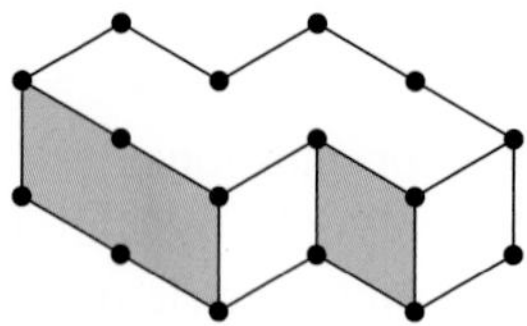

6 For the enlarged objects in questions 4 and 5 work out the ratio

$$\frac{\text{number of cubes in enlarged object}}{\text{number of cubes in original object}}$$

7 Draw an enlargement of the object in question 4 with the lengths of all edges *three* times the corresponding lengths of the original. Work out the ratio

$$\left(\frac{\text{number of cubes in enlargement}}{\text{number of cube in original}}\right).$$

Can you find a connection between the ratio you have found and the scale factor of the enlargement?

Planes of symmetry

- A plane of symmetry divides a 3-D shape into two congruent shapes. One shape must be a mirror image of the other shape.

The shaded plane is a plane of symmetry of the cube.

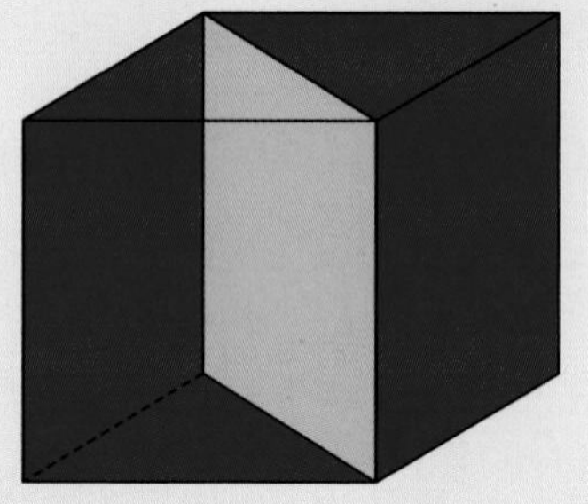

Exercise 2M

1 Here is a cuboid and a triangular prism (whose cross-section is an equilateral triangle).

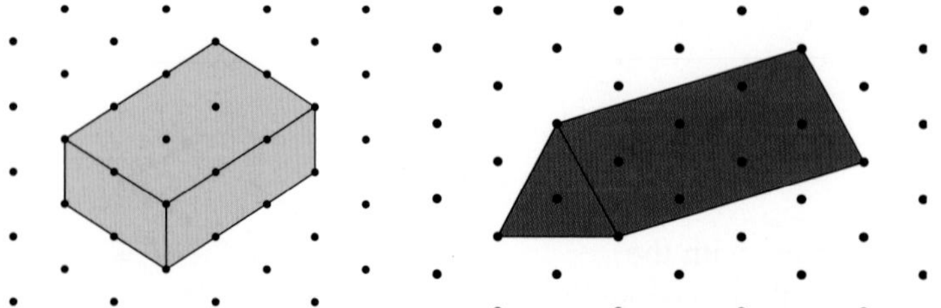

How many planes of symmetry does each shape have?

2 Here are two shapes made from four cubes. There are eight different shapes which can be made using four cubes.

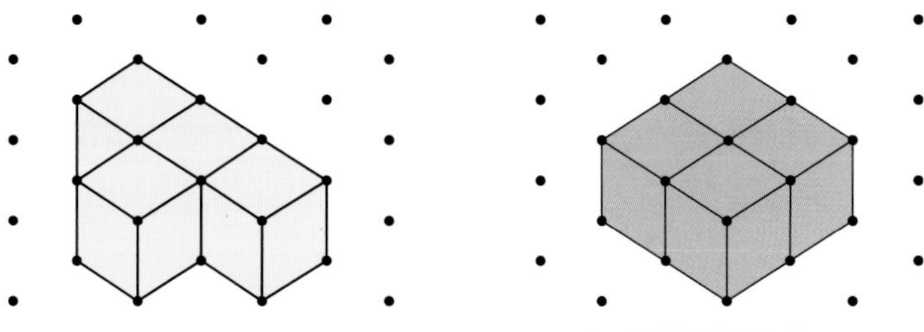

Make the eight shapes, using cubes, and draw them on isometric paper. Identify any planes of symmetry.

3 Visualise and describe all the planes of symmetry of:

(a) a square-based pyramid

(b) a cylinder

(c) a regular tetrahedron.

CHECK YOURSELF ON SECTIONS 3.3 AND 3.4

1. Rounding, estimating, errors in measurement

(a) Work out and round off as indicated.

(i) $\frac{7.91^3}{950}$ (2 d.p.) (ii) $\frac{565 \times 49.7}{2.4}$ (3 s.f.) (iii) $\frac{8.4 + 1.723}{7 - 2.63}$ (1 d.p.)

(b) (i) Estimate the mean price of four rings priced at £779, £69.90, £2499, £27.95

(ii) Give an estimate for the calculation

$$\frac{61.7 \times \sqrt{396.1}}{9.03}$$

(c) (i) The height of a door is measured at 212 cm to the nearest cm.

Write down the lower bound for the height of the door.

(ii) A book weighs 2.7 kg to the nearest 0.1 kg.

Write down the upper bound for the weight of the book.

2. Drawing and visualising 3D shapes

Here are three views of an object made from cubes.

Make the object and draw it on isometric paper. How many cubes are there?

front view

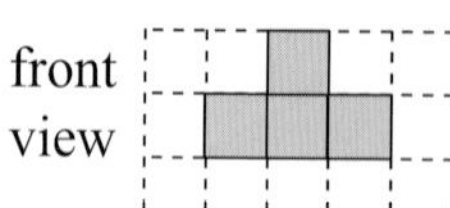

plan view

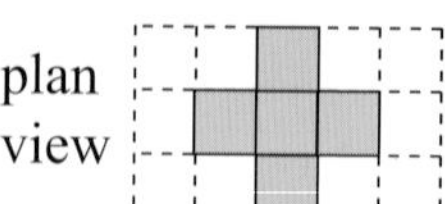

side view

3.5 Percentage change

In this unit you will:

- learn about percentage increase and decrease
- learn about reverse percentages
- answer mixed questions involving percentages

Percentage change

Suppose the price of a car was increased from £8000 to £8100 and the price of a computer was increased from £200 to £300.

The *actual* increase of £100 is the same for both items but the increase is far more significant for the computer! A good way of comparing price changes (up or down) is to work out the *percentage* change.

For an increase use the formula,

$$\text{percentage increase} = \left(\frac{\text{actual increase}}{\text{original value}}\right) \times 100$$

For the car above, percentage increase $= \left(\frac{100}{8000}\right) \times 100 = 1\frac{1}{4}\%$

For the computer, percentage increase $= \left(\frac{100}{200}\right) \times 100 = 50\%$

(a) Waitrose reduce the price of their own label cheesecake from £1.60 to £1.12. Find the percentage decrease.

The actual decrease = £0.48

Percentage decrease = $\left(\frac{0.48}{1.60}\right) \times 100$

= 30%

(b) The owner of a sports shop buys tennis rackets for £32 and sells them for £69.99. Find the percentage profit.

The actual profit = £37.99.

Percentage profit = $\left(\frac{37.99}{32}\right) \times 100$

= 118.7% (1 d.p.)

Exercise 1M

Give answers correct to 1 decimal place, where necessary.

1 Find the percentage increase when the price of a train ticket goes up from £8 to £9.

2 The number of pupils at a school increased from 250 to 290. Calculate the percentage increase in the number of pupils.

3 A pool table was bought for £400 and later sold for £280. What was the percentage decrease?

4 A footballer was paid £39 600 per week at Arsenal. After being transferred to Liverpool he was paid £53 000 per week. Calculate his percentage increase in pay.

5 During the first month of its life a kitten's weight increases from 650 g to 800 g. Calculate the percentage increase.

6 A man bought a car in an auction for £6350 and then quickly sold it for £7295. Calculate the percentage profit.

7 Calculate the percentage increase or decrease in each case.

	Original price	Final price
(a)	£160	£176
(b)	£200	£206
(c)	£410	£630
(d)	£240	£210
(e)	£880	£836
(f)	£22.50	£18.00

8 During a season when Liverpool were near the top of the league, their average crowd was 31 750. In the following season, they suffered a loss of form and the average attendance went down to 27 430. Calculate the percentage fall in the attendance.

9 Find the percentage increase when the price of a house goes up from £210,500 to £299,000.

10 Vijay's wages were increased from £115 per week to £130 per week. What was the percentage increase?

Exercise 1E

1 A baker made dough for bread and left it to rise.
The volume of the dough before it had risen was 970 cm^3.
The volume of the dough after it had risen was 1365 cm^3.
Calculate the percentage increase in the volume of the dough.

2 A shopkeeper bought a crate of 50 cans of drink at 18p per can. He sold 15 cans at 30p per can, and the rest of the crate for 25p per can.

(a) How much profit did he make?

(b) Express this profit as a percentage of his total cost price.

3 A cube originally had sides of length 40 cm. All the sides were then increased by 10%.

(a) *Without* doing any accurate calculations, estimate what you think the percentage increase in the volume of the cube was.

(b) Now work out the actual percentage increase in the volume.

4 A sports centre recorded the number of girls and boys who were admitted in 2011 and 2012.

	2011	2012	Total
Girls	22414	20904	43318
Boys	18715	27404	46119
Total	41129	48308	89437

(a) What percentage of the admissions in 2011 were girls?

(b) What percentage of the total admissions over the two years were boys?

(c) What was the percentage increase in the number of boys admitted between 2011 and 2012?

(d) What was the overall percentage increase in admissions between 2011 and 2012?

5 A box has a square base of side 20 cm and height 10 cm.

Calculate the percentage increase in the volume of the box after the length and width of the base are both increased by 20% and the height is increased by 15%.

6 One year a supermarket sold 'Hawaiian Crunch' in a 1.2 kg bag for £1.56. Next year they sold the same product in 1.5 kg bags for £2.04. Calculate the percentage increase or decrease in the price per gram of the cereal.

Teenager profits from the euro

THE introduction of the euro has brought winners and losers but one GSCE student found himself quids in in a big way after his first euro encounter.

Richard Shields, 15, changed his £10 pocket money for 16 euros to test out the new currency's spending power at his nearest department store.

Staff at his Debenhams in Luton, unfamiliar with the new currency, had failed to realise that the wrong exchange rate had been punched into their computer system. Instead of an exchange rate of 1.6 euros to the pound, their tills flashed up a rate of 0.6 euros to the pound.

Consequently Richard was charged considerably less than the marked price and was able to walk away with an armful of bargains. He bought a selection of leather wallets, fragrances and Tommy Hilfiger designer clothes after realizing that he could profit from the confusion.

He discovered something was amiss when he received his change in sterling for his first purchase. It was more than double the amount he had expected.

Realising his luck was in he made another trip between the bank and the department store.

Reverse percentages

After an increase of 4%, the price of a railway season ticket is £998.40. What was the price before the increase?

A common mistake here is to work out 4% of £998.40. This is wrong because the increase is 4% of the *old price*, not 4% of the new price.

$$104\% \text{ of the old price} = £998.40$$

$$\therefore \quad 1\% \text{ of the old price} = \frac{998.40}{104}$$

$$\therefore \quad 100\% \text{ of the old price} = \frac{998.40}{104} \times 100$$

$$\text{The old price} = £960$$

Exercise 2M

1 After an increase of 10%, the cost of one litre of petrol is £1.21. What was the cost before the increase?

2 In the first two weeks of its life the weight of a foal increased by 8%. Find its weight at birth if it weighed 27 kg after two weeks.

3 After an increase of 7%, the price of a squash racket is £58.85. Find the price of the racket before the increase.

4 After being heated, the volume of a metal ingot is increased by 3%. Find the volume of the unheated ingot, if the volume after being heated is 463.5 cm^3.

5 Because of falling sales the pay of a salesman was cut by 15% so he got £23 375 per year. How much was he paid previously?

6 Between 1980 and 1990 the population of a town fell by 4%. Find the population of the town in 1980 if it was 252 960 in 1990.

7 

As it descends, ballast is rapidly thrown overboard from a hot air balloon to reduce its weight by 3%. After the ballast is thrown the weight is 339.5kg. Find the weight of the balloon before.

8 To increase sales, the price of a book is reduced by 25%. Find the original price if the new price is £7.35.

Exercise 2E

1 Tesco has a special offer on its own brand pizza. Find the missing number.

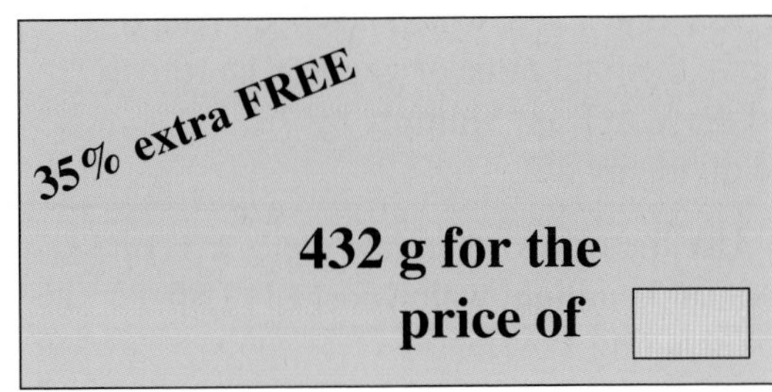

2 In a restaurant V.A.T., at 17.5%, is added to the cost of a meal. The total cost of a meal is £42.30 including V.A.T. Find the cost of the meal before the V.A.T. was added.

3 

At the top of a mountain a drink froze and its volume increased by 12%. The volume of the frozen drink was 420 cm^3. Find the volume of the drink before it froze.

4 In May the price of a magazine went up by 10% and then in August the new price went up by a further 4%. After the second increase, the price of the magazine was £2.86. What was the price of the magazine before the first increase?

5 The diagram shows two rectangles. The length of rectangle B is 20% greater than the length of rectangle A.

The width of rectangle B is 15% greater than the width of rectangle A.

Use the figures given to find the length and width of rectangle A.

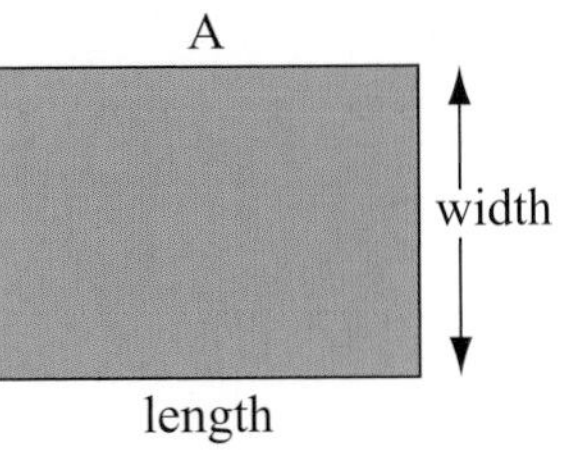

B

Area = 41.4 cm^2

7.2 cm

6 In the first week after waking up from its hibernation, a squirrel increases its weight by 2%. In the second week it increases its new weight by a further 10% so that it then weighs 5.61 kg. Find the weight of the squirrel when it first awoke from hibernation.

7 Businessmen use the '747 Rule' to work out the V.A.T. at $17\frac{1}{2}$% which has been added to give the total price of goods. The rule to find the V.A.T. is 'Multiply by 7 and divide by 47'.

(a) Use the rule to calculate the V.A.T. on a car headlight which cost £112.80, including V.A.T.

(b) Check that the rule works by calculating $17\frac{1}{2}$% of the price without the V.A.T.

Mixed percentage questions

Exercise 3 M/E

1 Compared to last year, the number of cars on the roads went up by 3.2%. This corresponded to an increase of 635 200 cars. How many cars were on the roads last year?

2 In 2012 the prison population was 2% higher than in the previous year. What was the prison population in 2011, if the increase was 1040 prisoners?

3 One day a dance school conducted a survey to find information about the people who were using its facilities.

Ages	Males	Females	Totals
under 10	68	23	91
10 → 14	215	347	562
14 → 18	307	269	576
18 and over	164	98	262

(a) What percentage of the 10–14 group was female?

(b) What percentage of the people using the dance school were 18 and over?

4 A cuboid made of special plastic has a square base of side 15 cm and height 25 cm. After immersion in water the sides of the base and the height all increase by 5.5%. Find the volume of the enlarged cuboid.

5 A FAX machine costs £329 including V.A.T. at $17\frac{1}{2}$%.
How much V.A.T. is paid?

6 When 240 litres are removed from a tank of fuel, the original quantity of fuel is reduced by 16%.
What was the final quantity of fuel left in the tank?

7 When Alex drives to work at an average speed of 15 m/s, her journey takes 20 minutes.

(a) How far is her journey to work?

(b) How much longer does her journey take when roadworks cause her average speed to be reduced by 8%? Give your answer to the nearest second.

8 Mrs Hawke's salary in 2015 is £20 000 per year.
Every year her salary is increased by 4%.

In 2016 her salary will be $20\,000 \times 1.04$ $= £20\,800$

In 2017 her salary will be $20\,000 \times 1.04 \times 1.04$ $= £21\,632$

In 2018 her salary will be $20\,000 \times 1.04 \times 1.04 \times 1.04$ $= £22\,497.28$

And so on.

(a) What will her salary be in 2021?

(b) What will her salary be in 2026?

[Hint. Use the x^y button on a calculator]

9 Mrs Hawke's daughter was paid £10 000 per year in 2015 but her salary is increased by 15% every year.

(a) What will be her salary in 2017?

(b) What will be her salary in 2026?

(c) (More difficult) In what year will Mrs Hawke be paid less than her daughter for the first time? [See Question 8]

CHECK YOURSELF ON UNIT 3.5

Percentage increase and decrease

(a) A shopkeeper bought a painting for £35
and later sold it for £54.25
Calculate the percentage profit.

(b) A camera shop had a closing down sale.
The sale started on Wednesday.
For each day of the sale, prices were reduced by 20% of the prices on the day before.

A camera had a price of £30 on Tuesday.
What was the price of the camera on Thursday?

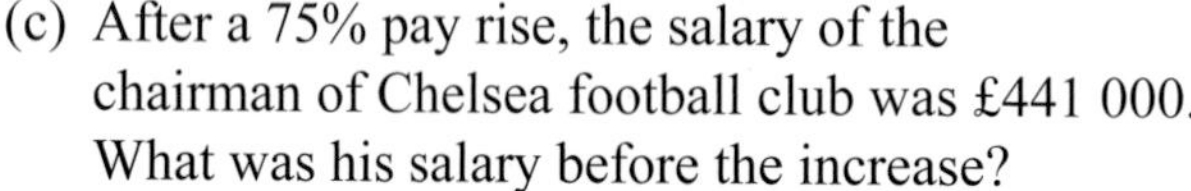

(c) After a 75% pay rise, the salary of the chairman of Chelsea football club was £441 000.
What was his salary before the increase?

UNIT 3 MIXED REVIEW

Part one

1 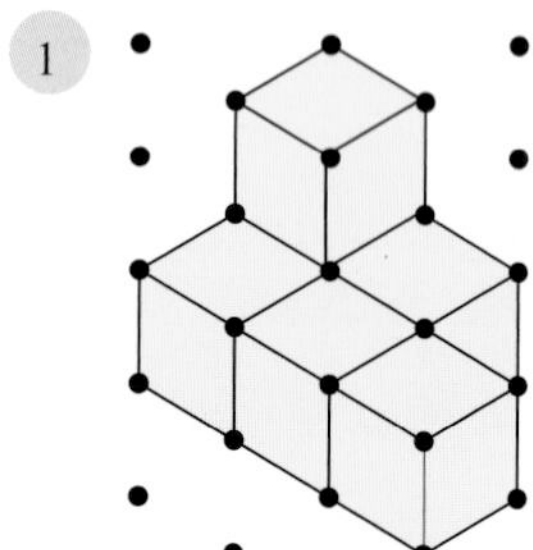

How many cubes are needed to make this shape into a $3 \times 2 \times 2$ cuboid?

2 Write in a more simple way.

(a) $3^5 \times 3^2$ (b) $a^{13} \div a^5$ (c) n^0 (d) $(2a^2)^3$

3 In each diagram there are w white squares and p pink squares.
How many white squares are there in the diagram which has n pink squares?

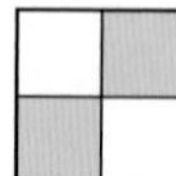

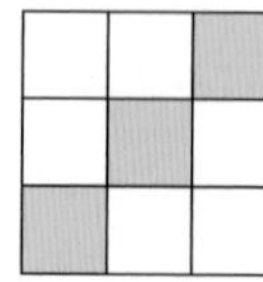

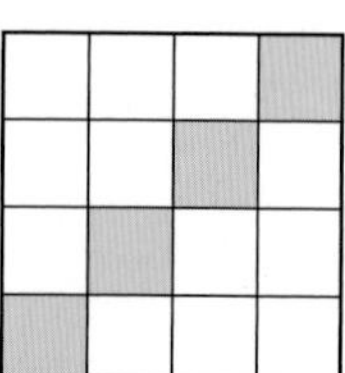

4 For each sequence find (i) the 10th term (ii) the nth term.

(a) 5, 10, 15, 20,
(b) 2, 4, 6, 8,
(c) $\frac{1}{2}, \frac{2}{3}, \frac{3}{4}, \frac{4}{5},$
(d) $\frac{1}{4}, \frac{2}{5}, \frac{3}{6},$
(e) 1, 4, 9, 16,
(f) 1, 10, 100, 1000,
(g) $4 \times 3, 5 \times 3^2, 6 \times 3^3, 7 \times 3^4,$
(h) 101, 201, 301, 401

5 

It is estimated that there are one hundred billion pebbles on the beach at Brighton.

How long would it take to count them at 1 pebble per second?

6 (a) A hammer costs £7.95. Estimate the cost of 207 hammers.

(b) Rex walks 0.78 m every stride.
Estimate how far he walks if he takes 511 strides.

7 (a) Answer true or false: $(a \times b)^3 = a^3 \times b^3$

(b) Copy and complete.

$(9 \times 4)^4 = \square^4 \times \square^4$ or $\square^4 \times \square^4 \times \square^4 \times \square^4$

8 A scientist used a computer to find the value of pi to 206,158,430,000 decimal places.

If this number was published in book form it would make a pile of books 22 times as high as the Eiffel Tower (300 m). Assume each book is 2 cm thick and has 400 pages.
How many digits of pi are on each page?

9 Work out these answers on a calculator and give the answers correct to two decimal places.

(a) $\frac{4.9}{1.6} - 1.24$ (b) $\frac{3.78}{1.9^2}$ (c) $\frac{5.74}{(1.74 + 2.015)}$

10 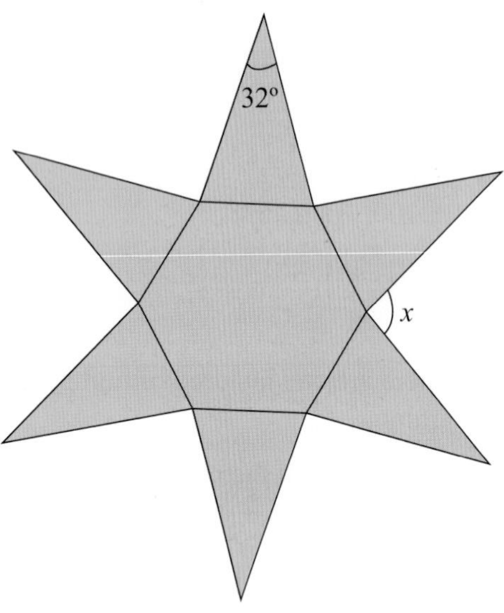

The diagram is a regular hexagon surrounded by six congruent isosceles triangles. Find the size of angle x.

11 (a) The nth term of a sequence is $\frac{n}{n+1}$.
Write down the first four terms of the sequence.

(b) The nth term of a sequence is 2^{n-1}.
What is the 10th term?

12 The diagram consists of a rectangle inside a semicircle.

Find the purple shaded area, correct to 3 significant figures.

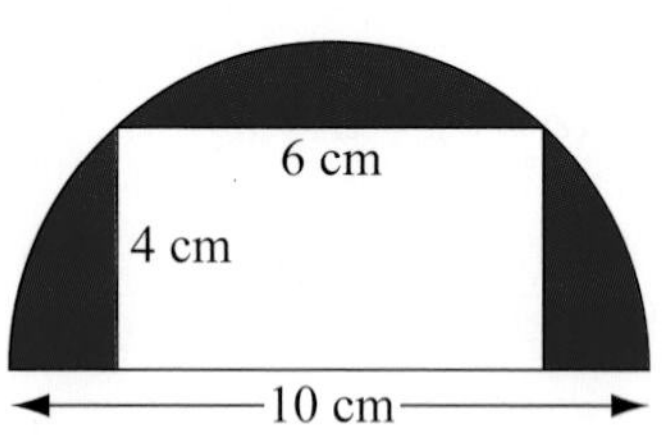

13 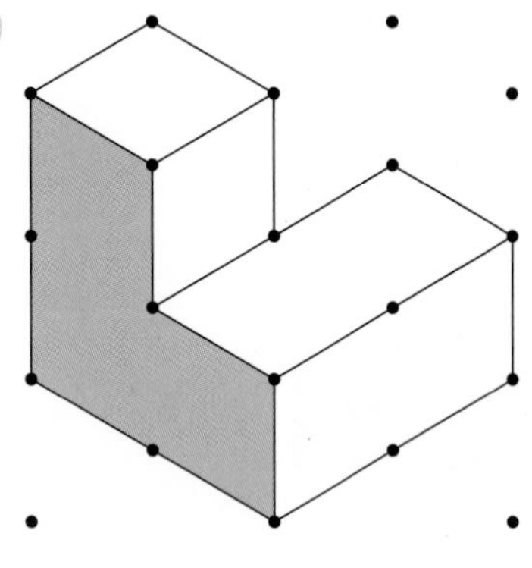

This objects falls over onto the blue shaded face. Draw the shape after it has fallen over.

14 (a) The point of the minute hand of a clock travels 21 cm in 20 minutes.
How long is the minute hand?

(b) The point of the hour hand travels 3 cm in one hour.
How long is the hour hand?

15 A concrete path, measuring 120 cm wide, is made to surround a lawn measuring 6 m by 5 m. If $4.824\ m^3$ of concrete is used, how thick is the path?

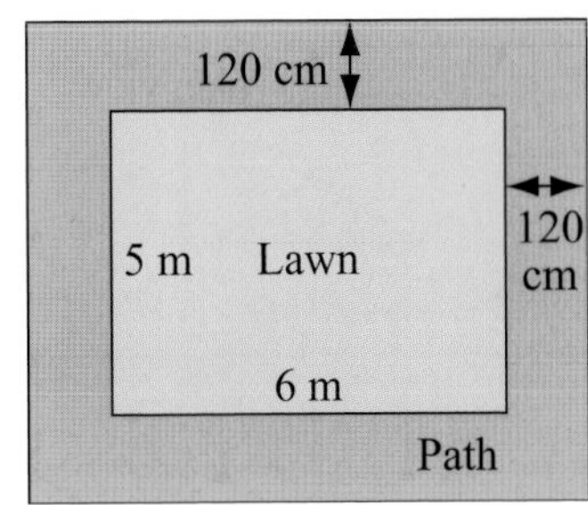

Part two

1

Matchstick oil rig sinks Titanic in record books

Southampton A retired oil rig worker has entered the record books with his matchstick replica of a North Sea oil platform.

David Reynolds, 51, from Southampton, spent 15 years on the project, using 4.075 million matchsticks. It has now been recognized by *Guinness World Records* as the biggest matchstick model, beating the 3.5 million used in a recreation of *Titanic*.

Mr Reynolds, who spent around £5,000 on matchsticks and glue, said: "It started as a hobby, but I guess it got out of hand." The model is 12ft tall, 21ft long and weighs ☐.

The Times October 20, 2009

(a) Matches are sold in boxes of 47. How many boxes did he need?

(b) Given that 47 matches weigh 12 g, copy and complete the final sentence in the article, stating the units.

2 Find the values of n and m if $n^3 - 1 = 37 \times 333\,667 \times m^4$

3 The prices for coating a metal plate with preservative are:

Up to 2000 cm^2	£300
From 2000 cm^2 to 4000 cm^2	£550
From 4000 cm^2 to 8000 cm^2	£850.

The measurements of a plate are shown.

(a) *Estimate* its area. Show your working.

(b) Using your estimate, what price would you pay for the coating?

(c) Without a calculator, work out the exact area of the plate.

4 A boat sails from point A on a bearing 040° to reach point B, which is 22 km from A. The boat then changes course and sails 35 km on a bearing 130° to reach point C. Draw a diagram to show the journey and hence *calculate* the distance between point A and point C.

5 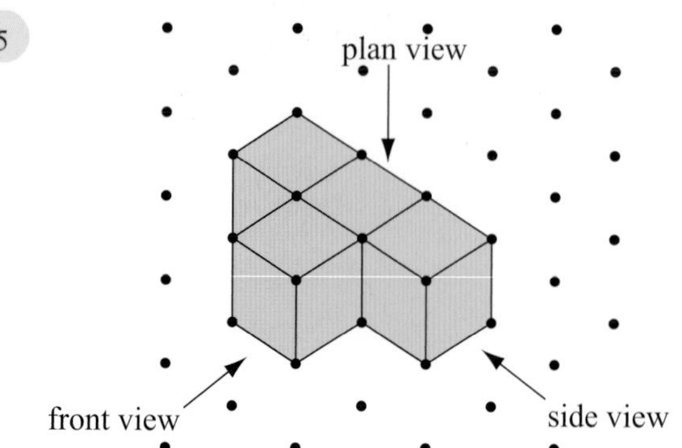

On squared paper draw the front view, the plan view and the side view of this object.

6 Here are four expressions involving an unknown number n

A	B	C	D
$2n + 1$	$n - 5$	$2n + 3$	$3n + 1$

(a) Find the value of n if the expressions A and B are equal.

(b) Find the value of n if the expressions C and D are equal.

(c) Which two expressions could never be equal for *any* value of n?

7 Rhodri eats x grapes in y days.
How many does he eat in a week?

8 The diagonal of a square has length 5cm.
What is the area of the square?

9 Find the percentage increase when the price of a lawnmower goes up from £140 to £151.20.

10 This is a series of shapes with blue and white tiles.

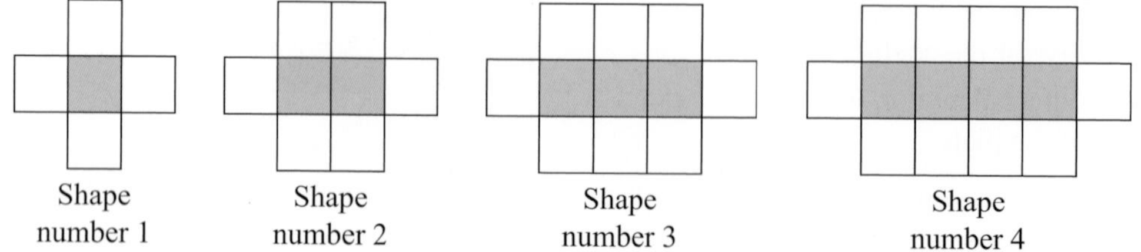

(a) How many blue tiles and how many white tiles are there in shape number 10?

(b) How many blue tiles and how many white tiles are there in shape number 150?

(c) How many white tiles are there in shape number n?

11 

After not eating for several weeks, the weight of a turtle went down by 10%. Find the original weight of the turtle if it weighed 24.3 kg after that time.

12 Which of the following statements are true?

$3^2 + 4^2 = 5^2$

$3^3 + 4^3 + 5^3 = 6^3$

$3^4 + 4^4 + 5^4 + 6^4 = 7^4$

$100^2 - 3^2 = 103 \times 97$

13 The cost of advertising in a local paper for one week is

28p per word plus 75p

(a) What is the cost of an advertisement of 15 words for one week?

(b) What is the greatest number of words in an advertisement costing up to £8 for one week?

(c) If an advertisement is run for two weeks, the cost for the second week is reduced by 30%. Calculate the total cost for an advertisement of 22 words for two weeks.

14 Find n% of $\left[\frac{224}{n} \times \left(\frac{n+1}{n-1}\right) \times 2^{n-1}\right]$, when $n = 8$.

15 At two minutes past ten on the morning of the first of October 2001 the time was 10.02.01.10.2001

This is a *palindrome* which reads the same backwards as forwards.

Think of another time when such an event occurred.

Hint. There is at least one in 2002 and another in the year 2112.

Puzzles and Problems 3

Puzzles

1 In these triangle puzzles the numbers a, b, c, d are connected as follows:

$a \times b^2 = c$
$c \times (b - 1) = d$

For example:

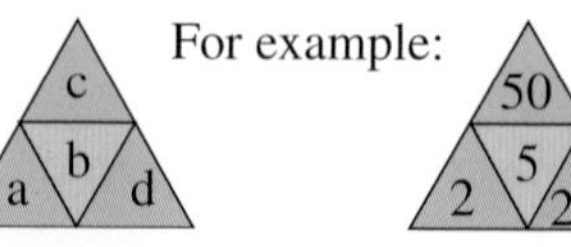

Copy and complete the following triangles:

(a)

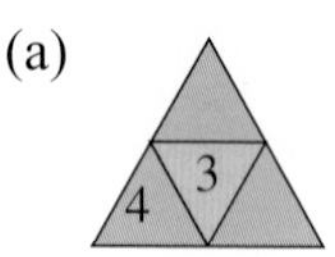

(b)

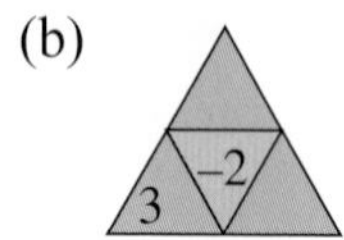

(c)

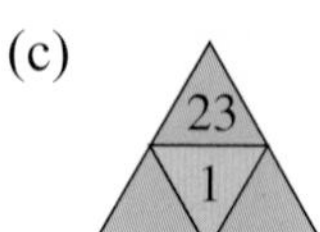

(d)

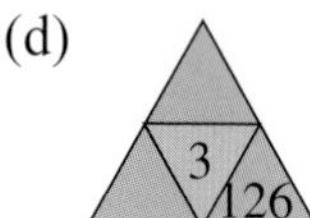

(e)

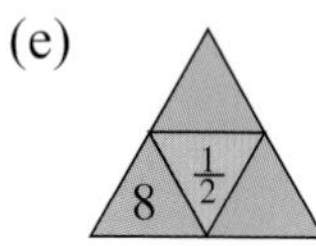

(f)

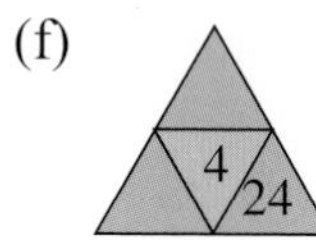

(g)

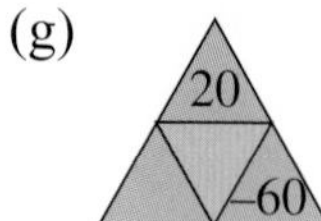

(h)

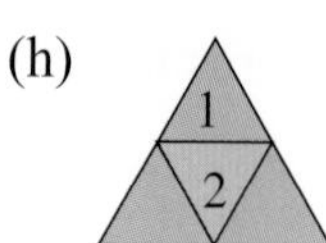

(i)

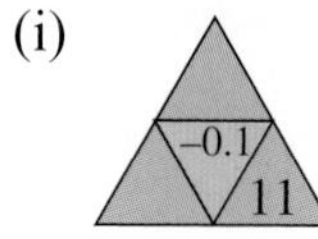

(j)

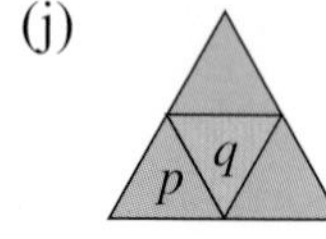

(k)

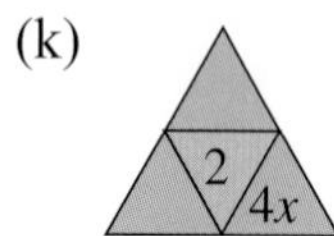

(l)

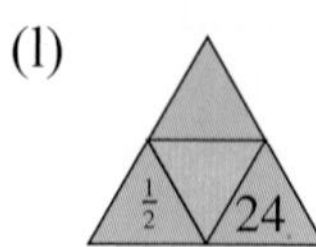

2 How many two-digit numbers have digits that add to fourteen?

3 How many three-digits number have digits that add to fourteen?

4 Using square 'dotty' paper, squares are drawn with their corners on dots. On the right are the three different squares which can be drawn inside a 2×2 grid. How many different size squares can be drawn inside a 10×10 grid?

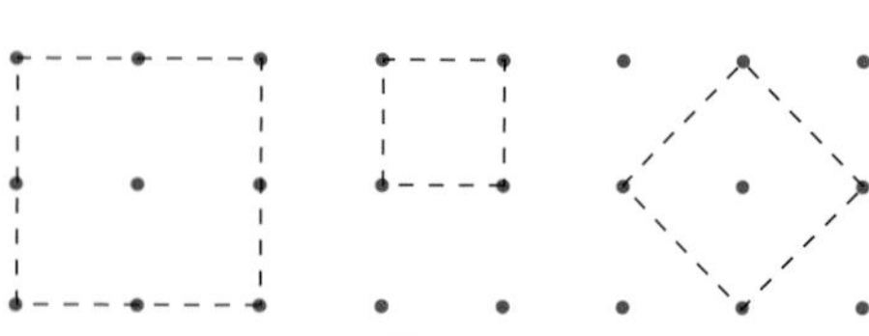

5 The circle has a radius of 1 unit. Find the total length of the arcs in the diagram. Give your answer as a multiple of π.

Hidden words

(a) Start in the top left box.

(b) Work out the answer to the calculation in the box.

(c) Find this answer in the top corner of another box.

(d) Write down the letter in that box.

(e) Repeat steps (b), (c) and (d) until you arrive back at the top left box. What is the message?

(f) Where necessary, numbers are rounded off to 2 decimal places.

1

92.2 Solve $\frac{3}{x} = \frac{1}{2}$	$\frac{7}{8}$ A $25.1 \div 0.1$	-8 E $\frac{1}{2} + \frac{1}{3} + \frac{1}{4}$	193.5 E $0.\dot{3} + 0.\dot{1}$	36 H $\frac{7.32}{8.1 - 1.94}$
5.5 S $(-3)^2 + (-2)^2$	1.5×10^{-10} O 3.2% of 2500	-1 F $1^3 + 2^3 + 3^3$	$-\frac{4}{7}$ S Solve $\frac{x}{3} + 4 = 7$	2×10^7 E $18 - 12 \div 3$
13 O Solve $3x - 1 = -4$	6 N $-7 - (-2) + (-3)$	9 H $\frac{3}{4} + \frac{1}{8}$	14 S $5.2 + 87$	$1\frac{1}{12}$ T Solve $\frac{3}{x+1} = 7$
$\frac{4}{9}$ L (5×10^{-3}) $\times (3 \times 10^{-8})$	$-\frac{3}{4}$ L (8×10^5) $\div (4 \times 10^{-2})$	80 T $12\frac{1}{2}$% of 44	1.19 O $-\frac{1}{2} + (-\frac{1}{4})$	251 V $\frac{3}{4}$ of 258

2

6.575 $(5.3 \times 10^4) \times (2 \times 10^9)$	3.6 O $(-12) \div (-\frac{1}{2})$	1.6×10^{-9} H $\frac{2.3^2 - 1.9^2}{8.2 - 7.71}$	3.55 I Solve $6 - 3x = 2$	$\frac{3}{5}$ T Half of 13.15
24 F $\frac{1}{6} + \frac{1}{7} + 0.2314$	–49 A $\frac{8.2 + 1.99}{1.7 \times 4.7}$	0.81 S Solve $3(x + 1) = 2(3 - x)$	106.26 U $\frac{2.75}{1.09} - \sqrt{\frac{1.21}{0.41}}$	36.96 P Solve $\frac{18}{x} - 1.5 = 3.5$
2.34 S $\frac{5}{6} - \frac{2}{5}$	–8 A 12% of $\frac{2}{5}$ of 770	1.06×10^{14} H $\frac{3}{2.51} + \frac{4}{1.7}$	$\frac{13}{30}$ A $(2.4 \times 10^{-6}) \div (1.5 \times 10^3)$	$\frac{4}{5}$ I $\sqrt{\frac{10}{\pi}} + \sqrt{\frac{\pi}{10}}$
$1\frac{1}{3}$ S Increase 250 by 5%	1.28 R $\frac{3}{5} \div \frac{3}{4}$	0.54 R $\frac{5^5 - 4^4}{3^3}$	262.5 C $(-7)^2 \times (-1)^3$	3.43 E $-7 + (-6) - (-5)$

3

$\frac{11}{20}$ $0.3 \times \frac{1}{3}$	$\frac{1}{2}$ U $-8 - (-3)$	16 L [right-angled triangle: sides 3 and 5, hypotenuse x] Find x	7.5×10^{10} H Solve $\frac{9}{x} + 7 = 10$	54.4 O $\frac{1}{2} \times \frac{2}{3} \times \frac{3}{4}$
4.17 T $(3 \times 10^4) \times (2.5 \times 10^6)$	6.71 P Decrease 64 by 15%	12 E $\frac{3}{5} + \frac{1}{2}$	2 I Increase 56.5 by 8%	$-\frac{1}{4}$ N $(-2)^2 \times (-3)^3$
61.02 S $3.984 - \left(\frac{2.61}{1.4}\right)$	$\frac{1}{4}$ I Solve $5(x + 1) = 3(1 - x)$	0.1 P Solve $\frac{1}{3}x = 9.9$	4.08 O $\frac{5}{12} - \frac{1}{4}$	210 E $\frac{1}{4} + (\frac{1}{2}$ of $\frac{3}{5})$
–108 T 6% of $\frac{2}{3}$ of 102	2.25×10^{-10} O Solve $\frac{3}{x + 1} = 2$	$\frac{1}{6}$ N $4.2 \div 0.02$	2×10^{-4} H $x^2 - 6x$, when $x = -2$	5.83 Y $\frac{2.9}{1.2 - 0.71^2}$
29.7 I $(-\frac{1}{2}) \div (-\frac{1}{4})$	3 R $3x^2$, when $x = 2$	–5 G 1% of 2%	1.1 E [right-angled triangle: sides 2 and x, hypotenuse 7] Find x	2.12 R $(1.5 \times 10^{-5})^2$

Mayan numbers

Decimal numbers use 10 digits and are based on powers of 10.

Quinary numbers use 5 digits and are based on powers of 5.
Some languages in the world use this number system.
12 in base 5 means $(1 \times 5) + (2 \times 1) = 7$ as a decimal number.
12 in base 10 means $(1 \times 10) + (2 \times 1) = 12$

The Mayan people lived in Central America. Over a thousand years ago they used a number system with base 20. They only used three symbols – dots, bars and shells. The numbers 0 to 19 are shown below.

0 1 2 3 4 5 6 7 8 9

10 11 12 13 14 15 16 17 18 19

Mayan numbers work vertically. When 20 is reached, the number of 20's appears above the remaining 0 to 19

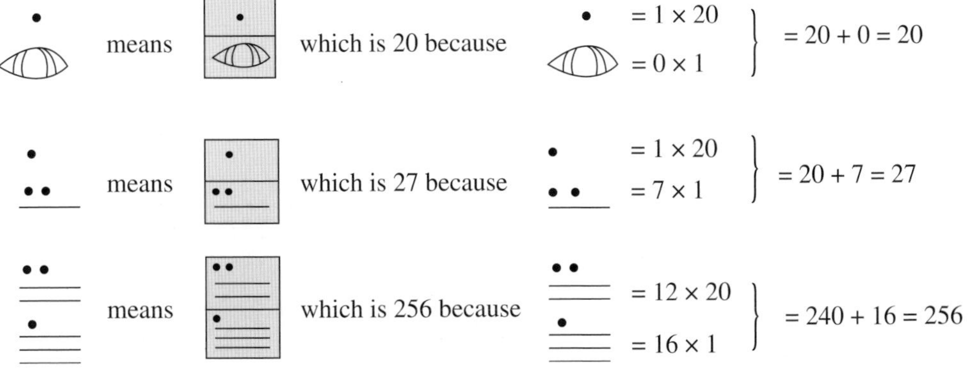

Larger numbers

When 20^2 (400) is reached, the number of 400s appears vertically above the remaining parts of the number.

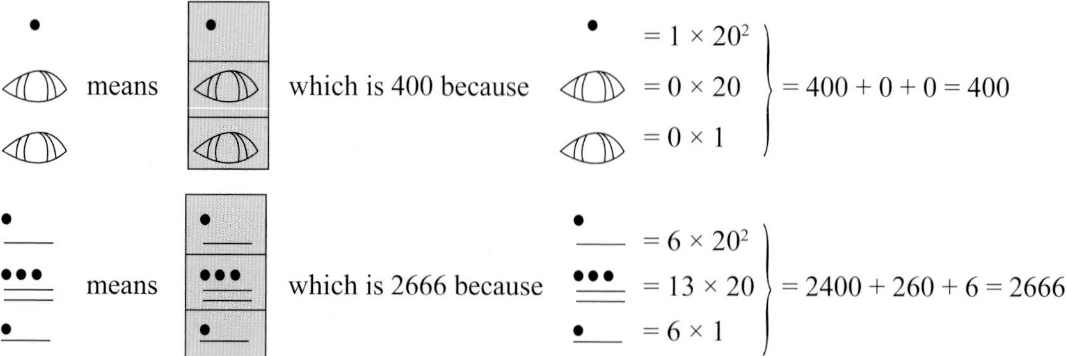

Addition

Add these two Mayan numbers giving your answer as a Mayan number.

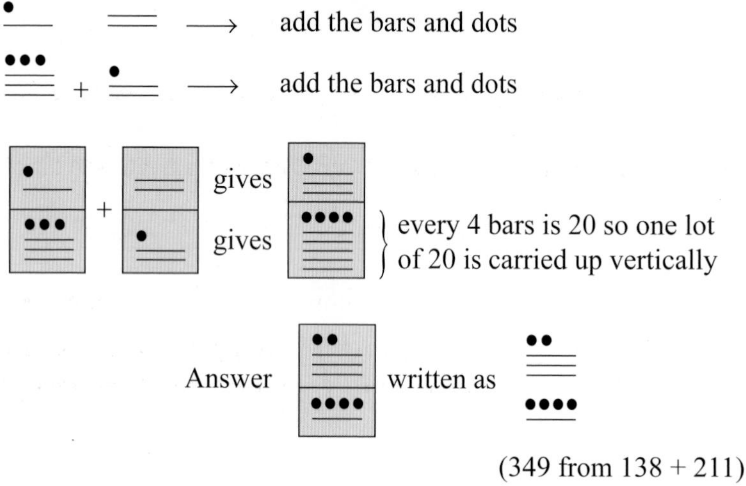

(349 from 138 + 211)

Exercise 1E

1 Change these Mayan numbers into ordinary decimal numbers.

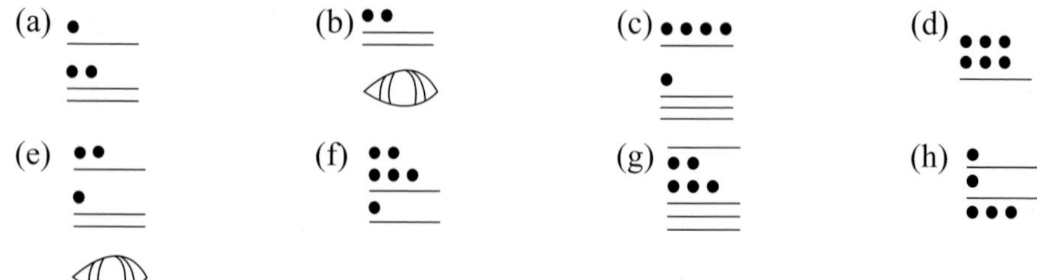

2 Write the following decimal numbers as Mayan numbers.

(a) 108 (b) 222 (c) 191 (d) 80 (e) 973 (f) 4244

3 Why do you think the Mayan people used a number system based on 20?

4 (a) 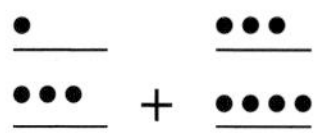 + (b) 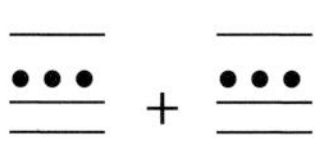 + (c) 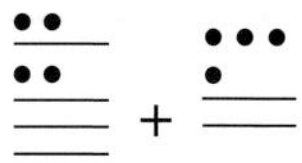 +

(d) 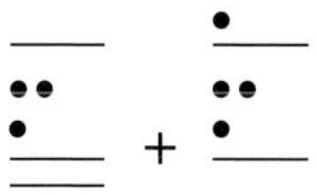 + (e) 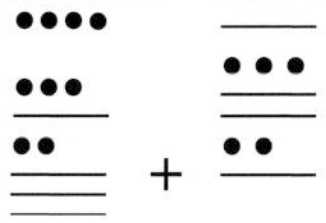 + (f) 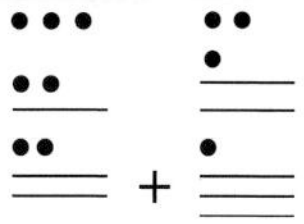 +

5 What do you think this Mayan number is as an ordinary decimal number?

6 Make up three Mayan numbers and add them together, giving your answers as a Mayan number.
Now give your three Mayan numbers to other people and see if they get the same answer when they add the numbers together.

7 **RESEARCH:**

(a) Find more ancient civilizations which used a number system which was not base 10.

(b) Hexadecimal numbers are widely used in computers and electronics. What base is used? Can you work out what the following three hexadecimal numbers are as ordinary decimal numbers?

(a) 200 (b) 3AC2 (c) FFFF

UNIT 4

4.1 Transformations

In this unit you will:

- learn how to use vectors to describe translations
- give complete descriptions of given single transformations
- answer questions involving successive transformations

Translation

In a translation an object 'shifts' from one position to another. There is no turning or reflection and the object stays the same size. A translation is described completely by its *vector*.

In the diagram:

(a) △ A is mapped onto △ B by the translation with vector $\begin{pmatrix} 3 \\ 2 \end{pmatrix}$

(b) △ A is mapped onto △ C by the translation with vector $\begin{pmatrix} 5 \\ -2 \end{pmatrix}$

(c) △ C is mapped onto △ B by the translation with vector $\begin{pmatrix} -2 \\ 4 \end{pmatrix}$

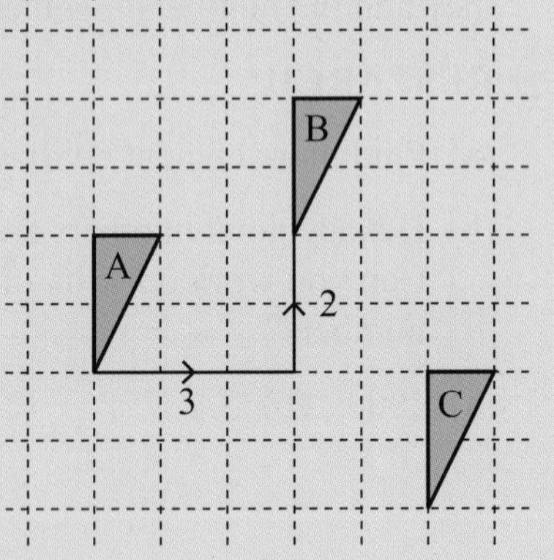

When performing a translation, concentrate your attention on *one* vertex of the shape.

The top number of a vector gives the number of units across (positive to the right). The bottom number gives the number of units up or down (positive upwards).

So $\begin{pmatrix} 5 \\ 2 \end{pmatrix}$ is 5 right → 2 up ↑, $\begin{pmatrix} 3 \\ -1 \end{pmatrix}$ is 3 right → 1 down ↓

Exercise 1M

1 Look at the diagram shown. Write down the vector for each of the following translations:

(a) △H → △P (b) △E → △A (c) △R → △S (d) △W → △C (e) △Y → △L

(f) △U → △F (g) △T → △A (h) △W → △G (i) △O → △Y (j) △U → △I

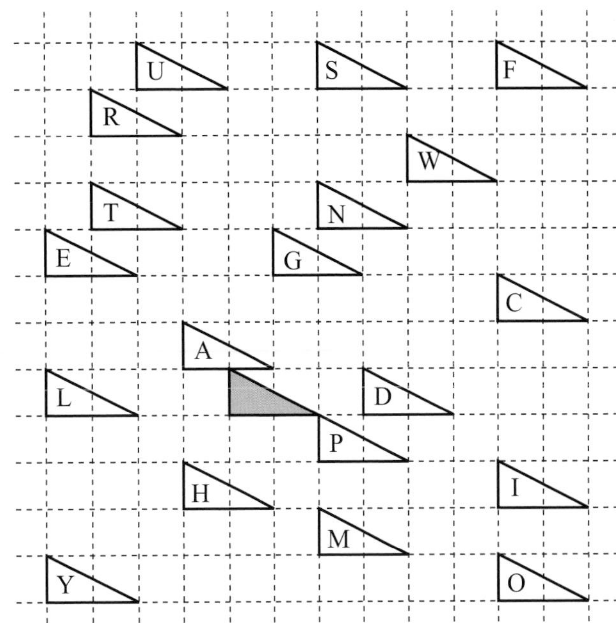

2 The vector $\begin{pmatrix}2\\7\end{pmatrix}$ translates the red triangle onto $\triangle$S. Similarly the vectors $\begin{pmatrix}-3\\4\end{pmatrix}, \begin{pmatrix}6\\-4\end{pmatrix}, \begin{pmatrix}2\\-1\end{pmatrix}$ translate the red triangle onto $\triangle$T, $\triangle$O, $\triangle$P. So you obtain the word 'STOP'.

(a) What word is given when the red triangle is translated using the vectors $\begin{pmatrix}-1\\1\end{pmatrix}, \begin{pmatrix}2\\-1\end{pmatrix}, \begin{pmatrix}2\\-1\end{pmatrix}, \begin{pmatrix}-4\\0\end{pmatrix}, \begin{pmatrix}-4\\3\end{pmatrix}$?

(b) Write down the vectors which translate the red triangle onto the letters of the word 'LAMP'.

3 Write the sentence given when the red triangle is translated using the vectors below.

$\begin{pmatrix}4\\5\end{pmatrix}\begin{pmatrix}-1\\-2\end{pmatrix}\begin{pmatrix}-1\\1\end{pmatrix}\begin{pmatrix}-3\\4\end{pmatrix} * \begin{pmatrix}3\\0\end{pmatrix}\begin{pmatrix}6\\-4\end{pmatrix} * \begin{pmatrix}-4\\-4\end{pmatrix}\begin{pmatrix}6\\-4\end{pmatrix}\begin{pmatrix}-2\\7\end{pmatrix} * \begin{pmatrix}6\\2\end{pmatrix}\begin{pmatrix}-1\\1\end{pmatrix}\begin{pmatrix}-4\\0\end{pmatrix}\begin{pmatrix}-4\\0\end{pmatrix} * \begin{pmatrix}-1\\1\end{pmatrix} * \begin{pmatrix}2\\-3\end{pmatrix}\begin{pmatrix}-1\\1\end{pmatrix}$

$\begin{pmatrix}2\\4\end{pmatrix} * \begin{pmatrix}4\\5\end{pmatrix}\begin{pmatrix}6\\-2\end{pmatrix}\begin{pmatrix}-3\\4\end{pmatrix}\begin{pmatrix}-1\\-2\end{pmatrix} * \begin{pmatrix}-1\\1\end{pmatrix} * \begin{pmatrix}4\\5\end{pmatrix}\begin{pmatrix}6\\-4\end{pmatrix}\begin{pmatrix}6\\-4\end{pmatrix}\begin{pmatrix}3\\0\end{pmatrix}\begin{pmatrix}-4\\3\end{pmatrix}\begin{pmatrix}2\\4\end{pmatrix} * \begin{pmatrix}-1\\-2\end{pmatrix}\begin{pmatrix}-4\\3\end{pmatrix}\begin{pmatrix}-1\\1\end{pmatrix}\begin{pmatrix}3\\0\end{pmatrix} * \begin{pmatrix}-4\\3\end{pmatrix}$

$\begin{pmatrix}3\\0\end{pmatrix}\begin{pmatrix}4\\5\end{pmatrix}\begin{pmatrix}-1\\1\end{pmatrix}\begin{pmatrix}-3\\6\end{pmatrix}\begin{pmatrix}3\\0\end{pmatrix} *$

4 What vector is twice as long as and parallel to the vector $\begin{pmatrix}3\\5\end{pmatrix}$?

5 What vector is twice as long as and opposite to the vector $\begin{pmatrix}1\\-2\end{pmatrix}$?

6 Write a vector which is perpendicular to the vector $\begin{pmatrix}2\\1\end{pmatrix}$

7 Under a certain translation, the image of the point (5, –2) is (3, –6). Find the image of the point (–2, 10) under the same translation.

8 Under a certain translation, the image of the point (–2, 0) is (6, –5). What point has (3, 3) as its image under the same translation?

Describing transformations

So far in you have studied four basic transformations. A full description of each transformation requires the information below.

- To describe a reflection you need the equation of the mirror line.
- To describe a rotation you need the angle, the direction and the centre of the rotation.
- To describe an enlargement you need the scale factor and the centre of the enlargement.
- To describe a translation you need the vector.

In the diagram the transformations are as follows:

$\triangle 1 \rightarrow \triangle 2$: Rotation 90° clockwise, centre (0, 0)

$\triangle 1 \rightarrow \triangle 3$: Reflection in $y = x$

$\triangle 1 \rightarrow \triangle 6$: Translation $\begin{pmatrix} 3 \\ -1 \end{pmatrix}$

$\triangle 4 \rightarrow \triangle 5$: Enlargement, scale factor 3, centre (3, –3)

$\triangle 1 \rightarrow \triangle 4$: Reflection in $y = 1\frac{1}{2}$

$\triangle 2 \rightarrow \triangle 6$: Rotation 90° anti-clockwise, centre (2, 1)

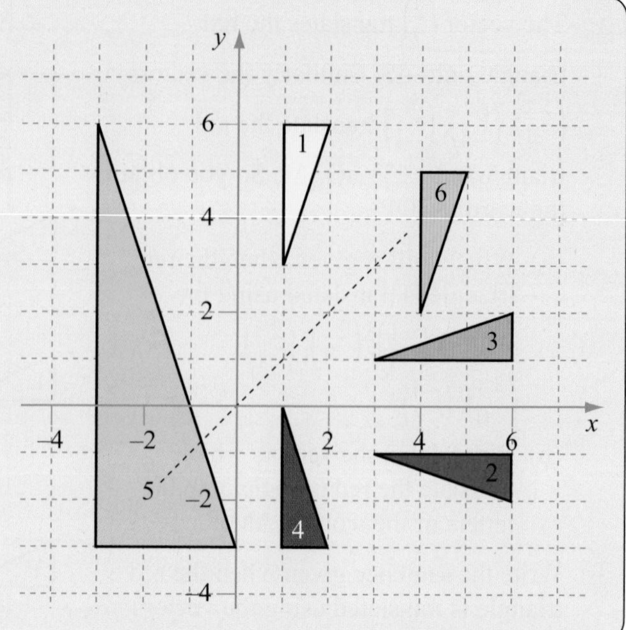

Exercise 2M

[Tracing paper will be helpful in this exercise.]

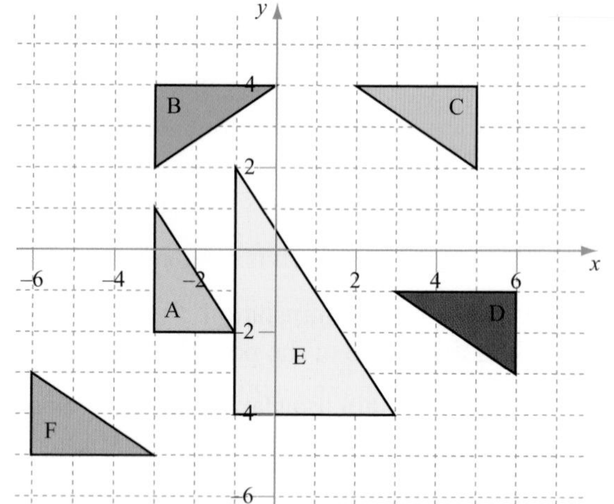

1. Copy the diagram so that you can draw construction lines.

   Describe fully each of the following transformations:

   (a) $\triangle A \rightarrow \triangle B$

   (b) $\triangle B \rightarrow \triangle C$

   (c) $\triangle C \rightarrow \triangle D$

   (d) $\triangle A \rightarrow \triangle E$

   (e) $\triangle D \rightarrow \triangle F$

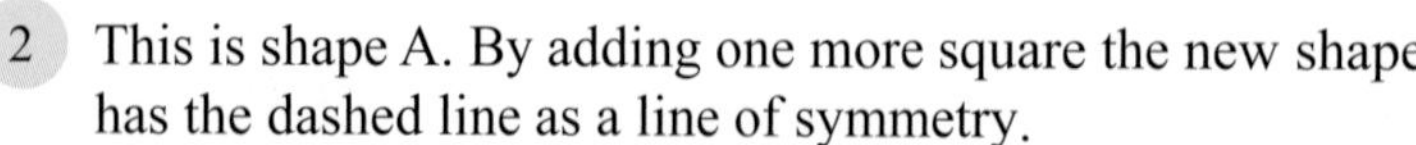

2. This is shape A. By adding one more square the new shape has the dashed line as a line of symmetry.

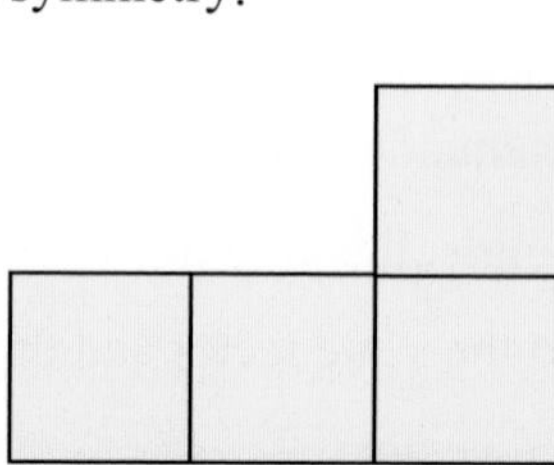

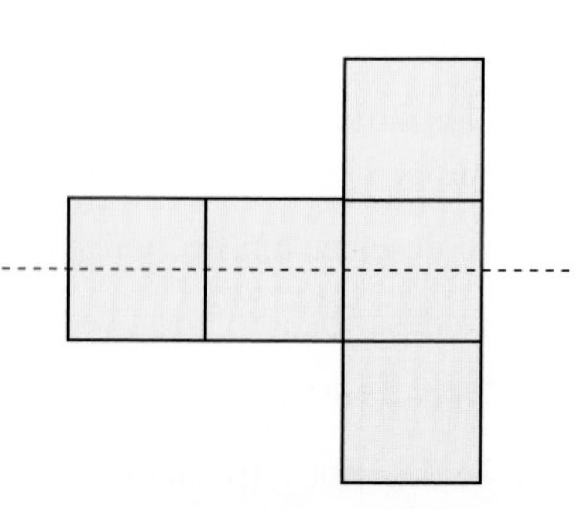

Copy each of the diagrams below and only add the number of squares stated so that the dashed line is a line of symmetry.

(a) 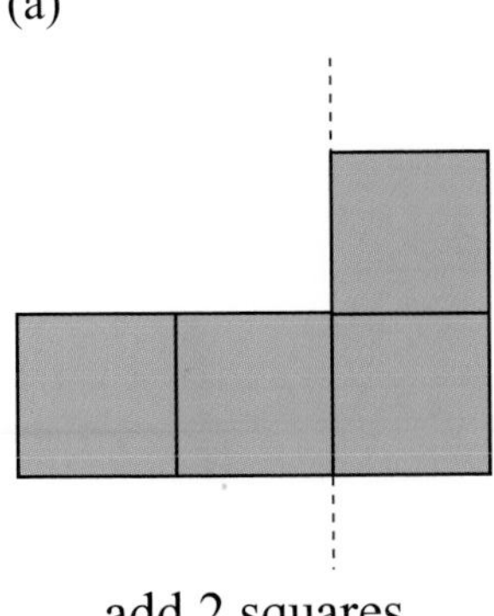

add 2 squares

(b) 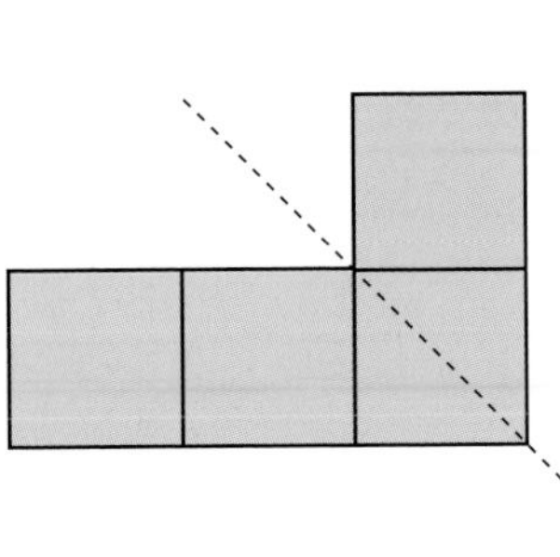

add 1 square

(c) 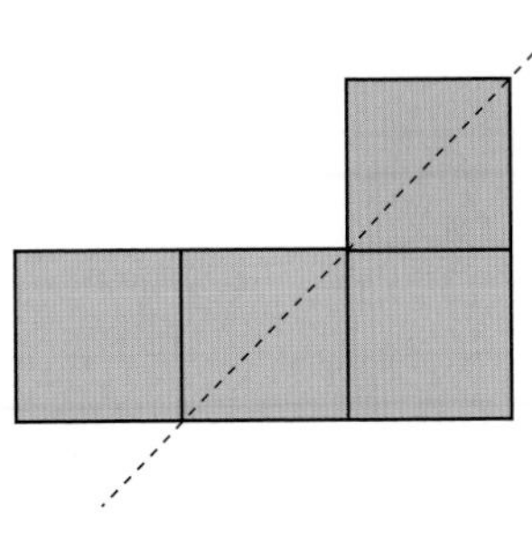

add 2 squares

3 (a) Find the image of the point (1, 3) after reflection in the line.

(i) $x = 4$ (ii) $y = 5$ (iii) $x = 50$ (iv) $y = x$ (v) $y = -x$

(b) Find the images of the points (7,3) (1,7) (99,3) (3,1) (–3,–1) (p, q) after reflection in the y axis.

4 Copy shape S inside the rectangle as shown. Shape S is enlarged so that it just fits inside the rectangle.

Draw the enlargement of shape S and mark the centre of enlargement.

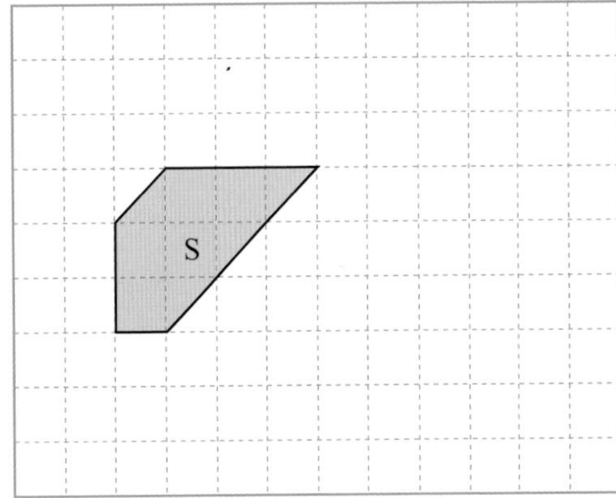

5 (a) Draw axes with x and y from –7 to +7.

(b) Plot and label $\Delta 1$ with vertices at (0, 0), (0, 2), (3, 2).

(c) Draw $\Delta 2, \Delta 3, \ldots \Delta 7$ as follows:

(i) $\Delta 1 \rightarrow \Delta 2$ Reflection in $y = 0$ (the x axis)

(ii) $\Delta 2 \rightarrow \Delta 3$ Reflection in $y = x$

(iii) $\Delta 1 \rightarrow \Delta 4$ Translation $\begin{pmatrix} -6 \\ 2 \end{pmatrix}$

(iv) $\Delta 4 \rightarrow \Delta 5$ Translation $\begin{pmatrix} 4 \\ 3 \end{pmatrix}$

(v) $\Delta 4 \rightarrow \Delta 6$ Reflection in $y = 0$

(vi) $\Delta 6 \rightarrow \Delta 7$ Reflection in $y = x$

(d) Describe each of the following single transformations:

(i) $\Delta 1 \rightarrow \Delta 3$
(ii) $\Delta 1 \rightarrow \Delta 5$
(iii) $\Delta 1 \rightarrow \Delta 7$

Successive transformations

Exercise 2E

1 (a) Copy the diagram on squared paper.

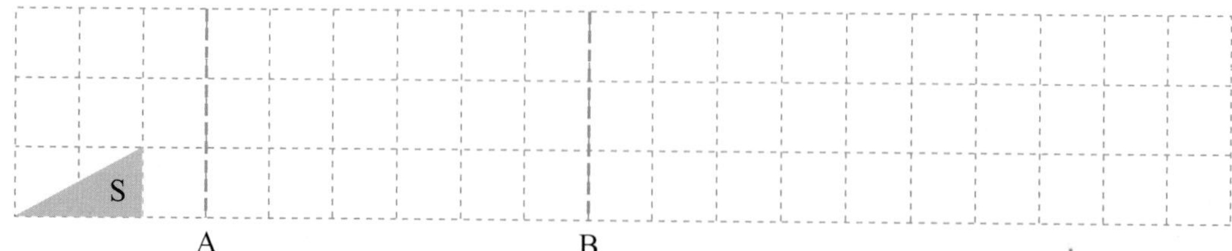

(b) Draw the reflection of shape S in line A. Label the image S_1.

(c) Draw the reflection of shape S_1 in line B. Label the image S_2.

(d) Describe the single transformation from S to S_2.

2 ABCD is mapped onto A′B′C′D′ by a reflection followed by a translation parallel to the *x* axis.

(a) Describe these two transformations as fully as possible.

(b) Would the image be the same if the translation was completed before the reflection?

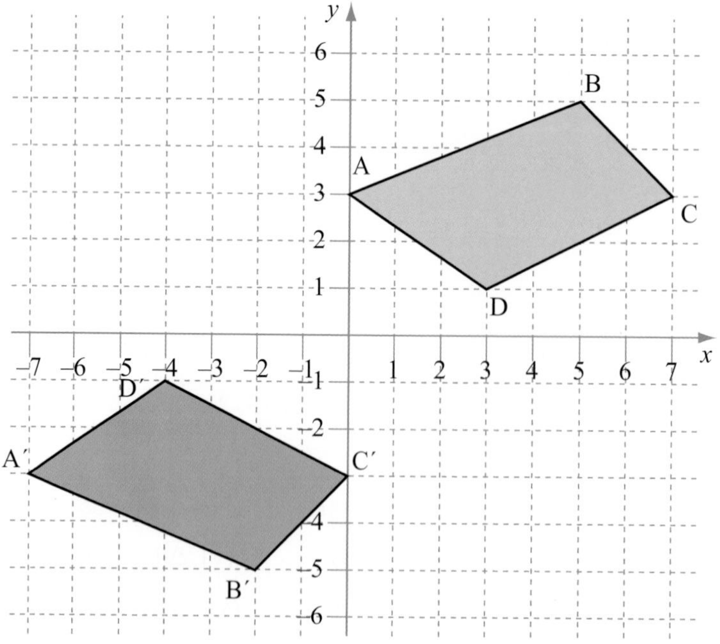

3 How could ABCD be transformed onto A′B′C′D′ by

(a) a single reflection,

(b) a reflection after a rotation of 90° anticlockwise about (0, 0)?

(c) Would the image be the same if the order of the rotation and reflection were reversed?

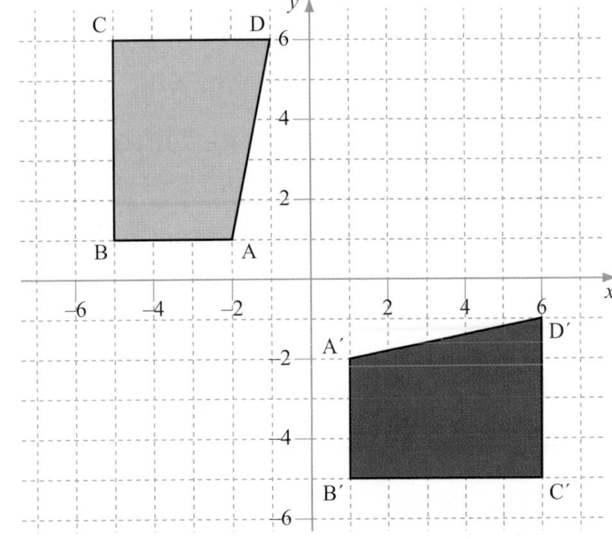

4 Draw axes for both x and y between –8 and +8.

Plot the points (1,1), (3, 1), (3, 2), (2, 2), (2, 4) and (1, 4) and join up to make an 'L' shape.

This is mapped onto the points (–2, –2), (–2, –6), (–4, –6), (–4, –4), (–8, –4), (–8, –2) by *two* transformations; an enlargement with centre (0, 0) followed by a reflection. Describe these transformations as fully as possible.

5 Draw axes for both x and y between –5 and +5.

Plot and label the points A (1, 1), B (3, 1), C (5, 3) and D (1, 2). Join these up to make a quadrilateral.

The images of these points after a translation parallel to the y-axis followed by a reflection are A′ (0,3), B′ (–2, 3), C′ (–4, 5) and D′ (0, 4). Plot A′B′C′D′ on the same set of axes. Describe fully the translation and reflection required.

6 Three transformations are required to map ABC onto A′B′C′, an enlargement centre (0, 0) followed by a translation parallel to the x axis and lastly a rotation about (0, 0). Describe these transformations as fully as possible.

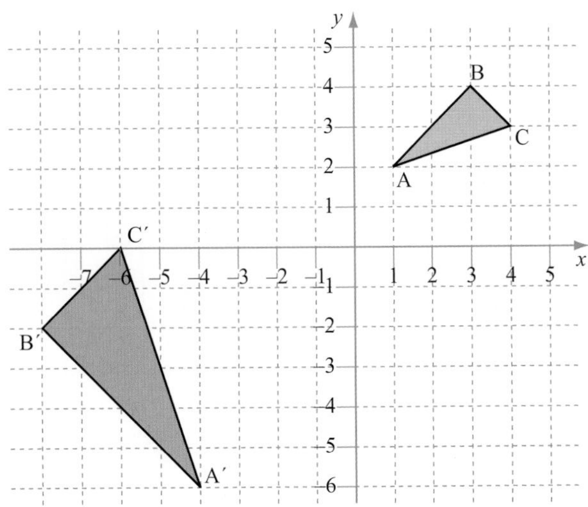

4.2 Reading and interpreting charts and graphs

In this section you will:

- answer questions involving pie charts, bar charts and scatter graphs
- interpret and draw line graphs and sketch graphs
- read and draw travel graphs

Pie charts and bar charts

Exercise 1M

1 540 people were asked how they travelled to work. The pie chart shows the results of the survey.

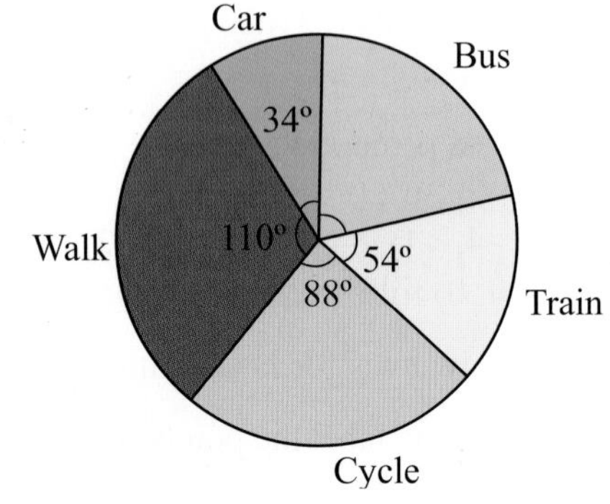

(a) How many people travelled by car?

(b) How many people travelled by bus?

(c) What percentage of the people travelled by train?

(d) In another survey of 540 people, 15% more people walked to work. What angle on a pie chart would represent this data?

2 The table shows the favourite types of books in a survey of 15 year-olds.

Work out the angle for each item on a pie chart.

Book	Frequency
horror	10
comedy	15
biography	3
romance	9
sports	8

3 The chart shows population growth rates in various parts of the world.

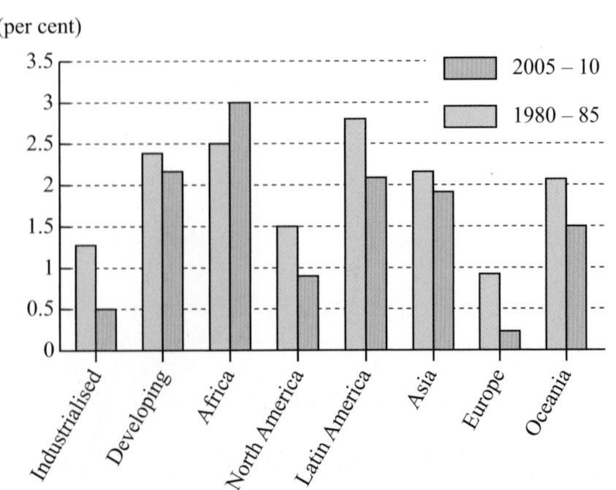

(a) What was the growth rate in North America between 1980 and 1985?

(b) Which region has seen an increase in growth rate?

(c) Which areas currently have the highest and lowest growth rates?

Try to think of reasons to explain the differences.

4 Describe briefly what each scatter graph shows.

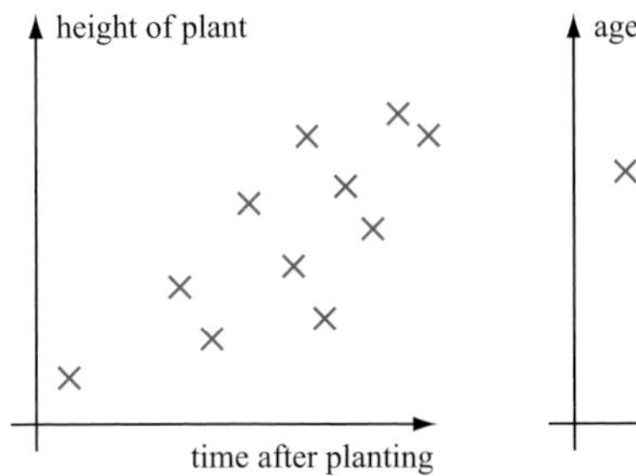

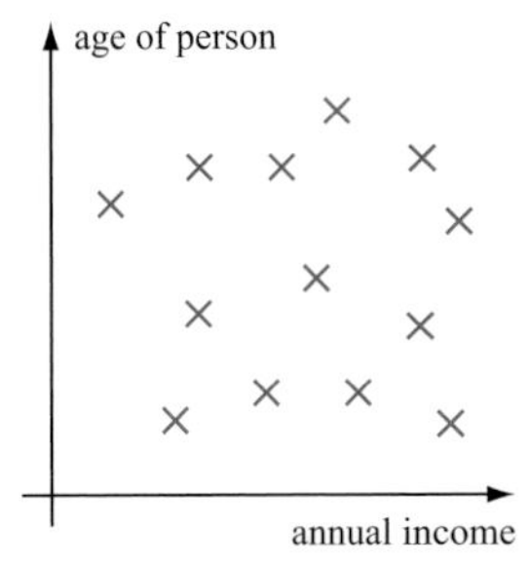

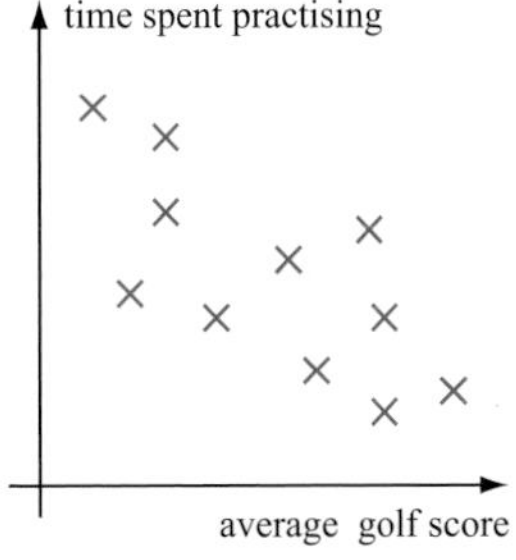

Exercise 1E

1 The charts show annual temperature and rainfall for two cities.

(a) What was the rainfall in Jakarta in April?

(b) What was the highest recorded temperature in Vladivostok?

Write one sentence about each chart to describe the main features.

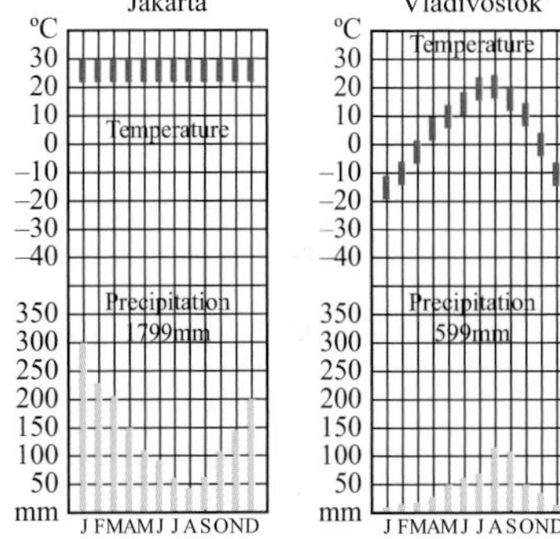

2 Here are population pyramids for Turkey and Australia. The charts show, for example, that about 4% of the male population of Australia is aged 0–4.

(a) About what percentage of males in Turkey were aged 30–34?

(b) What are the main differences in the two charts?
Try to explain why this might be so.

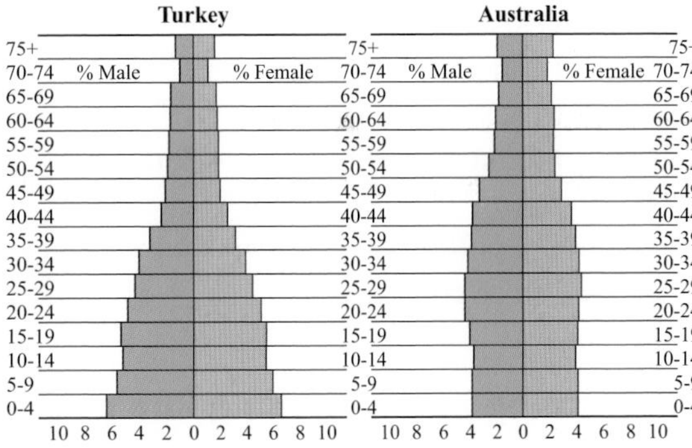

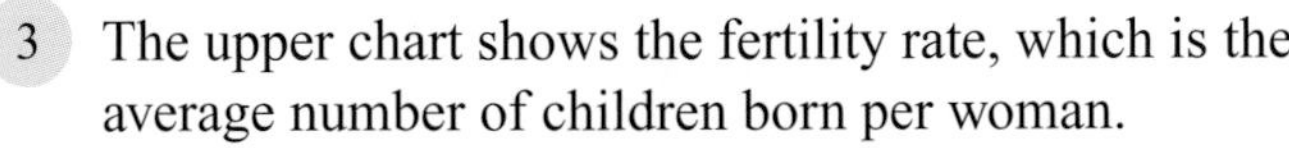

3 The upper chart shows the fertility rate, which is the average number of children born per woman.

The lower chart shows the percentage of females aged 12–17 in secondary education.

(a) What is the average number of children born per woman in Switzerland and in Nigeria?

(b) Describe the main differences that the graph shows for Denmark and Niger.

Why do you think these differences exist?

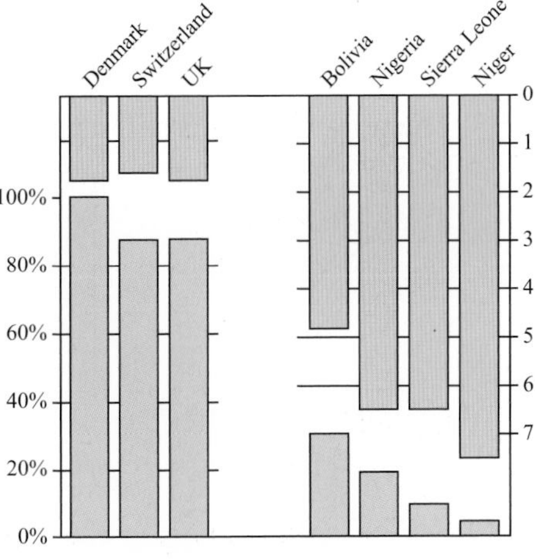

4 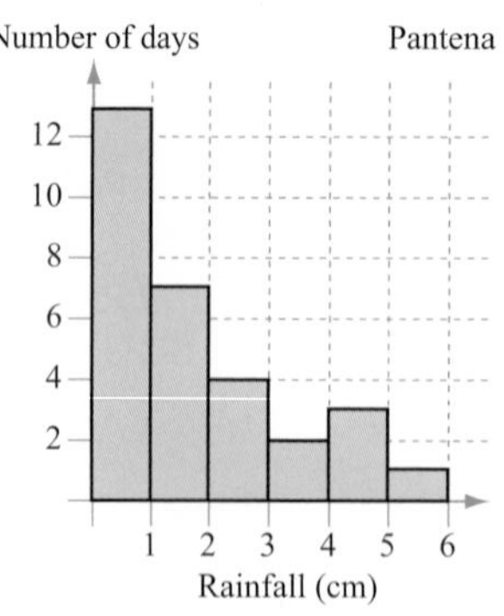

The sport of mud wrestling is best played when the ground is made soft by plenty of rainfall. The World Mudwrestling Association (W.M.A.) have to choose a venue for the 2015 championships. They have past rainfall data for the relevant month for two potential towns, Ortega and Pantena. Which venue would be more suitable? Explain your answer.

5 These charts show the ages of the people in four countries.

(a) In which country is about 75% of the population under the age of 30?

(b) Which country is the most likely to have good health care for the elderly?

(c) In one country there are many adult immigrant workers. Which country is that?

(d) One country was at war 20 years ago and its Supreme Leader called for mothers to have more babies to produce an army '20 million strong'.
The policy was later removed. Which country is that?

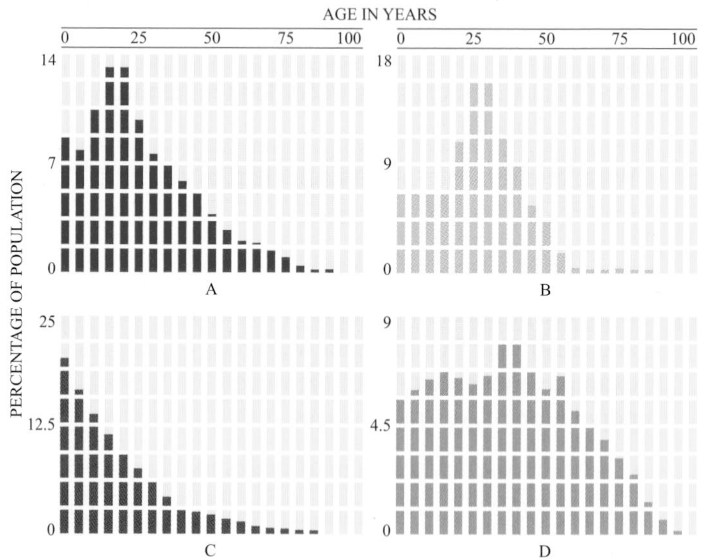

Interpreting and sketching line graphs

Exercise 2M

1 Which of the graphs A to D below best fits the following statement:

'The price of paint is still rising, but by less each month.'

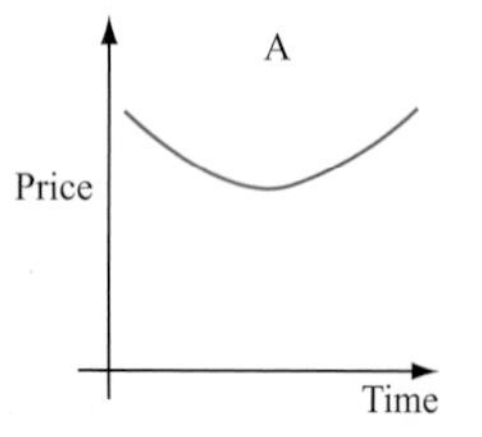

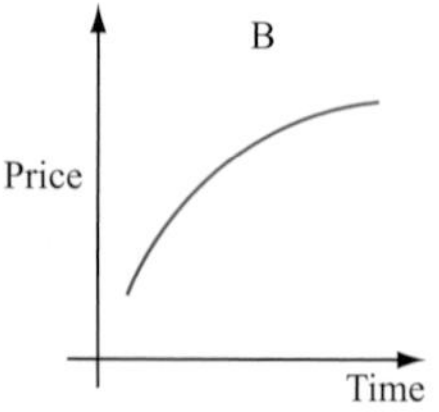

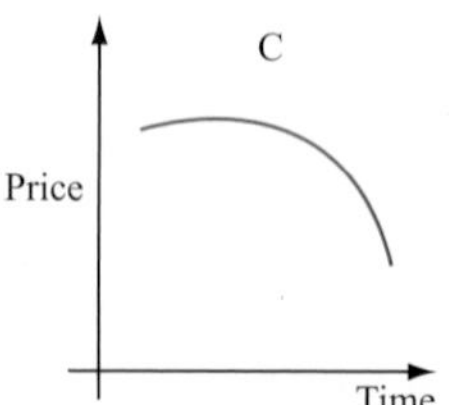

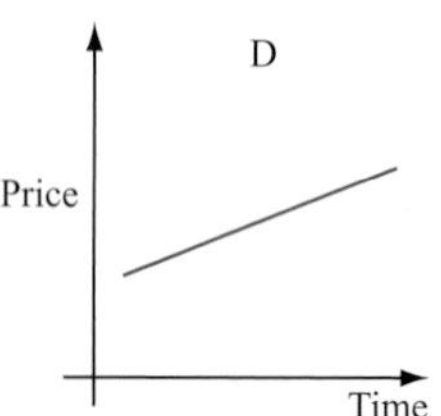

2 Which of the graphs A to D below best fits each of the following statements:

(a) The examination pass rate, which has been rising steadily, is now beginning to fall.

(b) The price of computers has fallen steadily over the last year.

(c) The birthrate was falling but is now steady.

(d) The cost of holidays, which rose slowly until 2009, is now rising fast.

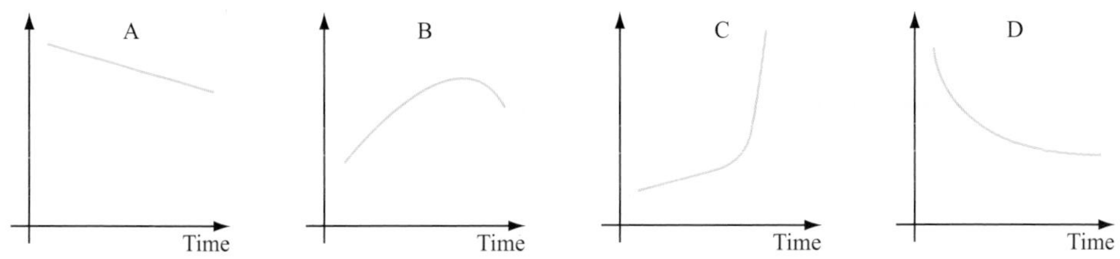

3 The step graph shows the cost of travelling on a bus. [Note that an open dot, o, means the overlap point is not included.] Find the cost of travelling

(a) 7 miles (b) 22 miles

(c) 10 miles

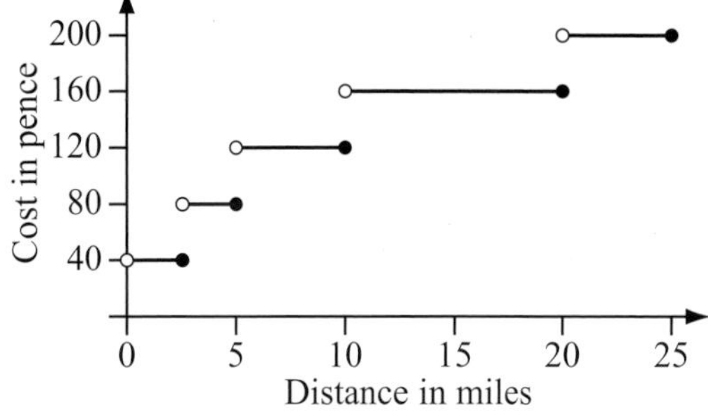

4 The graph below shows the depth of water at the centre of a puddle one summer day.

Describe what might be happening at each stage A–B, B–C etc.

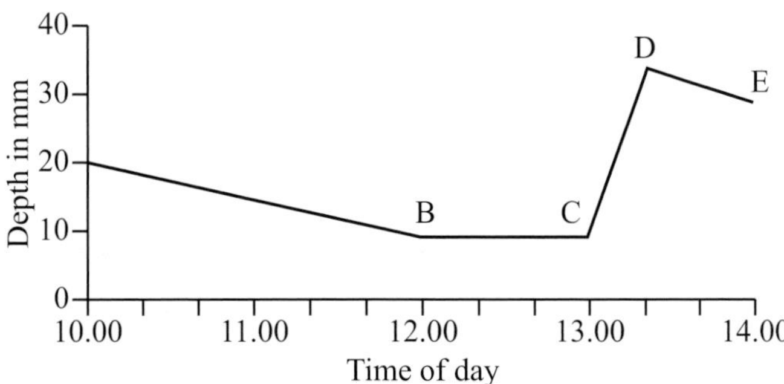

5 Here are two car racing circuits

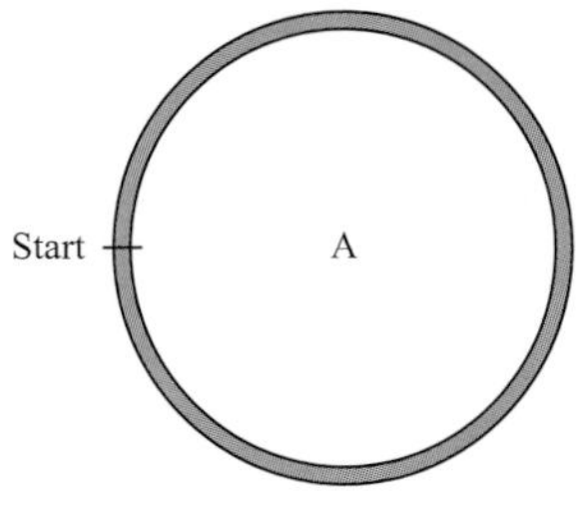

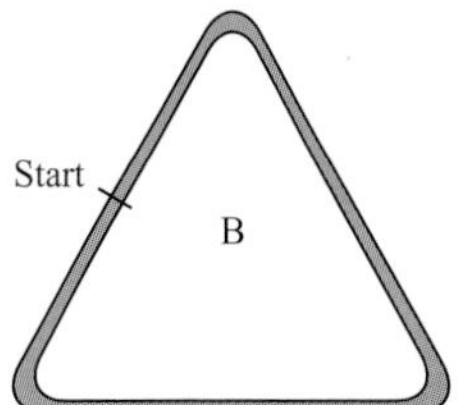

(a) Sketch a speed–time graph to show the speed of a racing car as it goes around one lap of each circuit in the middle of the race.

(b) Sketch a speed–time graph to show the speed of the car as it goes around the first lap on circuit A.

(c) Design a racing circuit of your own and sketch a speed–time graph for the speed of a car in a race.

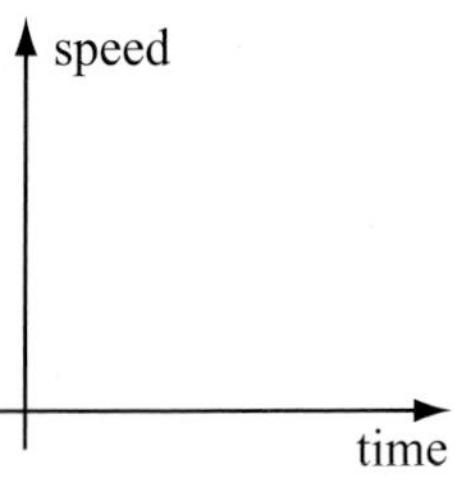

Exercise 2E

1 Water is poured at a constant rate into each of the containers A, B and C.

The graphs X, Y and Z shows how the water level rises.

Decide which graph fits each container. State your reasons.

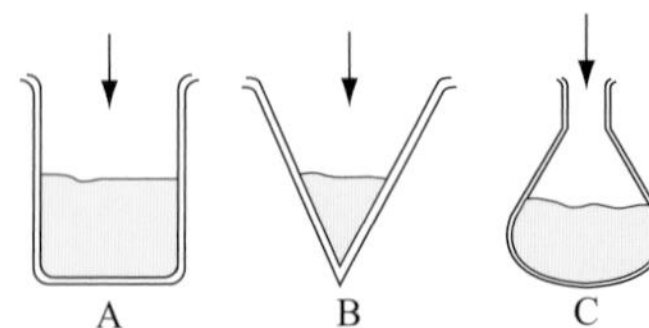

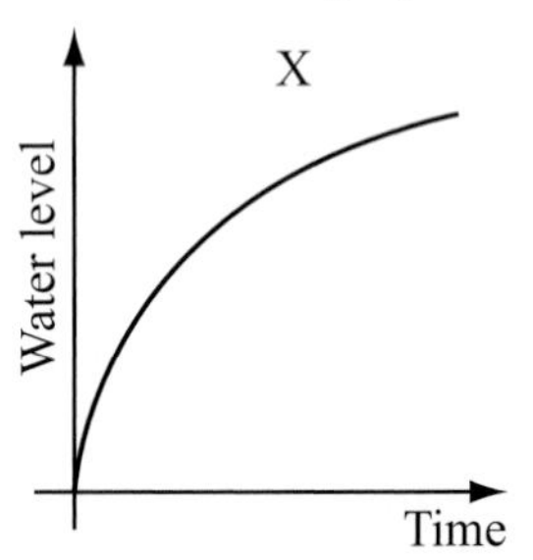

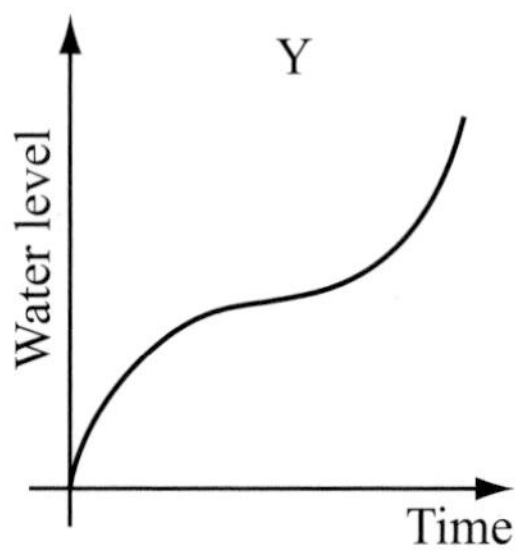

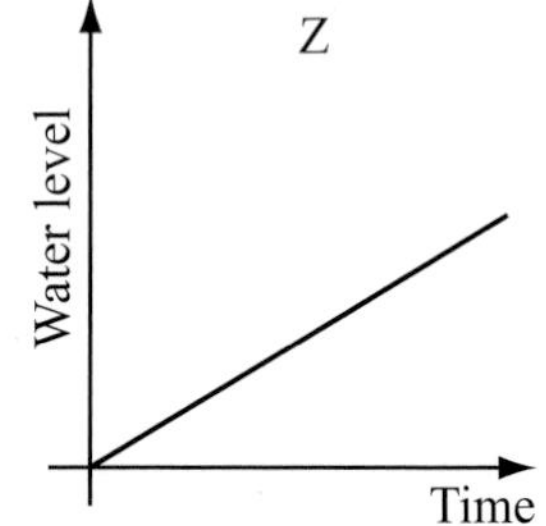

2 Water is poured at a constant rate into three different containers P, Q and R.

Draw sketch graphs, similar to those above, to show how the water level would rise in each one.

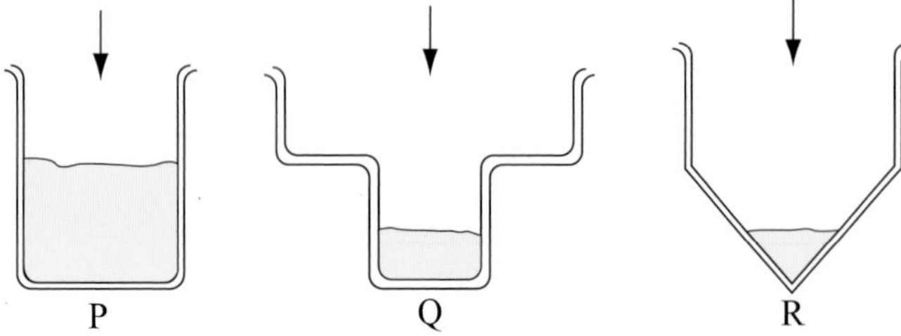

3 The line graph shows how the weight of an earthworm varies over the first 60 days of its life. Describe the main features of the graph and speculate about the possible causes of the main events.

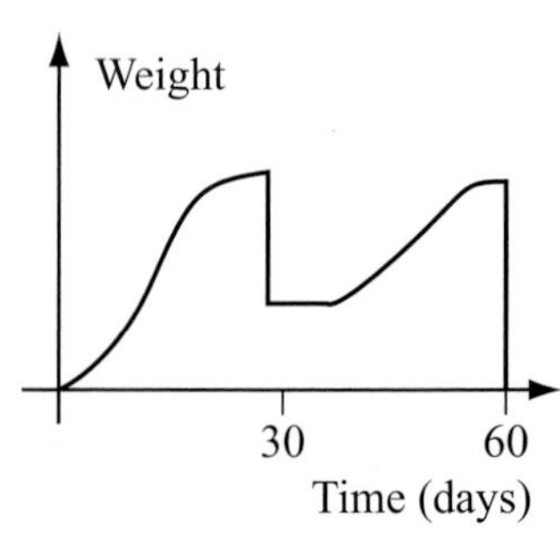

4 Sketch a speed–time graph of a parachutist from leaving a plane to landing on the ground.

5 Draw a sketch graph to show the height of a child from birth to age 20 years.

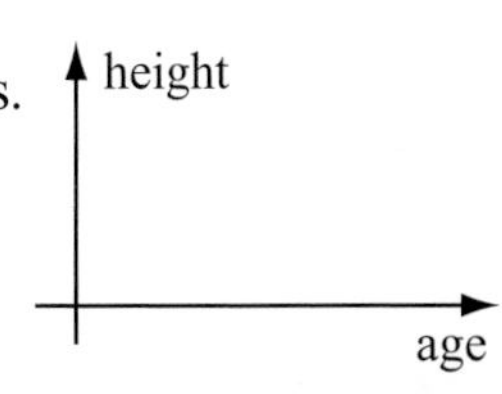

6 Draw a sketch graph to show the weight of a packet of chocolate biscuits as the biscuits are eaten over a period of 8 days.

7 A car was driven for a few miles around town before crashing.

Sketch a speed–time graph for the journey.

Travel graphs

Exercise 3M

1 The graph shows a car journey from York to Harrogate and back.

(a) When did the car arrive at Harrogate?
(b) When did the car return to York?
(c) At what speed did the car travel

(i) between 0900 and 1000,
(ii) between 1100 and 1200,
(iii) between 1000 and 1030?

(d) At what time was the car halfway between Harrogate and York on the return journey?

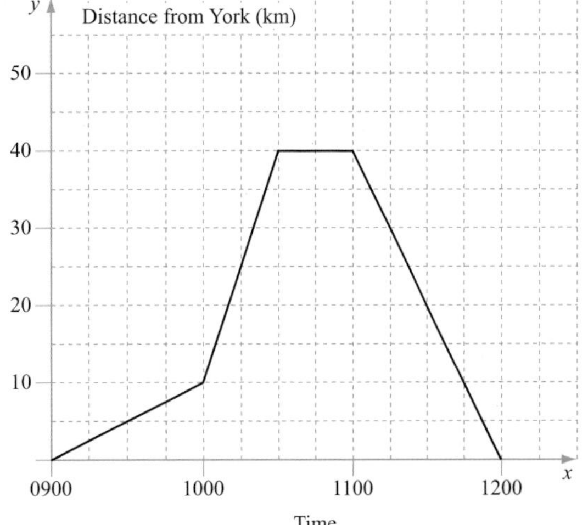

2 The travel graph below shows the progress of two cars, B and C, in a race from Leeds to Blackpool and back again.

(a) At what speed, in km/h, did car B travel between

(i) 2.00 and 3.15 (ii) 5.45 and 6.15 (iii) 4.45 and 5.45?

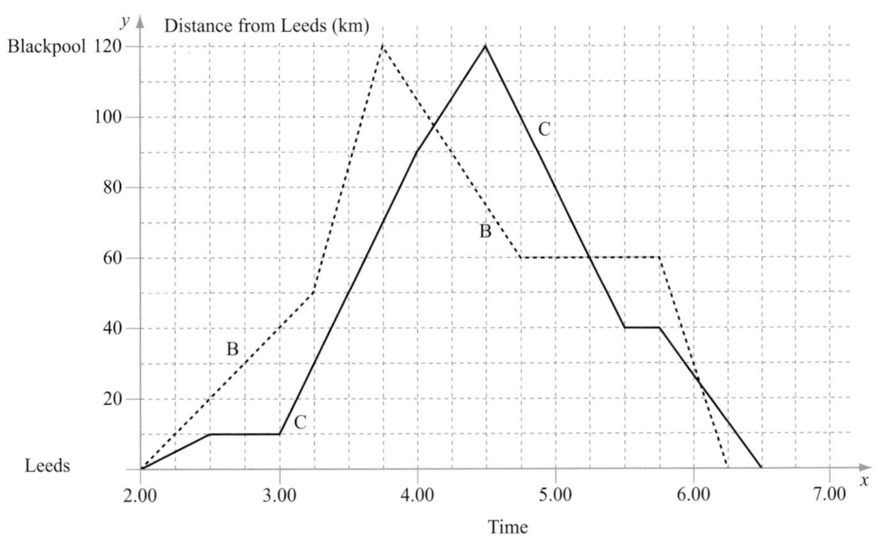

(b) Which car was leading in the race at
(i) 3.30 (ii) 4.15?

(c) What was the distance between the two cars at 4.45?

(d) What happened just after 6.00?

(e) Which car won the race?

3 At 0900 Kate leaves home and drives at a speed of 80 km/h. At 0930 she increases her speed to 100 km/h and continues to her destination which is 90 km from home. She stops for ¾ hour and then returns home at a speed of 90 km/h.

Draw a travel graph to show Kate's journey. Use the same scales as in Question 2, showing 'Distance from home' on the vertical axis.

At what time did she return home?

4 A car leaves Nottingham at 3.00 p.m. and travels at 60 km/h for ½ hour before stopping for ¾ hour. After that it continues towards York, which is 120 km from Nottingham, at 90 km/h. Also at 3.00 p.m. a lorry leaves York travelling towards Nottingham. The lorry travels at 40 km/h for the first hour but then breaks down. After repairs lasting ¾ hour the lorry returns to York at a speed of 40 km/h.

Draw a travel graph to show the journeys of the car and the lorry. Use the same scales as in Question 2, showing 'Distance from Nottingham' on the vertical axis.

(a) At about what time does the car overtake the lorry?

(b) At what time does the lorry arrive back in York?

(c) How far is the lorry from Nottingham at 3.45?

Using exponential and reciprocal graphs to approximate solutions to contextual problems

Exponential graphs

The graph of $y = 2^x$ is an example of an *exponential graph.*

For $y = 2^x$: when $x = 0, y = 2^0 = 1$

$x = 1, y = 2^1 = 2$

$x = 2, y = 2^2 = 4$

$x = -1, y = 2^{-1} = \frac{1}{2}$

$x = -2, y = 2^{-2} = \frac{1}{2^2} = \frac{1}{4}$

$x = -3, y = 2^{-3} = \frac{1}{2^3} = \frac{1}{8}$

[Reminder: see page 67 for explanation showing why $2^0 = 1$ and why $n^0 = 1$ for any non-zero value of n.]

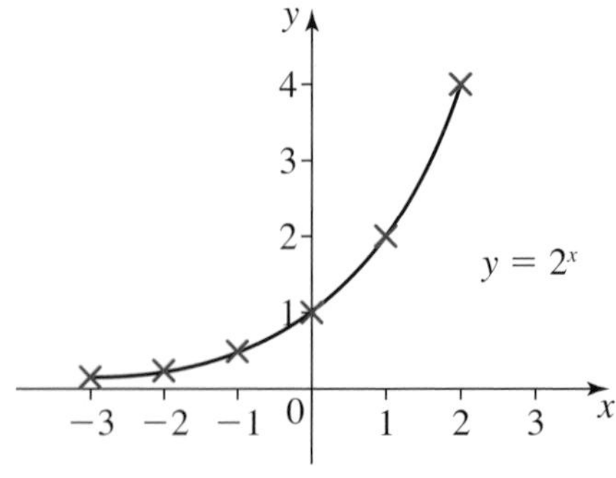

Notes: when $x = 0$, $y = 2^0 = 1$.
The line $y = 0$ is an asymptote.
The curve approaches the line $y = 0$ but never meets it.

Exercise 4M

1. Draw the graph of $y = 3^x$ for $-1 \leqslant x \leqslant 2$.

2. (a) Draw the graph of $y = 5^x$ for $-2 \leqslant x \leqslant 2$.
   (b) At what point does the curve cut the y-axis?

3. (a) Draw the graph of $y = 2^x + 1$ for $-2 \leqslant x \leqslant 3$.
   (b) At what point does the curve cut the y-axis?

4. Sketch the two curves given and state the number of times the curves intersect (in this context a straight line is called a curve).
   (a) $y = x^2$, $y = 5 - x$
   (b) $y = x^2$, $y = x^{-1}$
   (c) $y = 3^x$, $y = 10 - x$

5. At time $t = 0$, one bacterium is placed in a liquid in a test tube. The number of bacteria doubles every 5 minutes.
   (a) Draw a graph to show the growth of the bacteria from $t = 0$ to $t = 25$ minutes. Use a scale of 1 cm to 5 minutes across the page and 1 cm to 2 units up the page.
   (b) Use your graph to estimate the time taken to reach 24 bacteria.

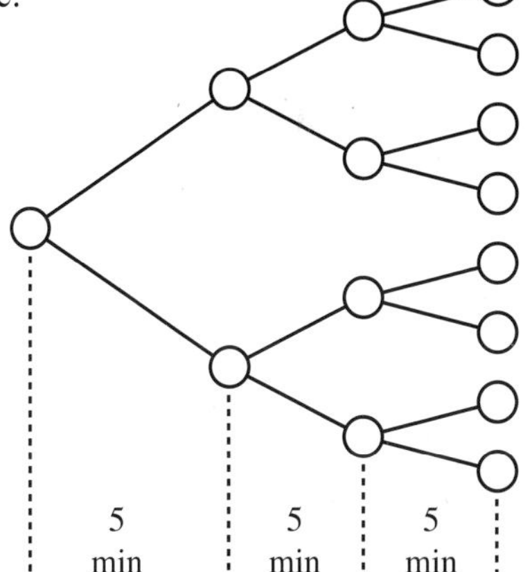

6. Initially there are 50 hamsters in the zoo. The number of hamsters in the zoo doubles each week. The table below shows the population of hamsters, H, after w weeks.

w	0	1	2	3	4	5
H	50	100	200	400	800	1600

   (a) Draw a graph to show this information.
   (b) The equation connecting H and w is $H = 50 \times 2^w$. Draw a graph of $H = 50 \times 2^w$ for values of H from 0 to 1600 and values of w from 0 to 5.
   (c) Use your graph to estimate the number of hamsters in the zoo after 3.5 weeks.

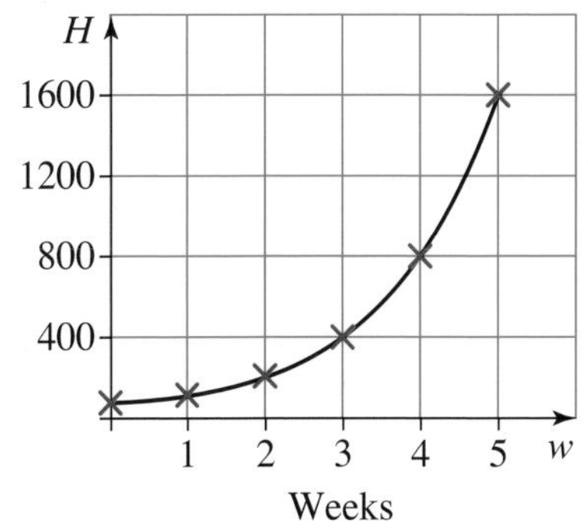

Reciprocal graphs

A reciprocal equation has the x term in the denominator of a fraction.

For example: $y = \frac{12}{x}$ $\quad y = \frac{20}{x+1}$ $\quad y = \frac{16}{x^2}$

Here is the table of values for $y = \frac{6}{x}$ for x from -6 to $+6$.

x	-6	-5	-4	-3	-2	-1	0	1	2	3	4	5	6
y	-1	-1.2	-1.5	-2	-3	-6	no value	6	3	2	1.5	1.2	1

Notice that when $x = 0$ there is no value for y. As x approaches 0 the curve approaches the y-axis but does not touch it.

Also as x gets larger and larger the curve approaches the x-axis but does not touch it. For this graph the lines $x = 0$ and $y = 0$ are *asymptotes* to the curve.

Here is the graph of $y = \frac{6}{x}$.

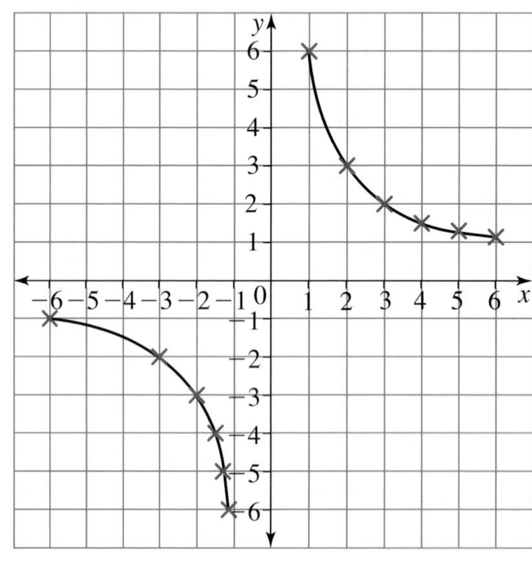

Exercise 4E

For questions 1 to 6 draw the curves. The scales given are for one unit of x and y.

1. $y = \frac{12}{x}$, for $1 \leqslant x \leqslant 10$ (scales: 1 cm for x and y)

2. $y = \frac{8}{x}$, for $\frac{1}{2} \leqslant x \leqslant 8$ (scales: 1 cm for x and y)

3. $y = \frac{12}{x+1}$, for $0 \leqslant x \leqslant 8$ (scales: 2 cm for x, 1 cm for y)

4. $y = \frac{x}{x+4}$, for $-3.5 \leqslant x \leqslant 4$ (scales: 2 cm for x and y)

5. $y = \frac{10}{x} + x$, for $1 \leqslant x \leqslant 7$ (scales: 2 cm for x, 1 cm for y)

6 $y = 3^x$, for $-3 \leqslant x \leqslant 3$ (scales: 2 cm for x, $\frac{1}{2}$ cm for y)

7 In the winter a farmer has 800 kg of food to feed his x cows.

The weight of food per cow, y kg, is given by the equation $y = \dfrac{800}{x}$.

(a) Copy and complete the table of values for $y = \dfrac{800}{x}$:

x	10	20	30	40	50	60	70	80	90	100
y										

(b) Draw the graph of $y = \dfrac{800}{x}$, for values of x from 10 to 100.

(c) Use your graph to estimate how much food each cow gets if the farmer has 74 cows.

8 In a laboratory germs were growing in a dish so that after t minutes the number of germs, g, was given by the formula $g = 2^t$.

(a) Copy and complete the table.

t	0	1	2	3	4	5
g	1	2				

(b) Draw the graph of $g = 2^t$ for values of t from 0 to 5.

(c) Use your graph to estimate the number of germs in the dish after 3.5 minutes.

9 Draw the graph of $y = \dfrac{18}{x}$ for $1 \leqslant x \leqslant 10$. Use the graph to find approximate solutions to the equations below:

(a) $\dfrac{18}{x} = x + 2$ (b) $\dfrac{18}{x} = 10 - x$ (c) $x^2 = 18$

10 A patient in hospital is treated with medicine to reduce the number of germs, g, in his body. After treatment the value of g is given by the equation $g = (0.8)^x$, where $x =$ the number of hours after the treatment began.

(a) Copy and complete the table of values for $g = (0.8)^x$.

x	0	1	2	3	4
g	1	0.8			0.41

(b) On the grid, draw the graph of $g = (0.8)^x$ for values of x from 0 to 4. Use scales of 2 cm for 1 unit for x and 1 cm for 0.1 units for g.

(c) Use your graph to solve the equation $(0.8)^x = 0.76$.

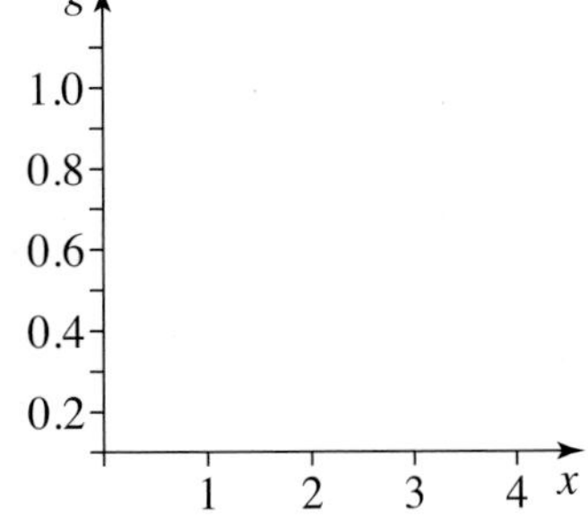

Exercise 5E

1 Find a, b and c.

(i) $3^a = 81$ (ii) $b^5 = 1$ (iii) $2^{c+1} = 32$

2 Solve these equations.

(a) $10x^3 = 270$ (b) $10^n = 0.1$ (c) $5n^3 = 0$

3 Use a calculator to find solutions to the following equations, correct to two significant figures.

(a) $x^x = 5.67$ (b) $3^n = 729$ (c) $\frac{1}{n} = 10^3$

4 Work out 5% of $\frac{2}{3}$ of 6% of $\frac{1}{(0.1)^4}$

5 (a) Look at the number pattern below.

$$1 = 1^3$$
$$3 + 5 = 8 = 2^3$$
$$7 + 9 + 11 = 27 = 3^3$$

(b) Write down the next three lines of the pattern.

(c) *Predict* (without working it out) the sum of $43 + 45 + 47 + 49 + 51 + 53 + 55$.

(d) Write the answer to part (c) as n^3 where n is to be found.

6 Find the solution to the equation $3^n = 59\,049$.

7 £1000 is invested in a bank and after n years the amount of money, M, in the account is given by the formula

$$M = 1000 \times 1.04^n$$

Find the amount of money in the account, to the nearest pound, after

(a) 2 years (b) 5 years

8 The number of fish, n, in a tank after w weeks is given by the formula $n = 200 \times (1.1)^w$. Find the value of n after 10 weeks.

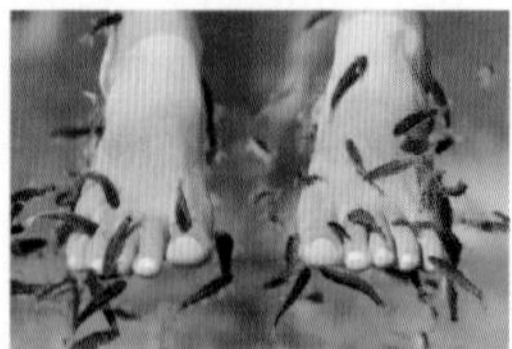

Sets, subsets and Venn diagrams

A set is a defined group of objects or symbols. The objects or symbols are called the **elements** of the set.

Here are the common symbols used in working with sets:

1. ∩ 'intersection' A ∩ B is shaded

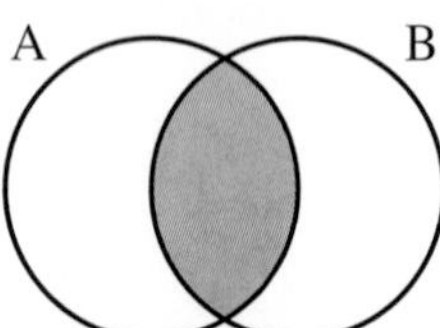

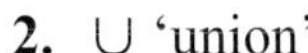

2. $\cup$ ‘union’ A $\cup$ B is shaded

3. $\subset$ ‘is a subset of’
P $\subset$ Q

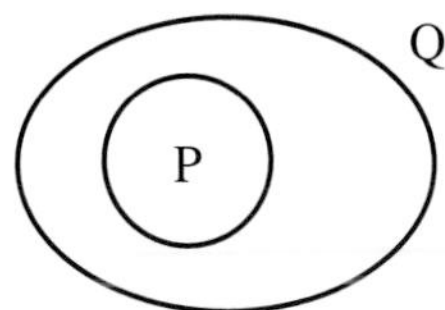

4. $\in$ ‘is a member of’
or ‘belongs to’
e.g. 7 $\in$ H

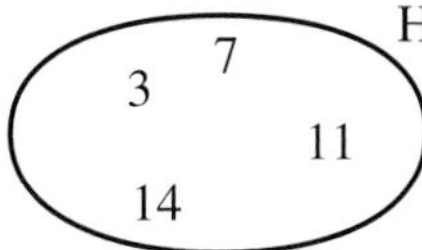

5. $\mathscr{E}$ universal set’
$\mathscr{E} = \{2, 3, 5, 7, 8\}$

$\mathscr{E}$

2 3 5

7 8

6. n(H) ‘the number of elements
of set H’
n(H) = 5

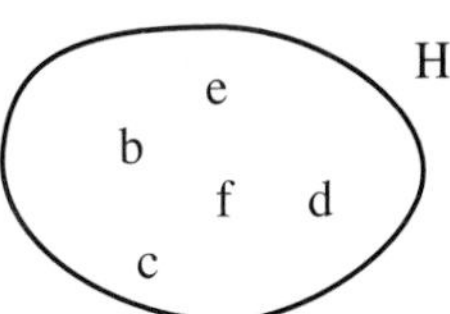

7. B = $\{x : x$ is an integer, $3 \leqslant x \leqslant 8\}$

The [set of] [such that]

8. $\varnothing$ or { } ‘empty set’

Using a Venn diagram to find the H.C.F. and L.C.M. of two numbers

HCF/LCM using a Venn diagram

Find all prime factors of the numbers (maybe using a factor tree).

Example 30 and 75

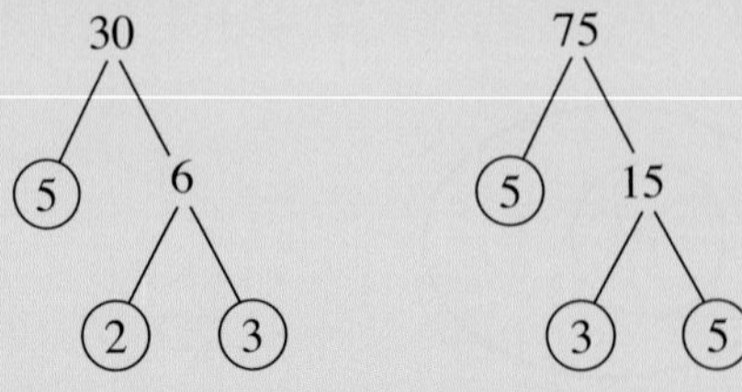

Write the prime factors in a Venn diagram with the common prime factors in the intersection part (i.e. the blue part where the rings for each number overlap).

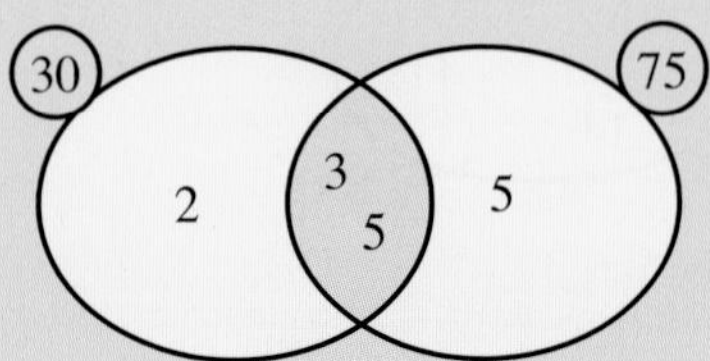

- multiply *all* prime numbers inside the Venn diagram to give the LCM.
  LCM $= 2 \times 3 \times 5 \times 5 = 150$
- multiply *all* prime numbers in the *intersection* (blue) part of the Venn diagram to give the HCF.
  HCF $= 3 \times 5 = 15$

Exercise 1M

1 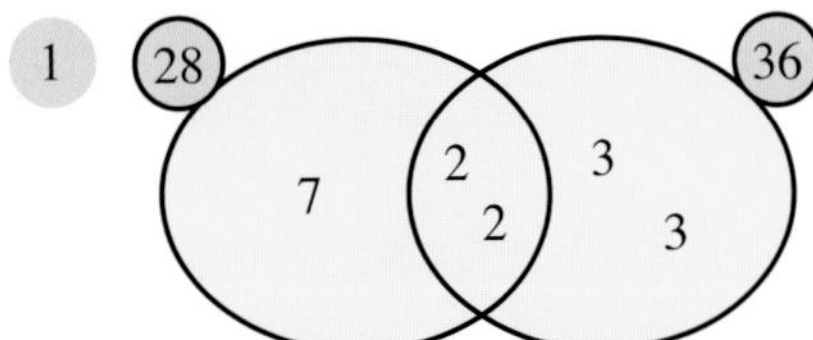

Use this Venn diagram to find
(a) the HCF of 28 and 36
(b) the LCM of 28 and 36.

2 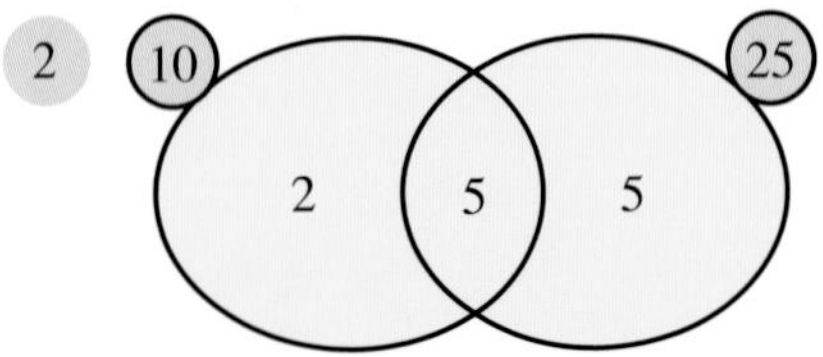

Use this Venn diagram to find
(a) the HCF of 10 and 25
(b) the LCM of 10 and 25.

3 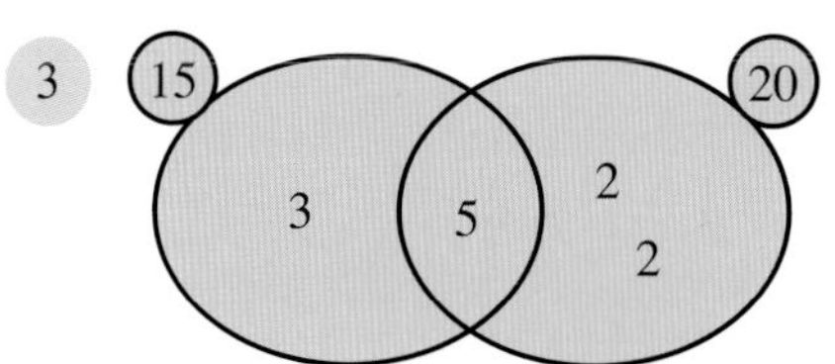

Use this Venn diagram to find
(a) the HCF of 15 and 20
(b) the LCM of 15 and 20.

4 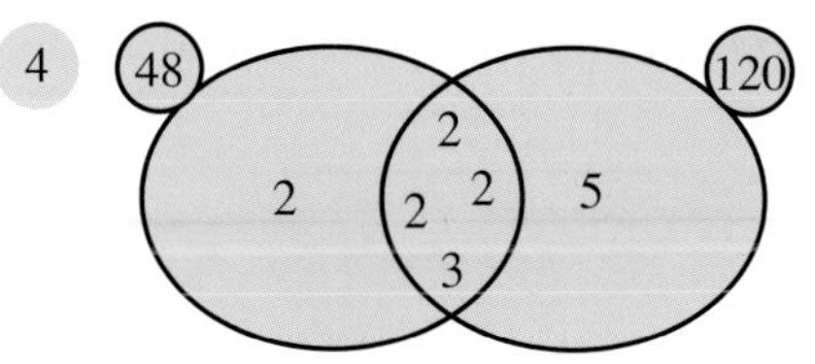

(a) Find the HCF of 48 and 120.
(b) Find the LCM of 48 and 120.

5 This Venn diagram shows the prime factors of 14 and 18.
Find the L.C.M. of 14 and 18.

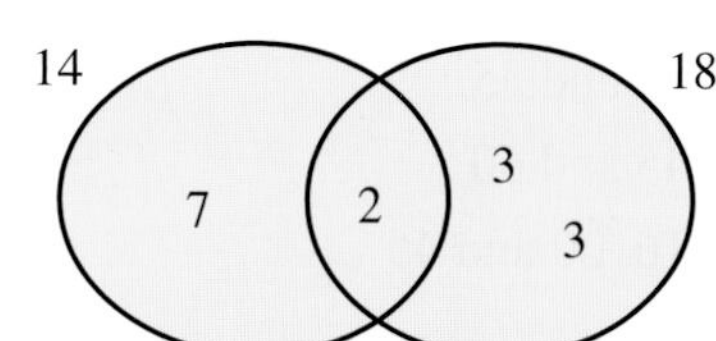

6 Find the L.C.M. of 12 and 21 using the Venn diagram which shows the factors of 12 and 21.

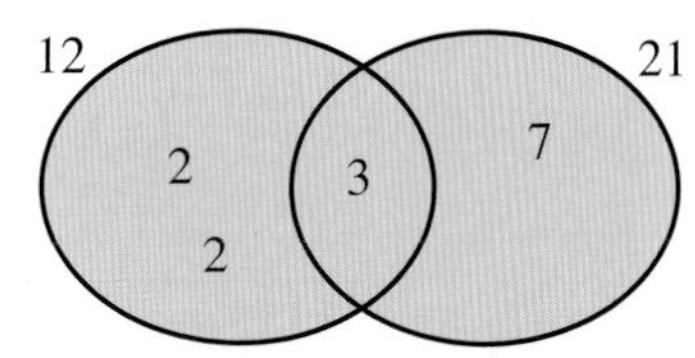

7 Draw a Venn diagram showing the prime factors of 11 and 20.
Use the diagram to find the L.C.M. of 11 and 20.

8 Here is a list of numbers.

3 4 10 27 30

From the list, write down
(a) a multiple of 15 (b) a factor of 18
(c) a square number (d) a cube number.

9 (a) Write 24 as a product of prime factors.
(b) Find the LCM of 24 and 60.

10 P is a prime number.
Q is an odd number.
State whether each of the following is *always odd* or *always even* or could be *either odd or even*.
(a) $P \times (Q + 1)$ (b) $Q - P$

11 The table shows the factors and common factors of 12 and 18.

Number	Factors	Common factors
12 18	1, 2, 3, 4, 6, 12 1, 2, 3, 6, 9, 18	} 1, 2, 3, 6

(a) Write down the H.C.F. of 12 and 18.

(b) Draw a table like the one above and write the factors and common factors of 18 and 24.

(c) Write down the H.C.F. of 18 and 24.

12 Find the H.C.F. of

(a) 16 and 48

(b) 22 and 55

(c) 45 and 60

(d) 10, 20 and 45

13 (a) Find the H.C.F. of 30 and 105.

(b) Find the H.C.F. of 32 and 40.

14 $70 = 2 \times 5 \times 7$ and $1155 = 3 \times 5 \times 7 \times 11$

Find the H.C.F. of 70 and 1155.

15 $975 = 3 \times 5 \times 5 \times 13$ and $300 = 3 \times 2 \times 2 \times 5 \times 5$

Find the H.C.F. of 975 and 300.

16 Find the H.C.F. of 154 and 1365.

17 $2^x \times 3^y \times 625 = 4.5 \times 10^4$. Find the values of x and y.

18 Express 286 as the product of its prime factors.

Using Venn diagrams for probability

S = {pupils who can swim}
H = {pupils who can do a handstand}

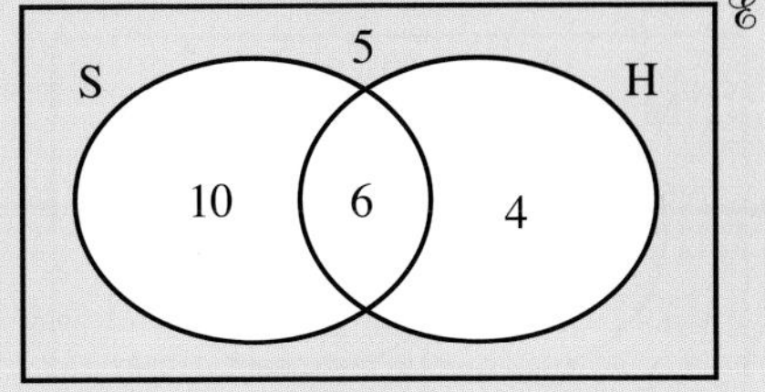

One pupil is selected from the class at random.
Find the probability that the pupil

(a) can swim
(b) can do a handstand
(c) can swim *and* can do a handstand
(d) can neither swim nor do a handstand.

Solution

(a) 16 pupils are in set S (can swim) and there are 25 in the class,
$p(\text{pupil can swim}) = \frac{16}{25}$

(b) 10 pupils can do a handstand
$\therefore\ p(\text{pupil can do a handstand}) = \frac{10}{25} = \frac{2}{5}$

(c) 6 pupils can swim *and* do a handstand
$\therefore\ p(\text{pupil can swim and do a handstand}) = \frac{6}{25}$

(d) $p(\text{pupil can neither swim nor do a handstand}) = \frac{5}{25} = \frac{1}{5}$

Exercise 2M

In this exercise do *not* cancel the fractions for the answers.

1 The Venn diagram shows the pupils in a class of 30.

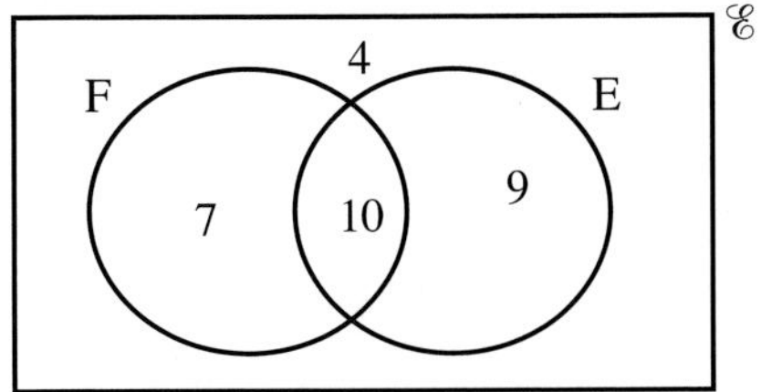

F = {pupils who like French}
E = {pupils who like English}.

Find the probability that one pupil, chosen at random, likes

(a) French
(b) English
(c) French and English
(d) English but not French
(e) neither English nor French.

2 The Venn diagram shows the 150 pupils in a primary school.

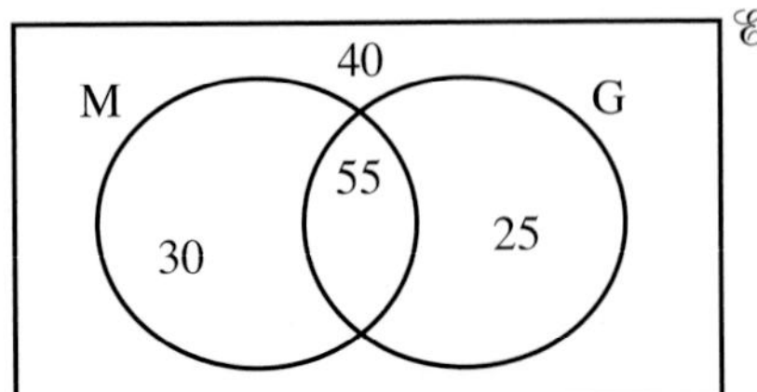

M = {pupils who like maths}
G = {pupils who like games}.

Find the probability that one pupil, chosen at random

(a) likes games
(b) likes maths
(c) likes maths and games
(d) likes games but not maths
(e) likes neither maths nor games
(f) likes maths but not games.

3 The Venn diagram shows the 34 pupils in one class of a mixed school.

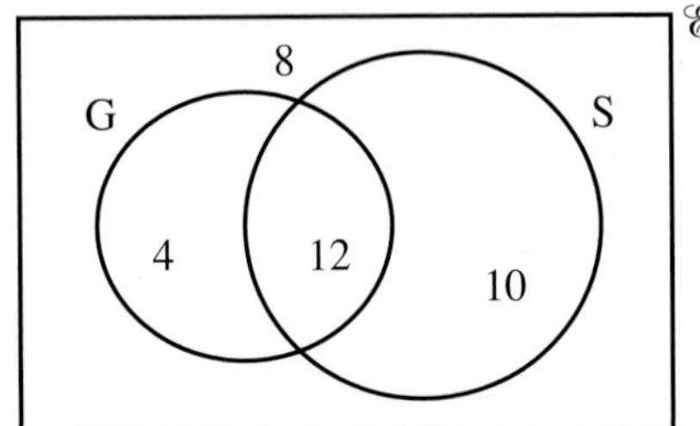

S = {pupils who can swim}
G = {girls}.

Find the probability that one pupil, chosen at random

(a) can swim
(b) is a girl
(c) is a boy
(d) is a girl who can swim
(e) is a boy who can swim
(f) is a girl who cannot swim.

4 The Venn diagram shows the 27 pupils in one class of a mixed school.

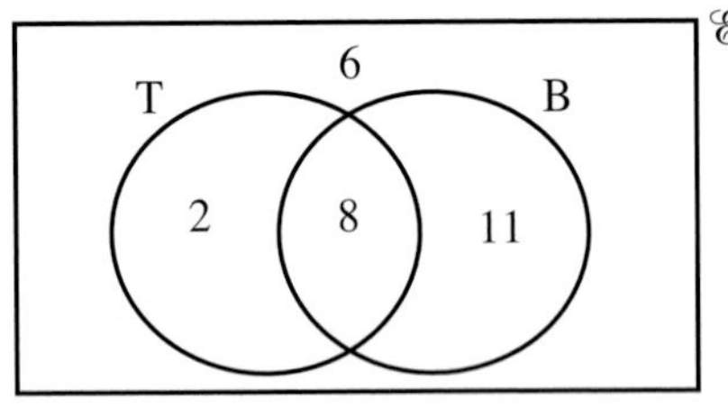

T = {pupils over 1.50 m tall}
B = {boys}.

Find the probability that one pupil, chosen at random

(a) is a boy
(b) is over 1.50 m tall
(c) is under 1.50 m tall
(d) is a girl
(e) is a boy over 1.50 m tall
(f) is a girl under 1.50 m tall.

5 The Venn diagram shows the 100 pupils in a junior school.

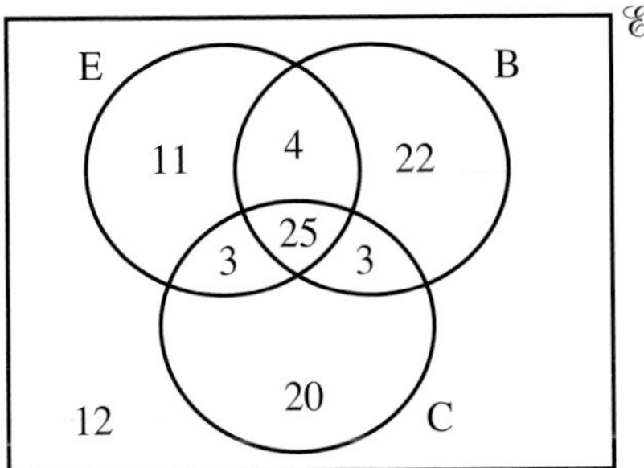

E = {pupils who like eggs}
B = {pupils who like bacon}
C = {pupils who like chips}.

Find the probability that one pupil, chosen at random

(a) likes eggs
(b) likes bacon
(c) likes chips
(d) likes both bacon and eggs
(e) likes both eggs and chips
(f) likes bacon, eggs and chips
(g) likes eggs only
(h) likes chips only.

6 The Venn diagram shows the 29 people on an activity holiday.

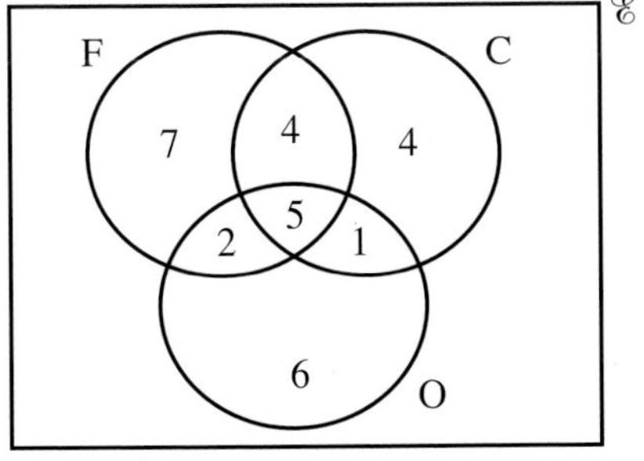

F = {people who like fishing}
C = {people who like canoeing}
O = {people who like orienteering}.

One person is chosen at random.
Find the probability that the person

(a) likes fishing
(b) likes canoeing
(c) likes orienteering
(d) likes both fishing and canoeing
(e) likes both orienteering and canoeing
(f) likes both orienteering and fishing
(g) likes fishing, canoeing and orienteering.

7 The Venn diagram shows the girls in a class.

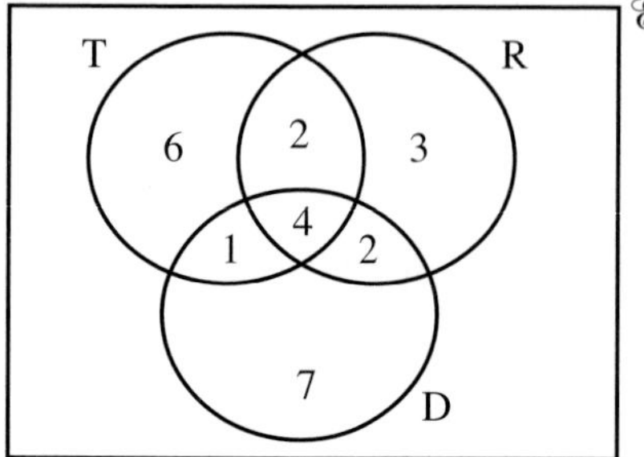

T = {girls who like T.V.}
R = {girls who like reading}
D = {girls who like dancing}.

One girl is selected at random. Find the probability that she

(a) likes T.V.

(b) likes reading

(c) likes dancing

(d) likes T.V. only

(e) likes both T.V. and reading

(f) likes both reading and dancing

(g) likes both T.V. and dancing

(h) likes T.V., reading and dancing

(i) likes reading only.

CHECK YOURSELF ON SECTION 4.1

1. Transformations

(a) Describe fully the following transformations.

(i) $\Delta A \to \Delta B$ (ii) $\Delta A \to \Delta C$

(iii) $\Delta C \to \Delta D$ (iv) $\Delta E \to \Delta A$

(b) Find any pair of successive transformations which will map ΔA onto ΔC.

(c) What vector is parallel to and twice as long as the vector $\begin{pmatrix} 3 \\ 5 \end{pmatrix}$?

(d) What vector is the same length but opposite to the vector? $\begin{pmatrix} 1 \\ -2 \end{pmatrix}$

(e) Write a vector which is perpendicular to the vector $\begin{pmatrix} 2 \\ 1 \end{pmatrix}$.

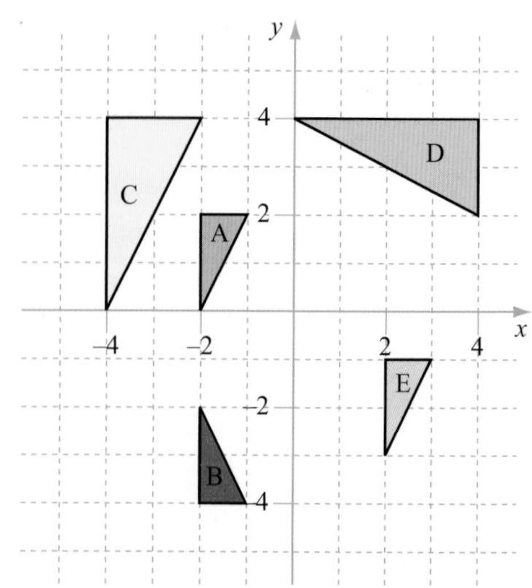

4.3 Area and volume

In this section you will:

- review the use of formulae for simple areas and volumes
- learn how to find the radius of a given circle
- solve a range of problems of increasing difficulty

Important formulae

(a) Triangle

Area $= \frac{b \times h}{2}$

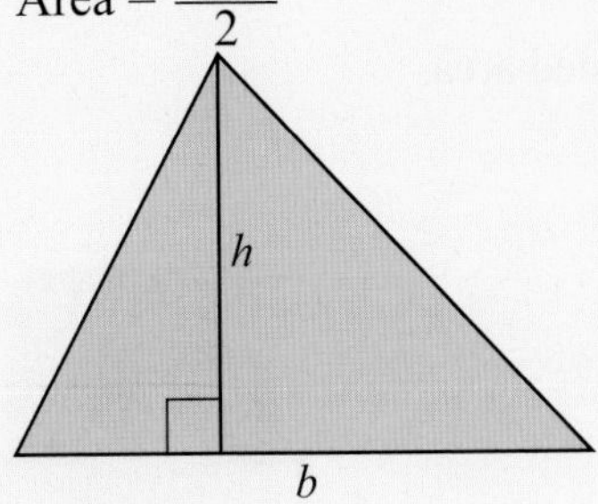

(b) Circle Area $= \pi r^2$

Circumference $= \pi d$

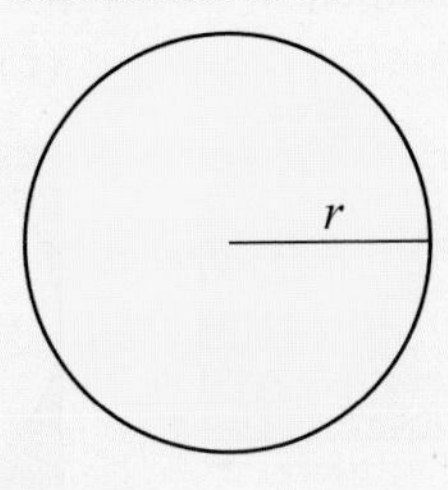

(c) Trapezium

Area $= \frac{h(a+b)}{2}$

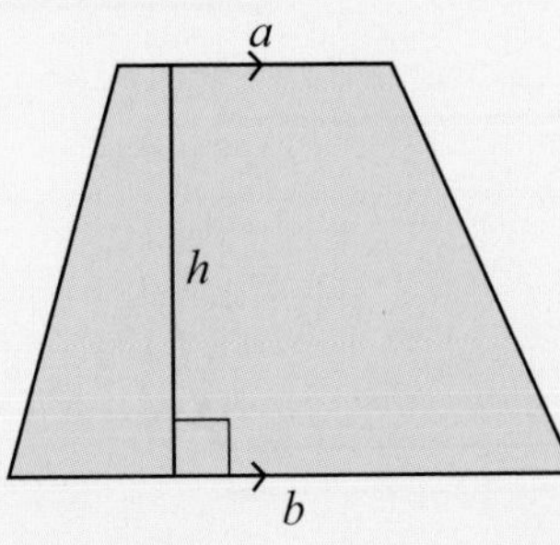

(d) A prism is a solid with the same cross-section throughout its length

Volume $= A \times l$

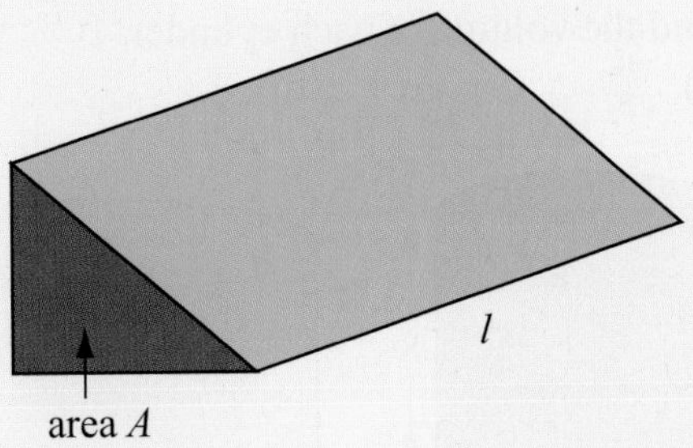

(e) Cylinder

Volume $= \pi r^2 h$ [A cylinder is a prism].

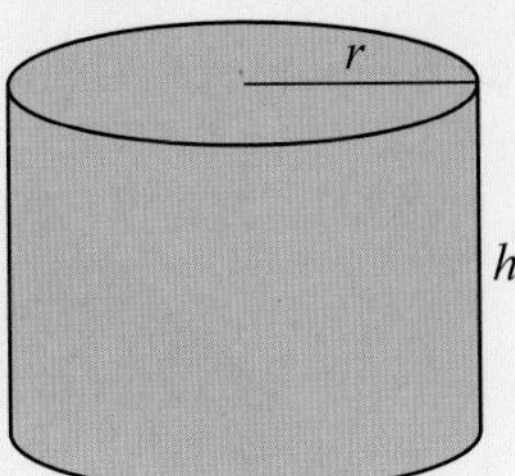

Exercise 1M

[Give answers correct to 3 s.f., where necessary. All lengths are in cm on diagrams.

1 Find the area of each circle.

(a)

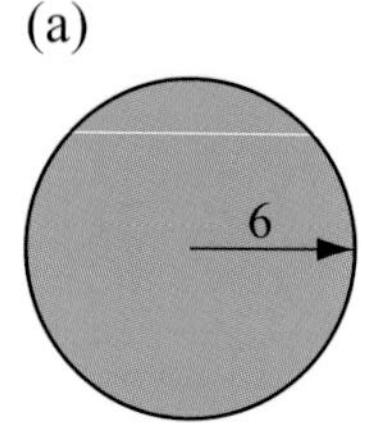

(b)

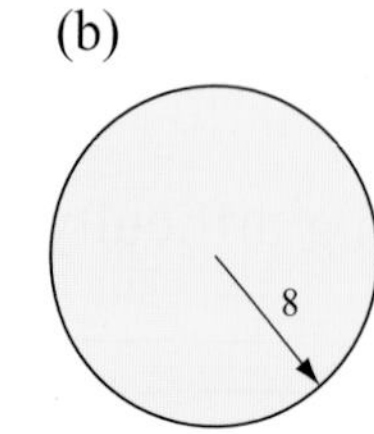

(c)

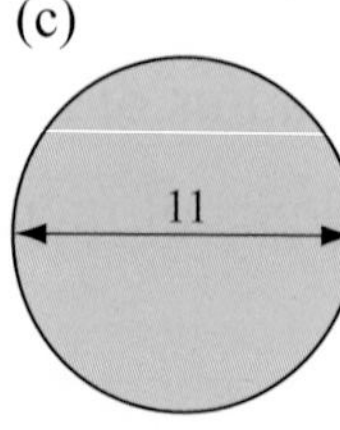

(d)

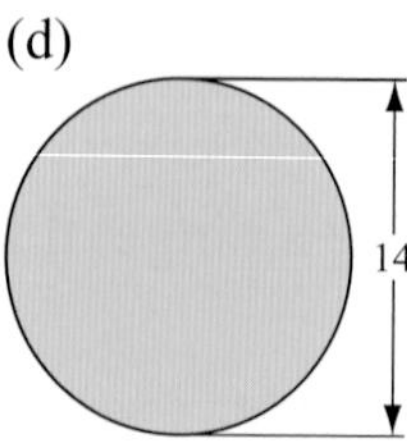

2 Find the circumference of each circle in question 1.

3 Find the area of the shapes.

(a)

12

(b)

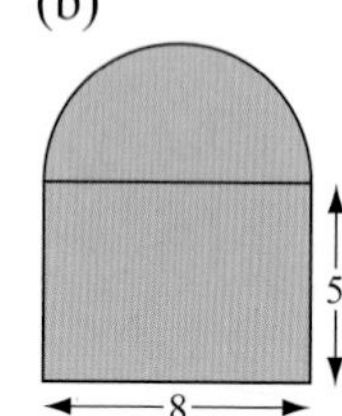

(c) Find the green shaded area.

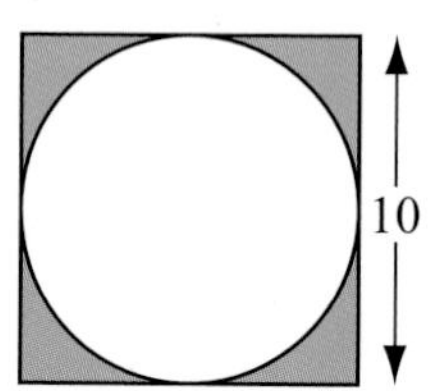

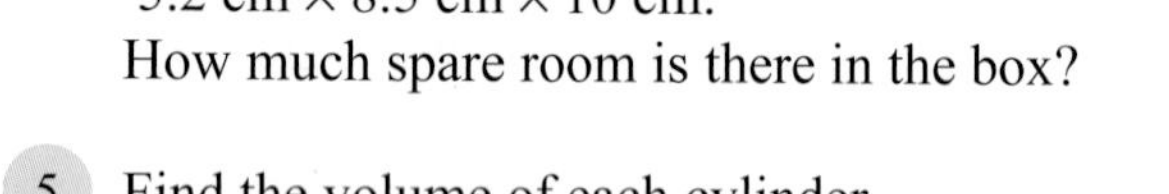

4 A hamster of volume 273 cm^3 lives inside a box measuring 5.2 cm × 8.5 cm × 10 cm.
How much spare room is there in the box?

5 Find the volume of each cylinder.

(a)

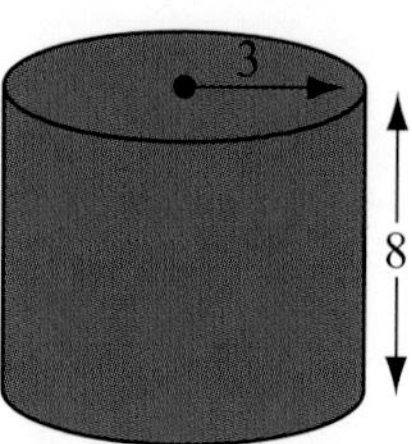

(b)

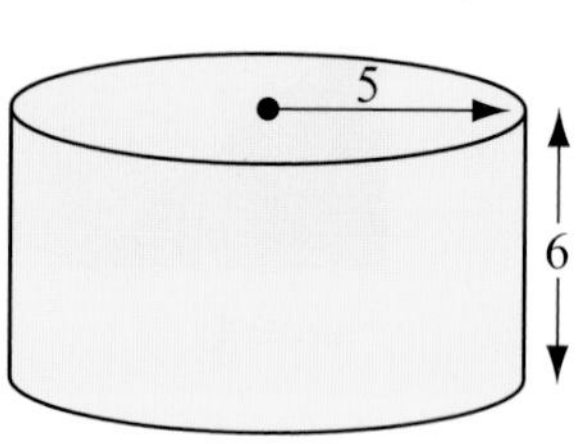

(c)

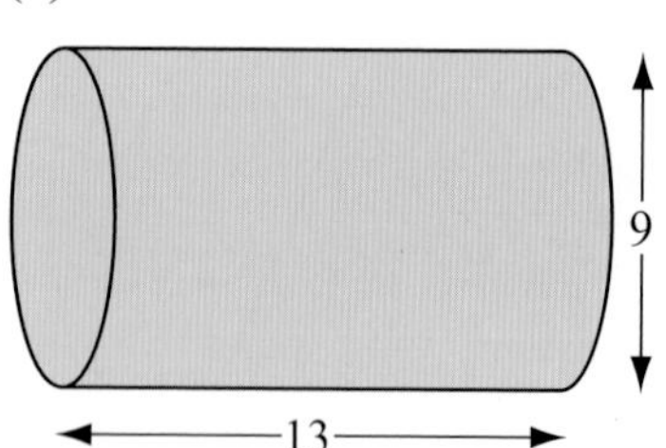

6 Find the volume of a cylinder of radius 5 m and height 8.2 m.
State clearly the units for the answer.

7 Find the area of each shape. All lengths are in cm.

(a)

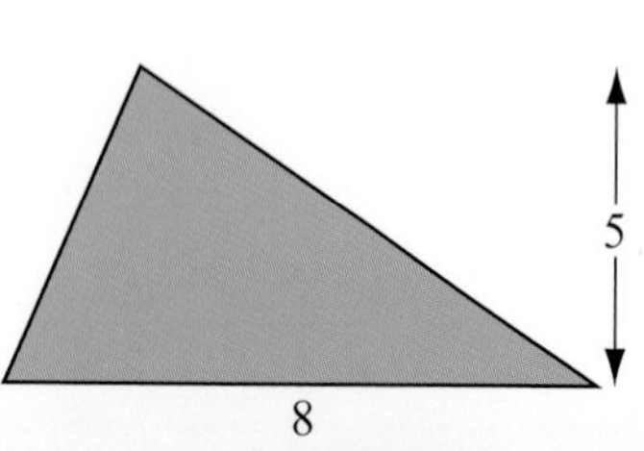

(b)

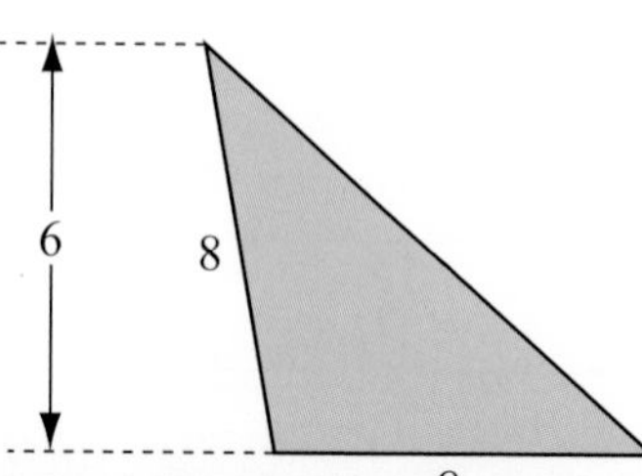

(c) Find the area shaded red

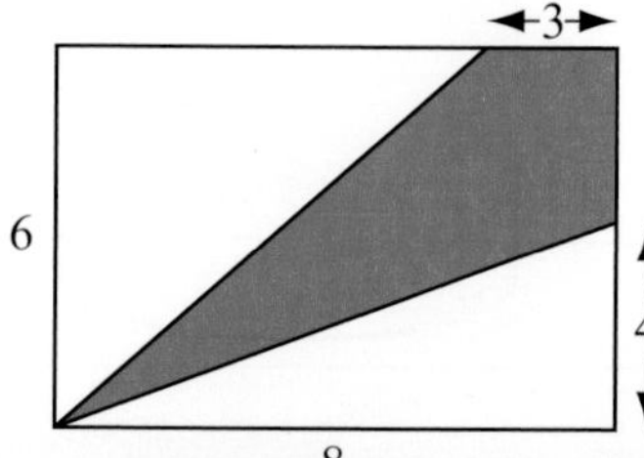

8 A right angled triangle has sides of length 6 m, 8 m and 10 m.
Sketch the triangle and then find its area.

9 The tower shown is made from cubes of side 4 cm.
Work out the volume of the tower.

10 A rectangle has area 24 cm^2 and perimeter 22 cm.
Find the sides of the rectangle.

11 Which of the solids below are prisms?

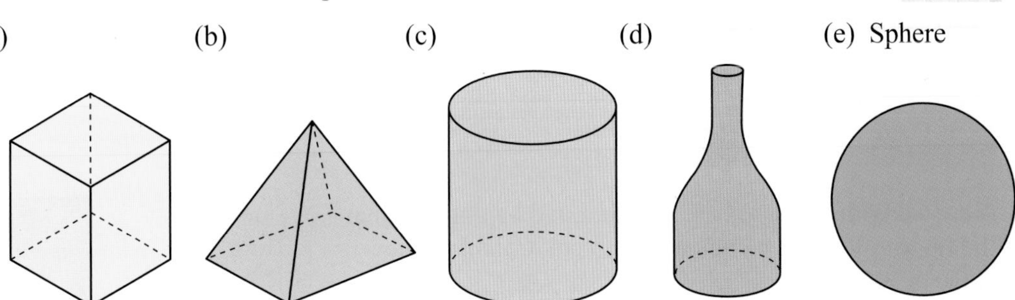

Exercise 1E

[Give answers correct to 3 s.f., where necessary] All lengths are in cm on diagrams.

1 Find the area of each shape.

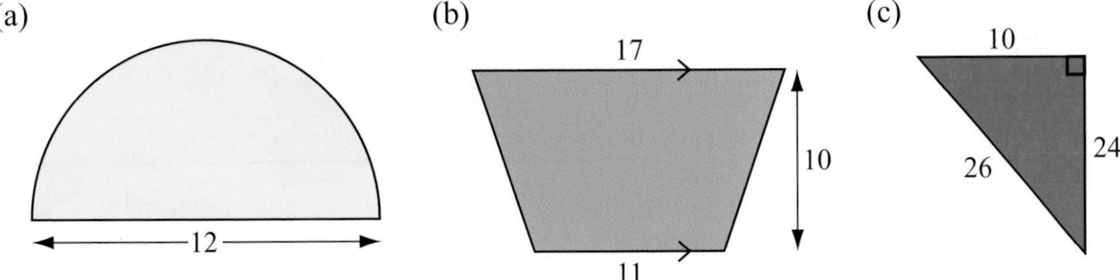

2 Find the area shaded.

(a)

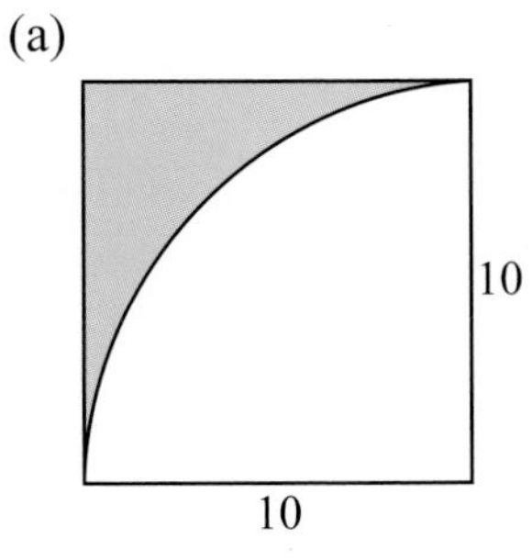

(b)

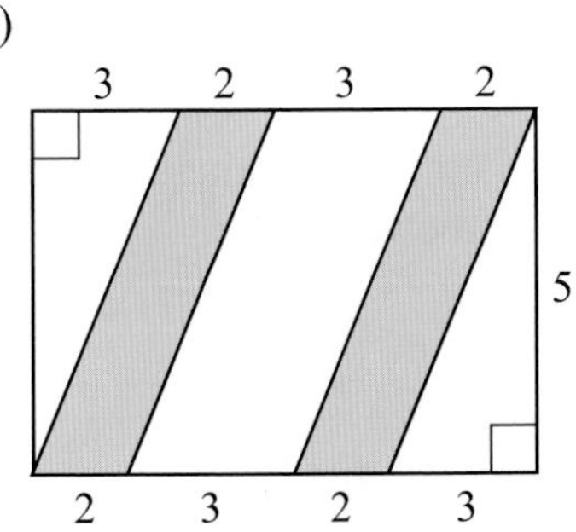

(c)

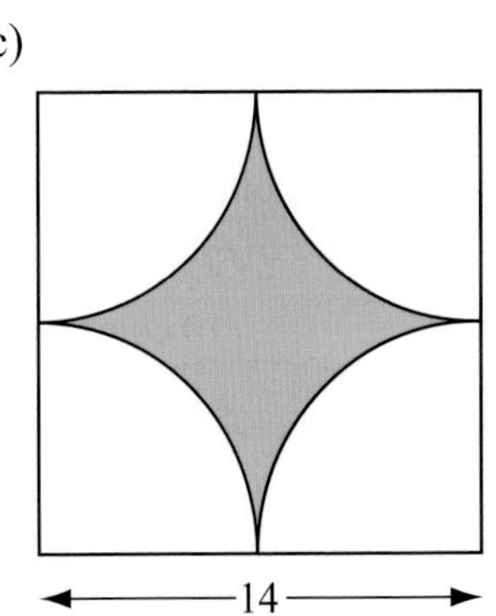

3 The diagonals of the kite shown are of length a and b and intersect at right angles.
Find an expression, in its simplest form, for the area of the kite in terms of a and b.

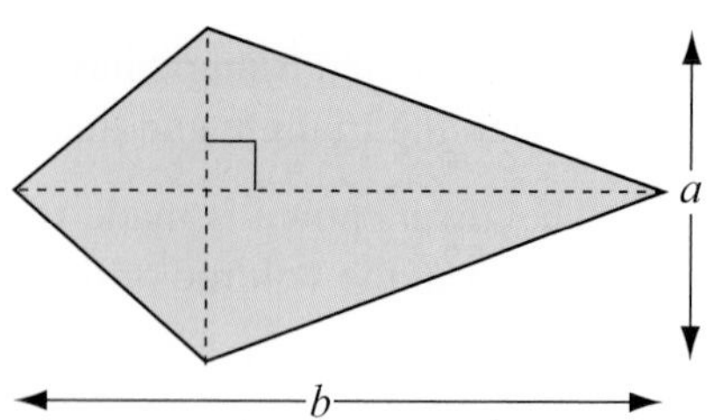

4 The area of a forest is 2.5 km^2. The land is sold at a price of £4200 per hectare. How much does it cost?

[1 hectare $= 10\,000\text{ m}^2$]

5 A cuboid with a square base of side x and height 4 cm has the same volume as a cube of side 6 cm. Calculate the value of x.

6 A long jump pit is 2.4 m wide by 18 m long and 20 cm deep. What volume of sand is required to fill it?

7 How many boxes of matches 10 cm by 2 cm by 6 cm will fit into a packing case 1 m by 80 cm by 48 cm?

8 Professor Gibson has calculated that in 100 000 years from now the Earth will collide with a seriously large flat object and will be transformed into a flat circular disc of thickness 1 km.

If the volume of the earth is $1.08 \times 10^{12}\text{ km}^3$, calculate the radius of the 'new' Earth.

9 A solid metal cube of side 1.2 cm weighs 15 grams. Calculate the mass of a cube of side 5 cm made of the same metal.

10 The total surface area of a cube is 121.5 cm^2. What is its volume?

11 Ten gold coins of radius 0.6 cm and thickness 0.3 cm are melted down to form a solid gold cube of side x cm. Calculate the value of x.

10 coins

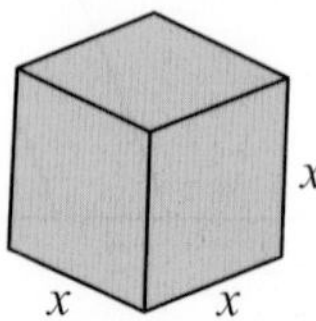

12 Rain falling onto a flat rectangular roof measuring 3.2 m by 5.5 m is drained off into a covered water tank with a square base 80 cm by 80 cm. If 5 mm of rain fell, by what depth would the water in the tank increase?

13 An ice rink with semicircular ends is to be filled to a depth of 10 cm with ice. If the straight sides are 60 m long and 30 m apart how many cubic metres of ice will be needed?

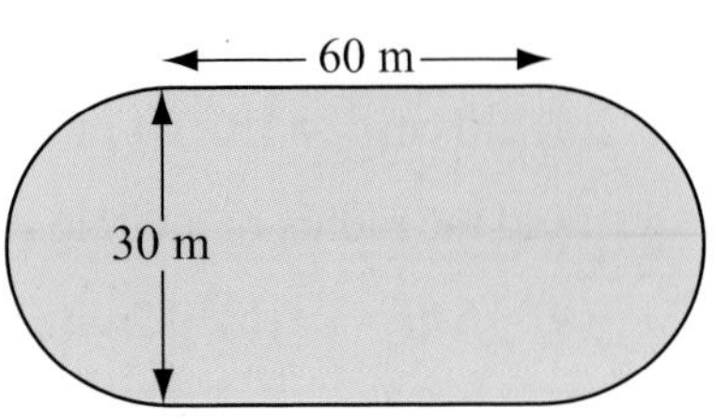

14 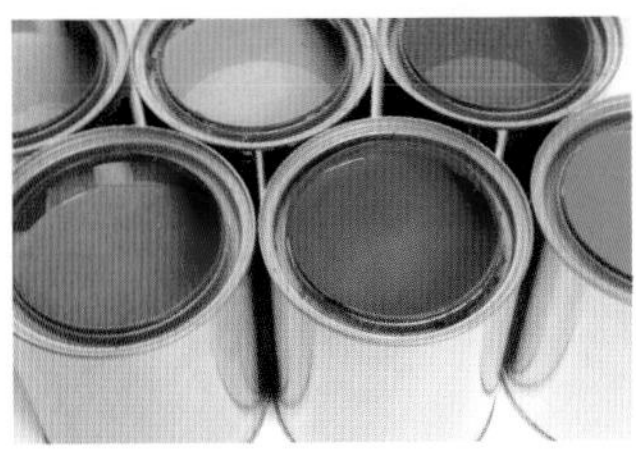

A business buys paint at £30 000 for 20 m^3. It puts the paint in tins of capacity 0.8 litres and sells them at £5.95 each.

Work out the profit.

Finding the radius of a circle

Reminder: Circumference of a circle = $2 \times \pi \times$ radius
(or $\pi \times$ diameter)

Area of a circle = $\pi \times (\text{radius})^2$

If we know the circumference or area of a circle we can find the radius by reversing these formulae.

Either $2\pi r = C$ or $\pi r^2 = A$

$$r = \frac{C}{2\pi} \qquad r = \sqrt{\frac{A}{\pi}}$$

(a) The circumference of a circle is 48 cm

$2\pi \times \text{radius} = 48$

$\text{radius} = \frac{48}{2\pi} = 7.64$ cm (3 s.f.)

(b) The area of a circle is 120 cm^2.

$\pi \times (\text{radius})^2 = 120$

$(\text{radius})^2 = \frac{120}{\pi}$

$\text{radius} = \sqrt{\left(\frac{120}{\pi}\right)} = 6.18$ cm (3 s.f)

(c) A cylinder of height 15 cm has a volume of 2250 cm^3.
Find its diameter.

Area of top A = $2250 \div 15 = 150$ cm^2

radius of top = $\sqrt{(150 \div \pi)} = 6.91$cm

diameter of cylinder = $2 \times$ radius = 13.8 cm (3 s.f.)

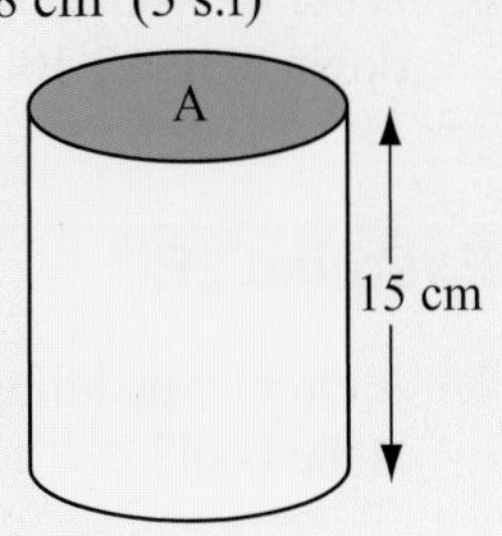

Exercise 2M

Give all answers to 3 sig. fig.

1 Find the radius of a circle with circumference of:

(a) 20 cm (b) 64 m (c) 120 cm

2 Find the radius of a circle with area of:

(a) 16 m^2 (b) 9.2 cm^2 (c) 42 cm^2

3 Find the diameter of each of the following cylinders:

(a)

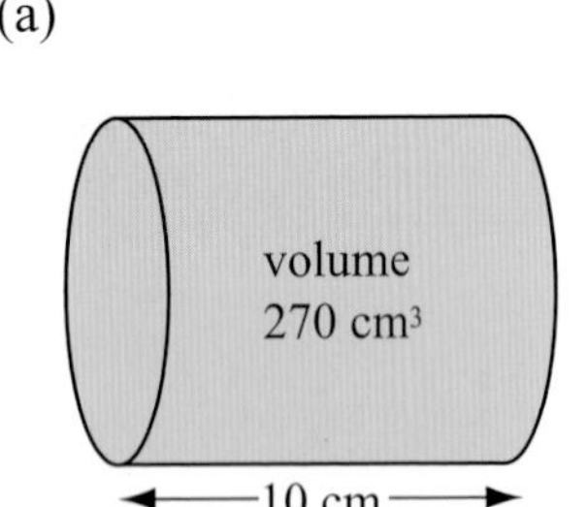

(b)

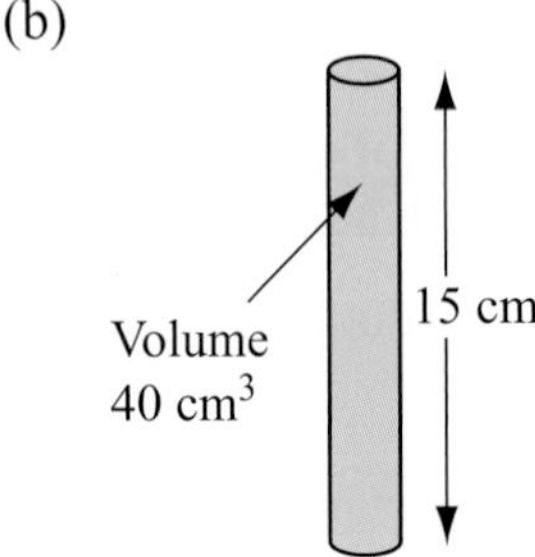

(c)

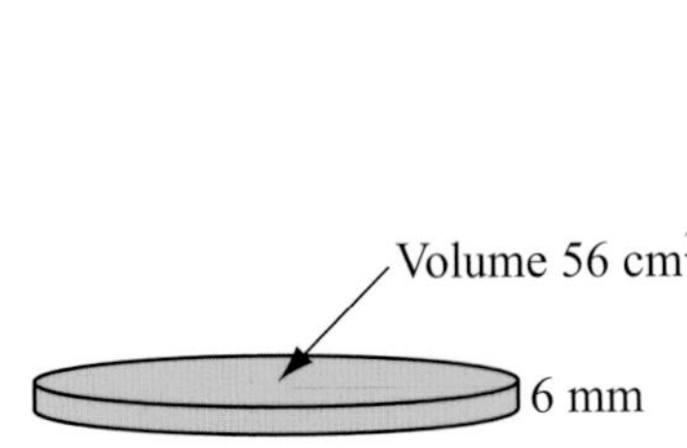

4 A litre of water is poured into a cylindrical glass jug. If the water in the jug is 8 cm deep, what is the diameter of the jug?
(1 litre = 1000 cm^3)

5 A trundle wheel is used by surveyors to measure distances along the ground.
It consists of a circular disc attached to a handle. One revolution of the wheel measures out exactly one metre. Find the diameter of the wheel.

6 Karen measures the girth of a tree trunk to be 1.8 metres.
What is its diameter?

7 When cycling 2.4 km to the beach, the wheels on Sue's bike rotated 1255 times. Find the diameter of the wheels.

8 A block of marzipan measuring 10 cm by 12 cm by 3 cm is rolled out to cover the top of a circular cake. If the marzipan is to be 1.5 cm thick, what is the maximum radius of cake that can be covered?

9 A bar of bronze that has a volume of 90 cm^3 is melted down to make 100 coins with a thickness of 3 mm. Find the diameter of the coins.

Exercise 2E

1 A circular paddling pool is filled to a depth of 25 cm. This takes 400 litres of water. How wide is the pool?

2 A rectangular piece of card 12 cm by 20 cm is rolled up to make a tube (with no overlap). Find the radius of the tube if
(a) the long sides are joined,
(b) the short sides are joined.

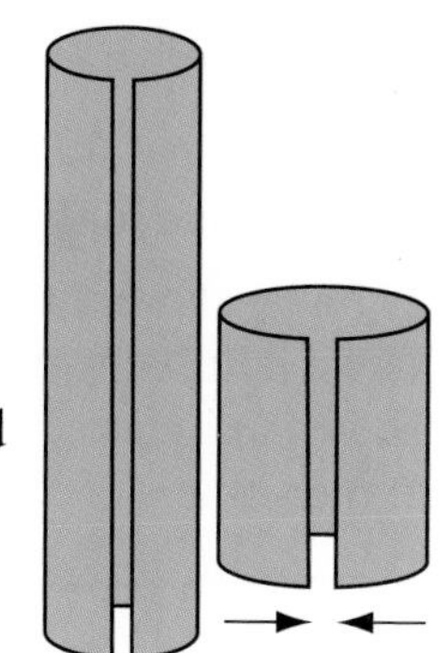

3 The point of the minute hand on a church clock travels 180 cm farther than the point of the hour hand in one complete revolution. If the hour hand is 60 cm long, how long is the minute hand?

4 The useable area on a CD is 10 000 mm^2. If the hole in the centre has a radius of 7.5 mm, what is the radius of the CD?

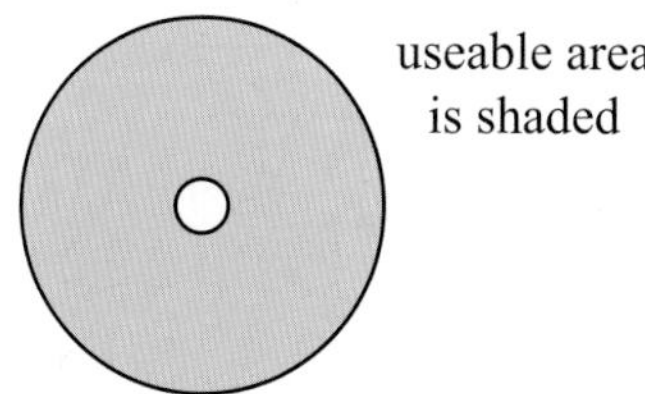

5 While on special offer, a tin of baked beans contains 25% extra free.

If the height of the tin is to remain the same and the area of the base of the original tin is 30 cm^2, find the diameter of the new tin.

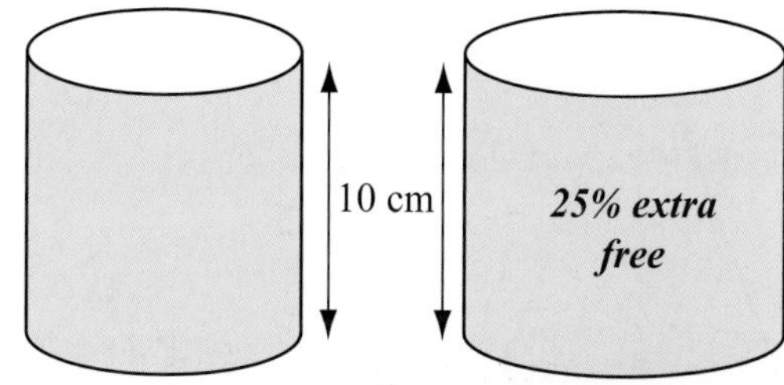

6 A running track consists of two straight sections with semi-circular ends. If the straight sections measure 100 metres and one complete lap on the inside of the track measures ½ km, what is the distance x between the two straights?

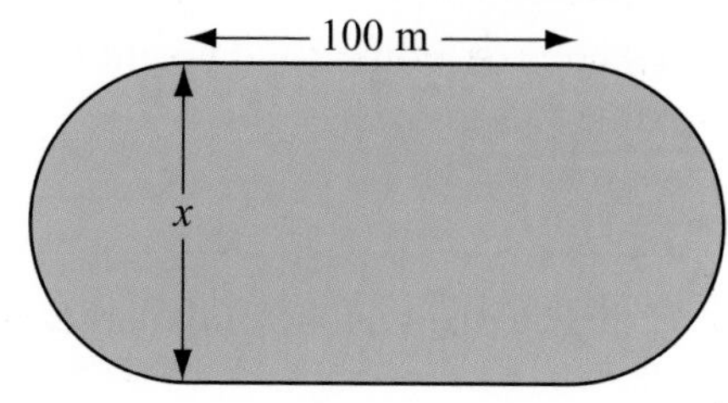

7 The perimeter of a lemon measures 18.8 cm. How many of these lemons could be put in a single layer in a box measuring 42 cm by 36 cm?

8 A rope 60 m long and 5 cm in diameter is coiled tightly as shown. Estimate, correct to one significant figure, the radius of the 'circle' formed.

Volume of pyramids, spheres and cones

Pyramid

The formula for the volume of a pyramid is demonstrated below.

Figure 1 shows a cube of side $2a$ broken down into six pyramids of height a as shown in Figure 2.
If the volume of each pyramid is V, then

$$6V = 2a \times 2a \times 2a$$

$$V = \frac{1}{6} \times (2a)^2 \times 2a$$

so $$V = \frac{1}{3} \times (2a)^2 \times a$$

$$V = \frac{1}{3} \text{ (base area)} \times \text{height.}$$

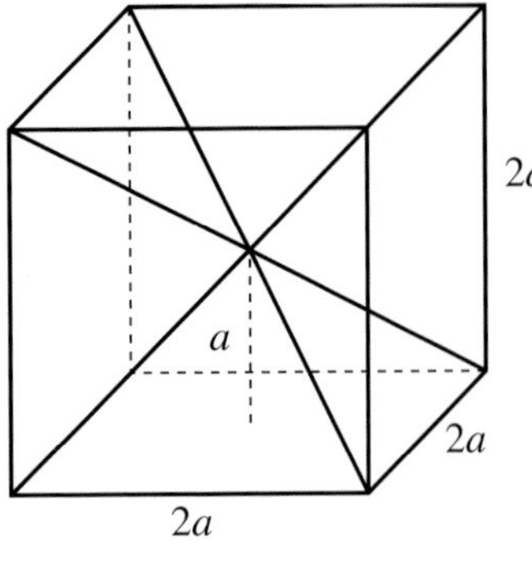

Figure 1

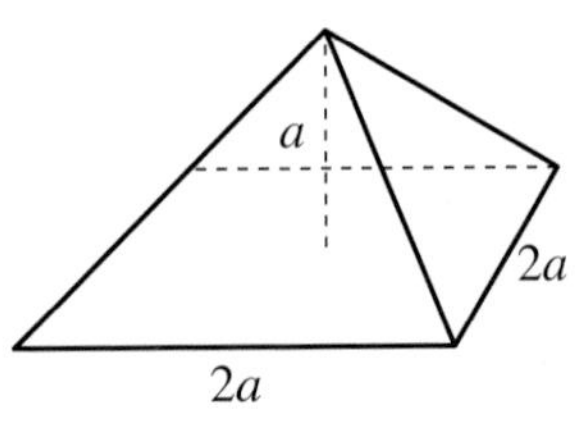

Figure 2

Learn this formula.

Cones

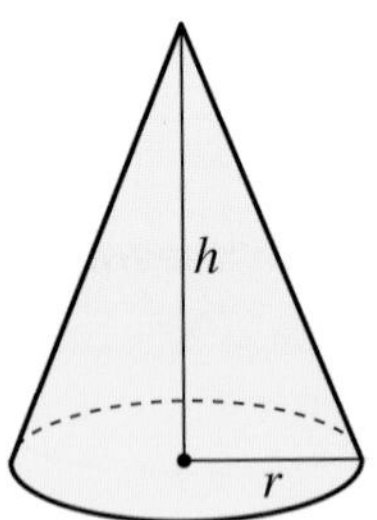

For a cone of radius r and height h, the volume V is given by

$$V = \tfrac{1}{3}\pi r^2 h$$

Sphere

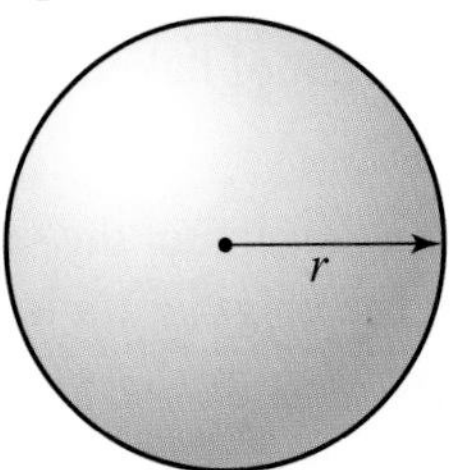

For a sphere of radius r

$$V = \tfrac{4}{3}\pi r^3$$

Calculate the volume of the objects shown.

(a)

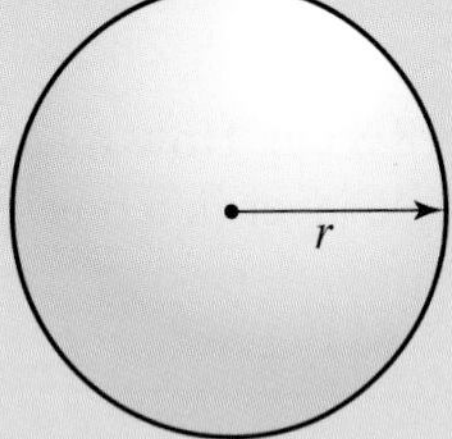

Calculate the volume of the sphere if $r = 2\text{ cm}$

Volume $= \frac{4}{3} \times \pi \times 2^3 = 33.5\text{ cm}^3$ (to 1 d.p.)

(b)

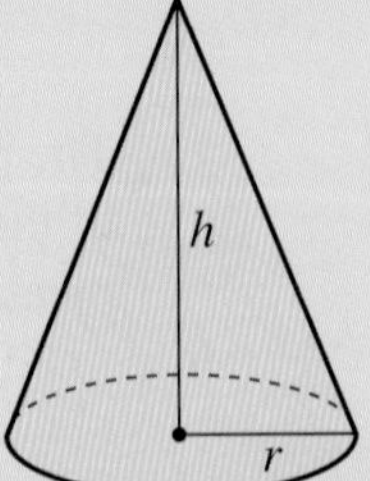

Find the volume of the cone if $r = 3\text{ m}$ and $h = 4\text{ m}$

Volume $= \frac{1}{3}\pi r^2 h$

$= \frac{1}{3}\pi \times 3^2 \times 4 = 33.7\text{ cm}^3$ (to 1 d.p.)

Exercise 3M

Give your answers correct to 1 d.p. where necessary.

1 Calculate the volume of a sphere of radius 3 cm.

2

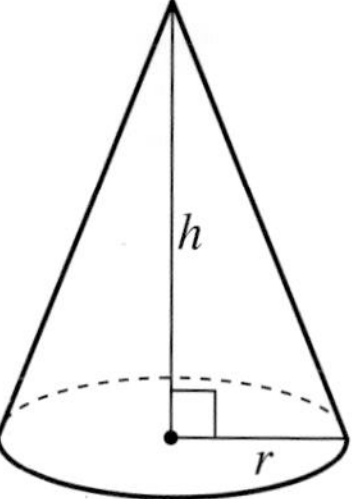

Calculate the volume of the cone if

(a) $r = 3$ m, $h = 4$ m

(b) $r = 2$ cm, $h = 5$ cm

3

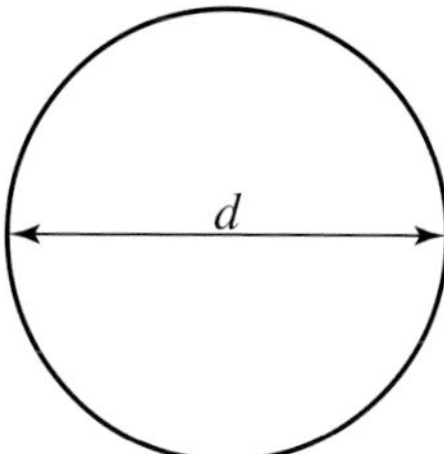

Calculate the volume of the sphere if

(a) $d = 2$ m

(b) $d = 6$ m

4 A pyramid has a square base of side 6 cm and vertical height 3.5 cm. Calculate the volume of the pyramid.

For questions 5 to 10 copy and complete the table.

	solid	radius	height	volume
5	sphere	3 cm	–	
6	cone	5 cm	4 cm	
7	cylinder	4 cm	8 cm	
8	sphere	7 m	–	
9	cone	10 m	1 m	
10	cylinder	6 mm	12 mm	

11 Calculate the capacity in litres of a sphere of radius 12 cm. (1 litre = 1000 cm^3)

12 Calculate the capacity in litres of a sphere of diameter 18 cm.

13 Calculate the capacity in litres of a cone of radius 10 cm and height 20 cm.

14 A solid sphere is made of metal of density 9 g/cm^3. Calculate the mass of the sphere if its radius is 5 cm.

15 Water is poured into an inverted cone, of diameter and height 30 cm, at a rate of 0.4 litres per second.
How long, in seconds, will it take to fill the cone?

16 A solid metal sphere of radius 2.5 cm is melted down and made into spheres of radius 0.5 cm.
How many of the smaller spheres can be made?

17 

Suzie has two boxes of volume 27 000 cm^3 and one box of volume 71 000 cm^3.

Find the lengths of the sides of one cubical box which has the same volume as the three boxes carried by Suzie.

Exercise 3E

1 A cake is made as a cylinder of radius 14 cm and thickness 3 cm.
A slice of the cake is cut with an angle of 40° at the centre of the cake.
Calculate the volume of this slice of cake.

2 The surface area, A, of a sphere of radius r is given by the formula $A = 4\pi r^2$.
Calculate the surface area of a sphere of radius 3 cm.
Give your answer correct to the nearest whole number.

3 

A large green sphere of radius 5 cm is melted down and made into small spheres of radius 0.4 cm.
How many small spheres can be made?

4 A solid metal sphere of radius 3 cm is recast into a solid cube.
Work out the length of each side of the cube.

5 An inverted cone of height 12 cm and base radius 6 cm contains water to a depth of 6 cm, measured from the vertex. Calculate the volume of water in the cone.

6 A telephone box has dimensions

$2.1\text{ m} \times 90\text{ cm} \times 80\text{ cm}$.

Calculate the total volume of the 12 boxes in the photo.

7 The cross-section of a prism is an equilateral triangle of side 8 cm. Work out the volume of the prism if its length is 24 cm.

8 A sphere of radius 3 cm has the same volume as a cylinder of radius 2 cm and length h cm. Find the value of h.

9 

The diameter of the Moon is 3474 km and the diameter of the Earth is 3.67 times as large. Calculate the volume of the Earth in km^3.

10 A lottery prize of £1 000 000 is paid in one pound coins. Each coin is 3 mm thick and 2.2 cm in diameter. Work out the total volume of all the coins in the prize.

11 A solid cylinder of height 8 cm and radius 8 cm is plated with a coating costing £9 per cm^2. Find the cost of the plating, correct to the nearest pound.

12 Calculate the radius of a sphere of surface area 500 cm^2.

Problem solving

A tent has an internal space of 0.864 m^3

If the tent is 2.4 m long and 90 cm wide, find its height.

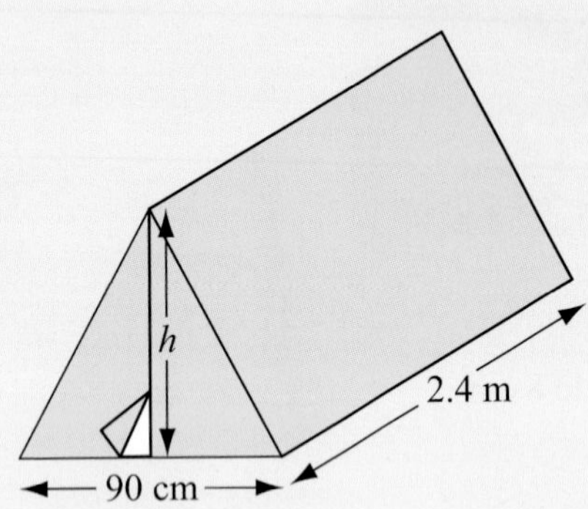

As the volume is in m^3 change all measurements to metres.

End area $= \frac{1}{2} \times h \times 0.9 = 0.45h$

Volume $= 0.45h \times 2.4 = 1.08h$

$\therefore\ 1.08h = 0.864$

$h = 0.864/1.08 = 0.8$ m or 80 cm

Exercise 4M

Give answers correct to 3 s.f. where necessary.

1 Find the missing lengths in the following prisms.

(a)

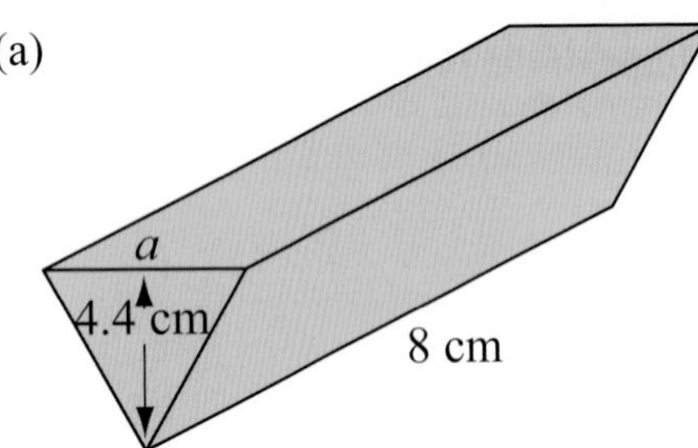

Volume = 88 cm^3

(b)

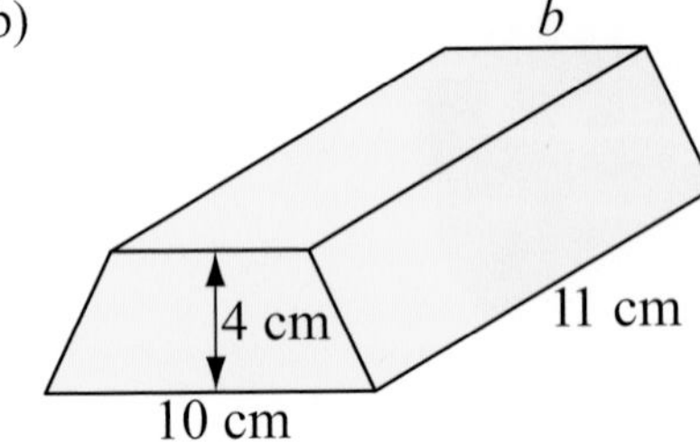

Volume = 396 cm^3

2 Gary's car is 4.4 m long. His garage has an internal volume of 28.2 m^3. Will his car fit in?

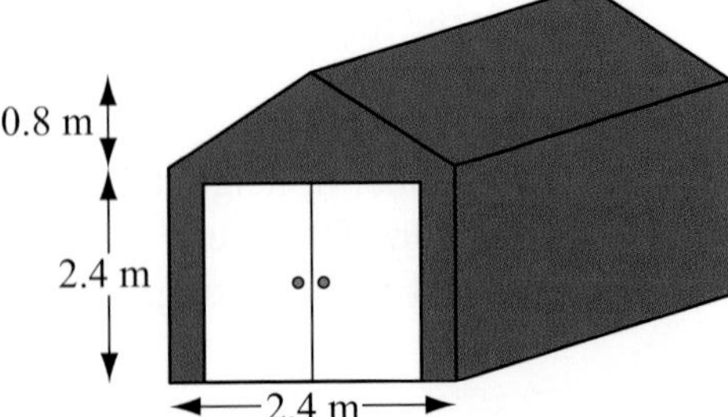

3 

Carol cuts a circular Bakewell tart into 5 equal wedge shape pieces. If the volume of tart in one of these pieces is 180 cm^3 and the wedge is 5 cm thick, find the diameter of the original tart.

4 The plastic guttering along the front of a house consists of a semicircular prism 8 m long. If it contains 35 litres of rain water before overflowing find the width, x, of the top of the guttering.

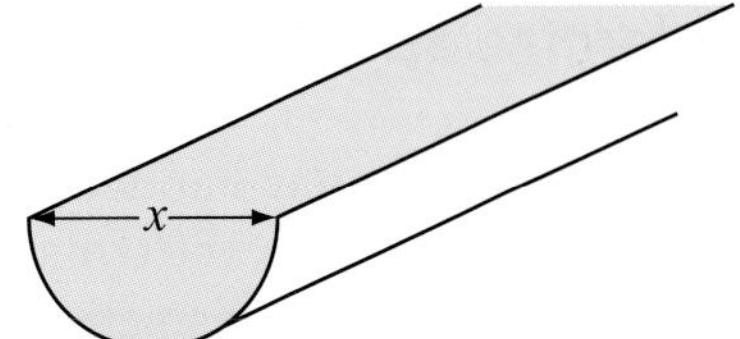

5 In some triangles you know the lengths of the three sides but you do not know the perpendicular height. Here is a famous formula which is used to calculate the area of a triangle when you know the three sides a, b and c.

Area $= \sqrt{s(s-a)(s-b)(s-c)}$, where $s = \dfrac{a+b+c}{2}$

Use this formula to calculate the area of each triangle below, correct to 3 s.f.

(a)

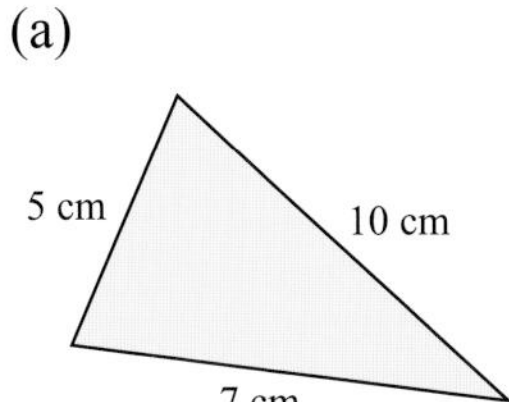

(b)

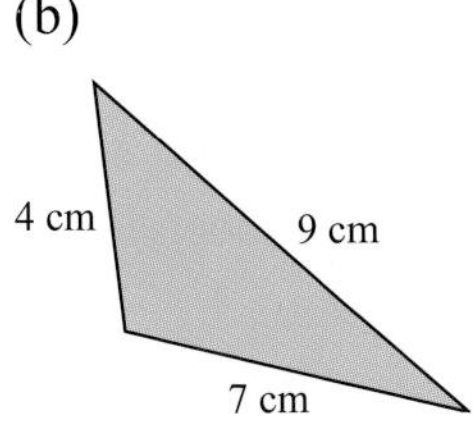

6 A kitchen roll consists of 144 sheets of absorbent paper, each measuring 24 cm by 24 cm and 0.02 cm thick.
These sheets are wound onto a cardboard tube 4 cm in diameter. Find the diameter of the finished roll of kitchen towels. Give the answer correct to 3 s.f.

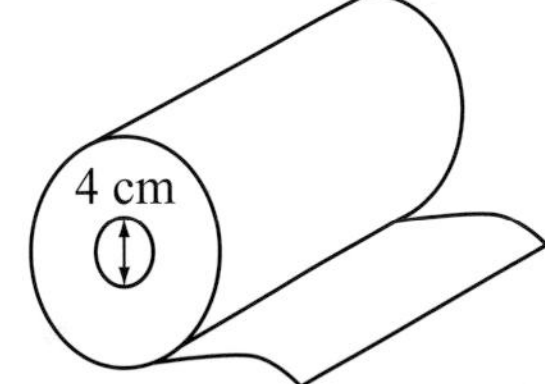

7 A barrel containing 50 litres of oil has been spilt. It has formed into two puddles each of a constant depth of 0.5 cm. The area of the larger puddle is exactly three times the area of the smaller one. Find the surface area of each puddle. (1 litre = 1000 cm^3)

8 A pig sty is made from a sheet of corrugated steel bent into a semicircular prism.
If the internal volume is 3.6 m^3 and it is 2.4 m wide at the front, find the dimensions of the original piece of steel.

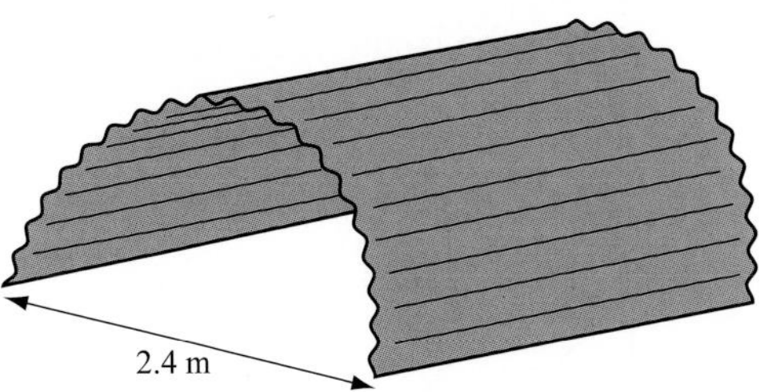

9 A triangle and a square are drawn on dotty paper with dots 1 cm apart. What is the area of the region coloured red?

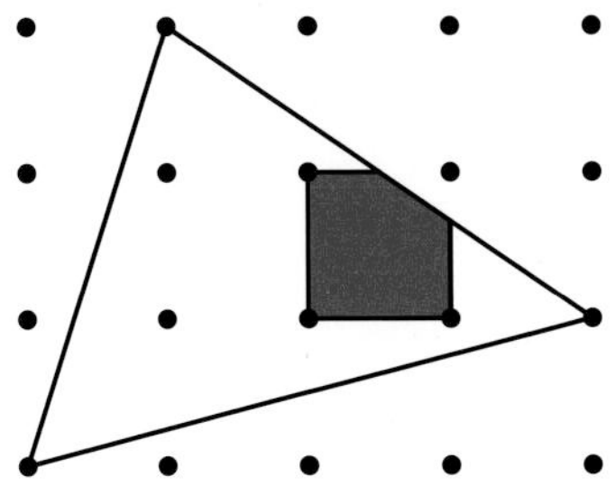

Exercise 4E (not easy!)

1 After harvesting Farmer Giles has 740 m^3 of hay. This is stored as 180 cylindrical bales. If each bale is 2.3 m long, what is its diameter?

2 Water flows into a circular pool at 0.4 litres per second. It takes 5 minutes to fill the pool to a depth of 20 cm. Find the internal diameter of the pool.

3

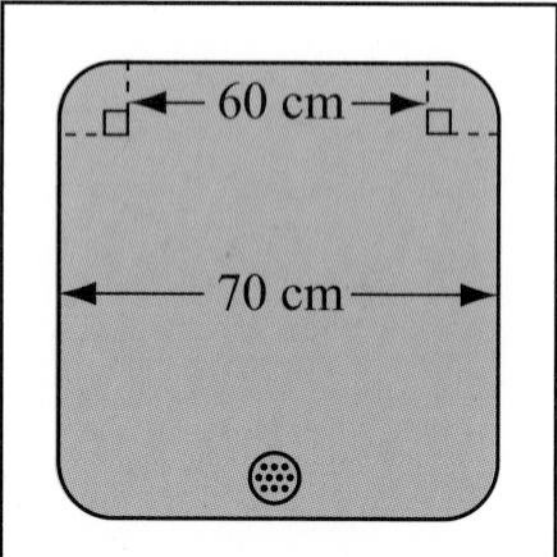

The top view of the square tray in the bottom of a shower cubical is shown.

If it is designed to hold 46 litres of water before overflowing, how deep is the tray?

4 A tiny island in the Pacific Ocean is the only place on Earth where the Gibson Oak grows. Each specimen of this magnificent tree requires a land area of 195 m^2 and the wood from each tree can be sold for \$550 000. The diameter of this circular island is 1.8 km. Calculate the value of the wood on the island. Assume the island is covered by the trees.

5

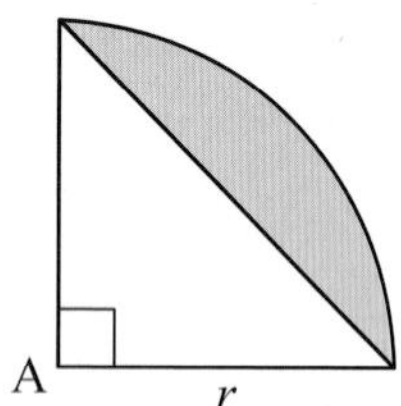

The diagram on the left consists of a quarter circle with centre A and a triangle. The pink shaded area is 200 cm^2. Find the radius r.

6 A solid cuboid has edges of lengths a, b, c. What is its surface area?

7 In the diagram a square of side a cm is surrounded by four equal isosceles triangles. Find the value of a if the area of the shape is 144 cm^2.

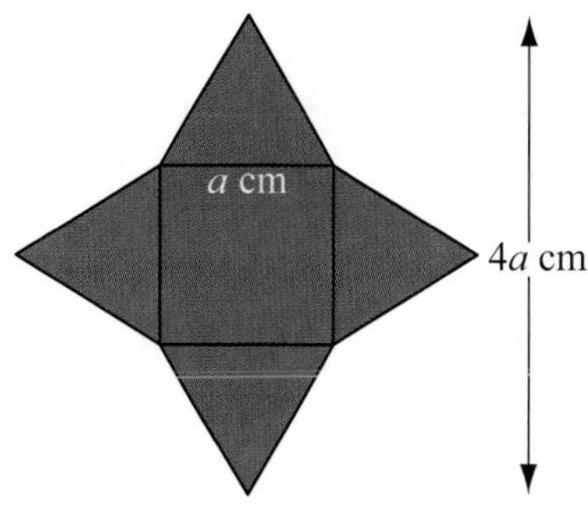

8 The diagram shows a semicircle inside a rectangle. The pink shaded area is 84 cm^2. Find x.

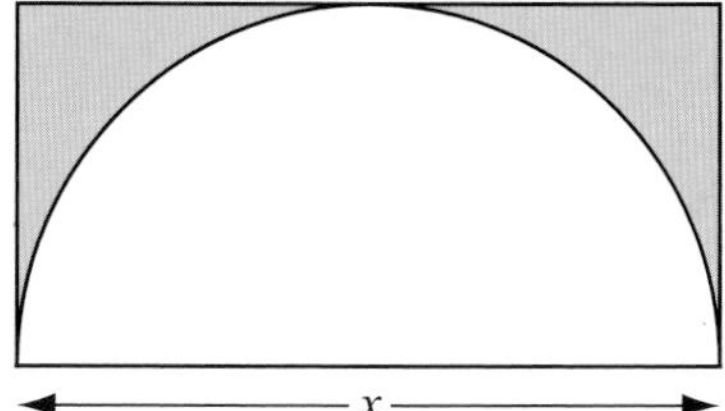

9 A wizard's hat is made by rolling up a sector of a circle into a cone as shown.

If the original piece of card has an area of 470 cm^2, what will be the slant height, x, of the cone?

The arc length AB becomes the circumference of the base of the cone. What is the base diameter of the hat?

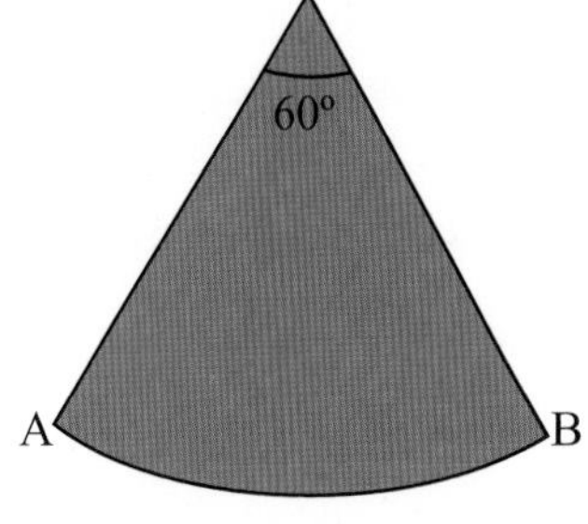

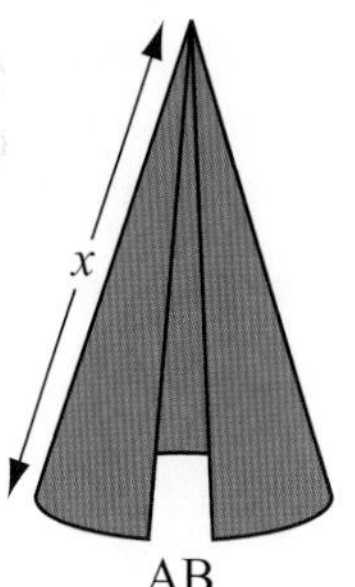

10 The photo shows part of a dart board. Calculate the area of one of the 'treble score' regions.

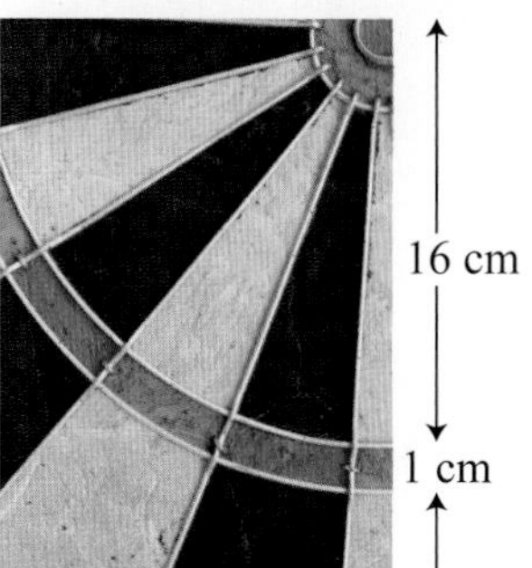

A dart board has 20 equal sectors.

4.4 Collecting and interpreting data

In this section you will:

- learn about collecting data and questionnaires
- learn about possible bias in data collection
- collect your own data to answer a question or solve a problem.

Questions involving data

In general we are concerned here with solving problems or answering questions for which data is required. In particular we can often use statistics to make predictions for the future. Here are some examples:

- Is the R.S.P.C.A. the most popular charity in the country?
- How much T.V. do adults and children watch?
- Do first class letters arrive next day?
- Will people use trains if they are cheaper and run on time?
- Which subject do people find most difficult at school?

Many problems of a statistical nature are made more clear when they are put in the form of a *conjecture*. A conjecture is a statement which may or may not be true. Here are some examples of conjectures:

- More money is donated to the R.S.P.C.A. than to any other charity.
- People aged 18 and over watch more T.V. than under 18 year olds.
- 90% of first class letters arrive next day.

The data relevant to each might be obtained from:

- A questionnaire or survey of a sample of people
- Published tables or from computer databases
- The internet

Collecting data

When you design a data collection sheet you must think ahead and decide what exactly is the purpose of the survey and what information does each question provide. Think also about the order of the questions.

Here are several points to consider when designing a data collection sheet.

- Keep it as short and simple as possible.

  People are (quite rightly) not prepared to spend a long time filling in forms.

- Do not ask questions if they are not relevant.

  Do not ask for the person's name unless you have to. People are more likely to cooperate if their replies are anonymous.

- Try not to ask questions that require written replies.

  You may get a hundred different points of view which makes analyzing the answers extremely difficult. It is much better to ask questions that can be answered with yes/no or by ticking an appropriate box. Do not *only* ask questions which can be answered yes/no.

- Try to avoid personal questions.

  If you ask someone their age, weight or income they will often be inclined to give you false information. A better approach would be to ask 'Which category do you fall into?'

under 16	16–19	20–29	30–49	50 or over

- Make sure you cover all possibilities.

  Do not leave a person thinking 'I don't belong to any of those categories'.

- Do not ask questions in such a way that the person feels forced to agree.

Example 1. Most people would find it difficult to say 'no' to a question such as 'Don't you agree that the cruel and inhumane way of transporting live animals should be abolished.'

Example 2. Do *not* ask: 'Do you agree that pupils in this school are given too much homework?

A better question is:

The amount of homework set to pupils in this school is:

Tick one box.

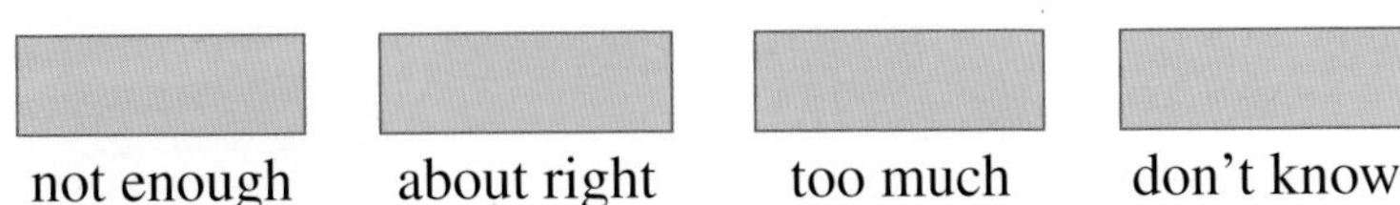

not enough   about right   too much   don't know

- Here are two data collection sheets.

good

I am collecting information to see if there is any connection between a person's height and the height of their parents.

1. Please tick one box — Male [ ] Female [ ]
2. Age: please tick one box — 13→15 [ ] 16→18 [ ] 19 and over [ ]
3. Please state your height, either in feet and inches or in cm. — height [ ]
4. Please state the height of your father [If you are not sure an estimate will be O.K.] — height of father [ ]
5. Please state the height of your mother — height of mother [ ]

Tell people what you are doing

Make it easy to answer.

Use the word 'please' frequently.

Not Good

State your name and age.

Name ______

Age ______

- How much television do you watch on average?

[ ] not much [ ] quite a lot [ ] a lot

- Which are your favourite programmes on T.V.?
- Do you agree that BBC1 provides the best news coverage?

[ ] agree [ ] disagree

No introduction

Not a good idea

People often don't like to state their age

Much too vague

You may get 100 different answers. This will be impossible to analyse.

Question is biased towards agreeing

Needs a box for 'don't know'

Exercise 1M

In Questions 1 to 6 explain why the question is not suitable for a questionnaire. Write an improved question in each case.

1 How much do you earn per month?

0–£100	£100–£200	£200–£500	£400–£700	more than £700

2 Wouldn't you agree that the present government is doing an appalling job?

3 Which sort of holiday do you most enjoy?

4 For how long do you watch the television each day?

2–3 hrs	3–4 hrs	5–6 hrs

5 Do you think that the disintegration of theological suppositions is leading to ethical degeneration?

6 Some of the money from the National Lottery goes to charities.

Tick one box:

The money going to charities is

Too little Too much

7 A group of pupils were asked to design a questionnaire to find out people's views about watching sport on television.

Comment on the following two pupils' efforts. Design an improved questionnaire to find out people's opinions.

(a)

Name ……….. Sex M/F

Age ……

Do you like sport ? …… Y/N

Do you have satellite TV?…… Y/N

Is there enough sport on TV? …… Y/N

(b)

Do you like sport?

Not at all
Not much
A bit
Quite a lot
I love it

Do you have cable or satellite TV?
Yes/No

How often do you watch sport?
Every day
Up to three times a week
Less than twice a month

Should there be more sport on television?
Yes/No

8

By Helen Rumbelow

…………………………..

Medical reporter

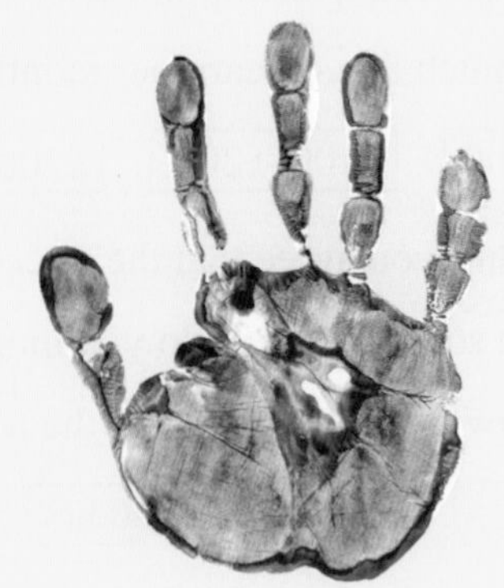

A SIMPLE measurement of a child's ring finger could predict whether he or she grows up to become a musical maestro, scientists announced yesterday.

Gifted musicians – of all instruments – tended to be born with much longer ring fingers than their index fingers, John Manning of Liverpool University said.

His team measured the ring fingers of all players in a large symphony orchestra – nearly all men – and compared them with a control group from the general population. All of the male musicians had a dramatically longer ring finger than other men.

To replicate Dr Manning's work, fingers should be measured from the crease nearest the palm to the tip: If the ratio of the index finger divided by the ring finger is less than 0.8, then an individual may have musical ability.

Read the article from a newspaper.

(a) Design a suitable questionnaire or data collections sheet to test this theory.

(b) What sort of graphical display could you use to display the results of your work?

(For example: bar chart, pie chart, scatter graph etc)

9 A new variety of soup, 'Cheese and Onion', is to be launched by a leading manufacturer. They wish to know if it will be popular and sell well. People are asked to try a free sample and comment on their impression.

Design a questionnaire to test people's opinions.

Bias

When a survey is conducted it is possible for the results to be misleading because of bias.

Bias can be either *intentional or unintentional*.

For example a company selling pizza might want to exagerate the popularity of its product.

It might conduct a survey but deliberately choose people who already buy the product.

Similarly, a political party might choose to collect a 'random' sample from visitors to the Chelsea Flower Show on the assumption that its own supporters would be more likely to visit the flower show.

Also the *wording* of a question can introduce bias because it might lead the respondent to agree with a certain statement.

Unintentional bias can occur in many ways:

In a recent large scale experiment, people were asked to choose a 'representative' sample by selecting 20 stones from a mixed collection of 1200 stones of varying sizes.

It was found that people tended to pick samples whose mean weight was significantly higher than the mean weight for the whole collection. This was true for 30 out of 36 samples. People used their own judgement to choose a mixture of small, medium and large stones for their sample but the 1200 stones in fact contained far more small stones.

In your own work you can easily introduce bias by choosing a sample from your friends rather than across a whole year group. If the question is relevant to both boys and girls, you should ensure that your sample contains equal numbers from both sexes.

Even in professionally conducted surveys people sometimes refuse to answer questions like 'Which political party would you vote for?' This can introduce bias because respondents who hold 'unpopular' views might not be willing to express them to a stranger and thus their views would not be represented in the survey.

The best way to avoid bias in choosing a sample is to select people using a random number table or, in simple cases, by 'picking names from a hat.'

You own work, testing a conjecture

- A conjecture is a statement which may or may not be true.

  'Spurs are the best team in the world.'
  'Tall people are less likely to wear glasses than short people.'
  'Most people in schools find French the hardest subject.'
  "People who are good at Maths are also good at Science."

- A conjecture can often be tested by conducting a survey in which a large number of people respond to a questionnaire.

- When you design a questionnaire you should think ahead to how you will display your results. In general graphs or charts are easier for other people to understand than tables of numbers.

You might use:

Pie charts;
Bar charts;
Scatter graphs;
Frequency polygons.

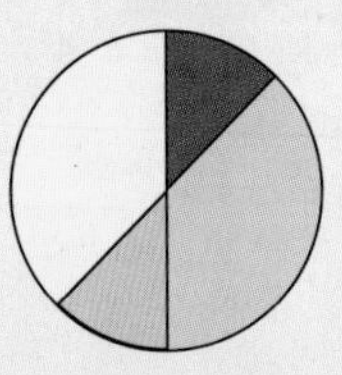

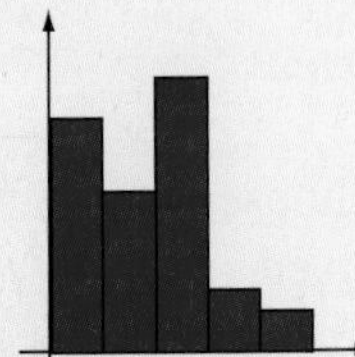

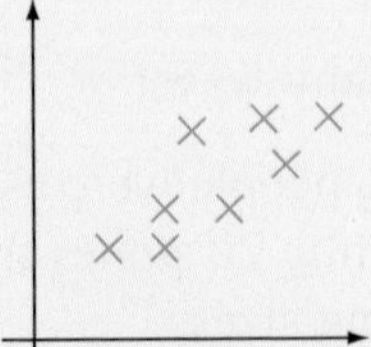

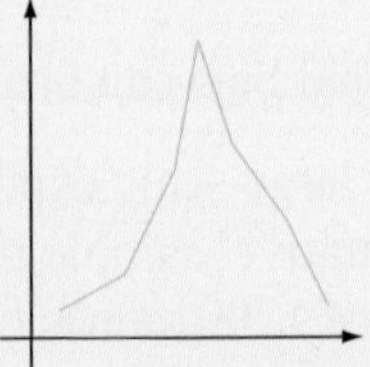

- *Do* use colour in your work and *do* write a short and clear summary of your results. Comment on whether your results support or do not support your conjecture. *Don't* produce page after page of repetitive, uninteresting results without any comments or observations.
- It is always a good idea to ask a few people to try out your questions in a *pilot survey*. Then if there are any problems with the questions these can be corrected. You might also get ideas for additional questions.
- You will almost certainly design a more interesting questionnaire if *you* choose the topic or the conjecture to be tested.

CHECK YOURSELF ON SECTIONS 4.3 AND 4.4

1. Area and volume.

Chocolates are sold in the boxes shown.

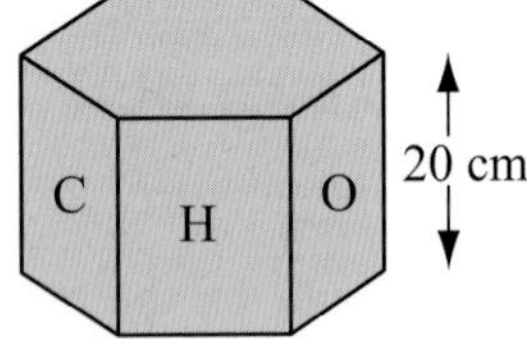

(a) The area of the lid is 165 cm^2. Work out the volume of the box.

(b) The label that goes round the tin has an area of 960 cm^2. Work out the distance around the tin.

length

C	H	O	C	S	!

20 cm

(c) A cylindrical tin of height 12 cm has a volume of 3000 cm^3. Find the diameter of this tin.

2. Collecting and interpreting data

A local council wanted to conduct a survey about life on a new development. Here are two possible questions which were suggested.

(1) 'Why do you like living here?

(2) 'Tick the box which explains why you like living here.'

☐ Close to the train station

☐ Good local schools

☐ Friendly neighbours

(a) Which do you think is the better question?

(b) How could the second question be improved?

4.5 Applying mathematics in a range of contexts 2

In this section you will

- solve a wide range of problems by applying appropriate mathematical knowledge

Exercise 1

1 Find these answers to two decimal places.

(a) $\frac{5.16 - 0.3}{3.7}$ (b) $\sqrt{\frac{46}{9}} + 3.89$ (c) $\frac{7.63}{8.2^2} + \frac{5.17}{1.3^2}$ (d) $\frac{5.68^2 - 17.4}{\sqrt{32.9}}$

2 The rectangle and the square have the same area. Find x.

3 How many pears at 11p each would be a fair exchange for 33 apples costing 18p each?

4 Copy and complete the following bill.

$3\frac{1}{2}$ kg of parsnips at 76 p per kg	= £ ☐
☐ tins of peaches at 69 p per tin	= £3.45
2.5 kg of cod at ☐ per kg	= £18
Total	= £ ☐

5 A garden 9 m by 12 m is to be treated with fertilizer. One cup of fertilizer covers an area of 3 m^2 and one bag of fertilizer is sufficient for 18 cups. Find the number of bags of fertilizer needed.

6 Without a calculator, work out which is the largest of $\sqrt{666}$ $6\sqrt{6}$ $66\sqrt{6}$
Show your working using appropriate estimates.

7 (a) Find two consecutive numbers with a product of 552
(b) Find four consecutive numbers with a total of 130
(c) Find *any* two numbers with a product of 1397
(d) Find a pair of numbers with a sum of 19 and a product of 48.

8 A rectangle is divided into four triangles as shown. Find the area of the biggest of the triangles. All lengths are in cm.

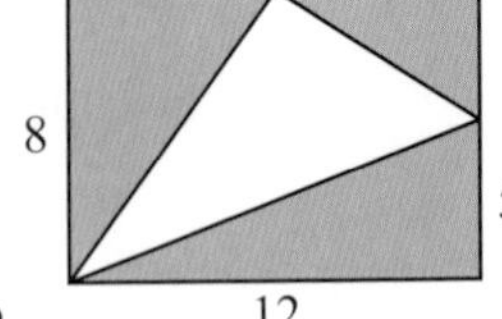

9 (a) What is the smallest number which rounds off to 7.4 correct to one decimal place?
(b) What is the smallest number which rounds off to 5.27 correct to two decimal places?

10 Jack has a packet of 64 sweets.
He gave 3/8 of his sweets to his friend Harry.
Harry then gives 1/4 of his share to James and eats the rest.
Meanwhile Jack eats 2/5 of his remaining sweets.
(a) How many sweets does Jack have left at the end?
(b) How many sweets does Harry eat?

Exercise 2

1 The triangle shown is isosceles.
Find the two possible values of f.

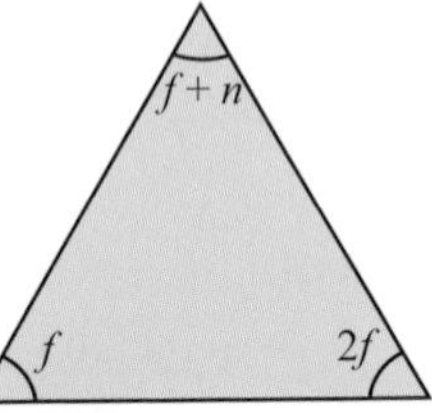

2 A pound coin has radius 1.1 cm and thickness 3 mm.
(a) Calculate the volume of a pile of pound coins of total value £1000.
(b) Calculate the value of the coins in a pile of volume 28.51 cm^3.

3 Find the exact answer to the following by first working out a rough answer and then using the information given. Do *not* use a calculator.
(a) If $142.3 \times 98.5 = 14016.55$ find $140.1655 \div 14.23$
(b) If $76.2 \times 8.6 = 655.32$ find $6553.2 \div 86$
(c) If $22.3512 \div 0.268 = 83.4$ find 8340×26.8
(d) If $1.6781 \div 17.3 = 0.097$ find 9700×0.173

4 Find the missing digits

(a) □ 7 × 1 □ = 611

(b) $8\overline{)\square 9 \square 8}$ = 366

(c) □ 6 × 1 □ = 442

(d)
```
  6 □ 1
− □ 7 □
  2 6 3
```

(e)
```
  □ □ 5
     ×9
2 5 6 □
```

(f) $7\overline{)\square 3 \square 1}$ = 483

5 How many statements in the box are true?

1. 1 + 2 = 3
2. 4 + 5 = 9
3. 3 ÷ 3 = 0
4. 5 × 5 = 10
5. Exactly 3 statements in this box are true.

6 It has been estimated that it would take 54 years to travel over the entire road network of the world at a steady speed of 80 km/h. Calculate the length of the road network of the world, giving your answer in standard form.

7 Work out
(The number of spots on a dice) × (The probability of spinning 2 heads with 2 coins) × ($\sqrt{1 \div 0.0001}$)

8 A pentagon has 5 diagonals. A different polygon has 20 diagonals. How many sides has it?

9 The pie chart shows how the price of a C.D. costing £14.99 can be broken down.

(a) Work out the angle of the V.A.T. sector.

(b) What is the total royalty paid to the artist if 500 000 C.D.s are sold?

(c) Tax from the sale of C.D.s is collected in three ways:

(i) as V.A.T.

(ii) 40% of the Artist's royalty

(iii) 40% of shop's profit.

Calculate the total amount of tax paid when 500 000 C.D.s are sold.

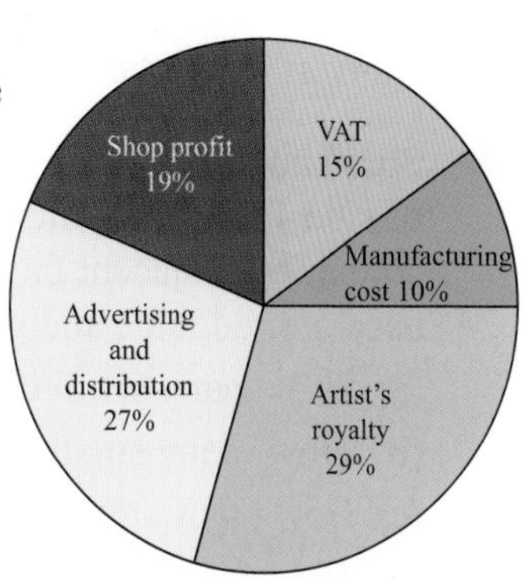

10 Three 9s can be used to make 2 : $\frac{9+9}{9}$

(a) Use four 5s to make 25

(b) Use four 8s to make 2

(c) Use four 7s to make 8

(d) Use four 6s to make 1

Exercise 3

1 It costs £5650 per hour to hire a recording studio. How much will it cost to hire the studio from 20.30 on Friday to 05.00 on the following Monday?

2 Bronze is made up of zinc, tin and copper in the ratio 1 : 4 : 95. A bronze statue contains 120 g of tin. Find the quantities of the other two metals required and the total weight of the statue.

3 The volume of paint in a tube is 150 cm^3. If this paint is squirted out in a straight line through a circular hole of diameter 5 mm, how long will this line be?

4 A car journey takes 3 hours 24 minutes. How long will it take at three quarters of the average speed?

5 The diagram shows a circle touching a semicircle.

Calculate the area of the coloured region.

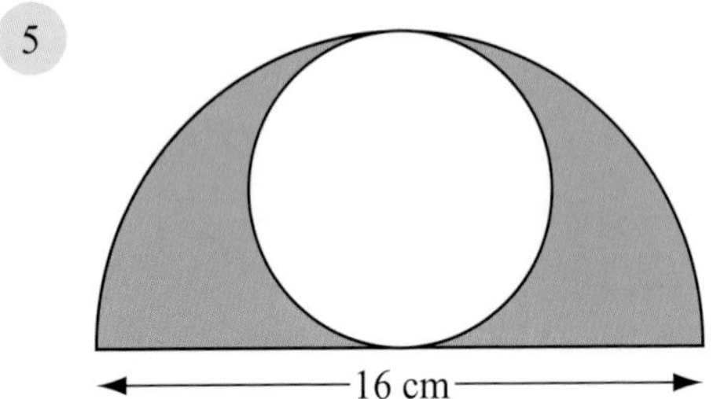

6 When the lid is left off an ink bottle, the ink evaporates at a rate of 2.5×10^{-6} cm^3/s. A full bottle contains 36 cm^3 of ink. How long, to the nearest day, will it take for all the ink to evaporate?

7 Convert 3.35 hours into hours and minutes.

8 Small cubes of side 1 cm are stuck together to form a large cube of side 4 cm. Opposite faces of the large cube are painted the same colour, but adjacent faces are different colours. The three colours used are red, blue and green.

(a) How many small cubes have just one red and one green face?

(b) How many small cubes are painted on one face only?

(c) How many small cubes have one red, one green and one blue face?

(d) How many small cubes have no faces painted?

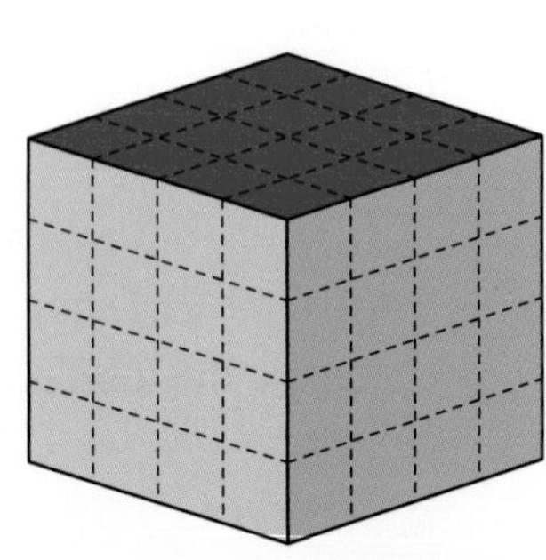

9 A sales manager reports an increase of 20% in sales this year compared to last year.

The increase was £70 800.

What were the sales last year?

10 Solve the equations

(a) $2(x + 4) = 3(3 - 2x)$

(b) $\frac{x + 2}{4} = \frac{4x - 1}{3}$

(c) $2^x = 1024$

Exercise 4

1 The diagram shows the frame for the roof of a house.

Calculate the length x.

2 Write the digits 1 to 9 so that all the answers are correct.

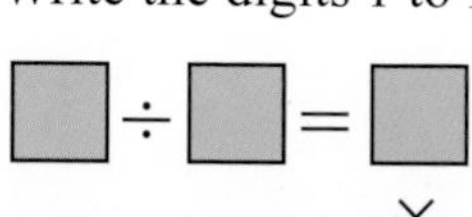

$\square \div \square = \square$

$\times$

$\square - \square = \square$

$\parallel$

$\square + \square = \square$

3 When I think of a number, multiply it by 6 and subtract 88, the answer is –10. What was the number I was thinking of ?

4 The total of each row in the table is given at the side

$1 - 2n$	$3(n + 7)$	x
7	$(n + 8)$	13

Find the values of n and x

5 A circle touches a square as shown.

Find the area of the coloured region.

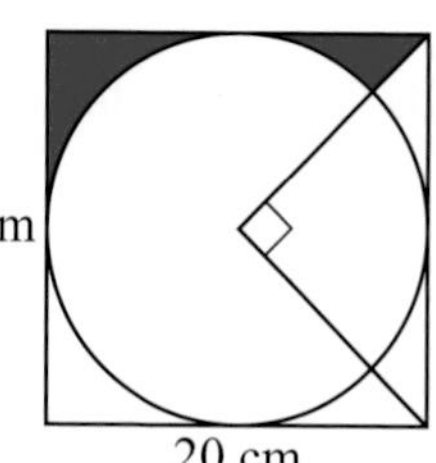

6 In quadrilateral ABCD, $B\hat{A}D = B\hat{C}D = 90°$, AD = 10, BC = 4, CD = 12. Find AB.

7 The rule for the number sequences below is '*double and add 1*'
Write down each sequence and fill in the missing numbers.

(a) ☐ → 5 → 11 → ☐

(b) ☐ → ☐ → ☐ → 63

(c) –1 → ☐ → ☐ → ☐

8 Hamish has the same number of 10p and 20p coins. The total value of the coins is £9.
How many of each coin does he have?

9 An aeroplane was due to take off from Heathrow airport at 18:42 but it was 35 min late. During the flight, thanks to a tail wind, the plane made up the time and in fact landed 16 min before its scheduled arrival time of 00:05. (Assume that the plane did not cross any time zones on its journey.)
(a) What time did the aeroplane take off?
(b) What time did it land?

10 It rained so hard that a 4 cm deep egg cup was filled in 20 minutes.
How much rain fell between 07:30 and 13:50?

Exercise 5

1 Draw a copy of the grid shown. The sum of the numbers in each column ↕ is the same as the sum of the numbers in each diagonal.

What number goes in the centre?

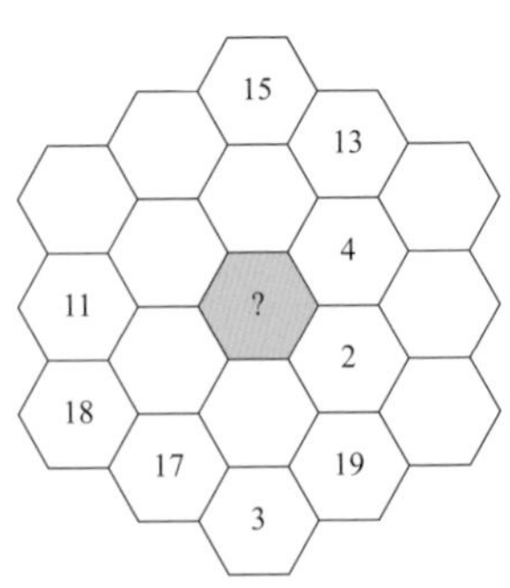

2 Street lights are placed 6 m apart next to a road of length 15 miles.
How many lights were required? [1km = 0.625 mile]

3 The area of the square exceeds the area of the rectangle by 13 m^2.
Find n

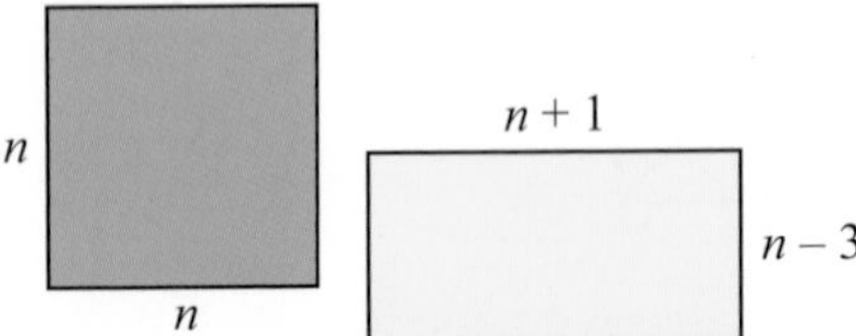

4 Which bag of apples is the better value:

Bag A, 6 kg for £4.14 or
Bag B, 2.5 kg for £1.80?

5 Water flows into an empty cylinder of diameter and height 60 cm at the rate of 300 cm^3/s. How long, to the nearest second, will it take to fill the cylinder?

6 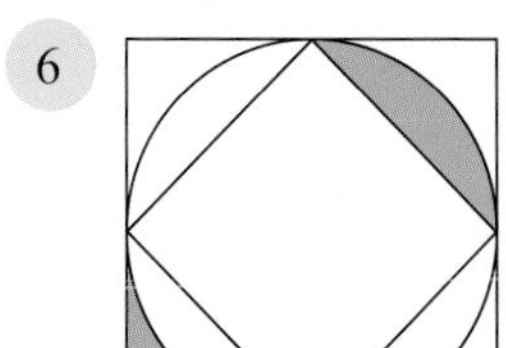

The diagram shows two squares and a circle of diameter 10 cm. Calculate the total area of the regions shaded green.

7 (a) Copy the table below and complete rows 4, 5 and 6.

Row				Sum of digits
1	4^2	=	16	7
2	34^2	=	1156	13
3	334^2	=	111556	19
4	3334^2	=	....	....
5	33334^2	=	....	....
6	333334^2	=	....	....

(b) Calculate the sum of the digits in the answer to 33333333334^2

8 In the diagram $\frac{5}{6}$ of the circle is shaded and $\frac{2}{3}$ of the triangle is shaded.

What is the ratio of the area of the circle to the area of the triangle?

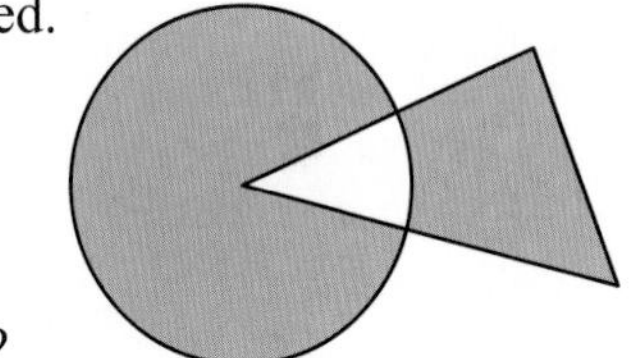

9 Do not use a calculator for this question.

(a) The square root of 161 lies between which two whole numbers?

(b) The cube root of 20 lies between which two whole numbers?

(c) Estimate the value of $\dfrac{\sqrt{897.2} \times 10.93}{\sqrt{16.75}}$

10 The diagram show a sketch of the graph $y = ab^x$

The curve passes through the points A(1,6) and B (2, 18).

The point (3, n) lies on the curve.

Find the value of n.

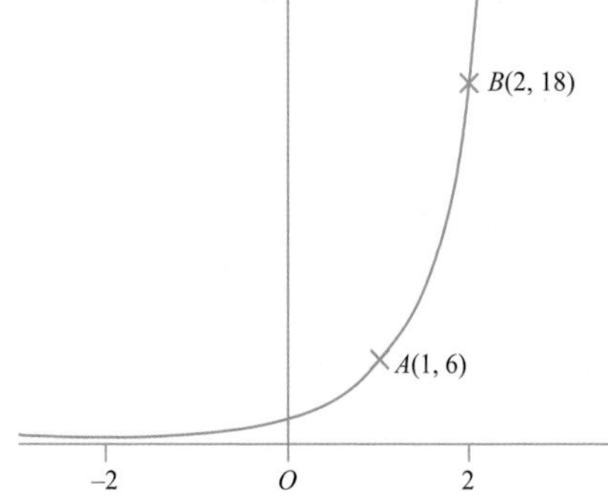

4.6 Simultaneous equations

In this section you will:

- learn how to solve simultaneous equations with a graph
- learn how to solve simultaneous equations algebraically
- solve problems by using simultaneous equations

What are simultaneous equations?

Up to now the equations you have solved have had just one unknown.

For example $3x - 1 = 1 - 4x$,

$5(1 - x) = 2(3x + 1)$,

$x(x + 1) = 100$.

The equation $3x + y = 8$ involves two variables x and y. There are many pairs of values of x and y which satisfy the equation.
For example, if $x = 1$ and $y = 5$, $(3 \times 1) + 5 = 8$

or, if $x = 4$ and $y = -4$, $(3 \times 4) + (-4) = 8$.

There is in fact an infinite number of pairs of solutions. Similarly the equation $2x + 5y = 1$ is satisfied by an infinite number of pairs of solutions.

When we solve a *pair of simultaneous* equations we find the one pair of values of x and y which satisfy *both* equations simultaneously. Confirm that the equations $3x + y = 8$ and $2x + 5y = 1$ are both satisfied by $x = 3$ and $y = -1$.

These are the solutions of the simultaneous equations.

Graphical solution of simultaneous equations

The equations $x + y = 7$ and

$2x - y = -1$

can be represented by straight lines as shown.

Since both lines pass through the point (2, 5), the solutions of the simultaneous equations

$$x + y = 7$$
$$2x - y = -1$$

are $x = 2$, $y = 5$.

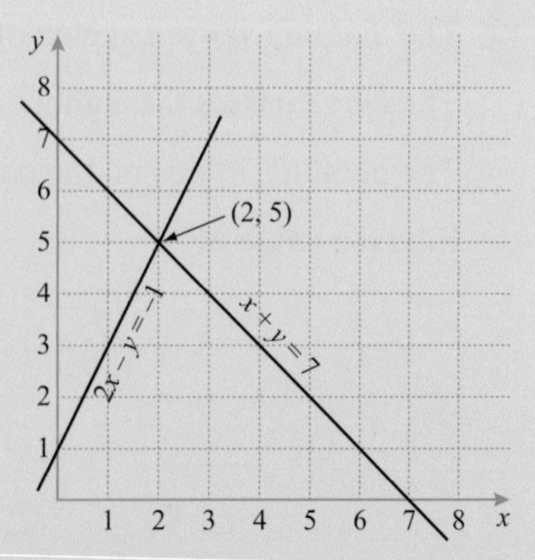

Solve the simultaneous equations

$2x + y = 6$

$x - 2y = -2.$

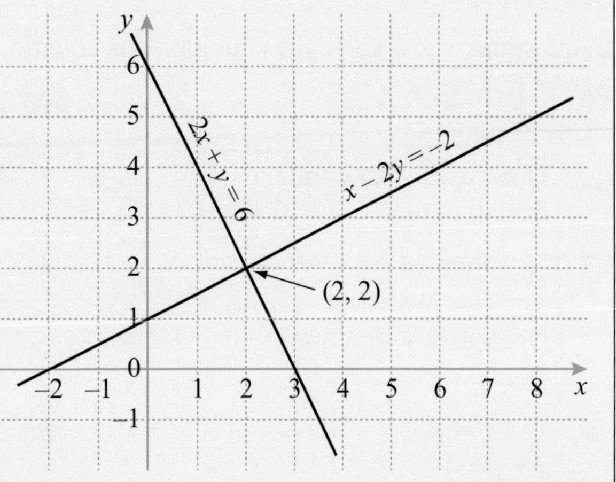

(a) Draw the line $2x + y = 6$.

When $x = 0$, $y = 6$
When $y = 0$, $x = 3$
When $x = 1$, $y = 4$

(b) Draw the line $x - 2y = -2$.

When $x = 0$, $y = 1$
When $y = 0$, $x = -2$
When $x = 6$, $y = 4$

(c) The lines intersect at (2, 2) so the solutions are $x = 2$, $y = 2$.

Exercise 1M

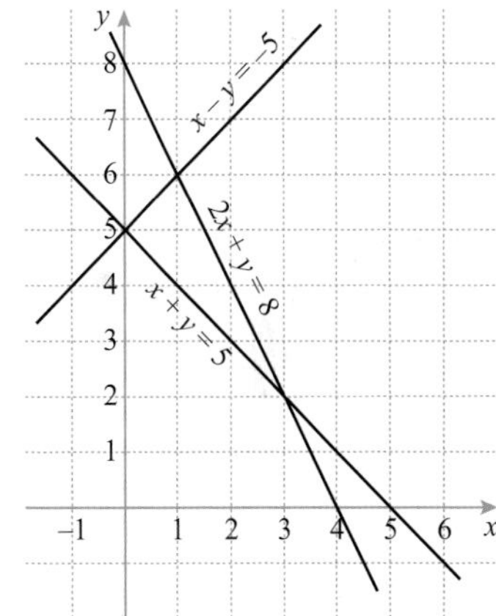

1 Use the graph to solve the simultaneous equations.

(a) $2x + y = 8$
$x + y = 5$

(b) $x - y = -5$
$x + y = 5$

(c) $2x + y = 8$
$x - y = -5$

2 Use the graph to solve the simultaneous equations.

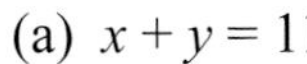

(a) $x + y = 11$

$x + 3y = 13$

(b) $2x - y = -2$

$x + y = 11$

(c) $x + 3y = 13$

$2x - y = -2$

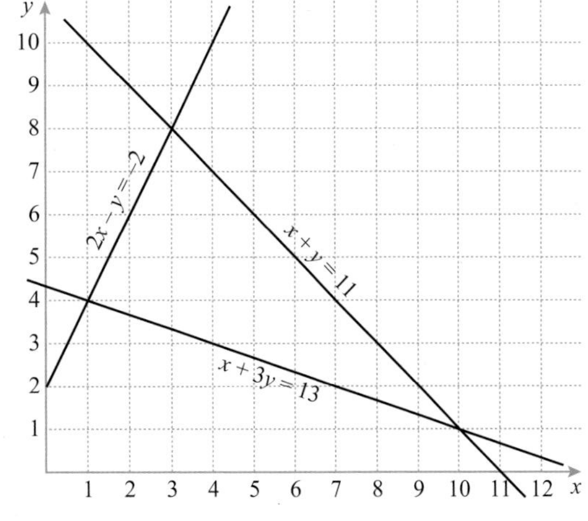

Exercise 1E

In questions 1 to 6 solve the simultaneous equations by drawing graphs.

1 $x + y = 6$
$y = x + 3$
Draw axes with x and y from 0 to 6.

2 $x + 2y = 11$
$2x + y = 13$
Draw axes with x and y from 0 to 13.

3 $3x + 4y = 24$
$3x + 2y = 18$
Draw axes with x and y from 0 to 9.

4 $x + y = 5$
$y = x + 2$
Draw axes with x and y from 0 to 5.

5 $y = 3x + 6$
$x + y = 4$
Draw axes with x and y from –2 to 6.

6 $2x + 5y = 17$
$2x - 3y = -3$
Draw axes with x and y from 0 to 6.
[Give your answers correct to 1 d.p.]

7 Use the graph to solve the equations below. Give your answers correct to 1 d.p. where necessary.

(a) $x + y = 9$
$y = 2x - 3$

(b) $x + 3y = 5$
$x + y = 9$

(c) $x + 3y = 5$
$y = 2x - 3$

(d) $y = 2x - 3$
$5y = 4x + 18$

(e) $5y = 4x + 18$
$x + 3y = 5$

(f) $x + y = 9$
$5y = 4x + 18$

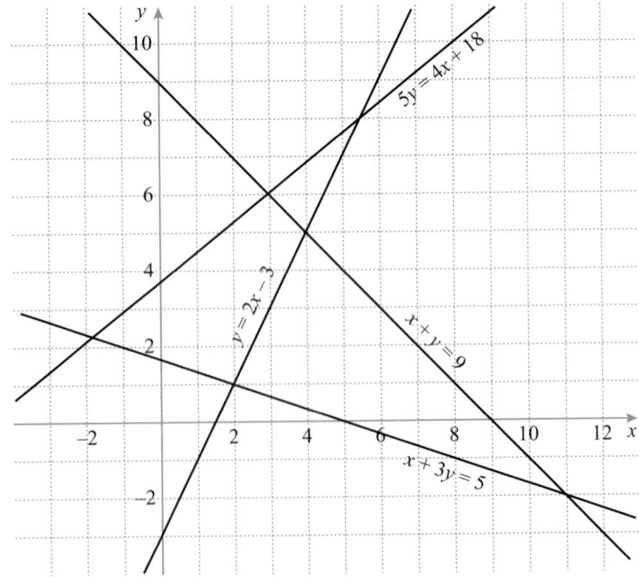

8 The simultaneous equations $x + 2y = 10$ and $x + 2y = 15$ have no solutions. What can you say about their graphs?

Algebraic solution of simultaneous equations

(a) Consider the simultaneous equations $5x + y = 21$ [1]
$3x + y = 13$ [2]

If we subtract equation [2] from equation [1] we eliminate the y terms.

We obtain $2x = 8$
$x = 4$

Now substitute $x = 4$ into equation [1] (or equation [2]).

$$(5 \times 4) + y = 21$$
$$y = 1$$

The solution is $x = 4, y = 1$

(b) Consider the simultaneous equations $x - y = 4$ [1]
$4x + y = 31$ [2]

If *we add* equation [1] to equation [2] we eliminate the y terms.

We obtain $5x = 35$
$x = 7$

Now substitute $x = 7$ into equation [1] (or equation [2]).

$$7 - y = 4$$
$$y = 3$$

The solution is $x = 7, y = 3$.

(c) Why can we add equations like this?

Equations are like scales which balance.

Equation [1]

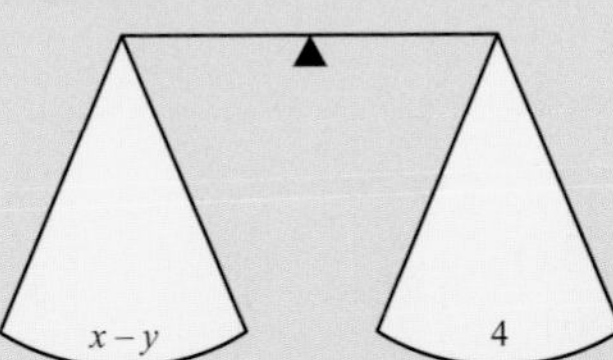

Equation [2]

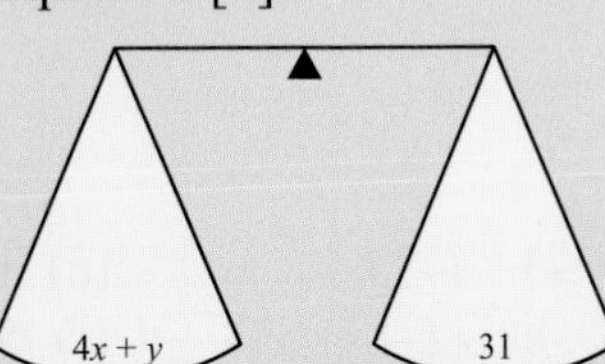

Both sets of scales balance. If we add the contents of the scales they will still balance.

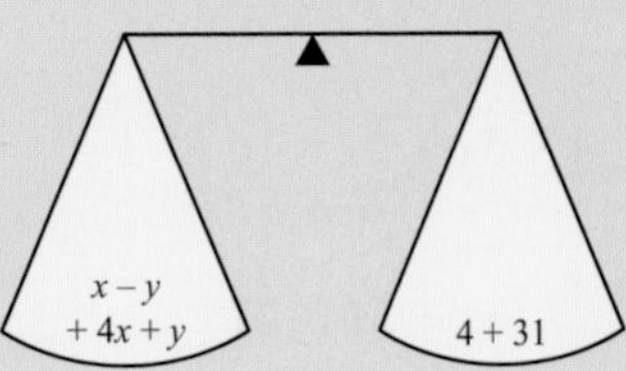

So $5x = 35$
$x = 7$

Solve the simultaneous equations

(a) $x + 2y = 7$ [1]
$x - y = 4$ [2]

Label the equations [1] and [2]

[1] – [2] gives $2y - (-y) = 3$
$3y = 3$
$y = 1$

Substitute $y = 1$ in [1]
$x + (2 \times 1) = 7$
$x = 5$
The solution is $x = 5$, $y = 1$.

(b) $3x + 2y = 10$ [1]
$5x - 2y = 14$ [2]

In this case to eliminate the y terms we *add* the equations.
[1] + [2] gives $8x = 24$
$x = 3$

Substitute $x = 3$ in [1]
$9 + 2y = 10$
$2y = 1$
$y = \frac{1}{2}$
The solution is $x = 3$, $y = \frac{1}{2}$.

Remember: 'If the signs in front of the letter to be eliminated are the *same* we *subtract*, but if the signs are different we add.'

Be careful with negative numbers when using this method. Look carefully at the following examples.

$2 - (-2) = 2 + 2$
$= 4$

$3y + (-3y) = 3y - 3y$
$= 0$

$-11 - (-3) = -11 + 3$
$= -8$

$3y - (+8y) = -5y$

$-2x - (-2x) = -2x + 2x$
$= 0$

$-4y + (-4y) = -4y - 4y$
$= -8y$

Exercise 2M

1 Simplify

(a) $-3 + (-4)$ (b) $-3 - (-2)$ (c) $x + (-3x)$
(d) $2y - (-2y)$ (e) $-8x - (-8x)$ (f) $5 + (-6)$
(g) $-3x - (-7x)$ (h) $a + (-a)$ (i) $8n - (-2n)$
(j) $4y + (-8y)$ (k) $-5p - (-p)$ (l) $3p - (5p)$

Solve the simultaneous equations.

2 $5x + y = 22$
$2x + y = 10$

3 $6x + y = 31$
$3x + y = 16$

4 $5x + 2y = 16$
$x + 2y = 4$

5 $7x + 4y = 17$
$3x + 4y = 5$

6 $x + 3y = 11$
$x + 2y = 9$

7 $3x + 5y = 21$
$3x - y = 3$

8 $4x + 5y = 9$
$4x - 2y = 2$

9 $x - 2y = 8$
$x - 5y = 17$

10 $4x + 3y = -5$
$7x + 3y = -11$

In questions **11** to **16** add the equations to eliminate the y terms.

11 $3x + y = 14$
$2x - y = 6$

12 $5x + 2y = 16$
$3x - 2y = 8$

13 $7x - 3y = 24$
$2x + 3y = 3$

14 $5x - y = -7$
$x + y = -5$

15 $6x - y = -26$
$5x + y = -18$

16 $x + 3y = -4$
$2x - 3y = -11$

Exercise 2E

In these questions either add or subtract to eliminate terms.

1 $3x + 2y = -1$
$3x - y = 5$

2 $a + b = 3$
$3a - b = 17$

3 $2a - b = 6$
$3a + b = 14$

4 $5a - 2b = 4$
$3a + 2b = 12$

5 $5x + y = -7$
$5x - 2y = -16$

6 $3x + y = 14$
$3x - y = 10$

7 $m - 2n = 0$
$9m + 2n = 30$

8 $3x - y = 16$
$6x - y = 31$

9 $3x - 2y = 11$
$7x - 2y = 27$

10 $4x - 5y = -17$
$2x - 5y = -16$

11 $3x = y + 10$
$3x - 2y = 4$

12 $x = 3y + 15$
$5x + 3y = 3$

Sometimes we cannot eliminate either x or y terms unless we multiply one equation or both equations by a suitable number or numbers. Examples (a) and (b) illustrate the method.

(a) $3x + y = 14$ [1]
$x + 2y = 3$ [2]

Multiply equation [1] by 2.
[1] × 2: $6x + 2y = 28$ [3]
[3] – [2]: $5x = 25$
$x = 5$

Substitute $x = 5$ in [1] (or [2])
$(3 \times 5) + y = 14$
$y = -1$

The solution is $x = 5$, $y = -1$

(b) $5x + 2y = 23$ [1]
$2x + 3y = 18$ [2]

Multiply both equations.
[1] × 3: $15x + 6y = 69$ [3]
[2] × 2: $4x + 6y = 36$ [4]
[3] – [4]: $11x = 33$
$x = 3$

Substitute $x = 3$ in [1] (or [2])
$(5 \times 3) + 2y = 23$
$y = 4$

The solution is $x = 3$, $y = 4$

Exercise 3M

Solve the simultaneous equations.

1 $4x + y = 14$
$5x + 2y = 19$

2 $2x + y = 5$
$5x + 3y = 12$

3 $4x + 3y = 25$
$x + 5y = 19$

4 $7a + 2b = 22$
$3a + 4b = 11$

5 $5m + 3n = 11$
$4m + 6n = 16$

6 $2x + 3y = 20$
$x + 5y = 31$

In questions **7** to **9** multiply one of the equations and then add to eliminate the y terms.

7 $3x + 2y = 19$
$4x - y = 29$

8 $5x - y = 8$
$7x + 4y = 22$

9 $8x - 3y = 30$
$3x + y = 7$

Exercise 3E

In the remaining questions multiply either one or both equations before eliminating the x or y terms.

1 $2x + 3y = 12$
$5x + 4y = 23$

2 $3x + 2y = 14$
$2x + 7y = 15$

3 $9a + 5b = 15$
$3a - 2b = -6$

4 $2x + 5y = 5$
$4x + 3y = 3$

5 $3x - 2y = 21$
$4x + 3y = 11$

6 $6x + 5y = 20$
$5x + 2y = 21$

7 $7x + 5y = 32$
$3x + 4y = 23$

8 $x - y = -1$
$2x - y = 0$

9 $y - x = -1$
$3x - y = 5$

10 $5x - 7y = 27$
$3x - 4y = 16$

11 $3x + 2y = 7$
$2x - 3y = -4$

12 $4x + 5y = -19$
$6x - 3y = 24$

13 $2x + 3y = 5$
$5x - 2y = -16$

14 $7a - 5b = 10$
$9a + 11b = -22$

15 $10x + 5y = 2\frac{1}{2}$
$7x - 2y = \frac{1}{10}$

Solving problems with simultaneous equations

Exercise 4M

Solve the problems by forming a pair of simultaneous equations. In questions **1** to **4** there are two numbers to be found.

1 Find two numbers whose sum is 9 and which have a difference of 6. [Let the numbers be x and y.]

2 Twice one number plus the other number adds up to 13. The sum of the numbers is 10.

3 Double the larger number plus three times the smaller number makes 19. The difference between the numbers is 2.

4 The mean of the two numbers is 11. The larger number is one more than twice the smaller number.

5 Angle A is 12° greater than angle C.

Find the angles of the triangle.

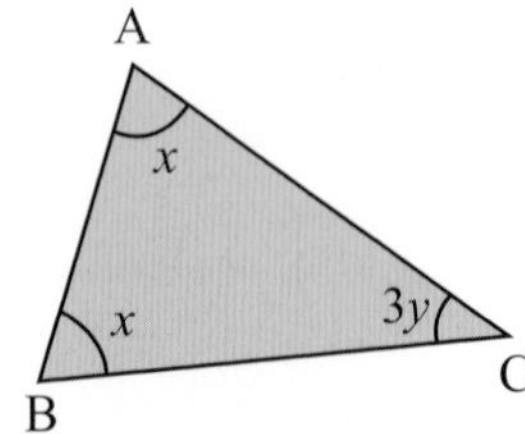

6 In the squares shown the sum of the numbers in each row and each column is given. Find the value of P and the value of Q in each case.

(a)

P	Q	P	Q	76
P	Q	P	P	92
Q	P	Q	Q	60
P	P	Q	Q	76
92	76	76	60	

(b)

P	Q	P	Q	P	25
P	P	P	Q	P	30
Q	P	Q	P	Q	20
P	P	P	P	Q	30
P	Q	P	Q	Q	20
30	25	30	20	20	

7 In this square there are three letters to be found. [Hint: Find A and B first.]

A	B	A	17
B	A	A	17
C	B	B	15
13	19	17	

Exercise 4E

1 76 football fans need to be transported to an away match. A minibus can take 12 people and a car can take 5 people. How many of each are needed if 11 vehicles are taken?
[Let the number of minibuses be m and let the number of cars be c].

2 A theatre sold 470 tickets at two different prices. A total of £5770 was made when x seats were sold at £15 and y seats were sold at £11. Find the values of x and y.

3 

In a small garden there are l ladybirds and d daisies.

There are five daisies for every ladybird. There are 228 more daisies than ladybirds. How many are there of each?

4 Stephen bought 4 cassettes and 2 CDs which came to a total of £69 while Amanda bought 3 cassettes and 3 CDs for a total of £66. Assuming that all cassettes are the same price, and all CDs are the same price, find the cost of each.

5 A box of 6 eggs costs 46p but a box of 12 eggs costs only 82p. If a total of 78 eggs are bought for a cost of £5.38, how many of each size box were bought?

6 Angle P is 20° greater than angle Q. Angle R is half the sum of angles P and Q. Find the values of m and n.

7 The line $y = mx + c$ passes through the points (2,1) and (4, 7). Find the values of m and c.

8 The six numbers around each pink hexagon add up to 100. Find a, b and c, given that $b + c = 29$.

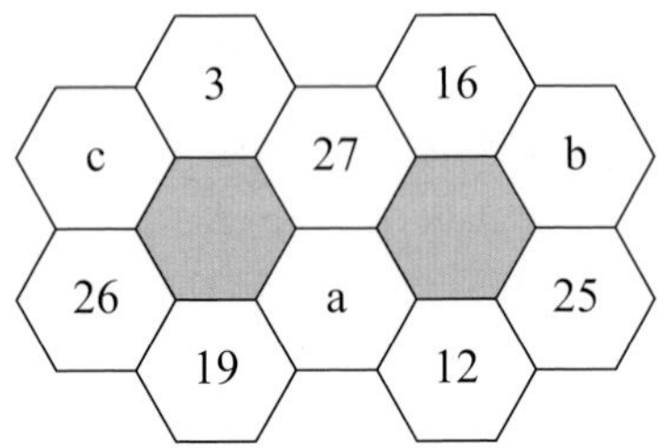

9 Here there are three simultaneous equations. Find a, b and c.

$$a + b + c = 9$$
$$a + 2b + c = 12$$
$$a + b - c = 7$$

10 Find x, y and z.

$$2x + y + z = 7$$
$$x + y - z = 1$$
$$5x + y + z = 19$$

11 The curve with equation $y = ax^2 + bx + c$ passes through the points (1,6) , (2, 13), (–1, 10). Find the values of a, b and c.

4.7 Sequences

In this section you will:

- learn about arithmetic progressions
- learn about geometric sequences
- learn how to find the nth term of a sequence
- learn about direct and inverse proportion

Arithmetic progression

A set of numbers written in a certain order where there is a simple rule to obtain the terms is called a **sequence** or **progression**.

Exercise 1M

Write down the next two terms in each of the following sequences:

1. 2, 4, 6, 8, …
2. 1, 4, 7, 10, …
3. 5, 10, 20, 40, …
4. $1^2, 2^2, 3^2, 4^2, \ldots$
5. 1, 2, 4, 8, …
6. 6, 3, 0, −3, …
7. $\frac{1}{2}, \frac{2}{3}, \frac{3}{4}, \frac{4}{5}, \ldots$
8. $\frac{1}{1} + \frac{1}{2} + \frac{1}{3} + \frac{1}{4} + \ldots$

In an *arithmetic progression* the difference between consecutive terms is constant and is called the *common difference*.

Here are three different arithmetic progressions (or *arithmetic series*).

$1 + 3 + 5 + 7 + \ldots + 13,$
$3 + 13 + 23 + 33 + \ldots + 83,$
$10 + 8 + 6 + \ldots - -20$

The arithmetic progression (A.P. for short) with first term a and common difference d is:

$$a + (a + d) + (a + 2d) + (a + 3d) + \ldots$$

You can see that the nth term is a + $(n - 1)d$

a Find the nth term of the arithmetic progression $2 + 7 + 12 + 17 + \ldots$
The first term, a, is 2 and the common difference, d, is 5.

The nth term $= a + (n - 1)d$
$= 2 + (n - 1) \times 5$
$= 2 + 5n - 5$
$= 5n - 3$

b Similarly the nth term of the arithmetic series $7 + 10 + 13 + 16 + \ldots$ is

$7 + (n - 1) \times 3$
$= 7 + 3n - 3$
$= 3n + 4$

Exercise 1E

1 Find an expression, involving n, for the nth term of the arithmetic progression
$3 + 7 + 11 + 15 + \dots$

2 Find an expression for the nth term of the following arithmetic progressions.

(a) $2 + 7 + 12 + 17 + \dots$ (b) $5 + 7 + 9 + 11 + \dots$

(c) $2 + 5 + 8 + 11 + \dots$ (d) $14 + 11 + 8 + 5 + \dots$

3 Which of the following are arithmetic progressions?

(a) $1 + 1.2 + 1.4 + 1.6 + \dots$ (b) $7.3 + 7 + 6.7 + 6.4 + \dots$

(c) $1 + 1.1 + 1.11 + 1.111 + \dots$ (d) $n + 2n + 3n + 4n + \dots$

4 Write down the terms stated in each of the following A.P.s.

(a) $2 + 7 + \dots$ 6th term (b) $12 + 19 + \dots$ 5th term

(c) $40 + 38 + \dots$ 10th term (d) $-7 - 1 + 5 + 11 + \dots$ 9th term

5 The picture shows letters and numbers made using screws. For example, the letter 'E' is made using 5 screws.

Here are five numbers and letters where the number of screws required to make them form an arithmetic sequence. 1, L, F, U, W.

What number or letter comes after the 'W'?

6 (a) Find the nth term of the A.P. $1 + 5 + 9 + \dots$

(b) Which term of the series is equal to 41?

(c) Hence find $1 + 5 + 9 + \dots + 41$.

7 Use a method similar to that in question 6 to find:

(a) $53 + 50 + 47 + \dots + 2$

(b) $\frac{1}{4} + \frac{1}{2} + \frac{3}{4} + \dots + 2$

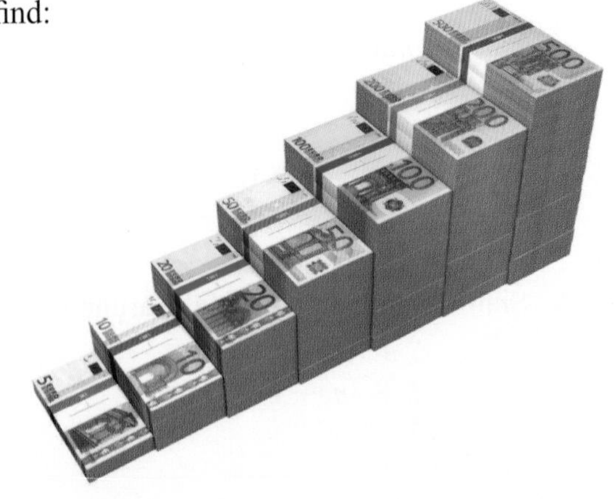

8 The picture shows bank notes in piles. The number of bank notes in each pile forms an arithmetic progression which starts 40, 80, 120, …

How many bank notes will there be altogether in the seven piles of notes shown?

9 Find the nth term of the following arithmetic progressions.

(a) $3 + 7 + 11 + \dots$ (b) $20 + 26 + 32 + \dots$

(c) $5 + 8 + 11 + \dots$ (d) $36 + 31 + 26 + \dots$

Geometric sequences

Another important sequence is the *geometric sequence*.
Here are some geometric sequences.

A: $1 + 2 + 4 + 8 + \dots$

B: $5 + 15 + 45 + 135 + \dots$

C: $1 + \frac{1}{2} + \frac{1}{4} + \frac{1}{8} + \dots$

In such sequences each term is obtained by multiplying the previous term by a constant number, called the *common ratio*.

In sequence A, above, the common ratio is 2.

In sequence B, above, the common ratio is 3.

In sequence C, above, the common ratio is $\frac{1}{2}$.

Exercise 2M

1 Which of the following are geometric sequences?

(a) $1 + 4 + 16 + 64 + \dots$ (b) $2 + 4 + 8 + 16 + \dots$

(c) $1 + 5 + 25 + 125 + \dots$ (d) $3 + 7 + 11 + 15 + \dots$

2 The 3rd term of a geometric series is 32 and the 4th term is 128.
Find the first term and the common ratio.

3 The 4th term of a geometric series is 27 and the 5th term is 81.
Find the first term and the common ratio.

4 Find the terms stated in the following geometric series:

(a) $4 + 8 + 16 + \dots$ 10th term

(b) $0.02 + 0.04 + 0.08 + \dots$ 6th term

5 Find the number of terms in the following geometric series:

(a) $1 + 10 + 100 + \dots + 1\,000\,000$

(b) $1 + 3 + 9 + \dots 243$

6 Which of the following are geometric sequences?

(a) $1 - 3 + 9 - 27 + \dots$ (b) $64 + 32 + 16 + 8 + \dots$

(c) $\frac{1}{5} + 1 + 10 + 50 + \dots$ (d) $80 - 40 + 20 - 10 + \dots$

(e) $1 + \sqrt{7} + 7 + \dots$ (f) $3 - 6 + 12 - 24 + \dots$

7 The first two terms of a geometric sequence are 2 and 8. What is

(a) the 3rd term?

(b) the 5th term?

8 The 4th term of a geometric sequence is 4 and the 6th term is 36. What is

(a) the common ratio of the sequence?

(b) the 7th term of the sequence?

9 Decide whether the sequence is an arithmetic or geometric sequence.

(a) 3, 8, 13, 18, 23, …

(b) $1\frac{1}{3}$, 4, 12, 36, …

(c) 2, 0.2, 0.02, 0.002, …

(d) 65, 59, 53, 47, …

Direct and inverse proportion

Direct proportion

(a) When a lorry driver buys diesel, the more he buys the more money he has to pay.
For example, if 3 litres cost £3.90, then 6 litres will cost £7.80.
The cost of diesel is **directly proportional** to the quantity bought.
To show that quantities are proportional, you use the symbol '$\propto$'.
So in the example above, if the cost of diesel is c pence and the number of litres of diesel is l, you write

$$c \propto l$$

The '$\propto$' sign can always be replaced by '$= k$', where k is a constant. So $c = kl$.
From above, if $c = 390$ when $l = 3$
then $390 = k \times 3$

$$k = \frac{390}{3} = 130$$

You can then write $c = 130l$, and this can be used to find the value of c for any value of l, and **vice versa**.

(b) If a quantity h is proportional to a quantity x, you can write $h \propto x$ or $h = kx$, where k is a constant (a number).

The graph of $h = kx$ is shown:

When h and x are directly proportional the graph connecting h and x is a straight line which passes through the origin, (0, 0).

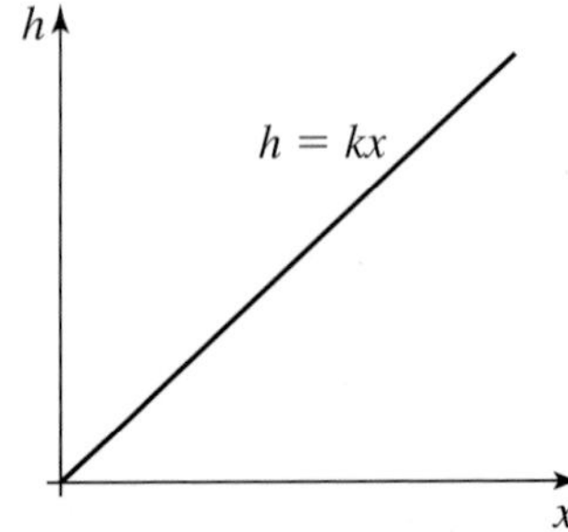

If p is proportional to z, and $p = 35$ when $z = 5$, find

(a) the value of p when $z = 9$

(b) the value of z when $p = 98$

We have $p \propto z$ so $p = kz$, where k is a constant.

When $p = 35$, $z = 5$, so (in $p = kz$), $35 = k \times 5$

so $k = 7$.

So $p = 7z$

(a) When $z = 9$, $p = 7 \times 9 = 63$

(b) When $p = 98$, $98 = 7 \times z$

$z = 98 \div 7 = 14$

Exercise 2E

1 Rewrite the statement connecting each pair of symbols using a constant k instead of '$\propto$'.

(a) $H \propto t$ (b) $y \propto x$ (c) $p \propto h^2$ (d) $T \propto \sqrt{m}$

2 y is proportional to z^2 and $y = 45$ when $z = 3$.

(a) Find the equation connecting y and z.

(b) Find the value of y when $z = 5$.

3 If 9 turkeys cost £81, how much would 5 turkeys cost?

4 If 10 shirts cost £75, how much would 2 shirts cost?

5 p is proportional to w and $p = 20$ when $w = 8$. Find

(a) the value of p when $w = 40$

(b) the value of w when $p = 30$.

6 If 3 sponges cost £4.02, how much would 7 sponges cost?

7 A cook takes 15 minutes to make 45 cakes.
How many cakes can he make in 10 minutes?

8 z is proportional to m and $z = 20$ when $m = 4$. Find

(a) the value of z when $m = 7$

(b) the value of m when $z = 60$.

9 A recipe for 3 people requires 162 g of chicken.
How much chicken is needed to make enough food for 7 people?

10 If 5 paint brushes cost £18.25, how much would you need to buy 14 of these paint brushes?

11 

Several apples are peeled to show the outline of India and the Middle East. Eleven of these special apples cost £72.05. How much would you need to buy twenty of these special apples?

12 If a machine takes 16 seconds to make 2 cereal bowls, how long would it take to make 11 similar bowls?

Inverse proportion 1

Example

If it takes 4 men 12 days to build a wall, how long would it take 3 men to build the wall?

This is an example of *inverse* proportion.
The more men there are, the less time it will take.

4 men take 12 days
1 man takes 48 days
3 men take 16 days.

Exercise 3M

1 If it takes 7 builders 4 days to build a wall, how long would it take 2 builders?

2 If it takes 8 machines 3 hours to make 1200 g of spaghetti, how long would it take 2 machines to make the same amount?

3 It takes 2 workers 18 minutes to unload a lorry.
How long would 9 workers take?

4 It took 10 cows 4 days to graze a field. How long would it have taken 8 cows to graze the field?

5 If 4 machines take 8 minutes to make 10 000 matches, how many machines would be needed to make 10 000 matches in 2 minutes?

6 At a bakery, 5 staff take 6 hours to make 300 doughnuts.
How long would 6 staff take to make the same number?

7 It took 4 workers 12 minutes to carry a load of sand across a bridge.
How long would the job have taken if there had been only 3 workers?

8 

If there are 128 people in front of you in a queue, it takes 36 minutes before you are served. How long would you have to wait if there were only 32 people in front of you?

9 It took 5 soldiers 6 hours to dig a trench.
How long would it have taken 3 soldiers to dig an identical trench?

10 If 5 machines can wrap 60 toys in a minute, how many toys would 3 machines wrap in the same time?

The time T to build a sand castle is proportional to the square of its volume, V.
It takes 10 hours to build a castle of volume 2 m^3.
How long does it take to build a castle of volume 3 m^3?

We have $T \propto V^2$, so we can write $T = kV^2$, where k is a constant (number).

We are given that $T = 10$ when $V = 2$, so $10 = k \times 2^2$

$$k = \frac{10}{4} = \frac{5}{2}$$

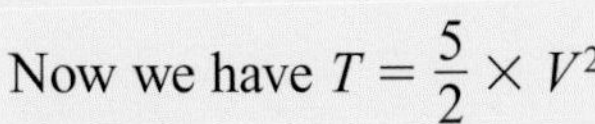

Now we have $T = \frac{5}{2} \times V^2$

So when $V = 3$, $T = \frac{5}{2} \times 3^2$ or $T = \frac{5 \times 9}{2} = 22\frac{1}{2}$ hours

Exercise 3E

1 In the tables below, y is directly proportional to x. We can write $y = kx$, where k is a constant (a number). In (a), (b) and (c) below find the value of k and then copy and complete the table.

(a)

x	3	8		18
y	6		22	

(b)

x	6	10		22
y	9		18	

(c)

x	1	3		$5\frac{1}{2}$
y	4		20	

2 y is proportional to t so that $y = kt$.
If $y = 9$ when $t = 6$, calculate the value of k and hence find

(a) the value of y when $t = 10$ (b) the value of t when $y = 6$.

3 A is proportional to r^2. If $A = 12$, when $r = 12$, calculate

(a) the value of A when $r = 4$ (b) the value of r when $A = 75$.

4 Given that $z \propto x$, copy and complete the table.

x	2	3		7.5
z	8		24	

5 Given that $P \propto x^3$, copy and complete the table.

x	1	3	4	10
P	3	81		

6 Given that $y \propto h$ and $y = 15$ when $h = 6$,
find the value of y when $h = 20$.

7 If y is directly proportional to x, state what happens to

(a) y if x is doubled (b) y if x is halved.

8

A model of the London Eye turns through one revolution in 2 minutes. How many degrees does it turn through in 1 second?

9 Find the cost of 10 km of pipe at 55p for every 25 cm.

10 Three men can build a shed in 10 hours.
How many men would be needed to build the shed in $7\frac{1}{2}$ hours?

11 In which of the graphs below is y directly proportional to x?

(a)
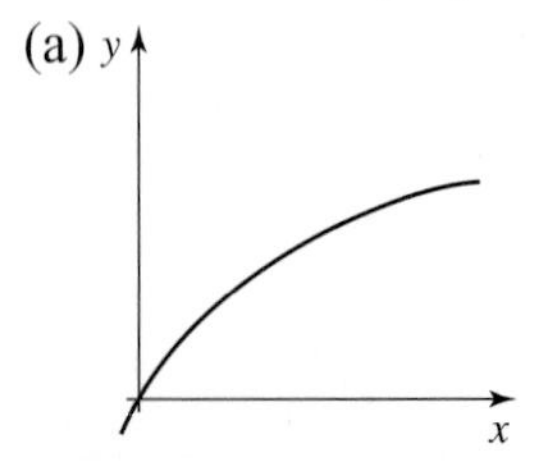

(b)
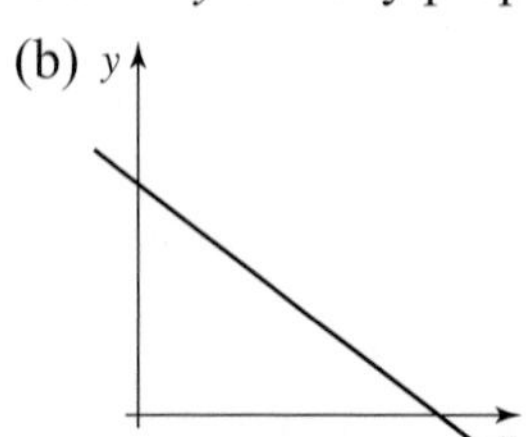

(c)
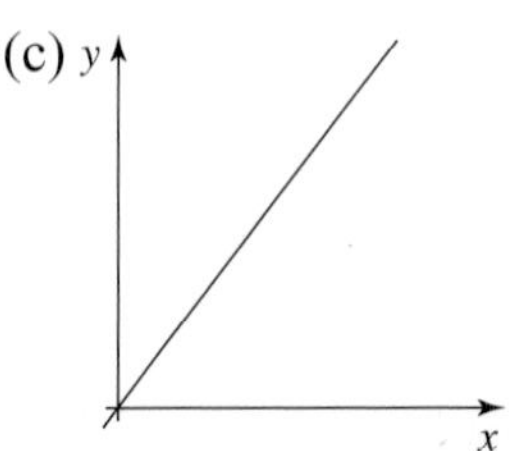

(d)
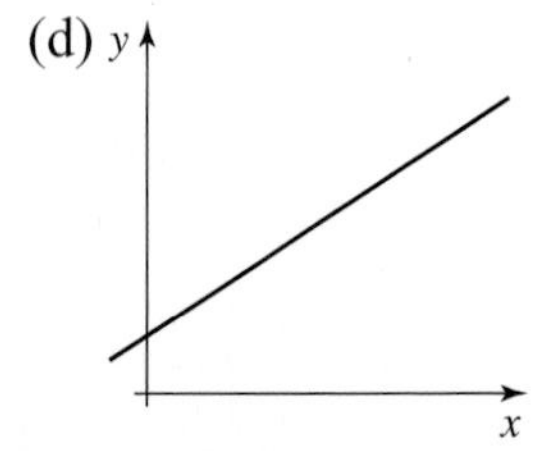

12 $y \propto x$ and $y = 76.8$ when $x = 6.4$. Find

(a) y when $x = 2.5$ (b) x when $y = 1212$.

13 One lorry carries enough food to supply 800 people for 20 days. How long would the food last for 500 people?

14 $h \propto m^2$ and $h = 1000$ when $m = 20$. Find

(a) h when $m = 30$ (b) m when $h = 202.5$

Inverse proportion 2

If a car travels 400 m at 10 m/s, the time taken is 40 s.
If the car travels 400 m at 20 m/s, the time taken is 20 s.
So as you *double* the speed, you *halve* the time taken.
For a fixed journey, the time taken is *inversely proportional* to the speed of travel.

If s is inversely proportional to t

you write $s \propto \frac{1}{t}$.

or $s = k \times \frac{1}{t}$

or $s \times t = k$

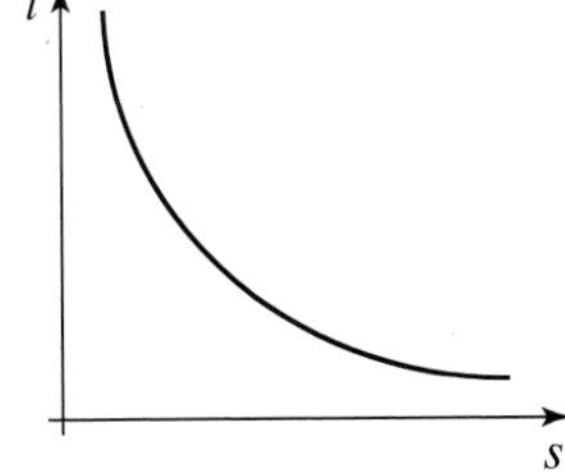

The graph connecting s and t is the curve shown above.

Notice that the shape of the curve is similar to the curve of $y = \frac{1}{x}$.

p is inversely proportional to s^2 and $p = 3$ when $s = 2$.
Calculate p when $s = 10$.

$p \propto \frac{1}{s^2}$ or $p = k \times \frac{1}{s^2}$

$p = 3$ when $s = 2$ so $3 = k \times \frac{1}{2^2}$

so $k = 3 \times 2^2 = 12$.

So $p = 12 \times \frac{1}{s^2}$.

When $s = 10$, $p = \frac{12}{10^2} = 0.12$

Exercise 4M/E

1 P is inversely proportional to s. When $P = 10$, $s = 2$.
Calculate P when $s = 5$.

2 h is inversely proportional to x^2. When $h = 10$, $x = 1$.
(a) Find the equation for h in terms of x [i.e. find $h = \ldots$].
(b) Find h when $x = 2$.

3 y is inversely proportional to $\sqrt{x}$. When $y = 2$, $x = 9$.
(a) Find the equation for y in terms of x [i.e. find $y = \ldots$].
(b) Find y when $x = 25$.

4 (a) Sketch the curve $y = \frac{12}{x}$ for values of x from 1 to 6.
(b) Find x when $y = 1.2$.

5 z is inversely proportional to $\sqrt{y}$. When $y = 100$, $z = 1.2$.
(a) Calculate the value of z when $y = 400$.
(b) Calculate the value of y when $z = 4$.

6 Sketch the graphs:
(a) $y = \frac{10}{x}$ for $0 < x \leqslant 10$
(b) $y = \frac{x}{10}$ for $-2 \leqslant x \leqslant 2$.

7 Here are four sketch graphs

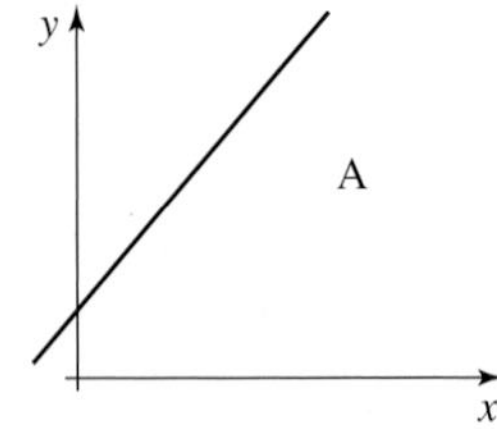

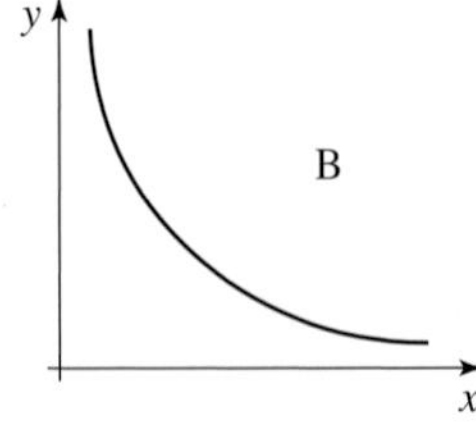

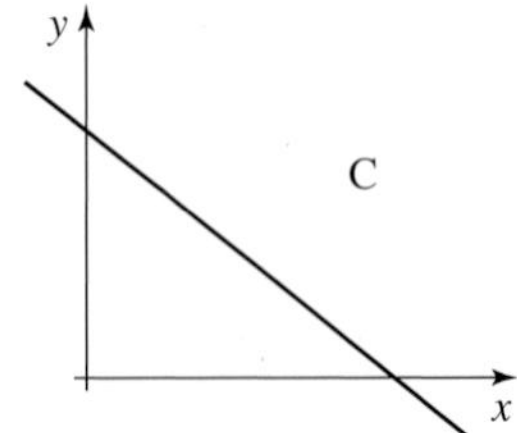

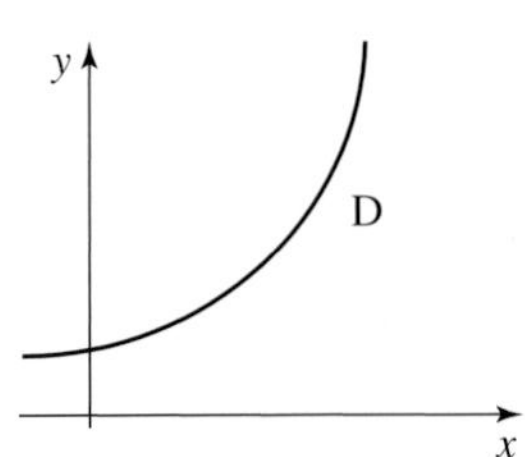

Decide which equation from the list below matches each graph.

$y = 2^x$ $\qquad$ $y = x + 3$ $\qquad$ $x + y = 8$ $\qquad$ $y = \frac{6}{x}$

8 You are given that the graphs below have equations:

$y = 5 - x$ $\quad$ $y = x + 2$ $\quad$ $y = \frac{10}{x}$ $\quad$ $y = x^2$ $\quad$ but not in this order.

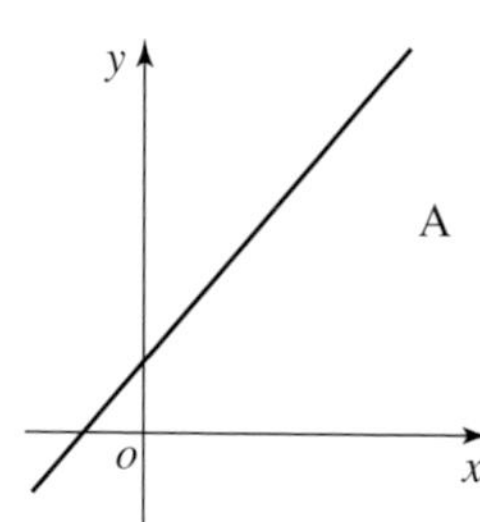

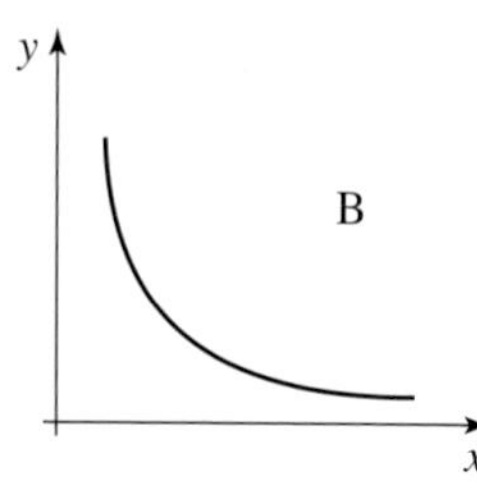

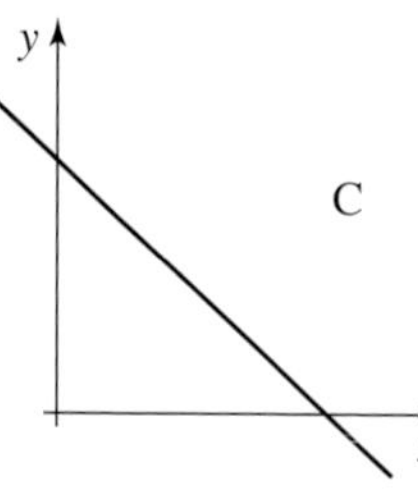

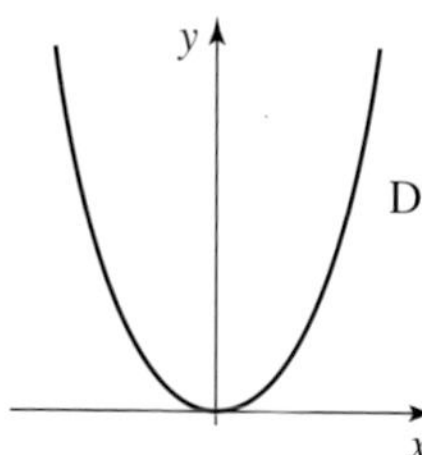

Copy and complete this list by choosing which equation fits each curve.

1. $y = x^2$ $\quad$ **2.** $y = 5 - x$ $\quad$ **3.** $y = \frac{10}{x}$ $\quad$ **4.** $y = x + 2$

9 The number of hours, H, needed to dig a certain hole is inversely proportional to the number of people who can dig.
When 6 people are digging, the hole takes 4 hours.

(a) How long would it take if 8 people were digging?

(b) If it takes half an hour to dig the hole, how many people are digging?

10 P is inversely proportional to s^2.
When $P = 3$, $s = 2$.

(a) Find the equation connecting P and s.

(b) Find the value of P when $s = 6$.

(c) Find the positive value of s when $P = 12$.

UNIT 4 MIXED REVIEW

Part one

1

This solid cube is made from alternate red and white centimetre cubes.

(a) Find the volume of the red cubes.

(b) How many centimetre cubes are on the outside of the cube?

2 The graph shows the water level in a bath. Use the letters A, B, C etc to describe when the events below occurred. [For example: A → B '............']

- John got out of bath
- Water drained from bath
- John got into bath
- Both taps on
- Hot tap on alone
- More hot water added when John was in bath
- John lies in bath, solving equations in his head.

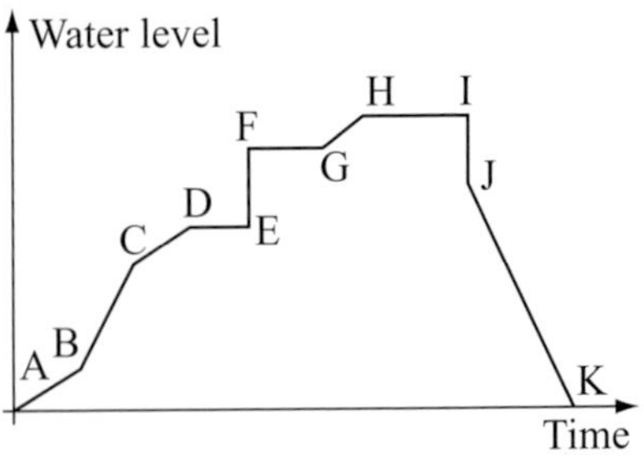

3 Copy shape A as shown. Shape A is enlarged so that it just fits inside the rectangle. Draw the enlargement of shape A and mark the centre of enlargement.

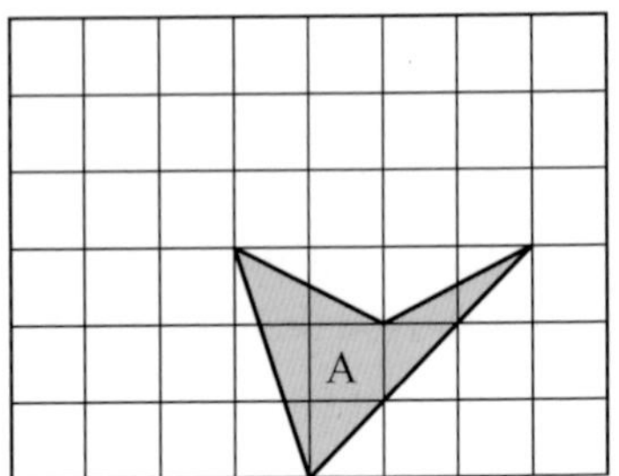

4

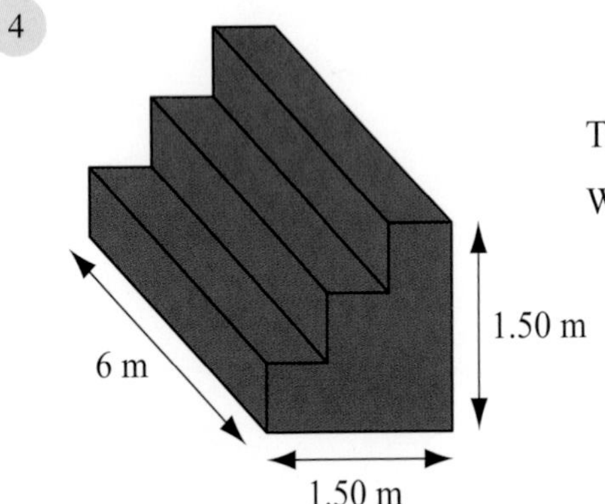

The diagram shows a set of steps made from concrete.

Work out the volume of the steps.

5 The circumference of a circular goldfish bowl is 124 cm. Work out the diameter of the bowl.

6 The cumulative frequency graph shows the weights of sheep in a field.

(a) How many sheep were weighed?

(b) What is the median weight?

(c) What is the lower quartile?

(d) What is the upper quartile?

(e) State the interquartile range.

(f) How many sheep weighed up to and including 45 kg?

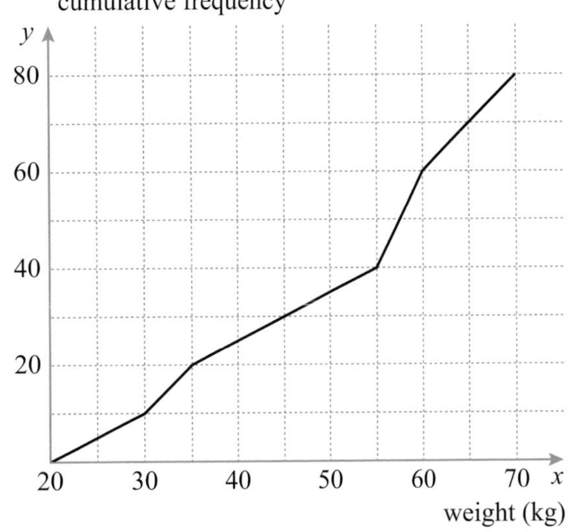

7 Emma's photo measures 4 cm × 6 cm.

(a) She wants to enlarge the photo so that it just fits a frame 12 cm × 18 cm.
By what scale factor should she multiply the original photo?

(b) Emma also wants a small photo to stick into an identity card. The small photo is 24 mm by 36 mm. By what scale factor should she multiply the original photo?

8 The mean weight of 8 apples is 120 g. If two extra apples weighing 135 g and 125 g are added, what is the new mean weight?

9 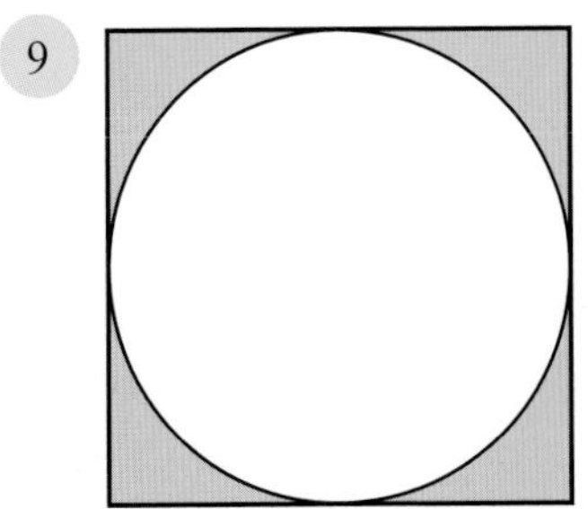

A circle is drawn inside a square of side 20 cm. Calculate the area of the pink shaded region.

10 Solve the simultaneous equations.

(a) $x + 4y = 6$
$3x - 2y = 11$

(b) $3x - y = -14$
$5x + 2y = -5$

11 Find the next term in each sequence.

(a)	(b)	(c)	(d)
4	1	5	1
10	6	16	3
18	15	39	19
28	28	80	85
?	?	145	261
		?	631
			?

12 A photograph measuring 5 cm by 3.5 cm is enlarged so that it fits exactly into a frame measuring 8 cm by x cm. Calculate the value of x.

13 Mr Davis is buying things for his new shop. He buys computers, televisions, videos and phones. He buys n computers.

Your answers to the following questions will involve n.

(a) He buys twice as many televisions as computers. How many televisions does he buy?
(b) He buys ten more videos than televisions. How many videos does he buy?
(c) He buys twice as many phones as televisions. How many phones does he buy?
(d) How many things does he buy altogether?

14 Cylinder A has radius 3.5 cm and height 8 cm.
Cylinder B has radius 5 cm.
If each cylinder has the same volume calculate the height h of cylinder B.

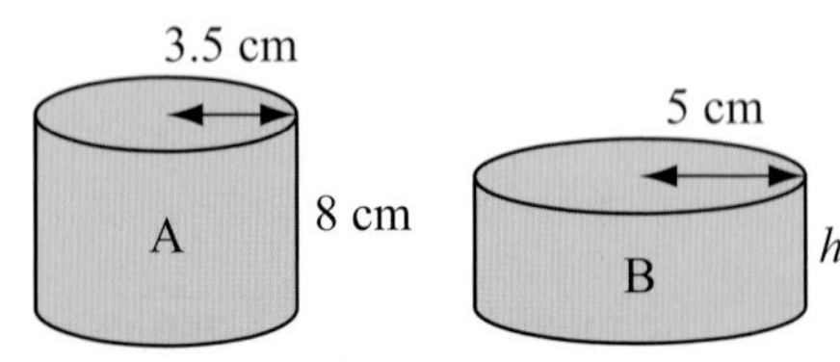

15 Draw x and y axes with values from –10 to +10. Plot and label the following triangles:

$\Delta 1$: (–1, –3) (–1, –5) (–5, –5)
$\Delta 2$: (1, 3) (1, 7) (3, 3)
$\Delta 3$: (3, –3) (7, –3) (7, –1)
$\Delta 4$: (–5, –5) (–5, –1) (–3, –1)
$\Delta 5$: (1, –6) (3, –6) (3, –5)
$\Delta 6$: (–3, 7) (–5, 7) (–3, 3)

Describe fully the following transformations

(a) $\Delta 1 \rightarrow \Delta 2$ (b) $\Delta 1 \rightarrow \Delta 4$ (c) $\Delta 1 \rightarrow \Delta 5$
(d) $\Delta 1 \rightarrow \Delta 6$ (e) $\Delta 5 \rightarrow \Delta 3$ (f) $\Delta 2 \rightarrow \Delta 3$

Part two

1 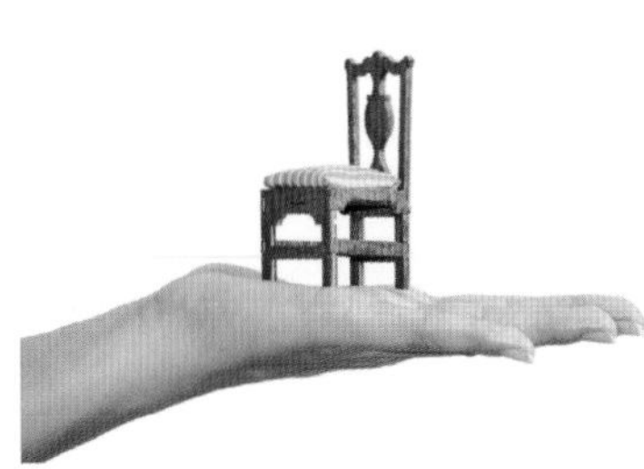

The photo shows an adult hand with a miniature chair. Make suitable measurements and estimate the scale to which the chair has been made.

2 Use the graph shown to solve the following pairs of simultaneous equations:

(a) $x - y = 2$
$3x + 5y = 30$

(b) $x - y = 2$
$2x + y = 7$

(c) $3x + 5y = 30$
$2x + y = 7$

[Give x and y correct to 1 d.p.]

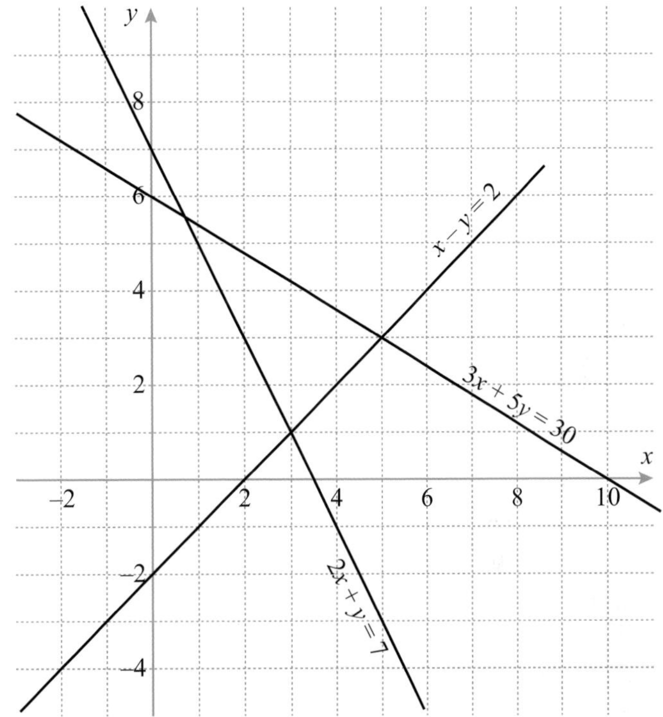

3 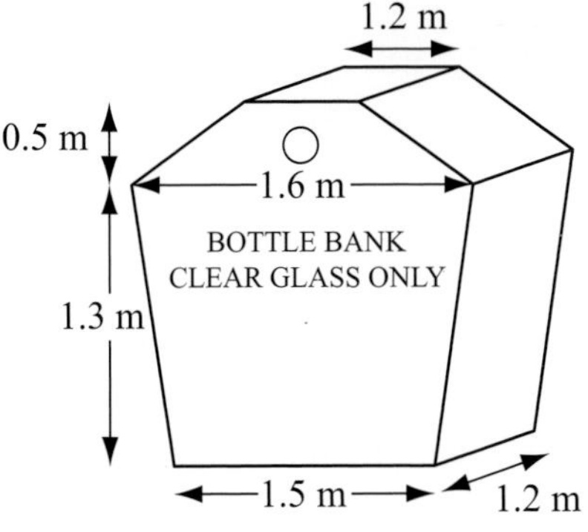

Find the volume of the bottle bank.

4 Write down the vector which is:

(a) parallel to and three times as long as the vector $\begin{pmatrix} -1 \\ 4 \end{pmatrix}$

(b) equal in length but opposite to the vector $\begin{pmatrix} 2 \\ -3 \end{pmatrix}$

(c) equal in length and perpendicular to the vector $\begin{pmatrix} 1 \\ -2 \end{pmatrix}$

5 A photograph measuring 6 cm by 4 cm is reduced to fit frame A and another copy of the photograph is enlarged to fit frame B.

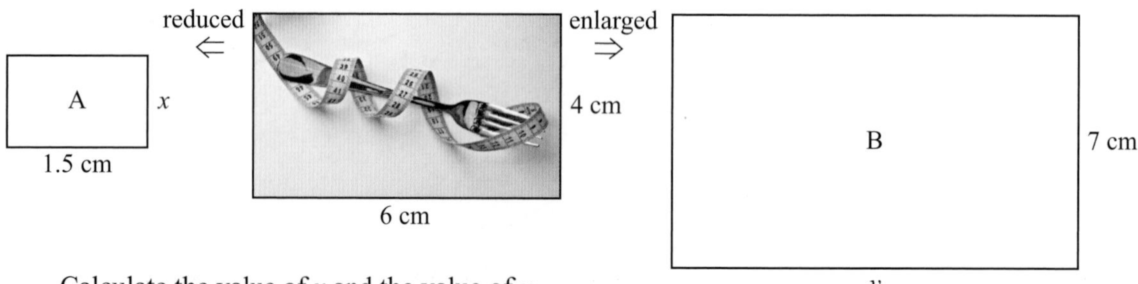

Calculate the value of x and the value of y.

6 The pie chart on the left shows the proportion of votes cast for each of the main political parties in a recent general election. The pie chart on the right shows the proportion of seats won by each party.

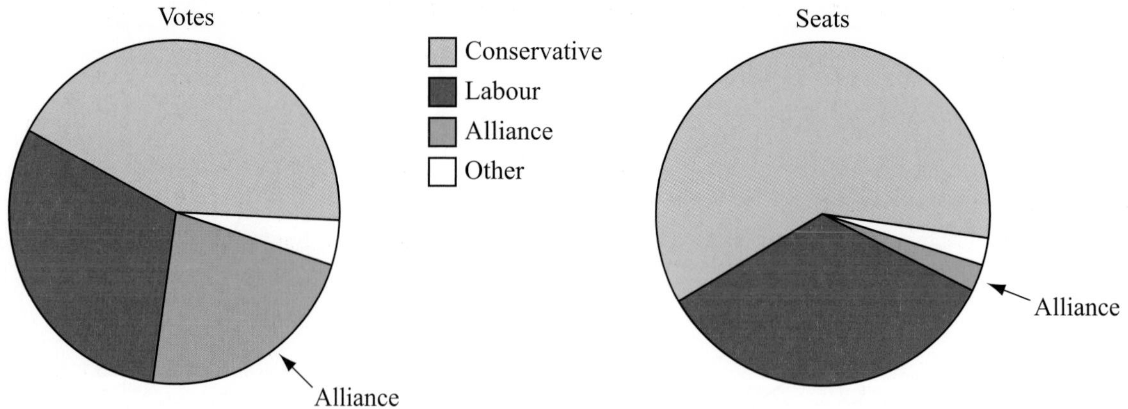

(a) There were 650 seats to be won in the election.

Estimate what percentage of the votes were cast for the Conservative party and estimate how many seats that party won.

Repeat these two calculations for the votes cast and seats won by the Alliance party.

(b) Comment briefly on your answers.

7 A railway tunnel 0.5 km long is to be cut through a hillside. The cross-section of the tunnel consists of a rectangle and a semicircle.

How much earth will have to be removed?

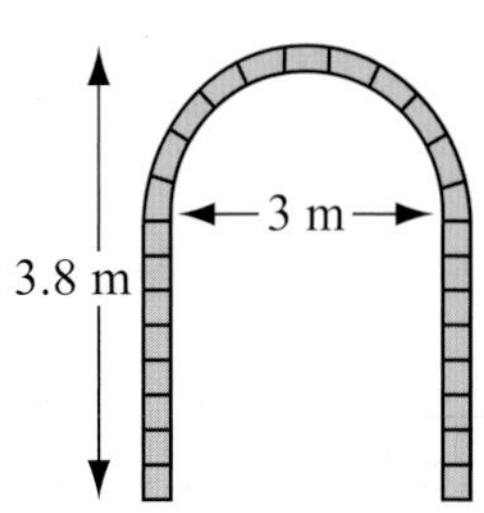

8 (a) Draw axes with x and y from –6 to +6.

(b) Plot and label Δ1 with vertices at (–6 , –2), (–6, –5), (–5, –2).

(c) Draw Δ2, Δ3, … Δ7 as follows:

(i) Δ1 → Δ2 Reflection in $y = x$

(ii) Δ2 → Δ3 Rotation 180°, centre (0, –5.5)

(iii) Δ3 → Δ4 Reflection in $y = -x$

(iv) Δ3 → Δ5 Rotation 90° anticlockwise, center (0, –3)

[Check that the right angle is at (2, –1)]

(v) Δ5 → Δ6 Enlargement, scale factor 3, centre (4, 0)

(vi) Δ5 → Δ7 Translation $\begin{pmatrix} -6 \\ 4 \end{pmatrix}$

(d) Describe fully each of the following single transformations:

(i) Δ7 → Δ6

(ii) Δ1 → Δ4

(iii) Δ2 → Δ5

9 Use trial and improvement to find one solution, correct to one decimal place.

(a) $x(x + 4) = 30$ (b) $x^3 + 3x = 100$

10 Find the value of each expression when $x = 3$, $y = -2$, $z = -1$.

(a) $x^2 + y^2$ (b) $xy + 3z$ (c) $2x^2$

(d) $yz - x^2$ (e) $\dfrac{x + y}{z}$ (f) $3y^2 + z^2$

11 The cross section of the prism shown is an equilateral triangle of side 8 cm. Calculate the volume of the prism.

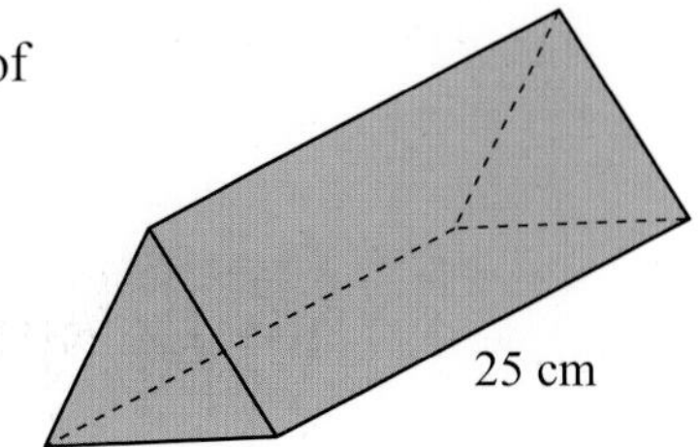

Surds

Numbers like $\sqrt{2}$, $\sqrt{3}$, $\sqrt{10}$ are called *surds*.

Using a calculator, $\sqrt{2} = 1.4142135 \ldots$

$\sqrt{2}$ is a non-terminating, non-recurring decimal.

The square shown has an area of 2 cm^2 and side length x cm.

2 cm² x x

So $x^2 = 2$

$x = \sqrt{2}$ cm This is the exact answer.

Rules for surds: $\sqrt{a} \times \sqrt{b} = \sqrt{ab}$ e.g. $\sqrt{4} \times \sqrt{9} = \sqrt{36}$
i.e. $[2 \times 3 = 6]$

$\frac{\sqrt{a}}{\sqrt{b}} = \sqrt{\frac{a}{b}}$ e.g. $\frac{\sqrt{36}}{\sqrt{4}} = \frac{6}{2} = 3$

Historical fact

The Greek word *a-logus* means 'irrational' but also means 'deaf'.

The Greek *a-logus* was translated as 'deaf', which in Latin is **surdus**.

So today numbers like $\sqrt{2}$, $\sqrt{5}$ … are called **surds**.

Note. An irrational number cannot be written in the form $\frac{a}{b}$, where a and b are whole numbers.

Exercise 1M

1 Sort these into four pairs of equal value.

A $\sqrt{9}$ B 5 C $\sqrt{100}$ D $2\sqrt{3}$

E $\sqrt{25}$ F $\sqrt{3} + \sqrt{3}$ G 3 H 10

2 Answer 'True' or 'False'.

(a) $(\sqrt{3})^2 = 3$ (b) $\sqrt{5} + \sqrt{5} = 2\sqrt{5}$ (c) $\sqrt{7} \times \sqrt{7} = 7$

(d) $3\sqrt{5} - \sqrt{5} = 2\sqrt{5}$ (e) $\sqrt{11} \times \sqrt{11} = 121$ (f) $3\sqrt{7} - \sqrt{7} = 3$

3 Simplify

(a) $\sqrt{9}$ (b) $\sqrt{5} \times \sqrt{5}$ (c) $2\sqrt{7} - \sqrt{7}$ (d) $\sqrt{3} \times \sqrt{3} \times \sqrt{3}$

(e) $\sqrt{2} \times \sqrt{8}$ (f) $6\sqrt{11} + 5\sqrt{11}$ (g) $(\sqrt{13})^2$ (h) $(\sqrt{2})^4$

4 Which of the following are true?

(a) $\sqrt{7} \times \sqrt{5} = \sqrt{35}$ (b) $\sqrt{9} + \sqrt{9} = \sqrt{18}$ (c) $\sqrt{18} = \sqrt{2 \times 9} = 3\sqrt{2}$

(d) $\sqrt{32} = \sqrt{16 \times 2} = 4\sqrt{2}$ (e) $\sqrt{12} = 2\sqrt{3}$

5 

$(\sqrt{7} - 1)$ cm

$\sqrt{7}$ cm

Find the area of this photo. Write your answer in a form involving surds.

6 Work out $(\sqrt{2})^4 + (3\sqrt{3})^2 - (\sqrt{5} \times \sqrt{5}) + (\sqrt{11})^4$

7 A satellite travels around the Earth in a circular orbit of radius $\sqrt{10\,000\,000}$ km. How far does the satellite travel in one orbit? (Take $\pi = 3.142$)

8 Simplify

(a) $(\sqrt{11})^4$ (b) $(\sqrt{27})^2 - (\sqrt{3})^2$ (c) $\sqrt{5} + \sqrt{5}$ (d) $6\sqrt{2} - \sqrt{2}$

(e) $\sqrt{3}(\sqrt{3} + 1)$ (f) $(3\sqrt{2})^3$ (g) $(2\sqrt{3})^4$ (h) $2\sqrt{5} \times 3\sqrt{2} - \sqrt{10}$

9 Which of the following numbers are rational?

(a) $\sqrt{3}$ (b) $\frac{\sqrt{3}}{2}$ (c) $(\sqrt{11})^2$ (d) $\frac{1}{3} + \frac{1}{9}$

(e) $\sqrt{5} - 1$ (f) $\sqrt{2.25}$ (g) $\sqrt{9} \times \sqrt{16}$ (h) $1 \div \sqrt{10\,000}$

10 Answer 'true' or 'false'.

(a) $\sqrt{28} = 2\sqrt{7}$ (b) $(\sqrt{7})^2 = 7$ (c) $\sqrt{2} + \sqrt{2} = 2\sqrt{2}$ (d) $\frac{\sqrt{64}}{16} = 0.5$

11 

$\sqrt{18 \times 2}$ cm

$\sqrt{25}$ cm

Work out:

(a) The perimeter of this photo.

(b) The area of this photo.

12 Write down which of the statements below are true.

(a) $\sqrt{2} \times \sqrt{2} = \sqrt{4}$ (b) $\sqrt{7} \times \sqrt{3} = \sqrt{21}$ (c) $\sqrt{5} + 3\sqrt{5} = 4\sqrt{5}$

(d) $\sqrt{300} = 10\sqrt{3}$ (e) $\sqrt{9} \times \sqrt{9} \times \sqrt{4} = 16$ (f) $\sqrt{11} + \sqrt{5} = 4$

13 Work out the following and give the answer in its simplest form.

(a) $\sqrt{5} \times \sqrt{7}$ (b) $\sqrt{8} \times \sqrt{2}$ (c) $\sqrt{7} \times \sqrt{13}$ (d) $\dfrac{\sqrt{100}}{\sqrt{10\,000}}$

14 The cube shown has sides of length $\sqrt{3}$ cm.

Work out: (a) the area of each face of the cube

(b) the volume of the cube.

Give your answers using surds, where necessary.

Exercise 1E

1 Without using a calculator, simplify the following.
Write your answers using surds where necessary.

(a) $\sqrt{7} \times \sqrt{2}$ (b) $\sqrt{32}$ (c) $\sqrt{200}$ (d) $\sqrt{5} + \sqrt{5}$ (e) $7\sqrt{3} - 2\sqrt{3}$

(f) $\sqrt{100} \times 7$ (g) $\sqrt{144} \times \sqrt{9}$ (h) $\sqrt{27}$ (i) $\sqrt{125}$

2 Find the area of each shape.

(a)

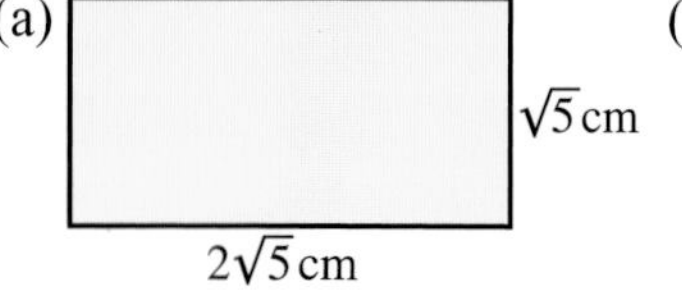

(b)

2√3 cm

√3 cm

(c)

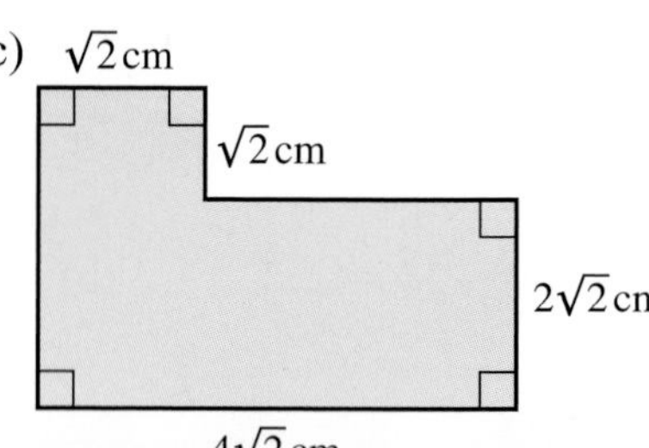

3 Simplify as far as possible.

(a) $5\sqrt{11} - 2\sqrt{11}$ (b) $\sqrt{16} \times \sqrt{9}$ (c) $(\sqrt{100})^3$ (d) $\sqrt{27} + 2\sqrt{3}$

(e) $\sqrt{100} + \sqrt{100}$ (f) $\sqrt{144} \div \sqrt{100}$ (g) $5\sqrt{5} + \sqrt{45}$

4

Some people think more clearly when they bury their head in the sand. Mr Neige is trying to work out $(\sqrt{5})^4$.
What is the correct answer?

5 Which of the statements below are true?

(a) $\sqrt{20} \div \sqrt{2} = \sqrt{10}$ (b) $\sqrt{19} - \sqrt{9} = \sqrt{10}$ (c) $\sqrt{169} - \sqrt{100} = \sqrt{69}$

6 Show that $(\sqrt{5} + \sqrt{2})(\sqrt{5} - \sqrt{2}) = 3$.

7 Find the exact value (using surds) of

(a) the area of this rectangle

(b) the perimeter of this rectangle.

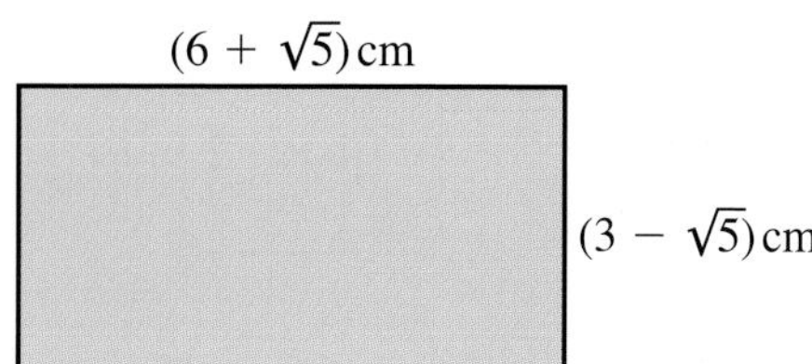

8 Simplify the following as far as possible:

(a) $8\sqrt{3} - 6\sqrt{3}$ (b) $7\sqrt{5} - \sqrt{5}$ (c) $\sqrt{8} + \sqrt{8}$

(d) $2\sqrt{5} \times 2\sqrt{5}$ (e) $\sqrt{10\,000} - \sqrt{100}$ (f) $(\sqrt{3} + 2)^3$

9 Answer 'true' or 'false': $\sqrt{16 + 9} = \sqrt{16} + \sqrt{9}$.

10 Write the following in the form $n\sqrt{3}$; where n is to be found.

(a) $\sqrt{12}$ (b) $\sqrt{27}$ (c) $\sqrt{300}$ (d) $\sqrt{75} - \sqrt{48}$

11 

The cube shown has sides of length $(4 - \sqrt{2})$ cm. Work out:

(a) the area of each face of the cube

(b) the volume of the cube.

Write your answers using surds.

12 Prove that $(\sqrt{6} + \sqrt{5})(\sqrt{6} - \sqrt{5}) = 1$.

13 Work out:

(a) the perimeter of this photo,

(b) the area of this photo.

Write your answers using surds.

Exercise 2E

1 Sort these cards into four pairs of equal value.

A	B	C	D
$\sqrt{20}$	$\sqrt{12}$	$\sqrt{3}$	$2\sqrt{3}$

E	F	G	H
2	$\sqrt{10} \times \sqrt{2}$	$\dfrac{\sqrt{20}}{\sqrt{5}}$	$\dfrac{\sqrt{15}}{\sqrt{5}}$

2 Answer 'true' or 'false'.

(a) $\sqrt{28} = 2\sqrt{7}$ (b) $(\sqrt{8})^2 = 8$ (c) $\sqrt{16} = \pm 4$

(d) $\sqrt{\dfrac{39}{3}} = \sqrt{13}$ (e) $\sqrt{4} + \sqrt{4} = \sqrt{8}$ (f) If $x^2 = 9, x = \pm 3$

3 Remove the brackets and simplify.

(a) $(1 + \sqrt{2})^2$ (b) $(2 - \sqrt{3})^2$ (c) $(\sqrt{2} + \sqrt{8})^2$

(d) $(3 - \sqrt{5})^2$ (e) $(\sqrt{2} + 2)^2$ (f) $(\sqrt{18} - \sqrt{2})^2$

4 Answer 'true' or 'false'.

(a) $\sqrt{2} + \sqrt{2} = 2\sqrt{2}$ (b) $\dfrac{\sqrt{8}}{2} = \sqrt{2}$ (c) $\sqrt{100} = \pm 10$

(d) $(\sqrt{2})^4 = 4$ (e) $\sqrt{9 + 16} = \sqrt{9} + \sqrt{16}$ (f) $(1 + \sqrt{3})^2 = 4 + 2\sqrt{3}$

5 Without using a calculator, simplify the following. Write your answer using surds where necessary.

(a) $\sqrt{8} \times \sqrt{2}$ (b) $\sqrt{32}$ (c) $\sqrt{300}$ (d) $\sqrt{18} \times 3$

(e) $\sqrt{5} + 4\sqrt{5}$ (f) $7\sqrt{3} - 2\sqrt{3}$ (g) $\sqrt{20} + \sqrt{45}$ (h) $\sqrt{75} - \sqrt{48}$

(i) $\dfrac{\sqrt{8}}{\sqrt{2}}$ (j) $\dfrac{\sqrt{27}}{\sqrt{12}}$ (k) $\dfrac{\sqrt{125}}{\sqrt{20}}$ (l) $\dfrac{\sqrt{80}}{\sqrt{45}}$

6 

The circular pond shown has radius $2\sqrt{7}$ m.
Work out the area of the pond.
(Use $\pi = \frac{22}{7}$)

Puzzles and Problems 4

Puzzles

1 The sum of three prime numbers is 50.
What is the smallest number?

2 A six-digit telephone number can start with any digit apart from zero.
The other five digits can be any number.
How many different six-digit numbers are there?

3278I4 921487 862103

3 Fill in the space in words so that it is correct:
'*This sentence has* _______ *letters*.'

4 The symbols *, ○, △, □, represent weights.
Use the information in (i), (ii), (iii) to answer part (iv).

(a) (i) * + △ = □

(ii) * = △ + ○

(iii) * + * + △ = □ + ○ + ○

(iv) △ = How many ○s?

(b) (i) ○ + ○ + □ = * + ○

(ii) * + * = ○ + ○ + ○

(iii) □ + * = ○ + ○

(iv) * = How many □s?

5 PQRS is a rectangle in which PQ = 2QR. Point E is such that PQE is an equilateral triangle which overlaps rectangle PQRS. M is the mid point of EQ. Find the size of angle QMR.

6 Show how the cross can be cut along the broken lines and the pieces rearranged to make a square.

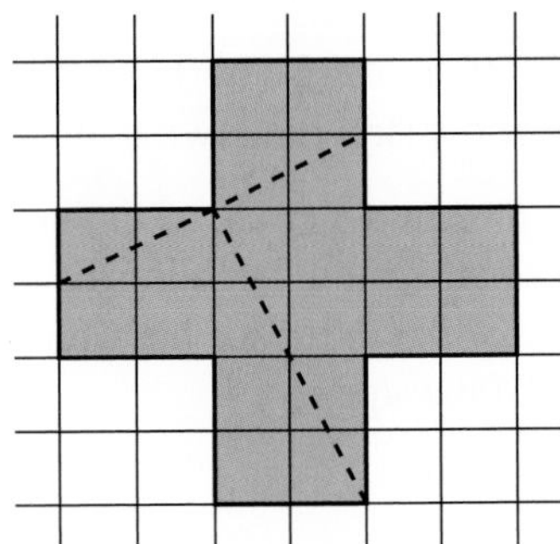

7 What is the sum of all the digits in the number $10^{30} - 90$?

8 The whole numbers from 1 to 789 are alternately added and subtracted:

$$1 - 2 + 3 - 4 + 5 - 6 + \ldots + 787 - 788 + 789.$$

What is the result?

9 The formula for converting degrees Celsius (°C) to degrees Fahrenheit (°F) is $F = \frac{9}{5}C + 32$.
At which temperature do both scales have the same reading?

10 Find (the sum of the first nine prime numbers) $\times (3\sqrt{2})^4 \times \sqrt{\dfrac{1}{0.0001}}$

11 Write in the simplest form:

(a) $1+\dfrac{2}{1+\dfrac{1}{1+2}}$

(b) $1+\dfrac{2}{1+\dfrac{1}{1+\dfrac{2}{1+2}}}$

12 The *factorial* notation uses an exclamation mark to show a product of decreasing integers. For example $4! = 4 \times 3 \times 2 \times 1$ and $7! = 7 \times 6 \times 5 \times 4 \times 3 \times 2 \times 1$.
How many zeros are at the end of 20!?

13 What is the radius of a circle whose area is $\dfrac{1}{\pi}$ square units?

14 Find the diameters of the circles if PQ = 9, PR = 7, QR = 5.

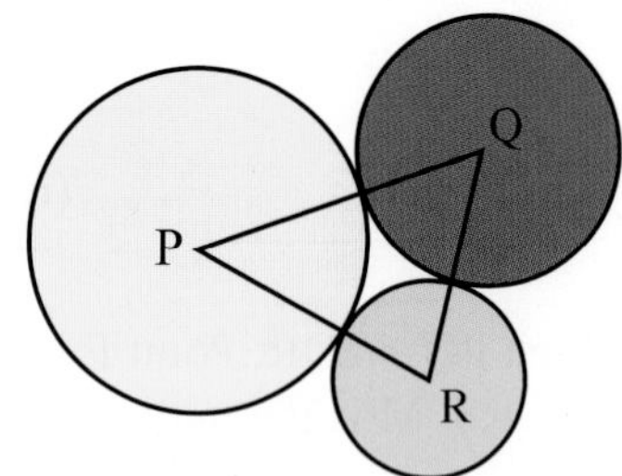

15 The Sun is 60° above the horizon. A vertical tree, 80 feet high, casts its shadow straight down a 30° slope. How long is the shadow?

16 The diagram shows a circle of radius 1 unit touching two sides of a square. Find the radius of the largest circle which could be drawn in the space between the circle and the corner of the square.

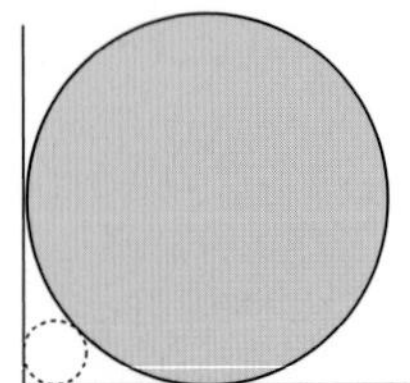

17 The Humber Bridge is seriously big! Its span is 1.37 miles and its two 533 ft towers are set almost 2 inches out of parallel to allow for the curvature of the Earth. In other words the distance between the towers is 2 inches greater at the top than at the base of the towers. Use the above information to calculate an estimate for the radius of the Earth.

A long time ago! 4

Pascal's triangle

							1							
						1		1						
					1		2		1					
				1		3		3		1				
			1		4		6		4		1			
		1		5		10		10		5		1		
	1		6		15		20		15		6		1	
1		7		21		35		35		21		7		1

This remarkable triangle of numbers was first discovered by Chinese then Arabic mathematicians.

Each number within the triangle is obtained by adding the two numbers directly above it.

Work out the next row of numbers then check it with your teacher.

The triangle is widely used in algebra and probability. It was finally named after the French mathematician, Blaise Pascal, who lived in the 17th century.

1. There are many number patterns to be found. Make your own copy of Pascal's triangle then highlight where the triangular numbers appear.

2. Look at the second number in each row of Pascal's triangle. If it is prime, what do you notice about the other numbers in the same row?

3. The top row is called row O.
The next row is called row 1, etc.

   Add up all the numbers in each row of your Pascal's triangle. The answers form a pattern. Describe it. Try to write down a formula for this number in row n

				1					→ row 0
			1		1				→ row 1
		1		2		1			→ row 2
	1		3		3		1		→ row 3
1		4		6		4		1	→ row 4

4 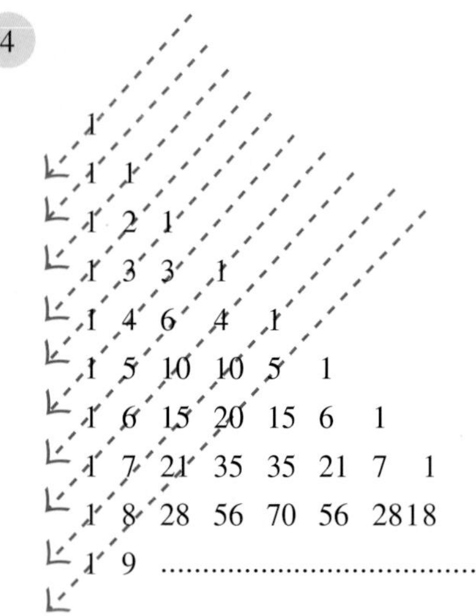

Here Pascal's triangle has been written in a slightly different format.
Add the numbers shown along each broken diagonal line.
The answers form a sequence.
Describe and name this sequence. Are you surprised to see it appear?

5 If you toss 2 coins, there are four possible outcomes.

H, H	H, T T, H	T, T
1	2 (one head, one tail)	1

If you toss 3 coins, there are eight possible outcomes.

H, H, H	H, H, T or H, T, H or T, H, H	H, T, T or T, H, T or T, T, H	T, T, T
1	3 (two heads, one tail)	3 (one head, two tails)	1

Amazingly these numbers are found in the rows of Pascal's triangle.

(a) Consider 4 coins. Use Pascal's triangle to predict how many possible outcomes there are for the following:

four heads
three heads, one tail
two heads, two tails
one head, three tails
four tails

(b) Check your answer to part (a) by drawing out each possibility using H and T as shown above.

6 As a group, design a poster to show your findings in this section.

UNIT 5

5.1 Trigonometry

In section 5.1 you will:

- learn how to find an angle or a side in a right angled triangle
- learn how to find the length of the hypotenuse
- learn how to use trigonometry to solve problems based on real life situations.

Sides of a triangle

In a right angled triangle we use different words to describe the three sides.

The longest side (opposite the right angle) is the *Hypotenuse*, HYP. The side opposite a known second angle, x, is the *Opposite*, OPP. The length touching both, x, and the right angle is the *Adjacent*, ADJ.

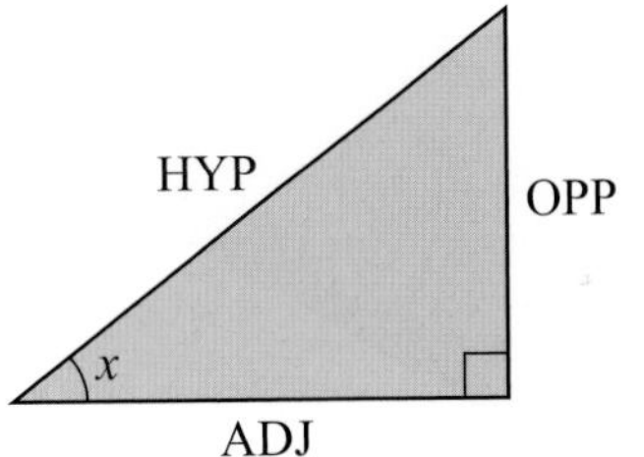

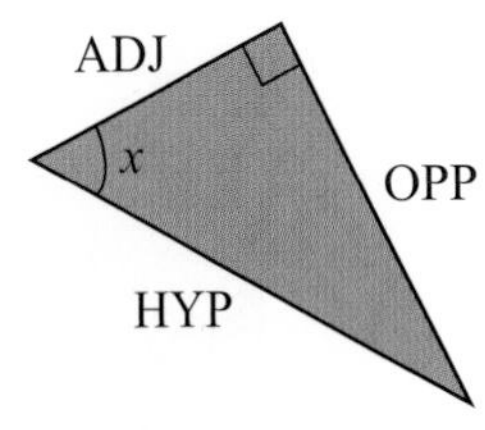

Exercise 1M

1 [This question can be done orally.] Use the small letters a, b, c, d etc to label the opposite, hypotenuse and adjacent in relation to the angle marked in each triangle.

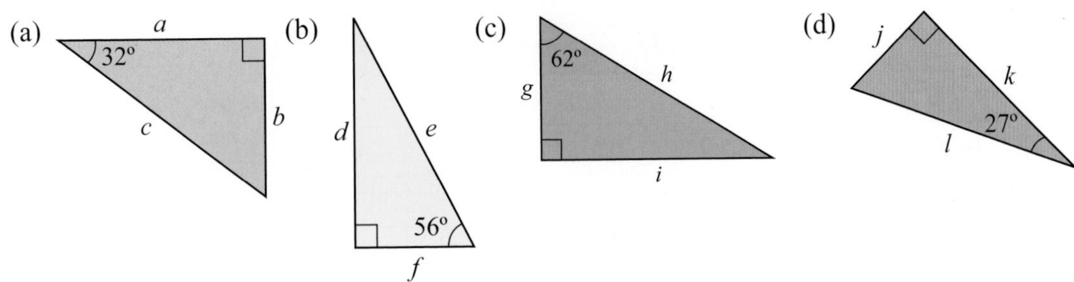

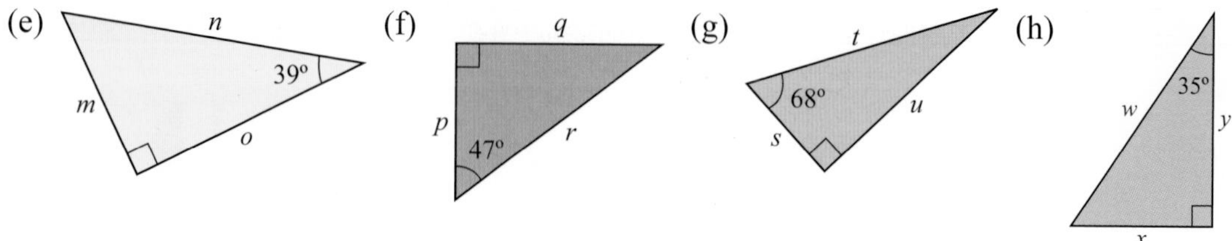

2 All the right angled triangles below have a 30° angle. Make a copy of the table on the next page and write in the measurements as accurately as possible. Calculate the ratios $\frac{\text{OPP}}{\text{HYP}}$, $\frac{\text{ADJ}}{\text{HYP}}$, $\frac{\text{OPP}}{\text{ADJ}}$, and write these in the table. The numbers for the first triangle have been completed for you.

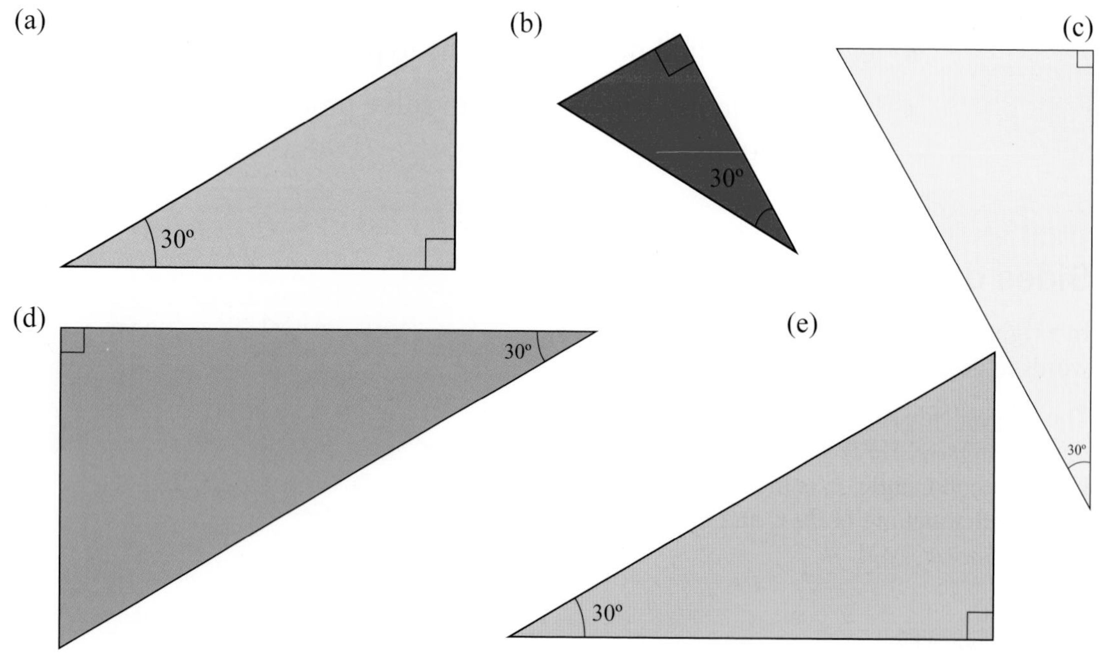

Triangle	Lengths			Ratios (to 2 d.p.)		
	Opp	Adj	Hyp	Opp÷Hyp	Adj÷Hyp	Opp÷Adj
(a)	2.95	5.1	5.9	0.5	0.86	0.58
(b)						
(c)						
(d)						
(e)						

3 Choose a different angle to 30° and draw five more right angled triangles of your own. Keep the angles the same but change the lengths of the sides. Make the table of results as before. Comment on what you notice.

Ratios of sides

You should have found that the ratios $\frac{\text{OPP}}{\text{HYP}}$, $\frac{\text{ADJ}}{\text{HYP}}$ and $\frac{\text{OPP}}{\text{ADJ}}$ remained constant if the angle remained the same. Any slight difference is due to the fact that it is impossible to measure with complete accuracy.

The ratios of these lengths remain constant for any given angle. Before we had calculators these values were printed in tables but now we literally have the answers at our fingertips.

$\frac{\text{OPP}}{\text{HYP}}$ = Sine of the angle	SIN	on a calculator
$\frac{\text{ADJ}}{\text{HYP}}$ = Cosine of the angle	COS	on a calculator
$\frac{\text{OPP}}{\text{ADJ}}$ = Tangent of the angle	TAN	on a calculator

On a calculator type SIN 30 =. The answer should be 0·5 (compare with the value you got for $\frac{\text{OPP}}{\text{HYP}}$ in question 2).

Finding a side using sine

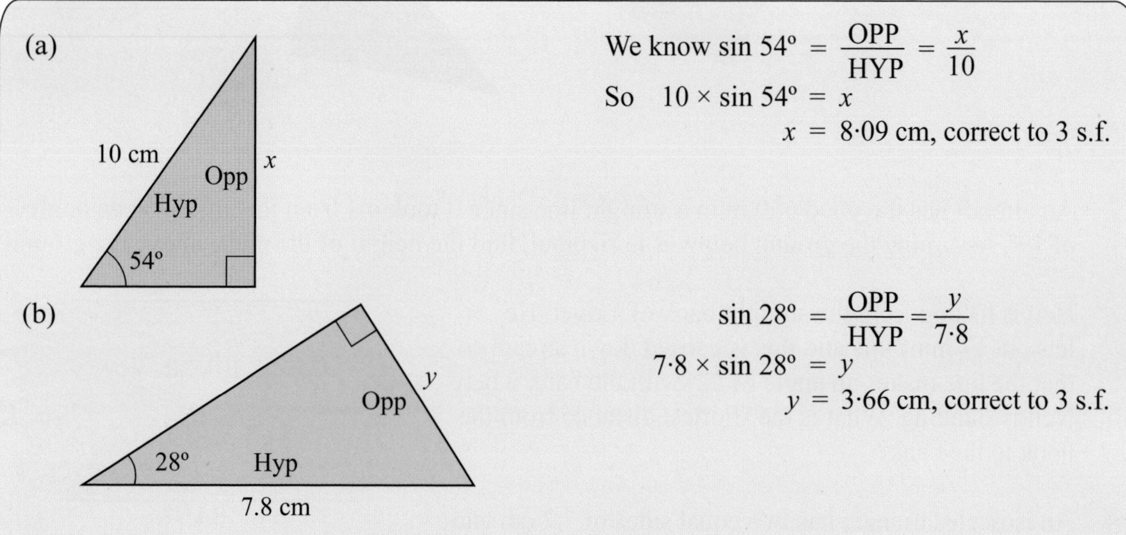

(a) We know $\sin 54° = \frac{\text{OPP}}{\text{HYP}} = \frac{x}{10}$

So $10 \times \sin 54° = x$

$x = 8{\cdot}09$ cm, correct to 3 s.f.

(b) $\sin 28° = \frac{\text{OPP}}{\text{HYP}} = \frac{y}{7{\cdot}8}$

$7{\cdot}8 \times \sin 28° = y$

$y = 3{\cdot}66$ cm, correct to 3 s.f.

Warning! Most calculators have 3 trigonometry modes: 'Deg', 'Rad' and 'Gra'. Make sure you work in 'Deg' mode.

Exercise 2M

1. Copy the following triangles and then use sine to find the required length, correct to 3 significant figures.

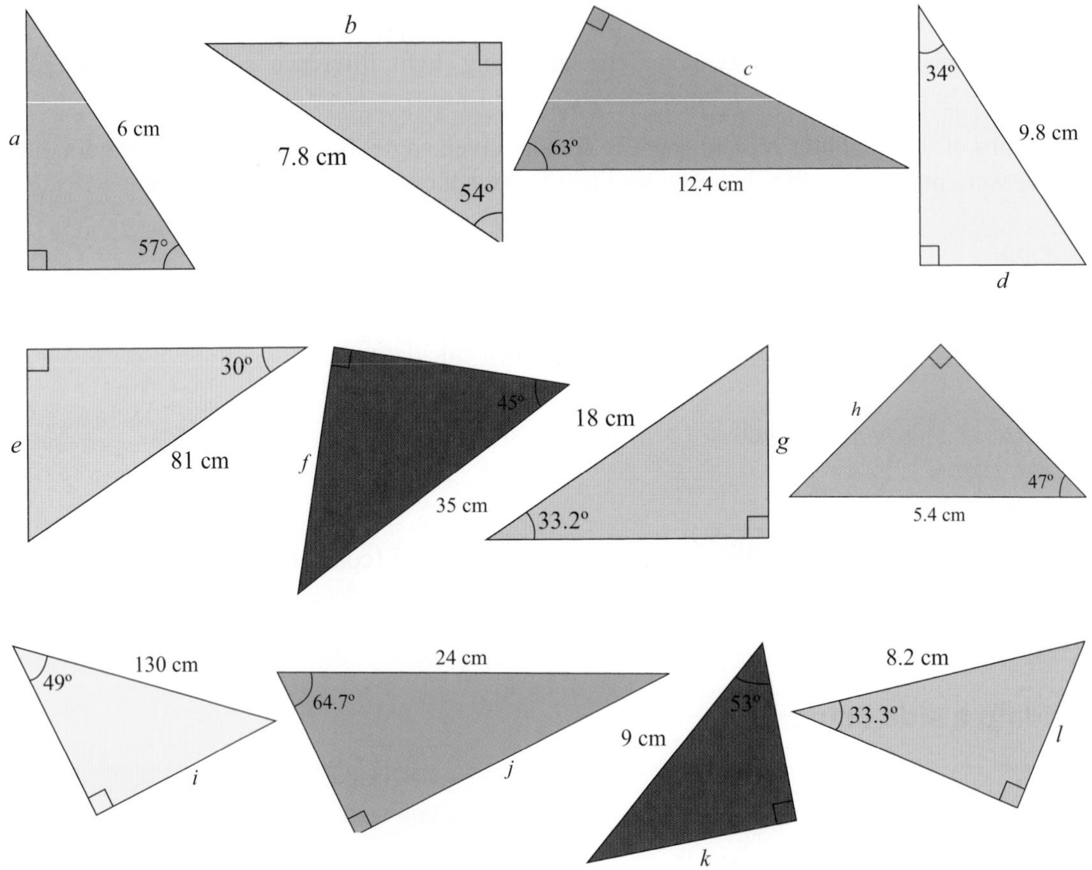

2. An aircraft has travelled 650 m in a straight line since it took off from the ground at an angle of 19°. Assuming the ground below is horizontal, find the height of the plane above the ground.

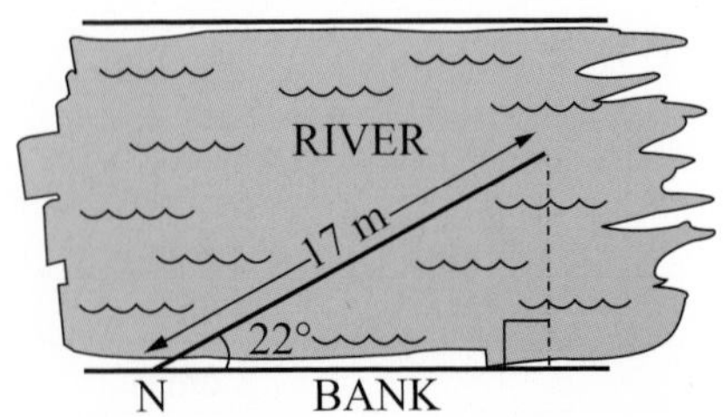

3. Neil is fishing from the straight bank of a river. He lets out 17 m of line and this is carried down stream so that the line makes an angle of 22° with the bank where Neil is standing. What is the shortest distance from the hook to the bank?

4. An isosceles triangle has two equal sides of 7.2 cm and equal base angles of 70°. Calculate the vertical height of the triangle.

5 A see-saw is made from a 6 foot plank of wood pivoting about the middle on a stand. The piece of wood makes an angle of 32° with the ground when one side of the see-saw is touching the ground. How high is the pivot stand?

6 Barbed wire of length 76m is fixed to opposite corners of a square field. How long are the sides of the field?

7 Sami walks for 1.7 km on a bearing of 042°. How far east has she walked from her starting position?

Finding a side using sine, consine or tangent

In the last exercise the questions were made easier because you used the sine of an angle every time. In general, when solving a right angle triangle, you may have to use sine, cosine or tangent.

Remember: $\sin x = \dfrac{\text{OPP}}{\text{HYP}}$ $\cos x = \dfrac{\text{ADJ}}{\text{HYP}}$ $\tan x = \dfrac{\text{OPP}}{\text{ADJ}}$

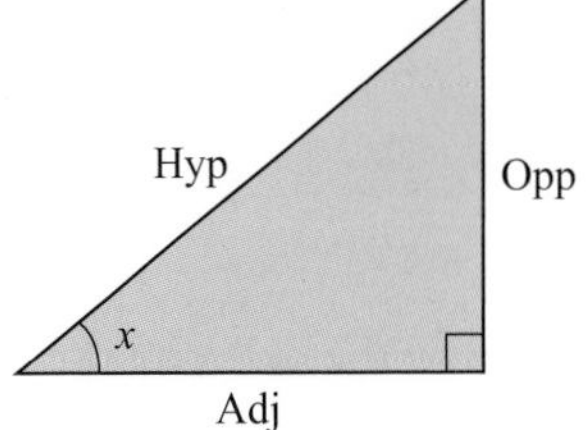

Many people use the word 'SOHCAHTOA' to help them choose the correct function. When solving triangles you should go through three stages:

1 Draw a diagram.

2 Label the sides Opp, Hyp, Adj relative to the given angle

3 Decide whether you need sin, cos or tan.

Find the sides marked with letters.

(a)

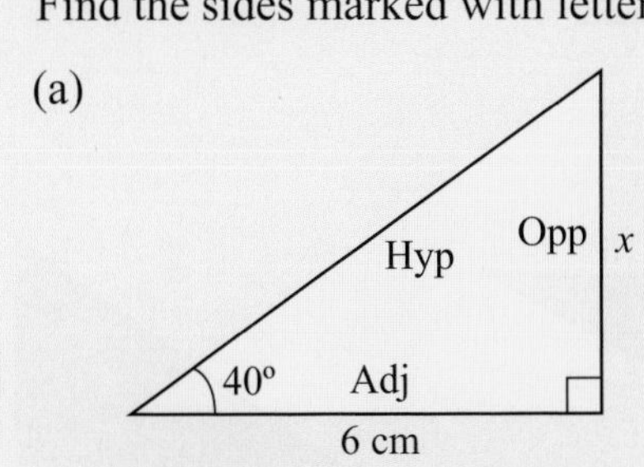

Label Opp, Hyp, Adj.
Since we want 'Opp' and we know 'Adj', choose tan.

$$\tan 40^\circ = \frac{\text{Opp}}{\text{Adj}} = \frac{x}{6}$$

$$6 \times \tan 40^\circ = x$$

$$x = 5{\cdot}03 \text{ cm, correct to 3 s.f.}$$

(b)

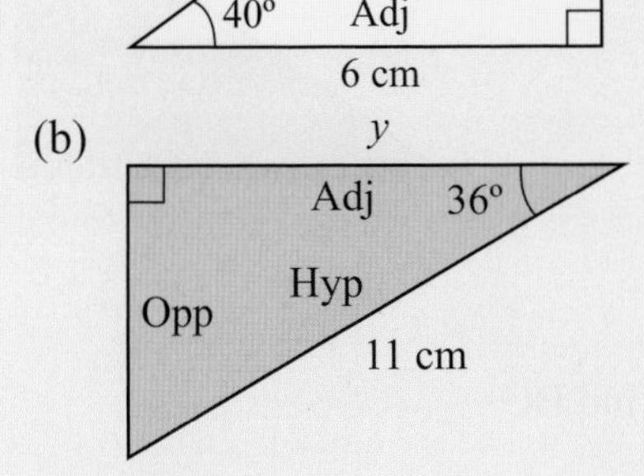

Label Opp, Hyp, Adj.
Since we want 'Adj' and we know 'Hyp', choose cos.

$$\cos 36^\circ = \frac{\text{Adj}}{\text{Hyp}} = \frac{y}{11}$$

$$11 \times \cos 36^\circ = y$$

$y = 8.90$ cm, correct to 3 s.f.

Exercise 3M

1 Sketch each triangle and find the sides marked with letters, correct to 3 s.f. All lengths are in cm.

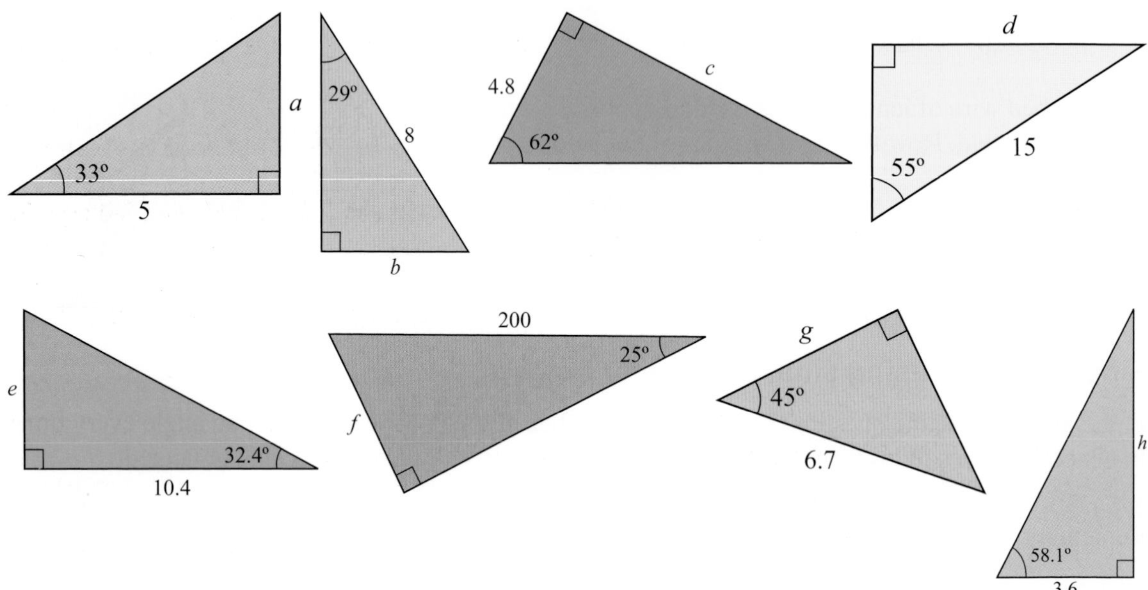

2 Find the sides marked with letters, correct to 3 s.f. All lengths are in cm.

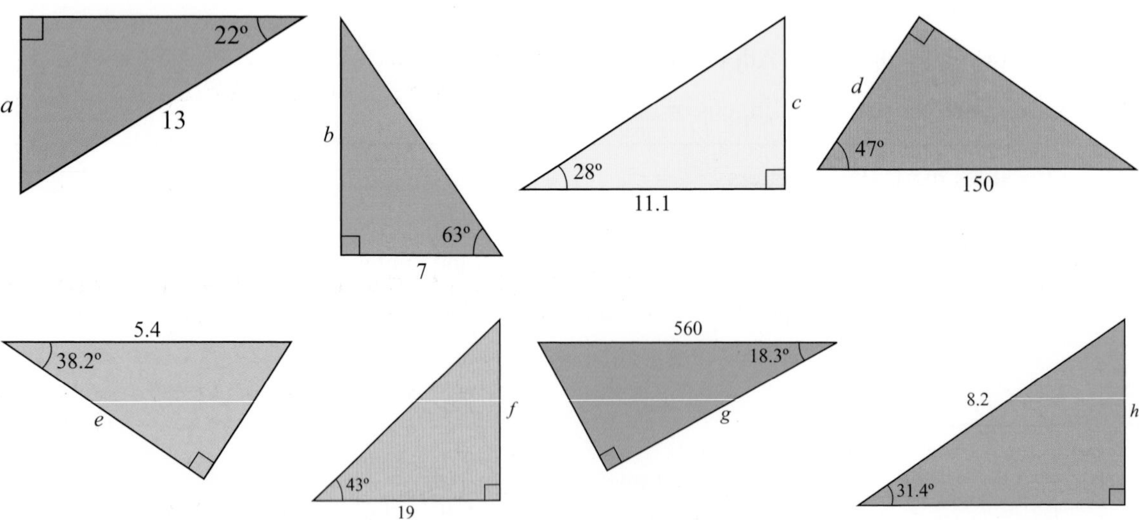

3 In triangle ABC, $A\hat{B}C = 90°$, $B\hat{A}C = 37°$, AC = 5 cm. Find BC.

4 In triangle DEF, $D\hat{F}E = 90°$, $E\hat{D}F = 42°$, DE = 8 cm. Find EF.

5 In triangle GHI, $G\hat{I}H = 90°$, $G\hat{H}I = 67°$, $GH = 8$ cm. Find HI.

6 In triangle PQR, $P\hat{Q}R = 90°$, $Q\hat{P}R = 35°$, $PQ = 10$ cm. Find RQ.

7 In triangle STU, $U\hat{S}T = 90°$, $S\hat{U}T = 43°$, $UT = 100$ cm. Find SU.

Exercise 3E

1 A ladder leans against a vertical wall so that it makes an angle of 28° with the wall. The top of the ladder reaches 3 m up the wall. How far from the wall is the base of the ladder?

2 A ladder of length 4 m rests against a vertical wall so that the angle between the ladder and the ground is 66°. How far up the wall does the ladder reach?

3 An isosceles triangle has two equal sides of 15 cm and equal base angles of 68°. How long is the base of the triangle?

4 The sail for a windsurfer is in the shape of a right angled triangle. If the height of the sail is 3.2 m and the longest side makes an angle of 32° with the mast how wide is the base of the sail?

5 Prince stands 30 m from the base of a tree. The angle of elevation to the top of the tree is 32°. How tall is the tree?

6 A girl is flying a kite from a string of length 45 m. If the string is taut and makes an angle of 34° with the horizontal, what is the height of the kite?

7 Robert is standing on the third floor of a block of flats. There is an office block that is 40 m across the street from him. Robert estimates the angle of elevation to the top of the block is 52° and the angle of depression to the base is 27°. Work out the height of the office block, correct to the nearest metre.

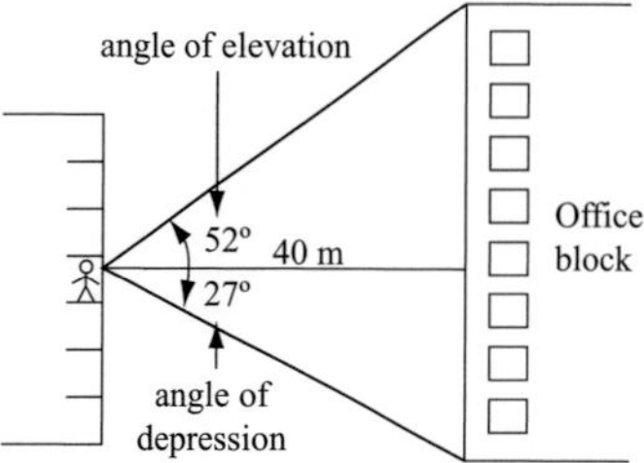

8 Two sides of an isosceles triangle are each 7 cm long. The angle between these sides is 66°. Work out the area of this triangle.

Finding an angle

(a)

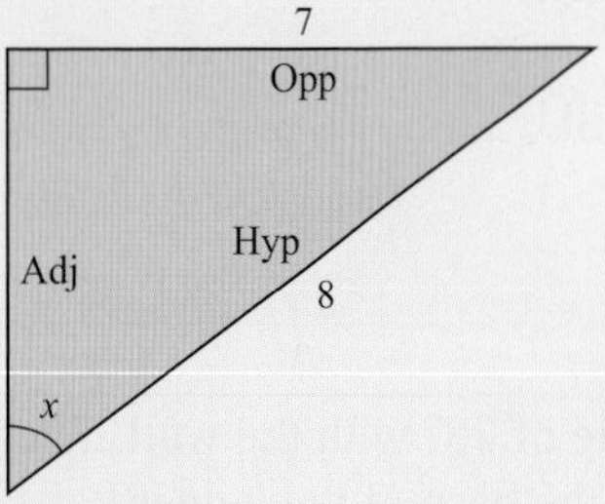

7 Opp, Adj, Hyp 8, x

Find angle x.

$$\sin x = \frac{\text{Opp}}{\text{Hyp}}$$

$$\text{so } \sin x = \frac{7}{8}$$

$$x = \sin^{-1}\frac{7}{8} = 61.0°, \text{ correct to 1 d.p.}$$

On a calculator press

7 ÷ 8 = SHIFT sin =

[or SHIFT sin (7 ÷ 8) =]

(b)

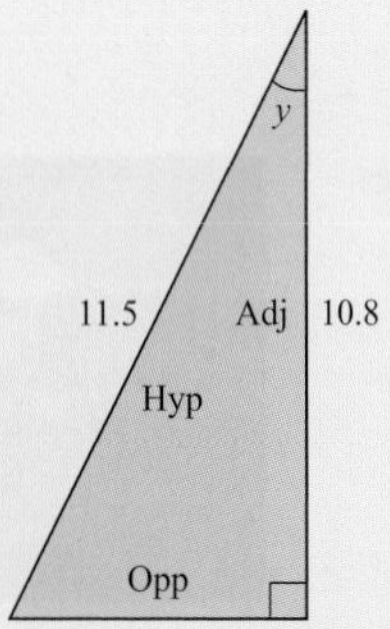

y, 11.5 Hyp, Adj 10.8, Opp

Find angle y.

$$\cos y = \frac{\text{Adj}}{\text{Hyp}}$$

$$\text{so } \cos y = \frac{10.8}{11.5}$$

$$y = \cos^{-1}\left(\frac{10.8}{11.5}\right) = 20.1°, \text{ correct to 1 d.p.}$$

Exercise 4M

1 Find the angles marked, correct to one decimal place. All lengths are in cm.

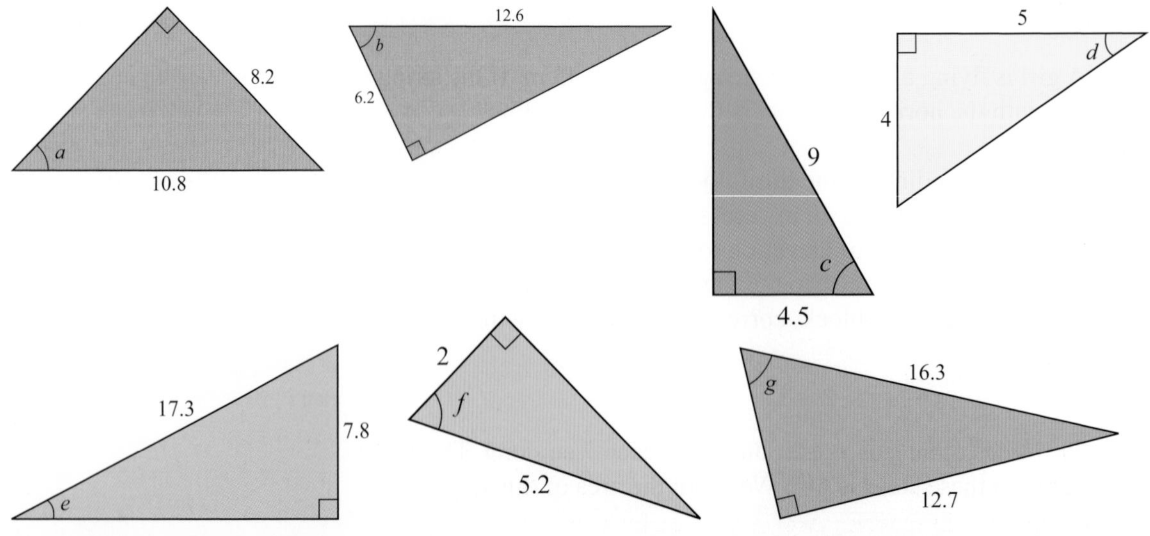

2 Find the angles marked, correct to the nearest degree.

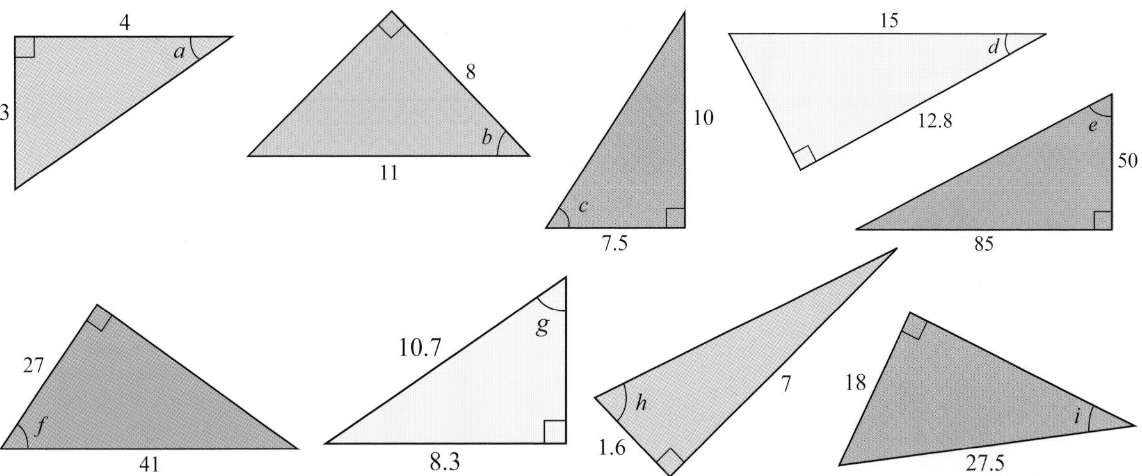

In questions 3 to 8 find the angles, correct to one decimal place.

3 In triangle ABC, $A\hat{B}C = 90°$, AC = 8 cm, BC = 5 cm. Find $B\hat{A}C$.

4 In triangle DEF, $D\hat{E}F = 90°$, DF = 4 cm, EF = 3 cm. Find $E\hat{D}F$.

5 In triangle GHI, $G\hat{H}I = 90°$, IG = 7 cm, HG = 6 cm. Find $H\hat{G}I$.

6 In triangle JKL, $J\hat{K}L = 90°$, JK = 7 cm, KL = 5 cm. Find $J\hat{L}K$.

7 In triangle MNO, $M\hat{N}O = 90°$, MN = 8 cm, NO = 10 cm. Find $M\hat{O}N$.

8 In triangle PQR, $P\hat{Q}R = 90°$, PR = 10 cm, RQ = 3 cm. Find $Q\hat{P}R$.

Exercise 4E

1 A ladder of length 4.2 m rests against a vertical wall so that the base of the ladder is 2 m from the wall. Calculate the angle between the ladder and the ground.

2 A point T is 80 m away from a flagpole, which is 27 m high. What is the angle of elevation to the top of the flagpole from T?

3 A chord AB of length 10 cm is drawn in a circle of radius 6 cm, centre O. Calculate the angle AOB.

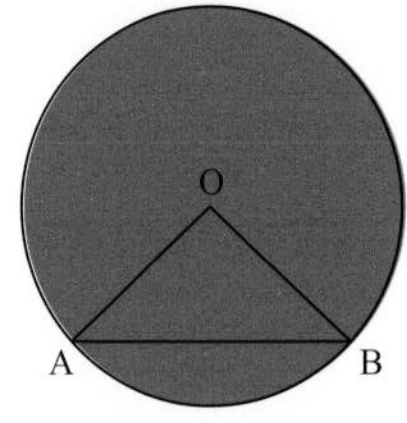

4 An owl sites on a branch 9.5 m from the ground vertically over the base of a tree. If he sees a mouse on the ground 6.2 m from the tree at what angle to the vertical must he swoop to catch his supper?

5 A very thin rigid book of height 28 cm is placed at an angle between two shelves 26 cm apart. What angle, to the nearest degree, will the book make with the bottom shelf?

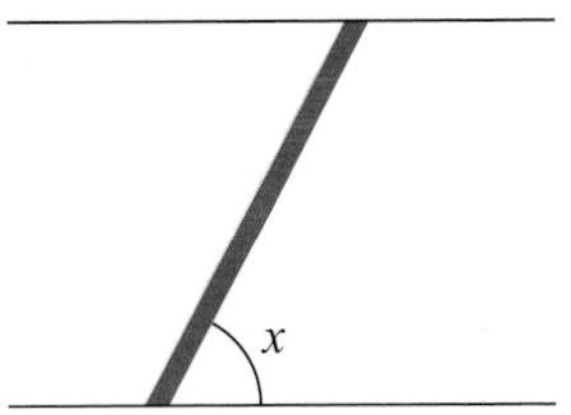

6 

The shadow of a cross in a war cemetery is 60 cm long. The angle of elevation of the Sun is 76°.

How tall is the cross?

7 Find the labelled angles in the rectangle.

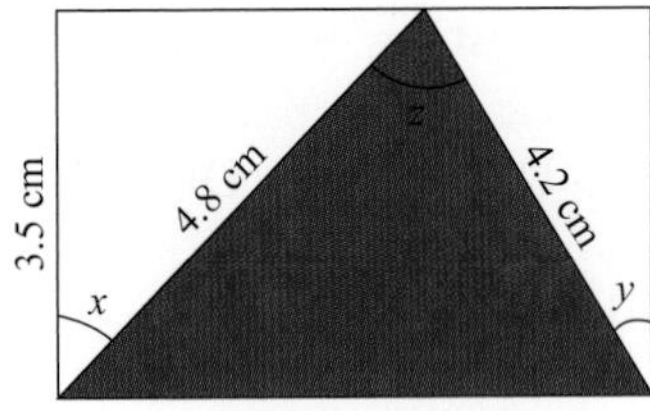

8 A ship sails 16 km due north then 5 km due east. Find the bearing and the distance of the ship from its start position.

9 Find the labelled angles in the following shapes.

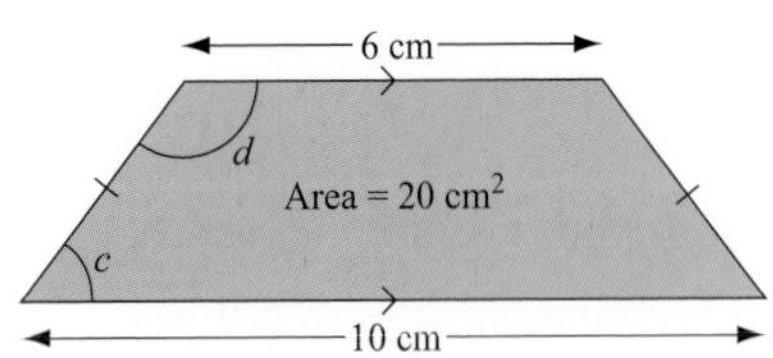

Area = 9.52 cm²
f
e
3.4 cm

10 Find the labelled angles in the kite.

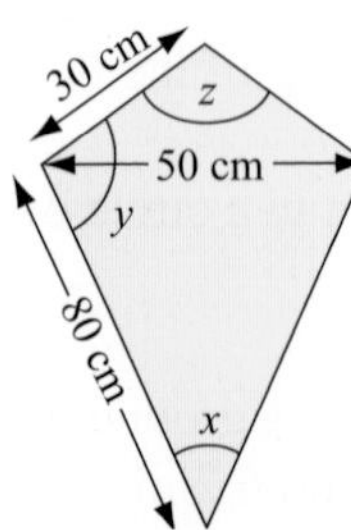

Finding the hypotenuse

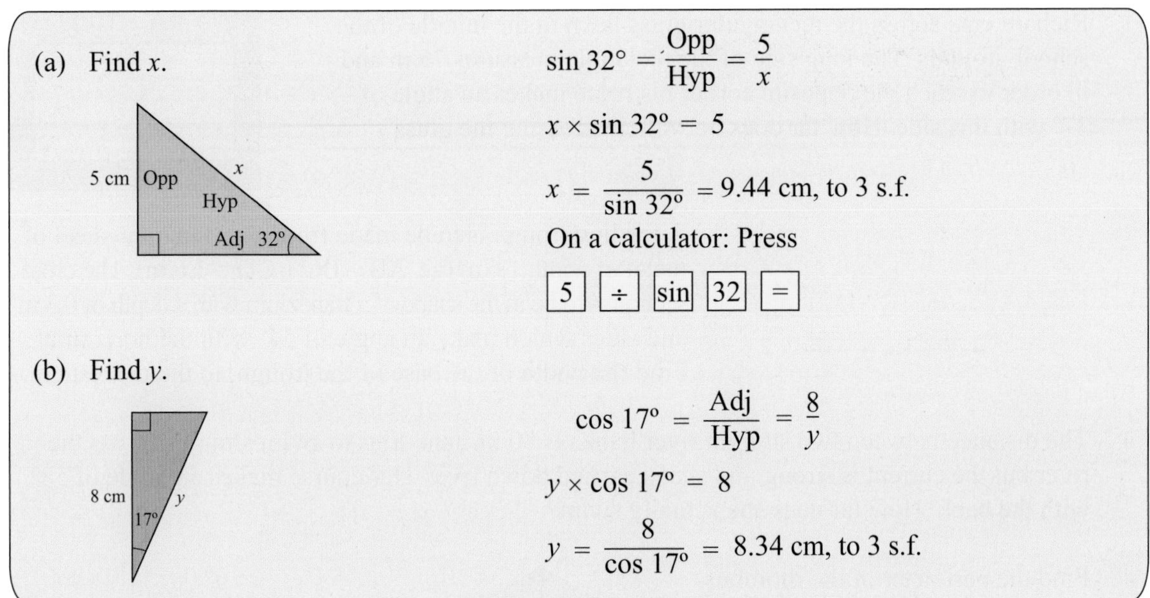

(a) Find x.

$$\sin 32^\circ = \frac{\text{Opp}}{\text{Hyp}} = \frac{5}{x}$$

$$x \times \sin 32^\circ = 5$$

$$x = \frac{5}{\sin 32^\circ} = 9.44 \text{ cm, to 3 s.f.}$$

On a calculator: Press

5 ÷ sin 32 =

(b) Find y.

$$\cos 17^\circ = \frac{\text{Adj}}{\text{Hyp}} = \frac{8}{y}$$

$$y \times \cos 17^\circ = 8$$

$$y = \frac{8}{\cos 17^\circ} = 8.34 \text{ cm, to 3 s.f.}$$

Exercise 5M

Give your answers correct to 3 s.f., unless told otherwise.

1 Find the hypotenuse in the following triangles.

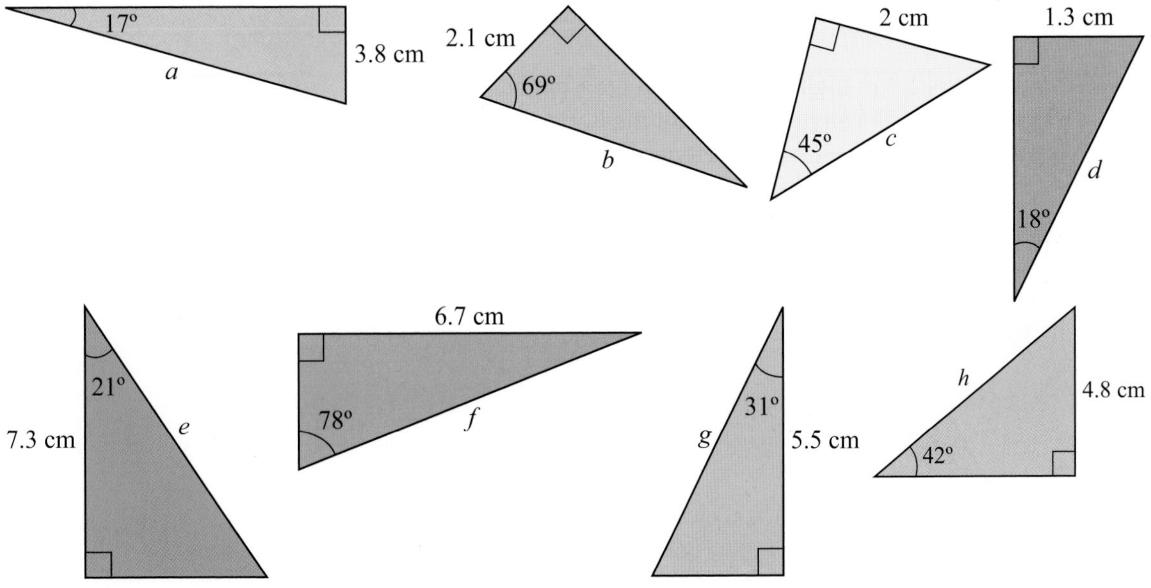

Exercise 5E

1 Richard cuts across the rectangular grass lawn in the middle of the school grounds. The long side of the rectangle measures 75 m and in order to reach the opposite corner his route makes an angle of 37° with this side. How far does he walk in crossing the grass?

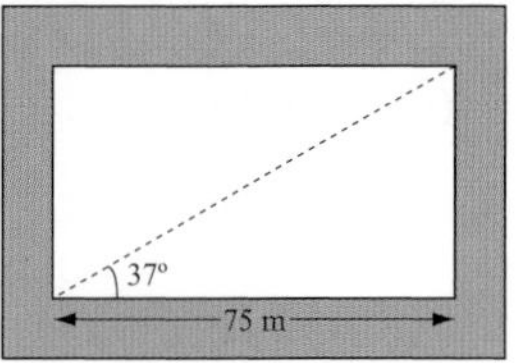

2 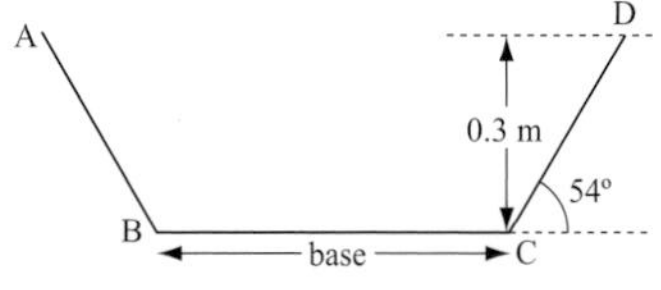

A feeding trough is to be made from a rectangular sheet of metal of width 1.6 m (i.e. AB + BC + CD = 1.6 m). The cross section is to be in the shape of a trapezium with a depth of 0.3 m and sides which make an angle of 54° with the horizontal. Find the width of the base of the trough, to the nearest cm.

3 The distance between two straight river banks is 80 m. Jane tries to swim straight across the river but the current is strong and she is carried down river. Her course makes an angle of 58° with the bank. How far does she actually swim?

4 Find the perimeter of the rhombus.

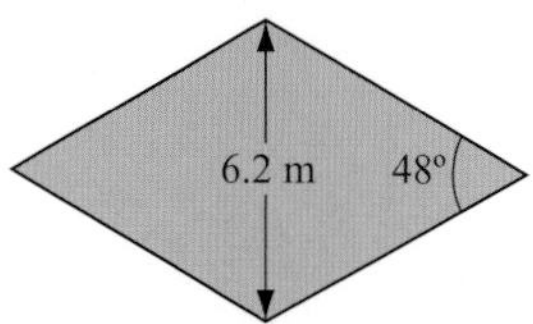

5 

The tips of the blades of a pair of scissors are 8.6 cm apart and the angle between the blades is 38°. How long is each blade to the point where they meet?

6 A farm gate is 1.3 m high. The diagonal crossbar has a width of 15 cm and makes an angle of 24° with the horizontal. Find the length of x and y in the diagram. Hence find the width of the gate.

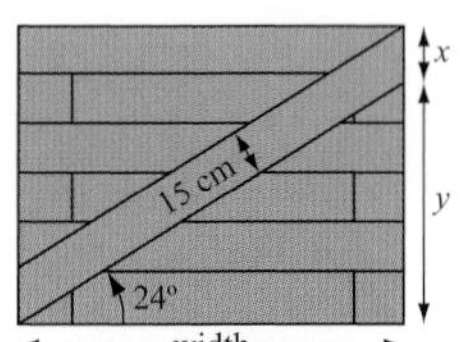

All your trigonometrical problems answered !!!!

If you can remember the following triangles they will help you to solve any trigonometry question in a right-angled triangle.

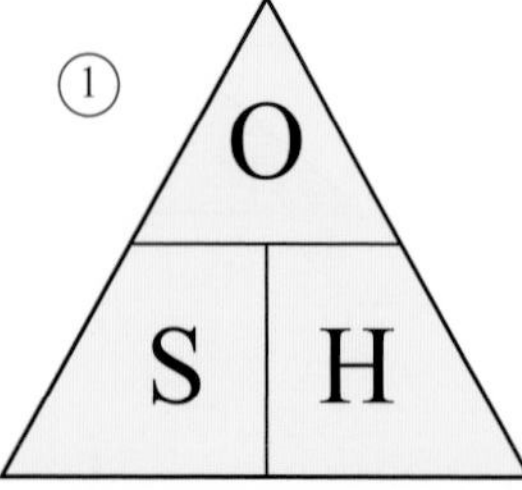

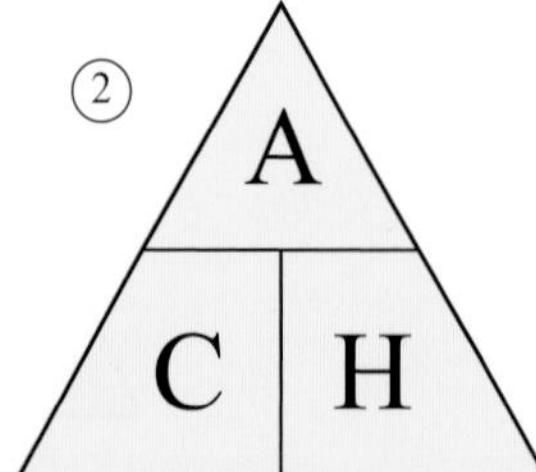

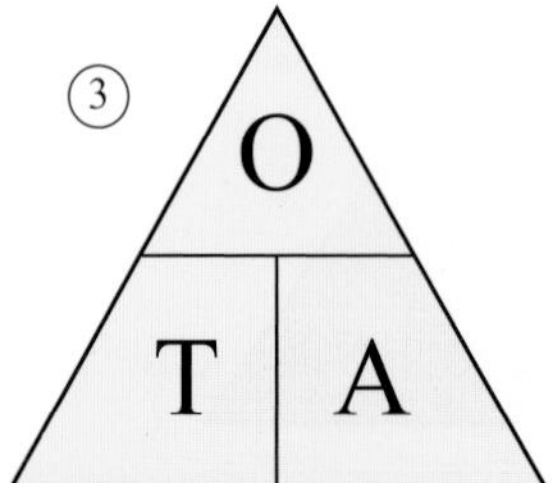

There are various rhymes which help you to remember the order of the letters. One of the 'worst', which usually means it is easier to remember, is:

Officers / Auburn / Offer

Some — Have — Curley — Hair — To — Attraction

Try to learn this or make up one of your own.

These triangles work in the same way as the distance, speed, time triangle.

You cover up what you are trying to work out and the triangle shows you how to calculate the answer.

Find the value of x in the following triangles.

(a)

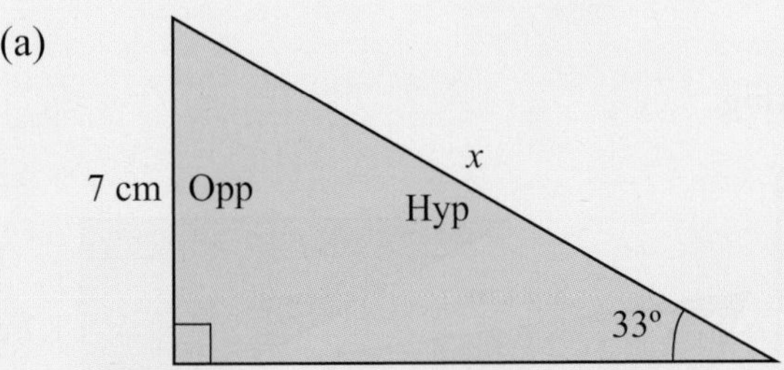

Here we are given the angle (33°) and the Opposite length and we want to calculate the Hypotenuse.

O and H appear together in triangle ①.

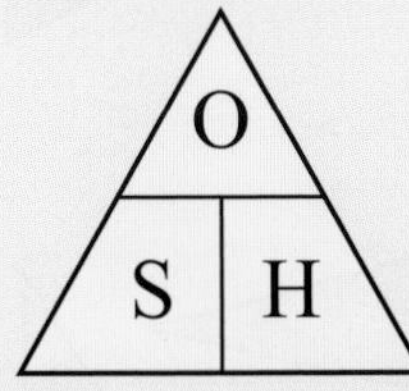

Cover up what we want to find . i.e. Hyp.

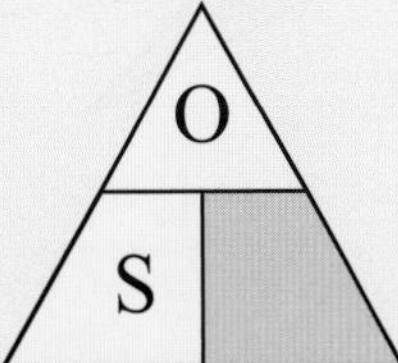

This gives us Hyp $= \dfrac{\text{Opp}}{\sin} = \dfrac{7}{\sin 33^\circ} = 12.9$ cm (3 s.f.)

(b)

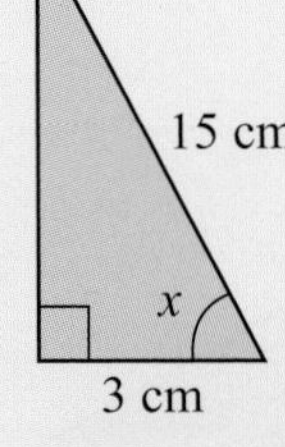

Here we have the Hypotenuse and the Adjacent and we want to work out the angle.

H and A appear together in triangle ②.

A

C | H

Cover up what we want to find. i.e. cos for the angle.

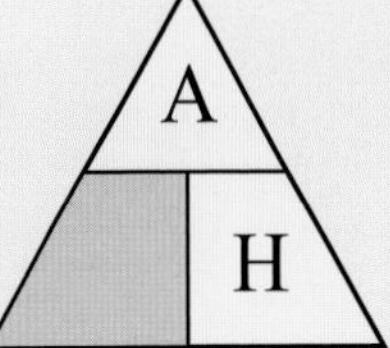

This gives us $\cos x = \dfrac{\text{Adj}}{\text{Hyp}} = \dfrac{3}{15} = 0.2$

$x = \cos^{-1}0.2 = 78.5^\circ$

(c) Here we have the Adjacent and the angle (48°) and we want the Opposite.

A and O appear together in triangle ③.

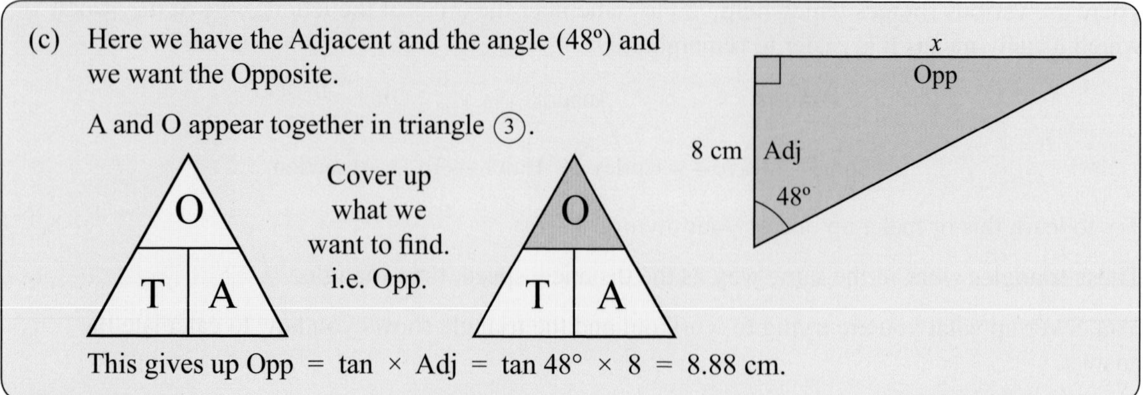

This gives up Opp = tan × Adj = tan 48° × 8 = 8.88 cm.

Exercise 6M

1 Find the labelled length or angle in the following

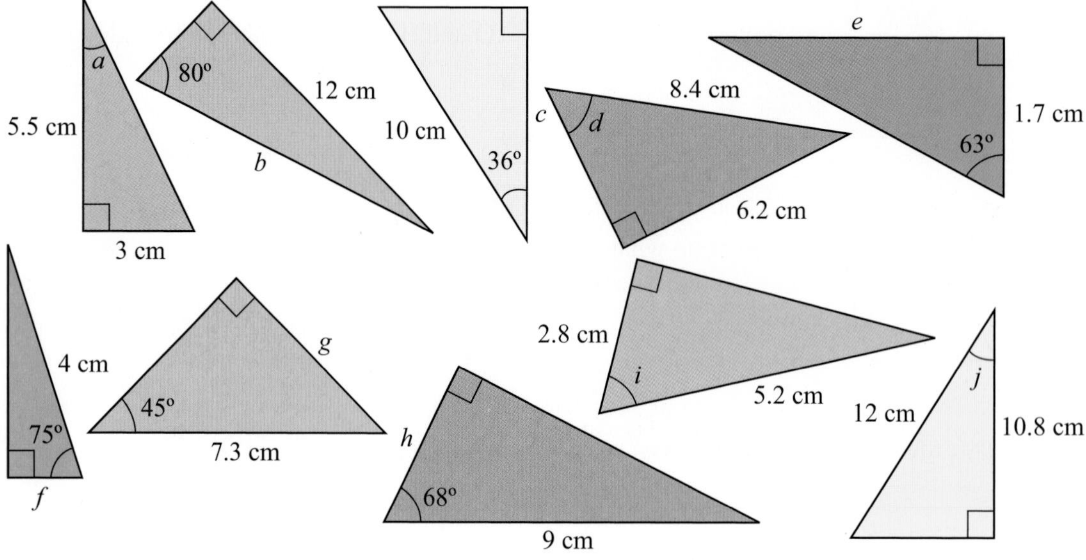

2 Find the lengths (a) AS (b) CS (c) BS

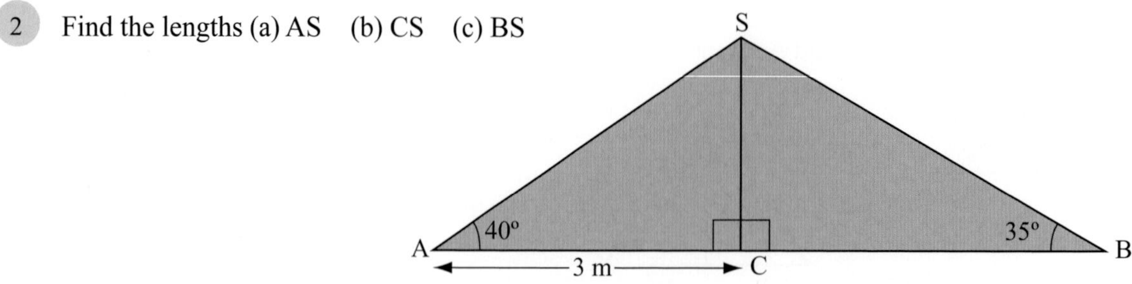

3 Calculate the area of rectangle ABCD.

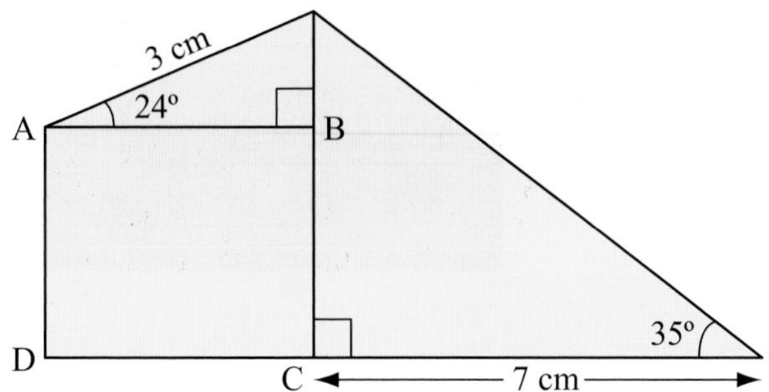

Exercise 6E

1 In rectangle ABCD, AB = 10 cm and AD = 6 cm. Calculate

(a) angle $A\hat{B}D$

(b) length AE

(c) length DF.

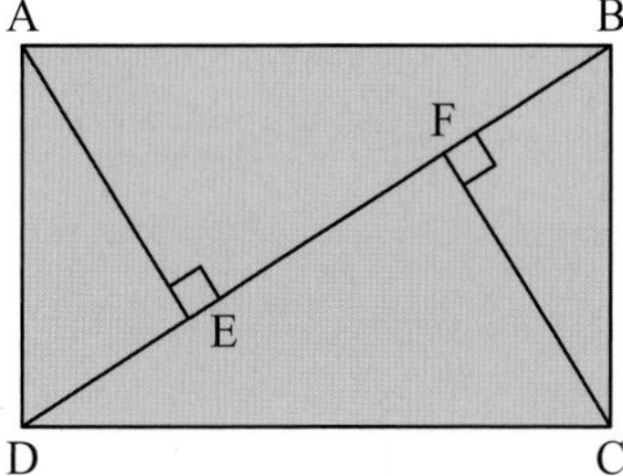

2 Diagram A shows a kitchen floor tiled with regular octogons and squares.

Diagram B shows an enlarged view of one octagon.

The squares have sides of length 12cm.

Find the width of the octagons.

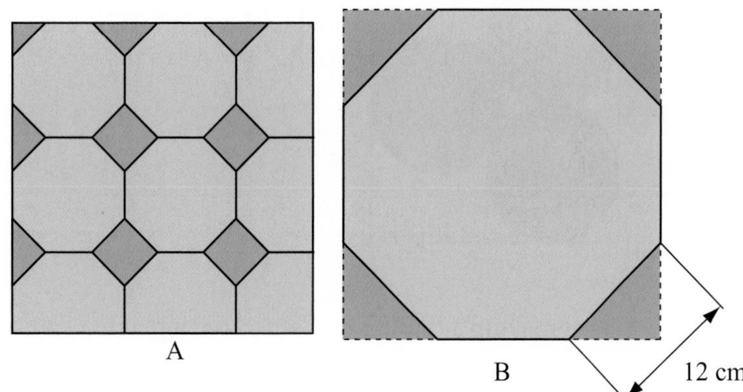

3 The pendulum of a grandfather clock consists of a circular disc of radius 5 cm attached to a straight arm of length 45 cm. If it swings through an angle of 33°, what is the minimum width of the body of the clock?

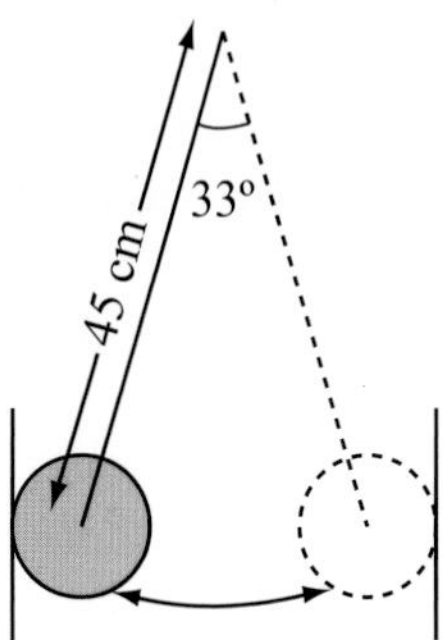

4 From the 'crossover' point the height of a crane is 37.2 m and the length of the horizontal arm is 40 m.

Find the angle of elevation of the end of the horizontal arm from the base of the vertical tower.

5 Find x. All lengths are in cm.

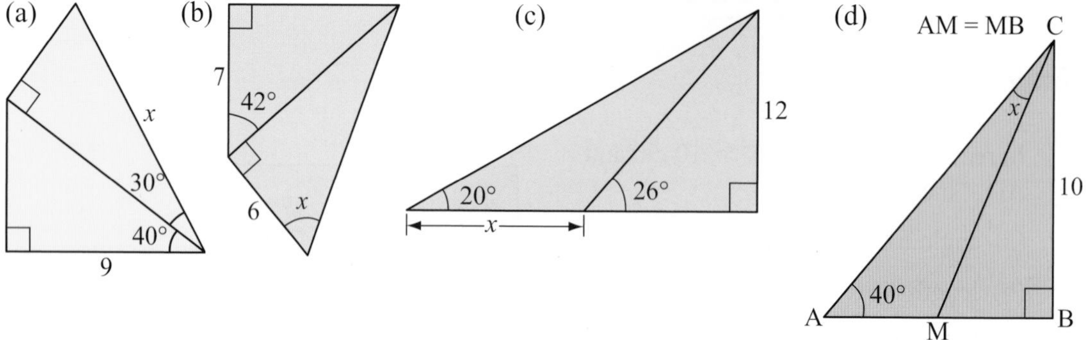

6 A baker wants to pack three individual apple pies, each of radius 4 cm, into a box as shown. Find the length and width of the box when the pies are packed as shown.

length

width

7 (a) Alan is making a 'House of Cards'. Each playing card measures 9 cm by 5.8 cm and is of negligible thickness. These cards are balanced against each other with their short sides touching and making an angle of 32° to one another. If Alan's house has five layers as shown, find its total height and the width of its base.

(b) Alan's first attempt soon falls down so he decides to try again, this time joining together the longer sides of the cards to see if this gives more stability. The angle at the top remains 32°. Find the new height and width.

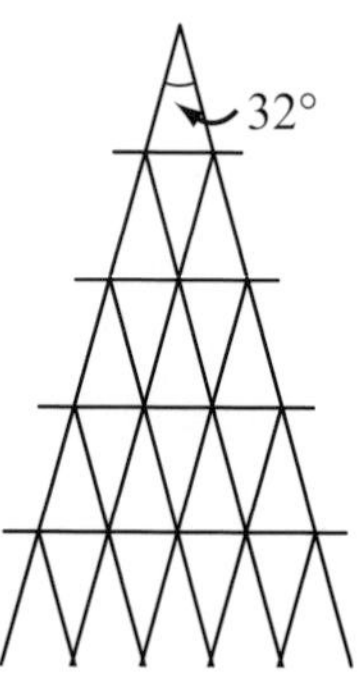

5.2 Inequalities

In this section you will:

- learn how to write and display inequalities
- learn how to solve inequalities
- learn about inequalities with two variables

Writing inequalities

$x < y$ mean 'x is less than y' [or 'y is greater than x']

$p \le q$ means 'p is less than or equal to q'

$a > b$ means 'a is greater than b'

$n \ge t$ means 'n is greater than or equal to t'

Notice that the inequality signs can be read from left to right or from right to left.

Here are some inequalities in everyday life.

- 'The weight limit for the hammock is 90 kg'

  We can write $w \le 90$, where w is the weight in kg.

- 'Each plant in the greenhouse produced more than 7 flowers.'

  We can write $f > 7$, where f is the number of flowers.

- 'Applicants for training as prison officers in Switzerland must be at least 1.70 m tall.'

  We can write $h \ge 1.70$ m, where h is the height of applicants.

Illustrate on a number line the range of values of x for which the following inequalities are true:

(a) $x > 1$

1

The circle at the left hand end of the range is open. This means that 1 is not included.

(b) $x \le -2$

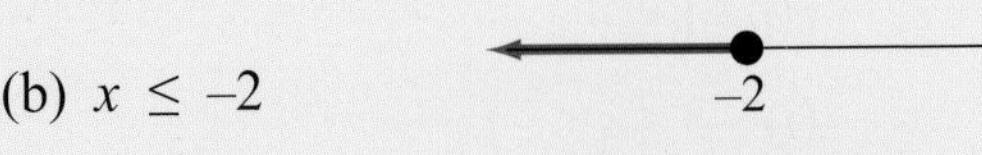

–2

The circle at – 2 is filled in to indicate that –2 is included.

(c) $-1 \le x < 3$

–1 3

[–1 included] [3 not included]

Exercise 1M

[The answers to questions 1 and 2 can be written down or discussed in class.]

1 Write an inequality for each statement.

(a) The maximum number of passengers, n, in the school minibus is 16.

(b) For best results the temperature of the oven, T, has to be between 180ºC and 215ºC.

(c) The minimum mark, m, for a pass in the Highway Code test is 80%.

(d) The speed limit, s, is 70 m.p.h.

(e) The percentage required for a grade B was between 49 and 62 inclusive.

2 Here is an advertisement for a job. Write the information given in the form of inequalities. Make up your own symbols for the relevant quantities.

> **Driver/Bodyguard Wanted**
>
> Age 20 to 50. Must have at least 5 years clean driving license and 3 tattoos.
>
> Applicants must have more than 2 GCSEs and weigh between 10 and 15 stones. Salary in excess of £300 per week.
>
> Phone 0182 996 13274.

3 Write down the inequalities displayed. Use x for the variable.

(a) 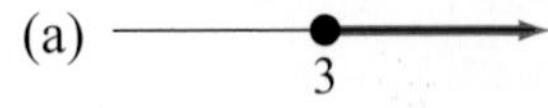

(b) 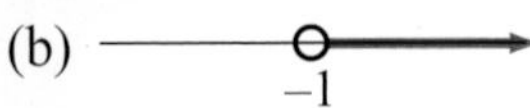

(c) 

(d) 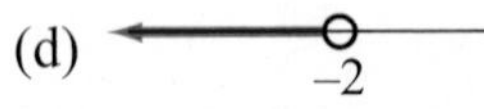

(e) 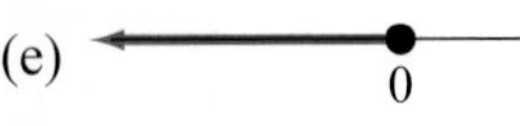

(f) 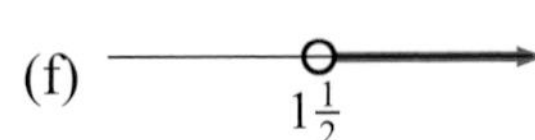

(g) 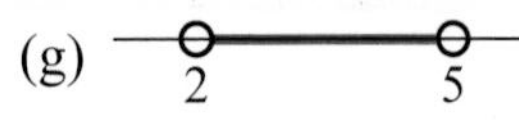

(h) –1 4

(i) 

(j) $\frac{1}{2}$ 1

(k) –3 3

(l) –1 6

4 Draw a number line to display the following inequalities.

(a) $x > -1$ (b) $x \leq 4$ (c) $a > -2$

(d) $n \leq 0$ (e) $-5 < p < 5$ (f) $-1 \leq y$

(g) $0 \leq x \leq 10$ (h) $-2 < t \leq 7$ (i) $-3 \leq s < -1$

5 Answer true or false:

(a) $71 > 701$ (b) $-3 < 1$ (c) $3\frac{1}{2} < 3.25$

(d) $-6 < -10$ (e) 1 metre > 1 yard (f) 1 kg > 1 pound

(g) 1 inch < 2 cm (h) $2^3 < 3^2$

6 Write a possible number for $\square$ in each of the following:

(a) $1000 < \square < 2000$ (b) $2540 < \square < 2550$ (c) $-3 < \square < 2$

(d) $2.1 < \square < 2.2$ (e) $16\,436 < \square < 16\,438$ (f) $9842 < \square < 9843$

7 The variable n satisfies each of these inequalities:

$2 \leq n \leq 5$ and $3 < n < 7$

Mark the solution set for n on a number line.

Solving inequalities

When we solve an equation, like $3x - 1 = x + 9$, we find one value of x which satisfies the equation.

When we solve an inequality, like $2x + 3 < 10$, we find the *range of values* of x which satisfy the inequality.

For example, the solution of the inequality $x - 3 < 11$ is $x < 14$. The variable x can be any value less than 14.

When solving inequalities we can:

- Add the same thing to both sides.
- Subtract the same thing from both sides.
- Multiply or divide both sides by the same *positive* number.

Note

If we multiply or divide by a *negative* number the inequality sign must be *reversed*.

(a) Consider the inequality $4 > -2$.

Now multiply both sides by (-1) $-4 < 2$.

↑ sign is reversed.

(b) Consider the inequality $-3 < 6$

Divide both sides by (-3) $1 > -2$

Again the inequality sign is reversed.

Solve the inequalities.

(a) $x - 3 < 4$
Add 3 to both sides.
$x < 7$

(b) $x + 5 > -2$
Subtract 5 from both sides.
$x > -2 - 5$
$x > -7$

(c) $5x \geq 350$
Divide both sides by 5.
$x \geq 70$

(d) $\frac{x}{3} \leq -2$
Multiply both sides by 3.
$x \leq -6$

Exercise 2M

Solve the inequalities.

1 $x - 10 \geq 2$

2 $x + 6 < 11$

3 $y - 6 > -3$

4 $7 + y < 11$

5 $3 + x \geq 9$

6 $x + 1 < 0$

7 $3n \geq 48$

8 $5y < 1$

9 $10x < 1000$

10 $x - 3 < -2$

11 $y + 7 > -7$

12 $5 + n \geq 4$

Find the range of values of x which satisfy each of the following inequalities and show the answer on a number line.

13 $\frac{x}{2} < 3$

14 $\frac{x}{5} > \frac{1}{2}$

15 $\frac{x}{3} \leq -1$

16 $-12 \geq 3x$

17 $\frac{1}{4} > \frac{x}{2}$

18 $\frac{3x}{2} > 6$

19 $x - 4 > 0$

20 $7 < x + 10$

21 $8 + x \leq 0$

In questions 22 to 26 list the solutions which satisfy the given conditions.

22 $3n < 30$; n is a positive integer (whole number).

23 $0 < a < 12$; a is an even number.

24 $\frac{3x}{5} < 7$; x is a positive integer.

25 $0 < 2y < 9$; y is an integer.

26 $\frac{p}{3} < 8$; p is a prime number.

27 State the smallest integer for which $5y > 21$.

28 Write down any value of x such that $2^3 < x < 3^2$.

Exercise 2E

In questions 1 to 8 write one inequality to show the values of x which satisfy both inequalities. If there are no values of x write 'impossible'.

1 $x > 0$ and $x < 3$

2 $x < 2$ and $x > 0$

3 $x > -3$ and $x < -1$

4 $x > 8$ and $x < 11$

5 $x < 6$ and $x > 7$

6 $2x < 3$ and $x > 0$

7 $5x > 1$ and $2x < 1$

8 $1 < 3x$ and $4x < 3$

In questions 9 to 12 solve each pair of inequalities and then find the range of values of x for which both inequalities are true.

9 $x - 3 < 1$ and $2x + 1 > 0$

10 $\frac{x}{2} + 1 < 3$ and $3x > 0$

11 $1 - 5x > 6$ and $2x + 7 > 3$

12 $\frac{x}{3} - 3 > 0$ an $12 - x > 1$

13 The height of each photo below has to be greater than the width. Find the range of possible values of n in each case.

(a)

$2(n + 1)$

$(n + 5)$

(b)

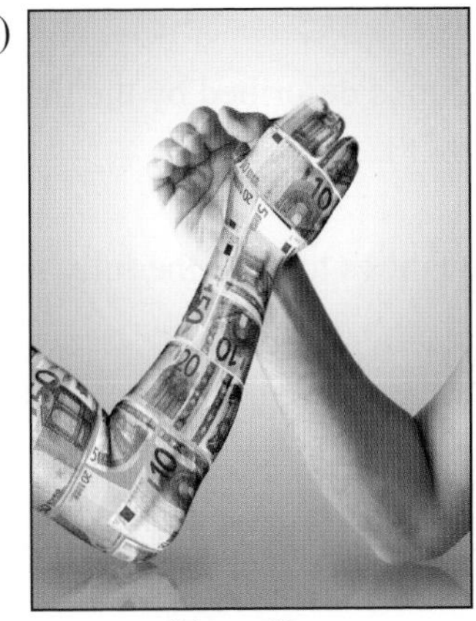

$(n + 3)$

$2(n - 3)$

14 Given that $1 \leq x \leq 5$ and $-3 \leq y \leq 1$, find

(a) the greatest possible value of $x - y$

(b) the least possible value of $x^2 + y^2$

15 Given that $1 \leq a \leq 10$ and $-5 \leq b \leq 6$, find

(a) the greatest possible value of $\frac{b}{a}$

(b) the greatest possible value of $b^2 - a$

(c) the greatest possible value of $a - b$

16 Given that $5x > 1$ and that $x - 2 < 3$, list all the possible whole number values of x.

17 If $3^x > 1000$, what is the smallest whole number value of x?

18 Look at the series $1 + 2 + 4 + 8 + \ldots\ldots\ldots\ldots\ldots$

After how many terms is the sum of this series greater than 1000?

19 Solve the inequality $2(x + 1) > x + 7$

20 Find the largest whole number n such that

$3n - 4 < 8 - 2n$

Inequalities in two variables

Exercise 3E

1 Copy and complete:

'The shaded region is described by the three inequalities
$y \leqslant x$, $x \leqslant 4$ and y ☐ 1

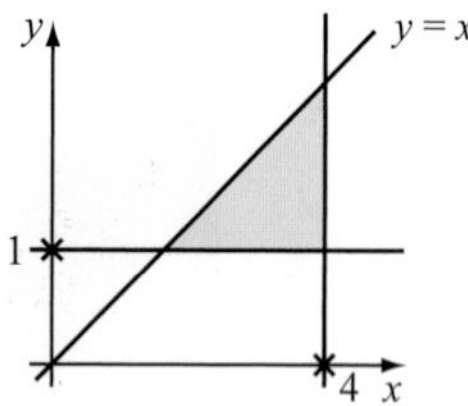

2 Write three inequalities to describe fully the shaded region.

(a)
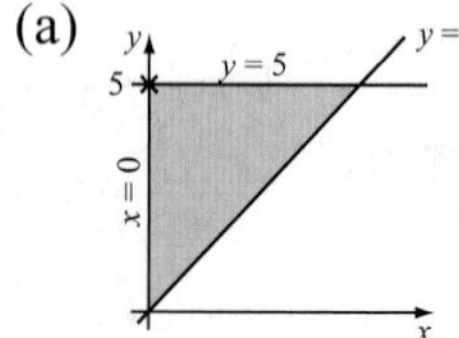

(b)
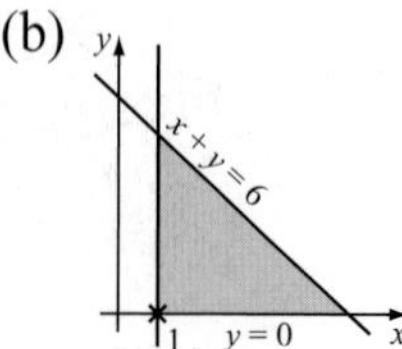

(c)
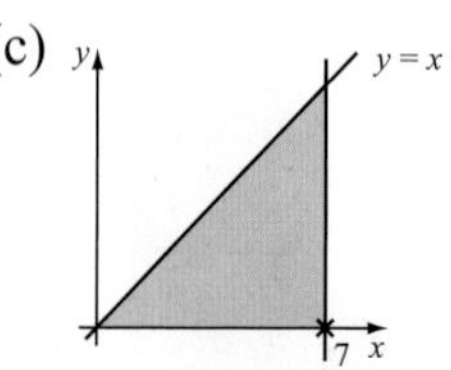

(d)
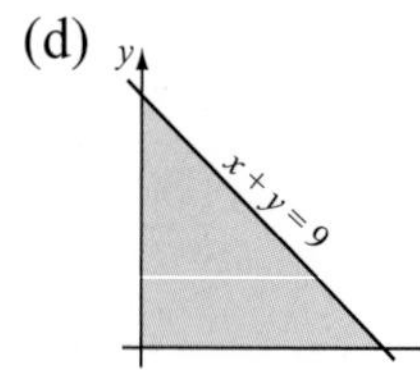

(e)
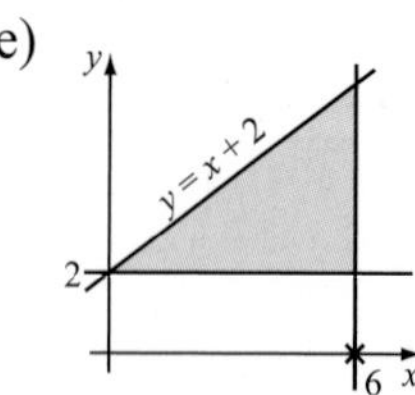

(f)
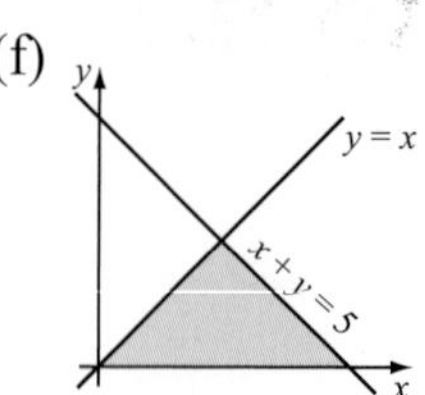

3 Draw sketch graphs and shade the regions indicated.

(a) $y \geq x,\ x \geq 1,\ y \leq 5$ (b) $y \leq x,\ x \leq 6,\ y \geq 0$

CHECK YOURSELF ON SECTIONS 5.1 AND 5.2

1. Trigonometry

(a) Find the angles x and y.

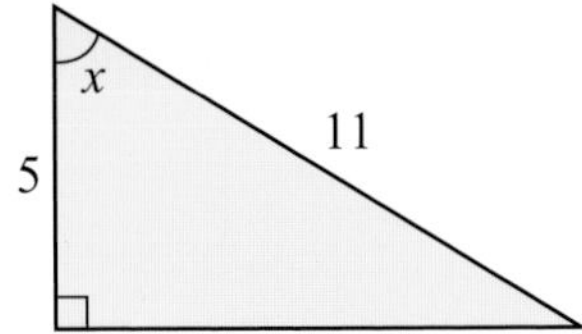

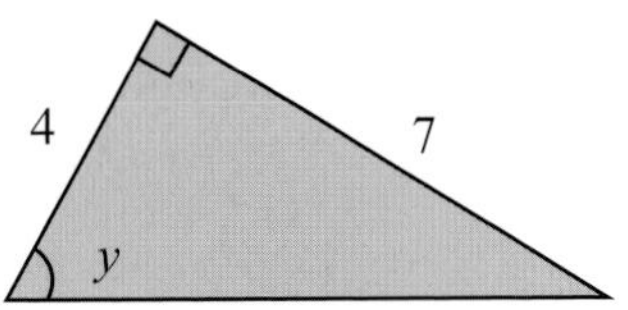

(b) In triangle ABC, $A\hat{B}C = 90^\circ$, $B\hat{A}C = 53^\circ$, AB = 4 cm. Find BC.

(c) In triangle DEF, $D\hat{E}F = 90^\circ$, $E\hat{D}F = 32.2^\circ$, DF = 15 cm. Find EF.

(d) Find the area of this triangle.

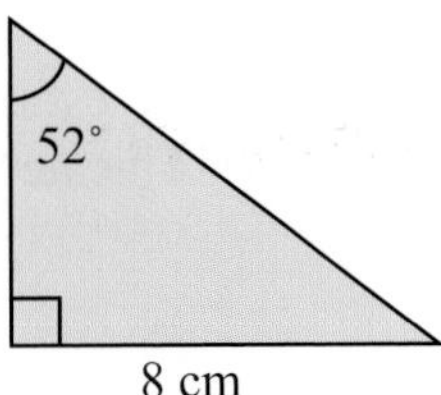

2. Inequalities

(a) Solve the inequalities.
   (i) $3x + 2 > 17$ (ii) $6x - 4 \leq 3x + 17$

(b) Write down the greatest positive whole number n which satisfies the inequality $4 - 9n > -23$.

(c) Draw a sketch graph to show the region where $1 \leq y \leq 7$.

(d) Find the whole number values of x which satisfy both the inequalities $3x > 10$ and $x - 2 < 5$.

5.3 Probability

In this section you will:

- learn about experimental probability
- learn about probability with one or two events
- learn about exclusive events

Probability

We can sometimes work out the probability of an event such as tossing a coin or rolling a dice. There are also many events which occur where it is very difficult (but not impossible) to estimate the probability of the event happening. This newspaper item illustrates one such event.

> **Birthday double**
>
> Monty and Madge Burton, whose two sons had daughters on the same day in June 1974, became great-grandparents twice on the same day this month when two of their nine grandchildren gave birth to daughters. Mrs. Burton, 80, from Leeds, said: "It's a very happy coincidence."

Relative frequency

- In Book 8H probabilities were worked out using equally likely outcomes. This is sometimes called the principle of *symmetry* (not to be confused with 'line symmetry' or 'rotational symmetry').
- In many situations this argument of symmetry cannot be applied. For example it is not easy to *work out* the probability of spinning a 5 on the spinner shown, which has unequal sectors.
- When a drawing pin is dropped onto a hard surface, it will come to rest either point up or point down. You might think that the probability of the pin landing point up is ½ because it must land either point up or point down. But a drawing pin is not a regular shape like a coin or a dice. Often the best way to find an estimate of the probability of an event, which cannot be predicted, is to perform an experiment.

Experiment: 'Spinning a five'

A spinner, with unequal sectors, is spun 10 times and the number of 5s obtained is recorded. This procedure is repeated several times and the results are recorded in a table.

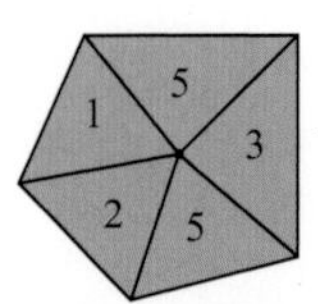

Relative frequency of spinning a 5 = $\left(\frac{\text{number of 5s obtained so far}}{\text{number of trials so far}}\right)$

For simplicity use √ for 'spinning a 5' and × for 'not spinning a 5'.

Results	Number of 5's obtained so far	Number of trials so far	Relative frequency of spinning a 5
√ × × √ × × × × × ×	2	10	= 0.2
× √ √ √ × √ √ √ × √	9	20	= 0.45
√ × × √ √ × √ × × √	14	30	= 0.467 (3 d.p.)
...	...	...	...

The experiment is continued until the number in the relative frequency column settles down to a fairly constant value.

A graph shows the progress of the experiment very clearly.

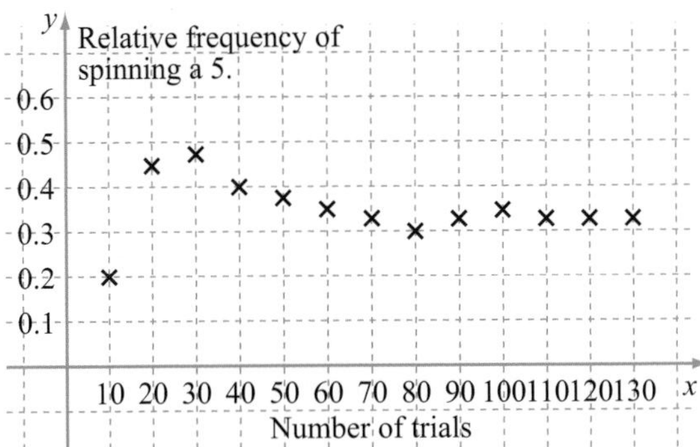

The graph may start by going up and down but after many trials the relative frequency settles down to a fairly constant number.

We can take the *relative frequency* of an event occurring as an estimate of the *probability* of that event occurring. The estimate improves as the number of trials is increased.

Exercise 1M

1 Karim randomly selects a card from a pack and notes whether it is a Heart, Spade, Diamond or Club. Here are his results:

S H D S S C H C C S D H H C S
C H C D S D H C D S H S S C H

(a) What was the relative frequency of selecting a Heart?

(b) What was the relative frequency of selecting a Diamond?

2 In an experiment Tom drops 12 drawing pins onto a hard floor. He does the experiment 10 times and counts how many pins land 'point up'. His results were

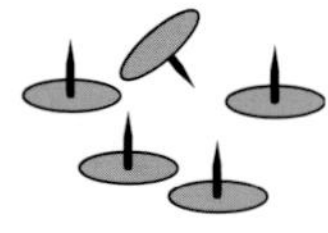

Number of the 12 drawing pins that landed 'point up'									
3	5	6	2	4	7	3	3	4	5

(a) Use Tom's data to work out the probability that a *single* drawing pin will land point up.

(b) Tom continues the experiment until he has dropped the 12 drawing pins 100 times. About how many drawing pins in total would you expect to land point up?

3 Four friends are using a spinner for a game and they wonder if it is perfectly fair. They each spin the spinner several times and record the results.

Name	Number of spins	Results		
		0	1	2
Alan	30	12	12	6
Keith	100	31	49	20
Bill	300	99	133	68
Ann	150	45	73	32

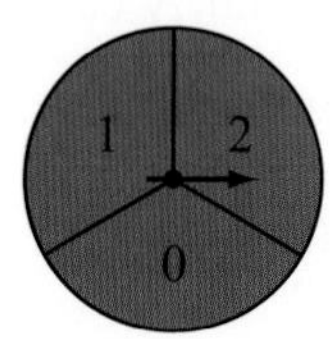

(a) Whose results are most likely to give the best estimate of the probability for getting each number?

(b) Make a table and collect together all the results. Use the table to decide whether you think the spinner is biased or unbiased.

(c) Use the results to work out the probability of the spinner getting a '2'.

4 The RAN# button on a calculator generates random numbers between .000 and .999. It can be used to simulate tossing three coins. We could say any *odd* digit is a *tail* and any *even* digit is a head. So the number .346 represents THH

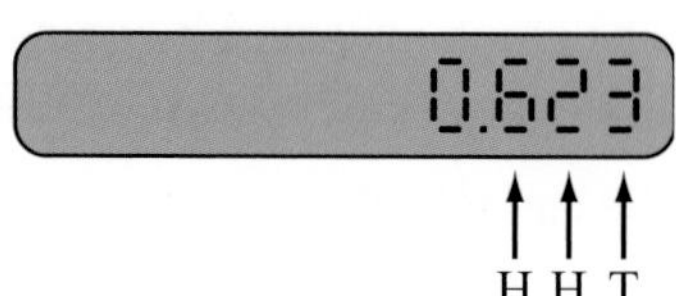

Use the RAN# button to simulate the tossing of three coins

'Toss' the three coins 100 or 200 times and work out the relative frequency of getting three heads.

Compare your result with the value that you would expect to get theoretically.

5 (**Practical**). To find the relative frequency of a drawing pin landing pointing up.

Drop a drawing pin (or perhaps 10 drawing pins) onto a hard surface and count the number of times it lands point up. Record the results in groups of 10 trials in a table. Use √ for 'point up' and × for 'point down'.

Draw a graph of relative frequency against number of trials, similar to the one above, and state the relative frequency of the event occurring after a large number (say 200) trials. (Combine results with other people).

Working out probabilities

Exericse 2M

1 Seven balls, numbered as shown, are put in a bag. One ball is selected at random. Find the probability that it is

(a) a 9 (b) not a 9

(c) an even number (d) a prime number

2 One ball is selected at random from the box shown. Write down the probability that it is

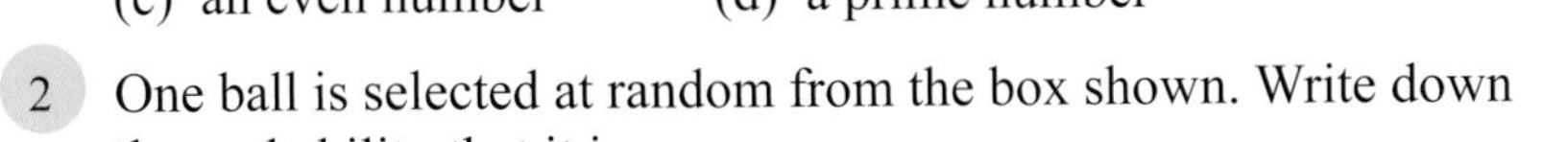

(a) blue (b) green

3 One card is picked at random from a pack of 52. Find the probability that it is

(a) the Jack of diamonds

(b) a two of any suit

(c) a diamond

4 A bag contains 9 balls: 3 red, 4 white and 2 yellow.

(a) Find the probability of selecting a red ball.

(b) The 2 yellow balls are replaced by 2 white balls. Find the probability of selecting a white ball.

5 Ella and Bo play 'rock, paper, scissors' 18 times. How many times would you expect Ella to win?

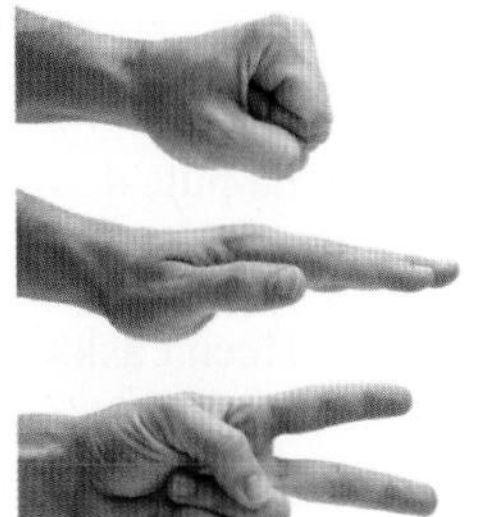

6 A fair dice is rolled 120 times. How many times would you expect to roll a two?

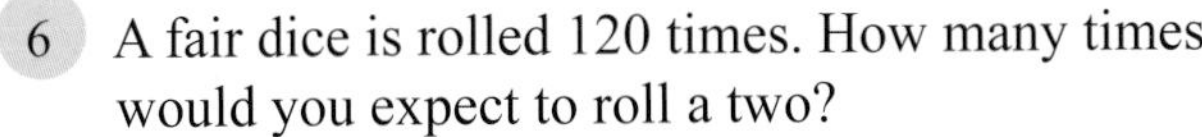

7 Neil played a card game with Phil. The cards were dealt so that both players received two cards. Neil's cards were a seven and a four. Phil's first card was a six.

Find the probability that Phil's second card was

(a) a seven

(b) a King or a Queen of any suit.

8 One ball is selected at random from the bag shown and then replaced. This procedure is repeated 400 times. How many times would you expect to select:

(a) a blue ball (b) a white ball?

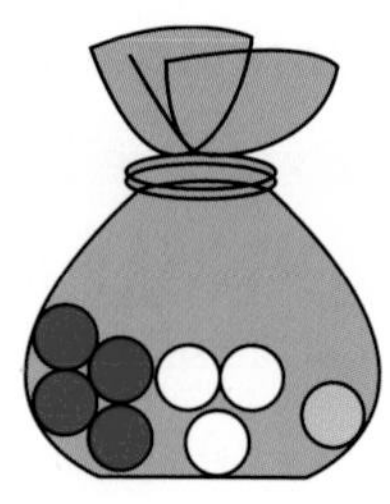

9

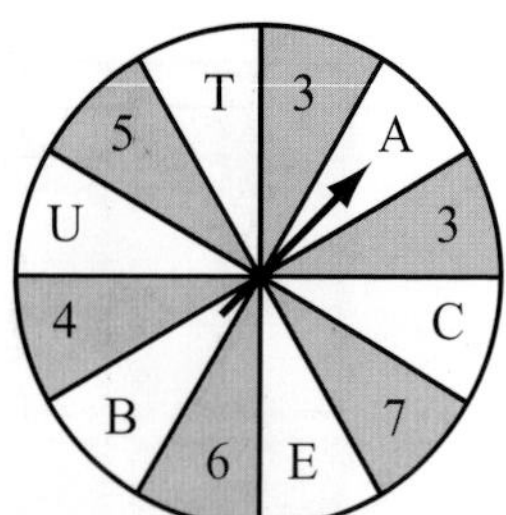

A spinner, with 12 equal sectors, is spun 420 times. How often woud you expect to spin:

(a) an E (b) an even number (c) a vowel?

10 Cards numbered 1 to 50 are placed in a bag and one card is picked at random. Write down the probability of picking:

(a) the number 27 (b) a square number (c) a multiple of 10.

Exercise 2E

1 The probability of Suki holing a six foot put is 0.3.

One week she had 30 six foot puts. How many would you expect her to hole?

2 Heena puts 4 white balls and 1 black ball in a bag. She then takes out one ball without looking.

(a) Heena asks her parents about the probability of getting a black.'
Her mum says,
'It is ¼ because there are 4 whites and 1 black.'
Her dad says,
'It is ⅕ because there are 5 balls and only 1 black.'
Which of her parents is correct?

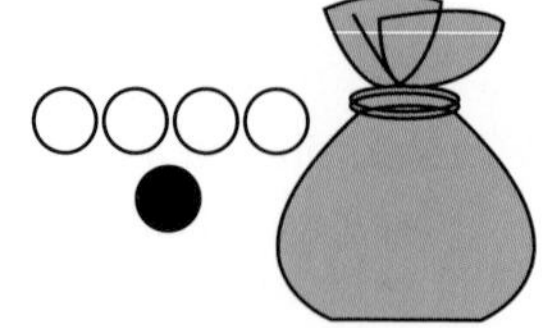

(b) Carl has another bag containing red and white balls. The probability of picking a red ball from Carl's bag is $^4/_7$.
What is the probability of picking a white ball from Carl's bag?

(c) How many balls of each colour *could* be in Carl's bag?

(d) Write down another possibility for the number of balls of each colour that could be in Carl's bag.

3 The number of people visiting the London Eye one day was 11,249. How many of these people would you expect to celebrate their birthdays on a Tuesday in the year 2013?

4 The cubes from the pyramid are separated and put into a bag and one cube is selected at random. What is the probability of selecting the red cube?

5 When playing Monopoly, Philip knows that the probability of throwing a 'double' with two dice is $\frac{1}{6}$. What is the probability that he does *not* throw a double with his next throw?

6 Kevin bought one ticket in a raffle in which 200 tickets were sold. What is the probability that Kevin did not win the first prize?

7 A coin is biased so that the probability of tossing a head is 56%.

(a) What is the probability of tossing a tail with this coin?

(b) How many tails would you expect when the coin is tossed 500 times?

8 One ball is selected from a bag containing x red balls and y blue balls. What is the probability of selecting a red ball?

9 One ball is selected from a bag containing n yellow balls, m red balls and 7 white balls. What is the probability of selecting a yellow ball?

10 There are 28 green marbles and x blue marbles in a box. One marble is selected at random. Given that the probability that it is blue is $\frac{1}{5}$, calculate the value of x.

Listing possible outcomes

When an experiment involves two events, it is usually helpful to make a list of all the possible outcomes. When there is a large number of outcomes, it is important to be systematic in making the list.

- Coins
- Using H for 'head' and T for 'tail', two coins can land as:

H	H
H	T
T	H
T	T

Two dice

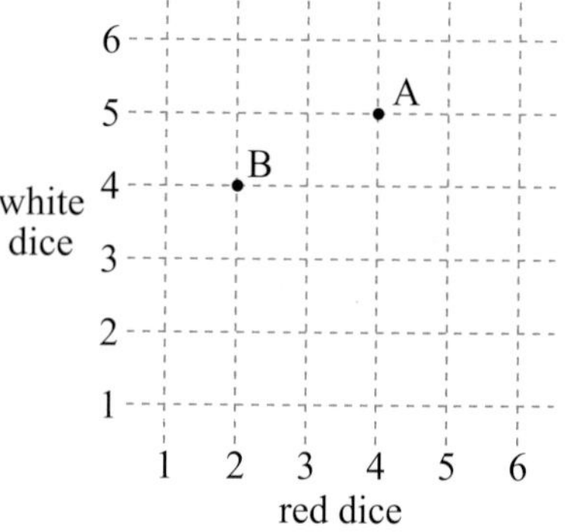

When a red dice is thrown with a white dice, the outcomes are (red dice first):

(1, 1), (1, 2), (1, 3), (1, 4), (1, 5), (1, 6), (2, 1), (2, 2), (2, 3). . . . (6, 6).

The 36 equally likely outcomes can be shown on a grid. Point A shows a 4 on the red dice and a 5 on the white dice. Point B shows a 2 on the red dice and a 4 on the white dice.

The probability of rolling a two on the red dice and a four on the white dice is $^1/_{36}$.

Exercise 3M

1 A 10p coin and a 20p coin are tossed together. List all the possible outcomes, heads or tails, for the two coins.

2 Three coins are tossed together. List all the possible outcomes for the three coins.

What is the probability of tossing three heads?

3 A red dice and a white dice are thrown together.

(a) Draw a grid to show all the possible outcomes.

(b) What is the probability of:

(i) getting the same number on each dice?

(ii) a total score of 10?

(iii) the score on the red dice being double the score on the white dice?

4 Katy has these two spinners. She spins both spinners and adds up the numbers to get a total. For example a '10' and a '2' give a total of 12.

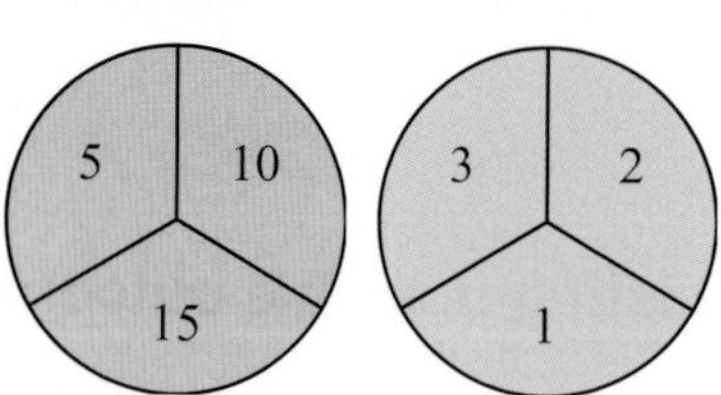

Make a list of all the possible totals.

What is the probability of getting a total of 8?

Exercise 3E

1 Amy, Beth, Chloe and Dee are in a dancing competition. The order in which they dance is decided by drawing cards with their names on from a bag. The names are taken out one at a time without looking.

(a) Write down all the possible orders of dancing with Chloe going first.

(b) In the main competition there are 12 dancers. The probability that Chloe dances first is $\frac{1}{12}$. Work out the probability that Chloe does *not* dance first.

2 A bag contains a 2p coin, a 5p coin and a 10p coin. Two coins are selected at random.

(a) List all the possible combinations of two coins which can be selected from the bag.

(b) Find the probability that the total value of the two coins selected is

(i) 15p (ii) 7p (iii) 20p

3 A coin and a dice are tossed together.

(a) List all the possible outcomes.

(b) Find the probability of getting

(i) a head on the coin and a 6 on the dice

(ii) a tail on the coin and an even number on the dice.

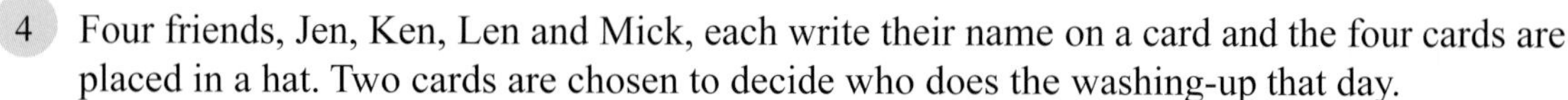

4 Four friends, Jen, Ken, Len and Mick, each write their name on a card and the four cards are placed in a hat. Two cards are chosen to decide who does the washing-up that day.

(a) List all the possible combinations.

(b) What is the probability that Ken and Len are chosen?

5 

(a) What is the probability of getting 2 sixes when 2 dice are rolled?

(b) What is the probability of getting 5 sixes when 5 dice are rolled?

6 The spinner is spun and the dice is rolled at the same time.

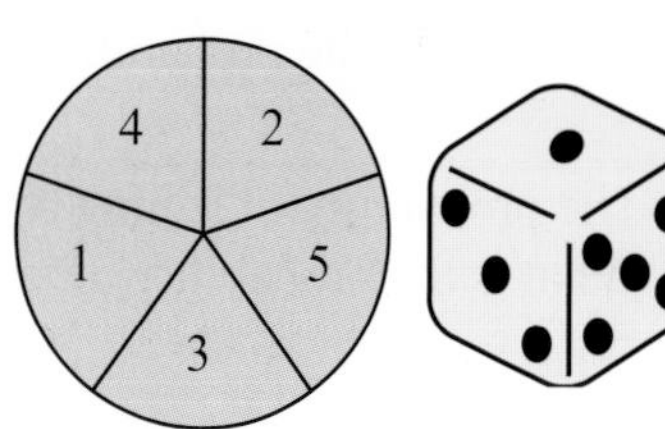

(a) Draw a grid to show all the possible outcomes.

(b) A 'win' occurs when the number on the spinner is greater than the number on the dice. Find the probability of a 'win'.

Exclusive events

Events are *mutually exclusive* if they cannot occur at the same time.

Examples

- Selecting a Queen } from a pack of cards
  Selecting a 3 }
- Tossing a 'head', Tossing a 'tail'
- Selecting a red ball from a bag
  Selecting a white ball from the same bag.

The sum of the probabilities of mutually exclusive events is 1

Adding probabilities: (The 'OR' rule)

If events A and B are mutually exclusive, p(A or B) = p(A) + p(B)

A bag contains balls which are either green, red or black.

The probability of selecting a green is 0.2

The probability of selecting a red is 0.35

What is the probability of selecting a black?

P(green or red) = p(green) + p(red) (The events are mutually exclusive.)
= 0.2 + 0.35 = 0.55

Sum of probabitities = 1

So p(black) = 1 – p(green or red)
= 1 – 0.55
= 0.45

Exercise 4 M/E

1 Kay has a drawer containing just yellow, blue or white T-shirts.
The probability of choosing a yellow T-shirt is 0.3
The probability of choosing a blue T-shirt is 0.5
(a) What is the probability of choosing a T-shirt which is either yellow or blue?
(b) What is the probability of choosing a white T-shirt?

2 The probability of rolling a 'six' with a biased dice is 0.22.
What is the probability of *not* rolling a 'six'?

3 The probability of a jumper's 'main' parachute opening is 0.998.
What is the probability of the main parachute not opening?

4 A bag contains balls which are either red, white or green.
The probability of selecting a red ball is 0.1
The probability of selecting a white ball is 0.6
(a) Find the probability of selecting a green ball.
(b) Find the probability of selecting a ball which is not red.

5 In a game using an electronic spinner, four possible symbols can be obtained.

The probability of each occurring is:

Star prize	$\frac{1}{16}$
Cat	$\frac{1}{8}$
Mouse	$\frac{1}{4}$
Lose	?

Find the probability of:

(a) losing

(b) getting 'cat' or 'mouse'

(c) not getting 'Star prize'.

6 A bag contains a large number of discs.

Most are numbered 1, 2, 3 or 4.
The rest are blank.
Here are the probabilities of drawing a disc with a particular number:

$p(1) = 0.2$
$p(2) = 0.15$
$p(3) = 0.25$
$p(4) = 0.1$

What is the probability of drawing a disc,

(a) marked 1 or 2?

(b) marked 2, 3 or 4?

(c) which is blank?

7 When a spinner with unequal sectors is spun, the probability of getting each colour and number is given in the tables.

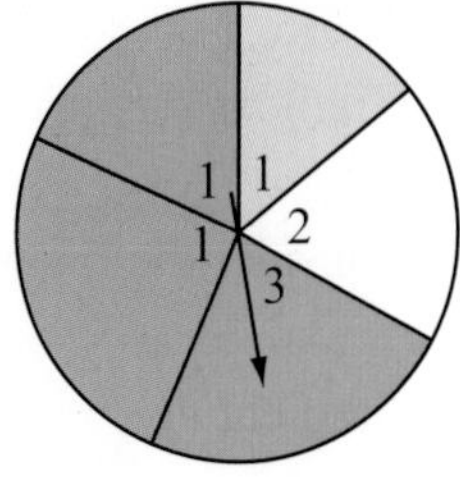

colour	probability
orange	0.45
green	0.25
white	0.2
blue	0.1

number	probability
1	0.55
2	0.2
3	0.25

(a) What is the probability of spinning either 1 or 2?

(b) What is the probability of spinning either 3 or white?

(c) Why is the probability of spinning either 3 or orange *not* 0.25 + 0.45?

5.4 Gradient of a line, $y = mx + c$

In this section you will:

- learn how to find the gradient of a line.
- learn how to find the y - intercept of a line.
- answer questions with straight lines in the form $y = mx + c$.
- learn about the gradients of parallel or perpendicular lines.

Gradient

- If we know the coordinates of two points on a line, we can use the formula

$$\text{Gradient} = \frac{\text{Difference between } y \text{ coordinates}}{\text{Difference between } x \text{ coordinates}}$$

The gradient of a line tells us how steep it is.

- Consider the line which passes through (1, 2) and (3, 6).

$$\text{Gradient} = \frac{6-2}{3-1} = \frac{4}{2} = 2$$

- Consider the line which passes through (−2, 3) and (3, 13)

$$\text{Gradient} = \frac{13-3}{3-(-2)} = \frac{10}{5} = 2$$

Notice that:

- a line sloping upwards to the right has a positive gradient;

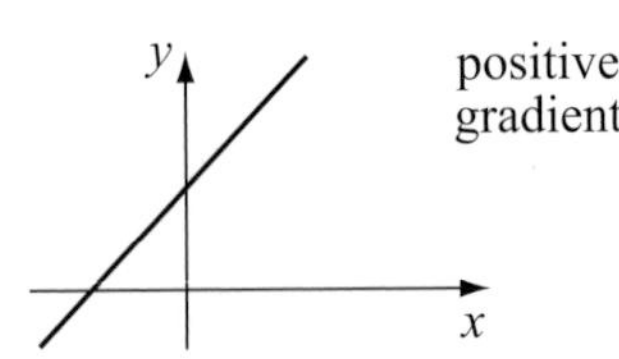

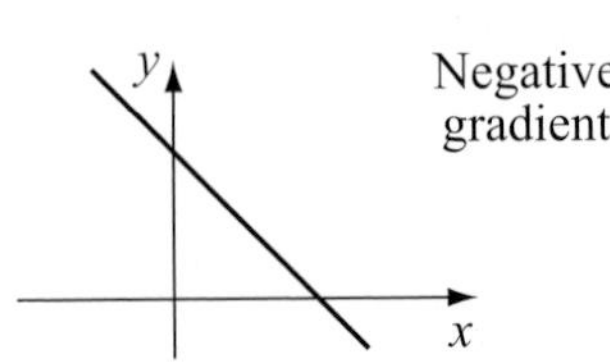

- a line sloping downwards to the right has a negative gradient.

Exercise 1M

1 Find the gradient of the line joining

(a) (1, 3) and (2, 6) (b) (1, 3) and (3, 7) (c) (2, 5) and (6, 7)

(d) (3, 9) and (9, 11) (e) (1, 4) and (3, 2) (f) (2, 5) and (5, –1)

(g) (6, 2) and (2, 10) (h) (3, –2) and (–3, 2) (i) (–2, –4) and (–1, 2)

(j) (2, –3) and (–2, 6).

2 Find the gradient of the line joining:

(a) A and B (b) B and C

(c) C and D (d) D and A.

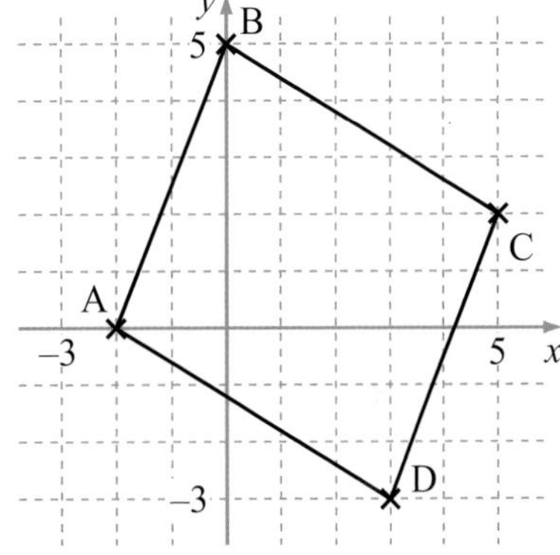

Gradient and intercept

A straight line can be described in terms of

(a) its gradient

(b) where it crosses the y-axis (the y-intercept).

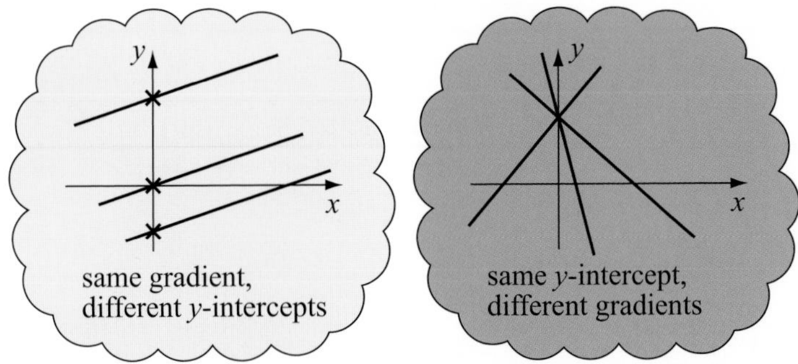

Exercise 2M

Sketch the following straight lines. Use a new pair of axes for each question. Draw about six sketches on one page of your book.

1 Gradient 2, y-intercept 3.

2 Gradient 1, y-intercept – 3.

3 Gradient 2, y-intercept 0.

4 Gradient –1, y-intercept 4.

5 Gradient –3, y-intercept 0.

6 Gradient –2, y-intercept –2.

7 Give the gradient and y-intercept of each line.

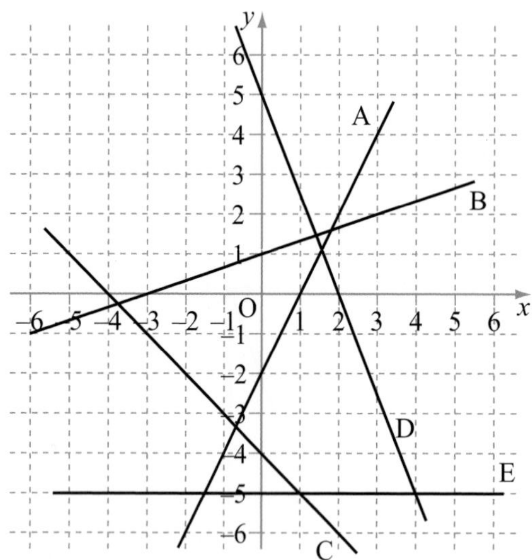

The line *y* = *mx* + *c*

$y = mx + c$ is the equation of a straight line with

- gradient m, and
- intercept c. [Hereafter the word 'intercept' is taken to be the y-intercept.]

Sketch the line with equation $y = 3x - 1$.

Gradient = 3.
Intercept = –1.

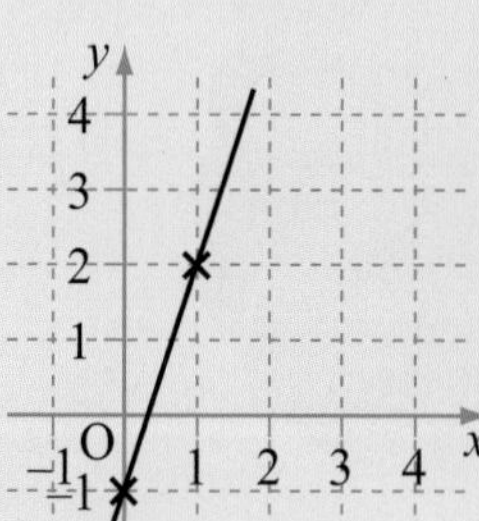

$y = 3x - 1$

Exercise 3M

Write down the gradient and intercept of each of the following lines:

1 $y = 2x - 3$

2 $y = 3x + 2$

3 $y = -x - 4$

4 $y = \frac{1}{2}x + 3$

5 $y = -\frac{2}{3}x - 4$

6 $y = 2 - 3x$

7 $y = 4 - 7x$

8 $y = 2x - 1$

9 $y = 3 - \frac{1}{2}x$

In questions **10** to **15** make y the subject and write down the gradient and intercept of the corresponding line:

10 $2x + y - 6 = 0$

11 $y - 3x + 7 = 0$

12 $y - 2x = 8$

13 $3x + 6y - 10 = 0$

14 $2x - 5y + 12 = 0$

15 $3y - 9x + 2 = 0$

Exercise 3E

1 Use the gradient and intercept to write down the equation of the lines A, B and C.

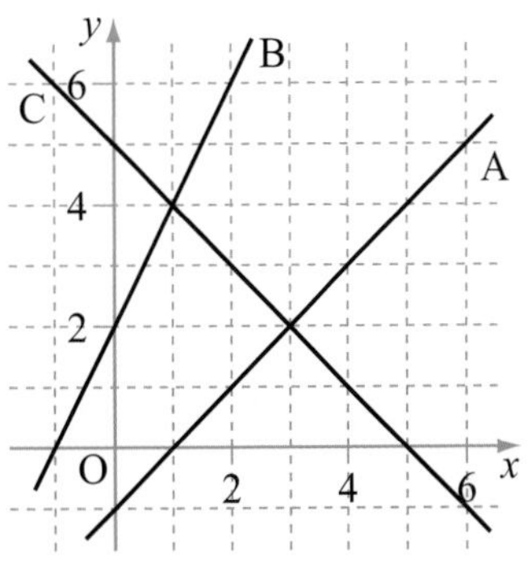

Sketch each of the following lines:

2 $y = x + 2$

3 $y = 2x - 4$

4 $y = 3 - 2x$

5 $y = \frac{3}{4}x - 1$

6 $y = 2 - \frac{1}{3}x$

7 $y - 2x + 2 = 0$

8 $2x + 4y + 1 = 0$

9 $3y - 9x - 1 = 0$

10 $2x - y + 6 = 0$

In questions **11** to **16** match each sketch with the correct equation from the list below.

11 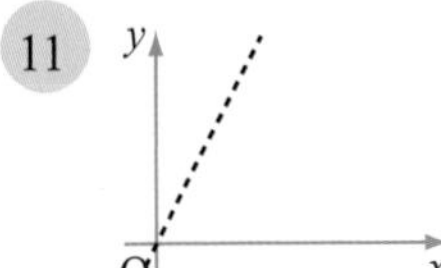

12 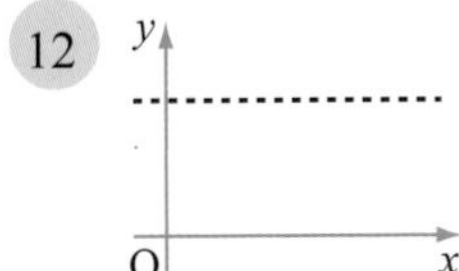

13 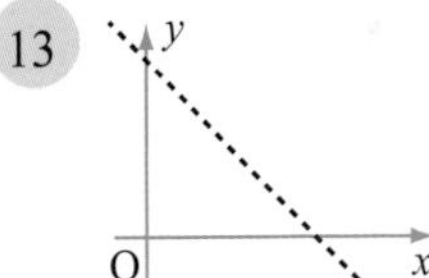

14 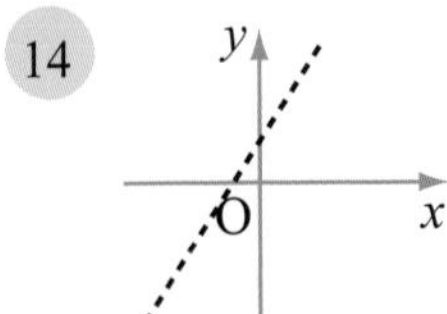

15 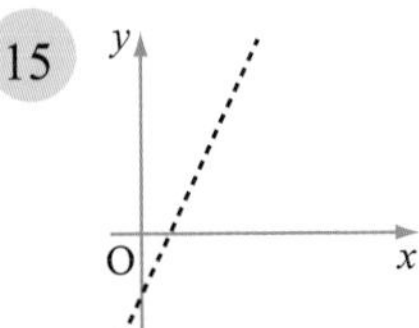

16 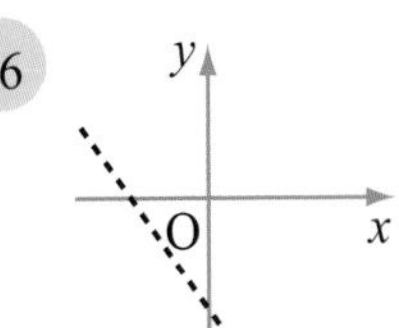

(a) $y = -x - 4$ (b) $y = 2x - 1$ (c) $y = 2x + 3$

(d) $y = 3x$ (e) $y = 3 - x$ (f) $y = 5$

17 Write down the equations of the lines A, B, C, D and E in question 7 of Exercise 2M

Parallel and perpendicular lines

Exercise 4E

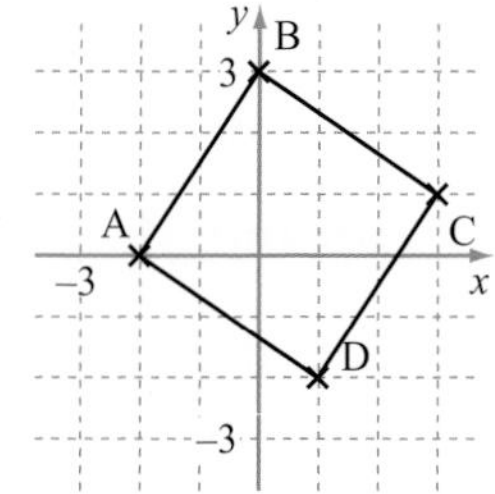

1 (a) Find the gradient of each side of the square shown.
(b) What do you notice about the gradient of AB and the gradient of BC?

Repeat with different squares.

(c) Copy and complete: 'For perpendicular lines the product of the gradients is ☐.'

2 Write down the equation of any line which is parallel to

(a) $y = 2x - 1$ (b) $y = 7x + 3$

3 Write down the gradient of a line which is perpendicular to a line of gradient

(a) 3 (b) –1 (c) $\frac{1}{4}$ (d) $-\frac{1}{2}$

4 Write down the equation of any line which is perpendicular to

(a) $y = 2x + 1$ (b) $y = -\frac{1}{4}x$ (c) $y = \frac{1}{3}x + 7$

5 Here are the equations of several straight lines.

A	$y = 3x - 1$	B	$y = x - 3$	C	$y = \frac{1}{2}x + 1$	D	$y = 3x + 5$
E	$y = -2x$	F	$y = -x + 7$	G	$y = 1 + 4x$	H	$y = 4x$

(a) Find two pairs of lines which are parallel.
(b) Find two pairs of lines which are perpendicular.

6 Find the equation of the line passing through the two points given.
A sketch graph may be helpful.

(a) (0, 4) and (2, 8) (b) (0, –2) and (4, 10) (c) (0, 5) and (5, 10)

(d) (0, 0) and (3, 9) (e) (0, –2) and (–4, 4) (f) (0, 1) and (–2, –4)

7 The sketch shows the graph of $2y + x = 8$.

Find
(a) the coordinates of A.
(b) the equation of the line which is the reflection of the line AB is the y axis.

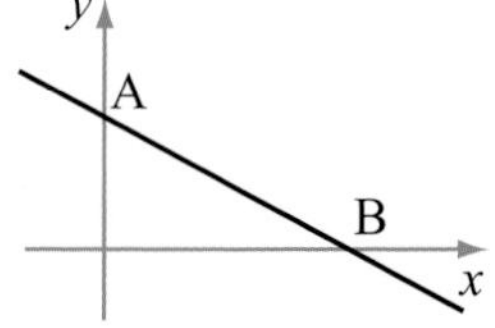

8 LMN is a right-angled triangle with vertices at L(1, 3), M(3, 5) and N(6, n). Given angle LMN is 90º, find n.

5.5 Mathematical reasoning, proof

In this section you will:

- Use a range of mathematical processes to solve problems and make predictions
- Prove geometric and algebraic results.

How many dots?

1 The diagram shows a 5×5 square of dots.

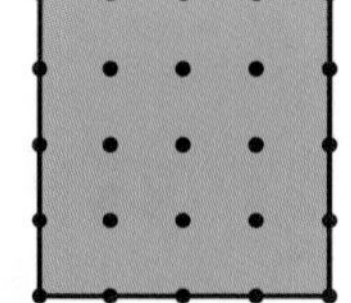

There are 16 dots on the perimeter and 9 dots inside the square.

(a) Draw a 3×3, a 4×4 and a 6×6 square of dots. For each diagram, count the number of dots on the perimeter and the number of dots inside the square.

(b) For a 100×100 square of dots, how many dots are on the perimeter?

(c) For a 57×57 square of dots, how many dots are inside the square?

2 Rectangles are drawn so that the width is always 1 unit more than the height. The number of dots on the perimeter and the number of dots inside the rectangle are counted.

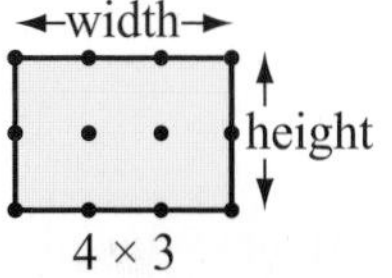

dots on perimeter = 10
dots inside = 2

(a) How many dots are on the perimeter of a 101×100 rectangle?

(b) How many dots are inside a 9×8 rectangle?

(c) (Much harder) How many dots are inside a 52×51 rectangle?

Creating numbers: a task requiring imagination

Your task is to create every number from 1 to 50.

You can use only the numbers 1, 2, 3 and 4 once each and the operations $+, -, \times, \div$.

You can use the numbers as powers and you must use all of the numbers 1, 2, 3, 4.

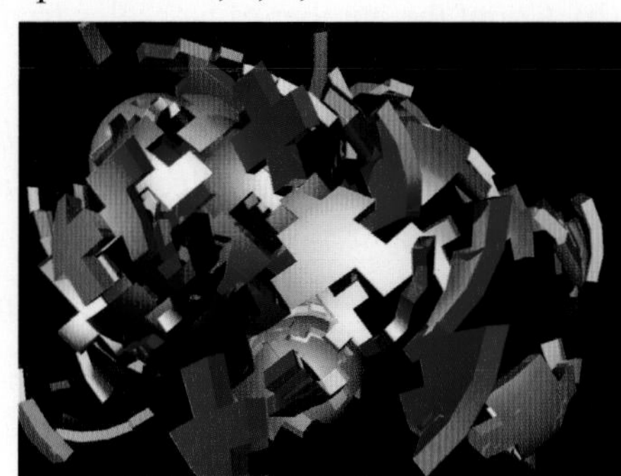

Here are some examples:

$1 = (4 - 3) \div (2 - 1)$

$20 = 4^2 + 3 + 1$

$68 = 34 \times 2 \times 1$

$75 = (4 + 1)^2 \times 3$

Diamonds and triangles

In this task you will draw rectangles on triangular dotty paper (make sure you have the paper the right way up!)

In each diagram you have :

A

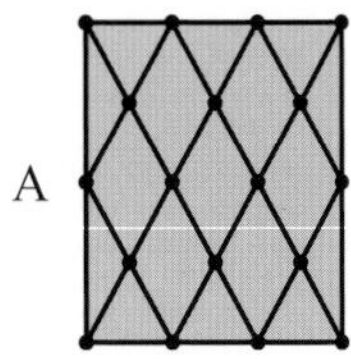

equilateral triangles (e),

isosceles triangles (i),

diamonds (d).

In all rectangles each corner must be on a dot.

This is correct.

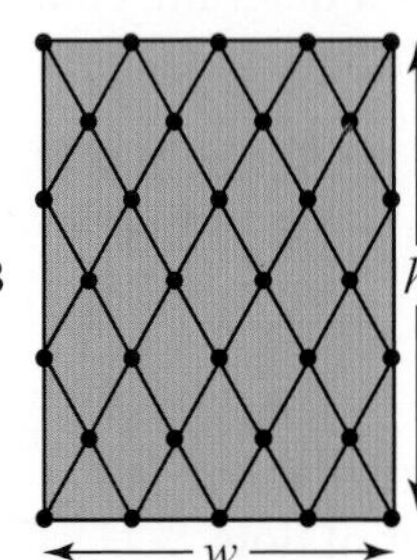

This is not allowed.

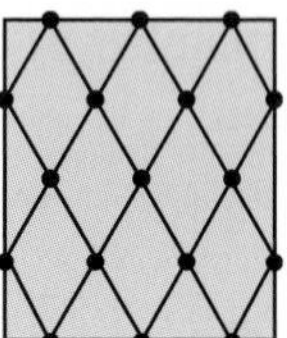

Each rectangle has width w and height h.

In rectangle A $\quad w = 3, h = 2$

In rectangle B $\quad w = 4, h = 3$

Both w and h must be whole numbers.

(a) Count the number of equilateral triangles e in diagrams A and B and in rectangles of your own.

Can you find a rule connecting e and w or a rule connecting e and h?

(b) Count the number of isosceles triangles i in your rectangles. Can you find a rule connecting i with either w or h?

(c) The rule connecting d with w and h is more difficult to find. Be systematic by putting your results in tables. First keep w the same and change only h.
For example:

(i)

w	h	d
2	2	4
2	3	?
2	4	?
2	5	?

(ii) Change to $w = 3$

w	h	d
3	2	?
3	3	?
3	4	?
3	5	?

(iii) Change to $w = 4$ etc.

Hints: As you look for a connection try the following:

in (i) write a column in the table for $3h$

in (ii) write a column in the table for $5h$

in (iii) write a column in the table for $7h$

Can you see a rule connecting, w, h and d for each of the different widths?

Try to write '$d =$ '

Now add a column for $w \times h \times 2$.

Can you now see a rule that works for any diagram you could draw?

Connect the transformations

The triangle ABC is mapped onto triangle A′B′C′ by a rotation followed by a translation.

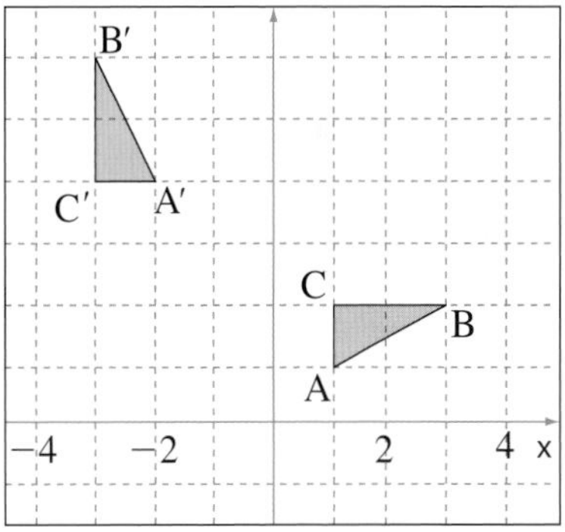

For example: Rotation 90° anticlockwise about (1, 1)

followed by translation $\begin{pmatrix} -3 \\ 3 \end{pmatrix}$.

or Rotation 90° anticlockwise about (3, 0)

followed by translation $\begin{pmatrix} -4 \\ 6 \end{pmatrix}$.

B′
C′
A′
C
B
A
−4
−2
2
4
x

Is there a connection between the centre of the rotation and the vector of the translation?

This is not an easy question to answer. You need to work methodically and to record your results in a table.

Suggestions:

(a) Take the following points as the centres of the rotation: (0,0), (1, 1), (2, 2), (3, 3) etc.

Record the results in a table.

Write down any connection you notice between the centre of rotation and the vector of the translation.

centre	translation
(0, 0)	$\begin{pmatrix} -1 \\ 3 \end{pmatrix}$
(1,1)	$\begin{pmatrix} -3 \\ 3 \end{pmatrix}$

(b) Now take a different set of points for the centres of the rotation: (0,0), (1, 0), (2, 0), (3, 0), etc.

Again write down any connections you notice.

(c) Can you use your results from (a) and (b) above to *predict* the vector of the translation if the centre of the rotation is (7,7) or (10, 0)?

(d) Investigate other sets of points for the centre of rotation. Can you find a general rule which predicts the vector of the translation for *any* centre of rotation?

In search of π

You have been using the fact that the circumference of a circle $= \pi \times$ diameter, where π is some value a bit more than 3. You may also have been told that π is an *irrational* number which means it does not have an exact decimal value, and that it has been calculated to many hundreds of decimal places. So how can we be sure this value is correct?

Firstly find the perimeter of a regular pentagon where the distance from the centre to the vertices is 0.5 cm.

A pentagon is made up of five isosceles triangles.

$z = 360° \div 5 = 72°$

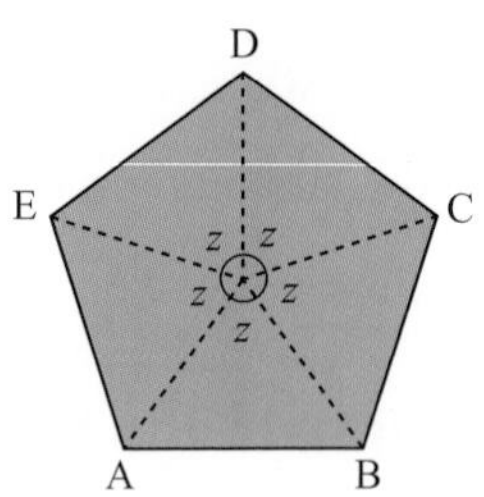

By splitting triangle AOB into two right angled triangles we can find AX, where X is the mid-point of AB.

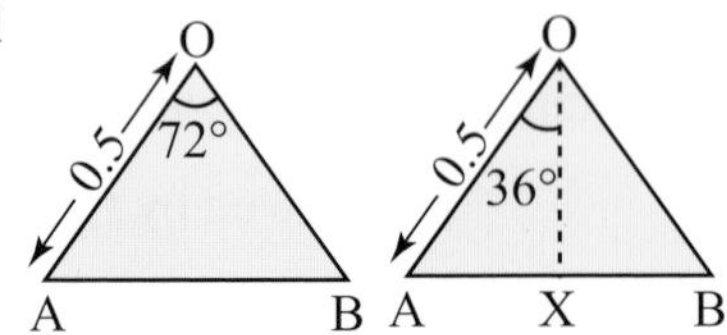

AX = 0.5 Sin 36°
AB = 2 AX = 2(0.5 Sin 36°)
AB = Sin 36° = 0.5877852523 (10 d.p.)
So perimeter of pentagon = 5 × 0.5877852523.

In a similar way find the perimeters of the following regular polygons with the same distance from the centre to the vertices.

(a) an octagon (8 sides)
(b) a decagon (10 sides)
(c) a 20 sided polygon
(d) a 100 sided polygon
(e) a 1000 sided polygon!

The more sides we take the closer our shape resembles a circle with a diameter of 1 cm and the nearer our perimeter gets to the circumference of a circle of diameter 1 cm.

Proof

- In the field of science a theory, like Newton's theory of gravitation, can never be proved. It can only be considered highly likely using all the evidence available at the time. The history of science contains many examples of theories which were accepted at the time but were later shown to be untrue when more accurate observation was possible.
- A mathematical proof is far more powerful. Once a theorem is proved mathematically it will *always* be true. Pythagoras proved his famous theorem over 2500 years ago and when he died he knew it would never be disproved.

  A proof starts with simple facts which are accepted. The proof then argues logically to the result which is required.

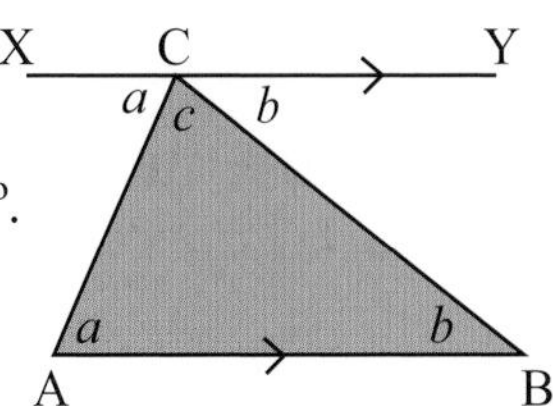

For example, in Book 8H, we used alternate angles to prove that the angle sum of any triangle is 180º.

We then *used* that result to prove that the angle sum of a quadrilateral is 360º.

It is most important to realise that a result *cannot* be proved simply by finding thousands or even millions of results which support it.

Exercise 1E

Questions **1**, **2**, **3** require a knowledge of the conditions for triangles to be congruent [i.e. SSS, SAS, ASA or RHS see section 2.2]

1 Copy and complete a proof that the opposite sides of a parallelogram are equal.

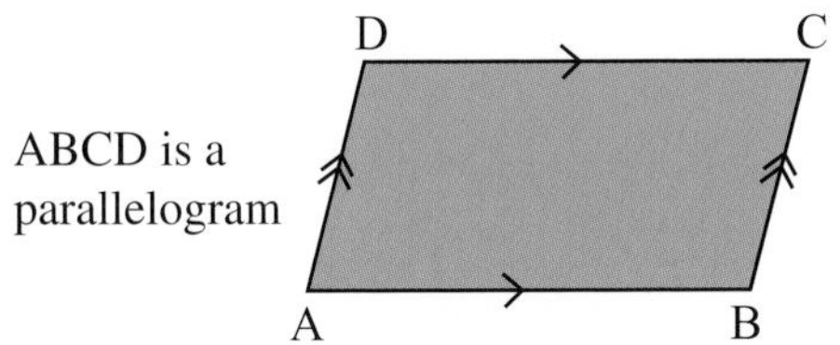

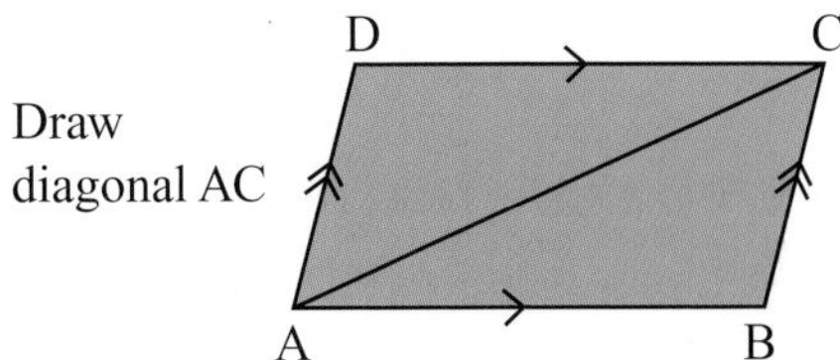

$B\hat{A}C = D\hat{C}A$ and $D\hat{A}C = B\hat{C}A$ (alternate angles)

AC is common to triangles ABC and DCA.

∴ Triangles ABC and [ ] are congruent (ASA)

∴ AB = [ ] which proves that opposite sides of a parallelogram are equal.

2 To prove that the two base angles of an isosceles triangle are equal.

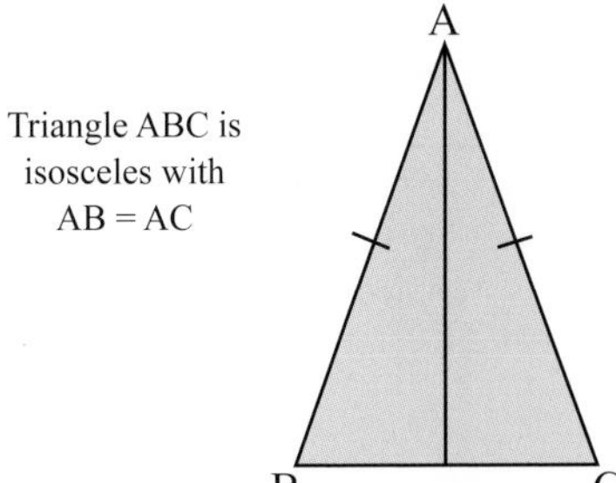

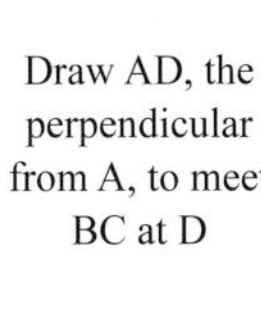

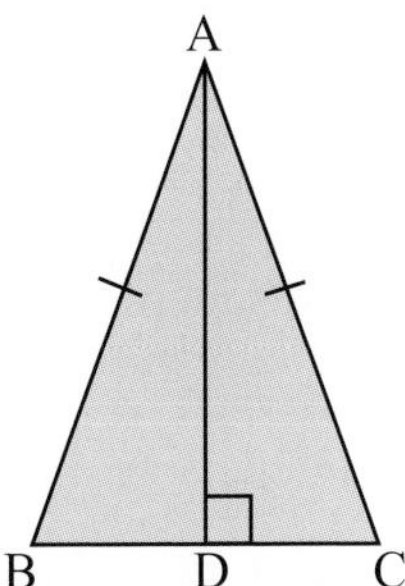

Prove that triangles ABD and ACD are congruent. [Hint: 'RHS']

Hence prove that the two base angles of an isosceles triangle are equal.

3 Draw any rhombus ABCD with four equal sides and opposite sides parallel.

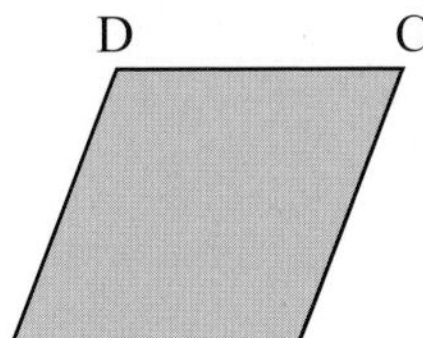

Draw diagonals AC and BD and introduce angles x and y.

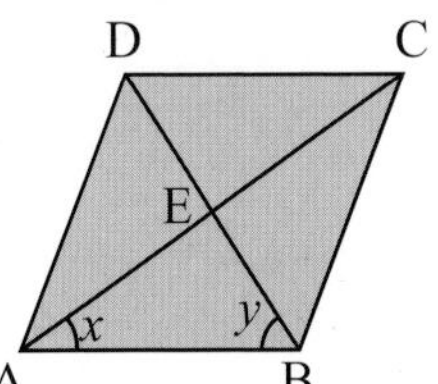

Use alternate angles and congruent triangles to prove that the diagonals of a rhombus bisect each other at right angles.

4 Triangle PQR is isosceles, with PQ = QR.
Prove that $R\hat{Q}S = 2 \times R\hat{P}Q$.

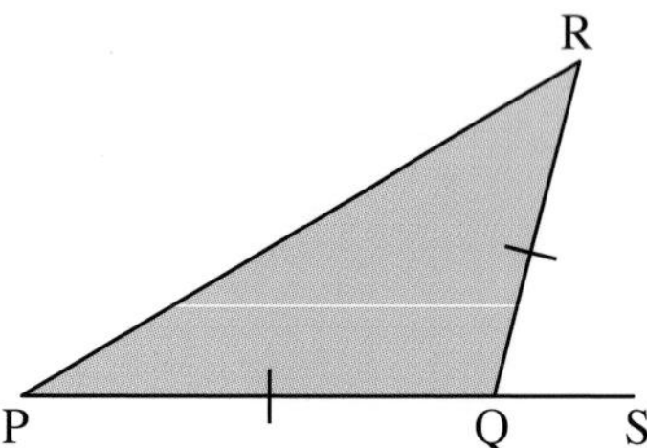

5 Given that AD = CD = DB, prove that angle ACB is a right angle.

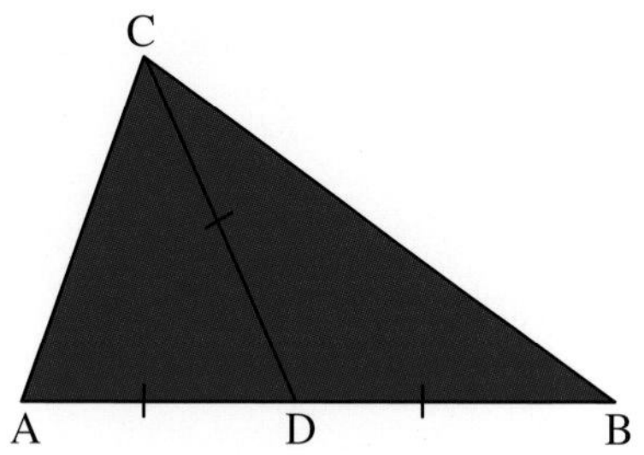

Algebraic proof

Prove that the sum of the squares of 2 consecutive integers is odd.

Proof
Let the 2 consecutive integers be n and $n + 1$.

$$\begin{aligned} n^2 + (n + 1)^2 &= n^2 + n^2 + 2n + 1 \\ &= 2n^2 + 2n + 1 \\ &= 2(n^2 + n) + 1 \end{aligned}$$

Now, since $2(n^2 + n)$ is even, $2(n^2 + n) + 1$ is odd, as required.

Prove that, if p and q are odd numbers, then $p + q$ is even.

Proof

If p is odd there is remainder 1 when p is divided by 2.
So p may be written in the form $(2m + 1)$ where m is a whole number.
In the same way q may be written in the form $(2n + 1)$.

So $p + q = 2m + 1 + 2n + 1$
$\quad = 2(m + n + 1)$

So $p + q$ is even, as required.

Exercise 2E

1 Prove that the answer to every line of the pattern below is 8.

$3 \times 5 - 1 \times 7$
$4 \times 6 - 2 \times 8$
$5 \times 7 - 3 \times 9$
$\vdots \qquad \vdots$

Hint: Write an expression for the nth line of the pattern. [i.e. $(n + 2)(n + 4) - n(n + 6)$]

2 (a) Without a calculator explain why 3^5 is an odd number.
(b) Again, without a calculator, determine whether $3^5 + 4^5 + 5^5$ is odd or even.

3 Prove that when 2 is subtracted from the sum of the squares of three consecutive numbers you always obtain 3 times a square number.

For example $4^2 + 5^2 + 6^2 - 2 = 16 + 25 + 36 - 2$
$= 75$
$= 3 \times 5^2$

[Hint: Let the three consecutive numbers be $n - 1, n, n + 1$.]

4 Prove that the cube of an even number is divisible by 8.

5 If p is odd and q is even, prove that pq is even.
[Let $p = 2n + 1$ and $q = 2m$, where n and m are integers (whole numbers).]

6 Prove that the product of four consecutive numbers is divisible by 4.

7 Five consecutive numbers can be written as

$n - 2, n - 1, n, n + 1, n + 2.$

Prove that the sum of the squares of five consecutive numbers is divisible by 5.

For example, $1^2 + 2^2 + 3^2 + 4^2 + 5^2 = 55 = 5 \times 11$

8 Prove that the sum of the squares of any two consecutive integers is an odd number.

9 Find the sum of the squares of three consecutive numbers and then subtract 2.
Prove that the result is always 3 times a square number.

10 Prove that the sum of the squares of two consecutive odd numbers is even.

11 Prove that the answer to every line of the pattern below is 3.

$2 \times 4 - 1 \times 5 =$
$3 \times 5 - 1 \times 6 =$
$4 \times 6 - 1 \times 7 =$
$\vdots \qquad \vdots$

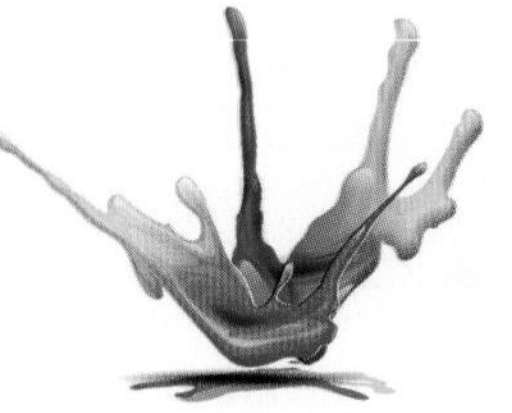

12 In any three consecutive numbers, prove that the product of the first and third numbers is one less than the square of the middle number.

13 A B C D E F G H
I J K L M N O
P Q R S T U V
W X Y Z
1 2 3 4 5 6
7 8 9 0

The letters of the alphabet are made using screws.

For example, there are 7 screws used to make the number '8'.

The number of screws used to make the letters, B, G, D, F form a sequence.

Which *letters* could be used to continue the sequence for the next term?

CHECK YOURSELF ON SECTIONS 5.3 AND 5.4

1. Probability

(a) Joshua threw an 8 – sided dice with faces numbered 1 to 8. Find the probability of throwing:
(i) a 5 (ii) a prime number

(b) One ball is selected from a bag containing x white balls and y red balls. What is the probability of selecting a red ball?

(c) The probability of winning a lottery prize is 0.05. What is the probability of *not* winning a prize?

2. Gradient of a line, $y = mx + c$

(a) The vertices of triangle ABC are at A (1, 2), B (2, 6) and C(5, 1)
  (i) Find the gradients of AB, BC and AC
  (ii) Is ABC a right-angled triangle?

(b) Find the gradient and y-intercept of the lines:
  (i) $y = 3 - 2x$ (ii) $3x - y + 2 = 0$

(c) Sketch each of the following lines:
  (i) $y = 2 + x$ (ii) $2y = 4x - 3$

UNIT 5 MIXED REVIEW

Part One

1 Write down all the whole number values of n which satisfy the inequality $2 \le n < 7$

2 The width of this photo is less than the height. Find the range of possible values of x.

$(x + 5)$

$3(x - 2)$

3 Carol walks for 1.7 km on a bearing of 042°. How far east has she walked from her starting position?

4 Copy and complete the magic square, in which each row, each column and both main diagonals have the same total.

0		
	–1	
–4		–2

5 A bag contains a large number of balls including some green balls. The probability of selecting a green ball is $\frac{1}{4}$. What is the probability of selecting a ball which is not green?

6 Find the angles in an isosceles triangle ABC if AB = BC = 7 cm and AC = 3 cm.

7 Describe an experiment you could perform to test a roulette wheel suspected of being biased. Roughly how many trials would you require?

8 Answer true or false:

(a) $3^7 > 9^3$ (b) $2^{21} \div 2^{16} = 32$ (c) $6^0 = 1$

9 Copy and complete the table for the straight lines 1 and 2.

Gradient of line 1	Gradient of line 2	Information
4	□	Lines are parallel
2	□	Lines are perpendicular
□	$-\frac{1}{3}$	Lines are parallel
-5	□	Lines are perpendicular
□	$\frac{3}{4}$	Lines are perpendicular

10 (a) Given that $x + 11 < 15$ and that $6x > 3$, list all the possible whole number values of x.

(b) If $3^n < 20000$, what is the largest whole number value of n?

11 Two dice are rolled. Find the probability of getting a total of 8 on the two dice.

12 Sabi wants to draw a circle. She lines her pencil up with the point of the compass. The length of the compass arm is 9 cm and she set the angle between the arms at 28°. What is the diameter of the circle she can draw?

13 A right angled triangle has sides of length 5 cm, 12 cm and 13 cm. Find the size of the smallest angle in the triangle.

14 A dice is biased and the probability of rolling a 'one' is 0.2. The dice is rolled 200 times. How many times would you expect to get a 2, 3, 4, 5, or 6?

15 A line of 215 680 dominoes was made ready to fall. Each domino fell 0.6 seconds after the previous one. How long, in hours, minutes and seconds, would it take for the whole line to fall?

Part Two

1 A bag contains balls which are either red, blue or yellow.

The probability of selecting a red is 0.3

The probability of selecting a blue is 0.4

What is the probability of selecting a yellow?

2 A shed roof is to be covered by a rectangular piece of asphalt. The shed is 2.8 m wide and 4.6 m long. The roof makes an angle of 48° with the horizontal. Calculate the area of the rectangle of asphalt.

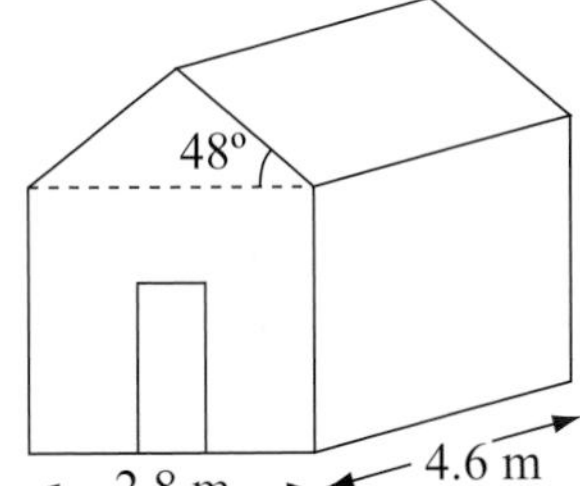

3 Solve the inequalities below.

(a) $\frac{x}{3} > -2$ (b) $\frac{4x+3}{7} \leq 5$

4 A room has a bed in the position shown.

[All the diagrams are views looking down on the room.]

Calculate if the room is wide enough to turn the bed as shown below into a new position.

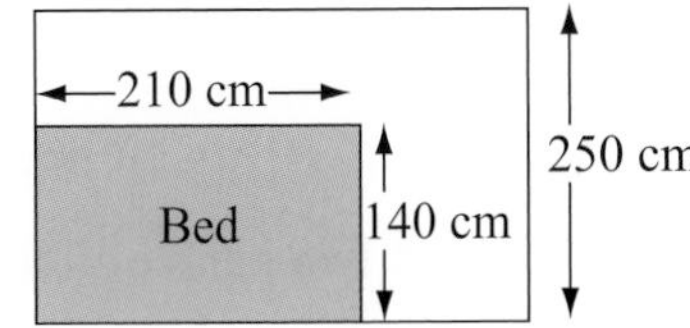

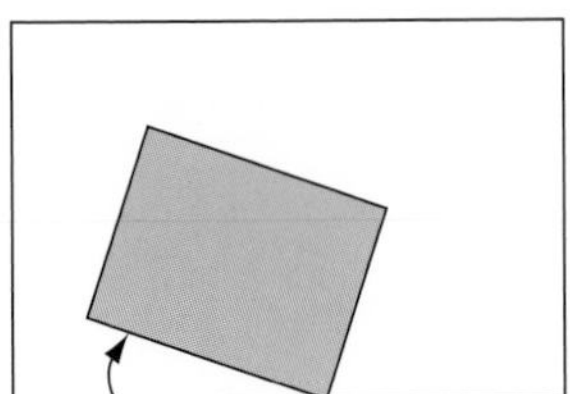

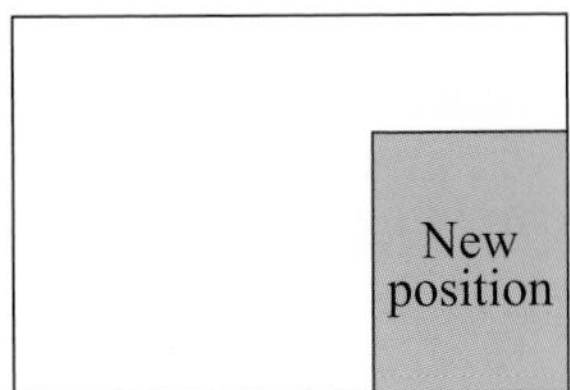

5 (a) On one graph sketch the lines $y = 3x + 1$ and $y = 5 - x$.

(b) At what point do the lines meet?

(c) The line PQ is perpendicular to the line $y = 5 - x$ and also passes through the point (2, 3). At what point does PQ meet the y axis?

6 A ladder AB leans against a vertical wall and a rope of length 1.8 m ties the ladder to the base of the wall.

The rope is perpendicular to the ladder. If the ladder rests at an angle of 72° to the ground, calculate the length of the ladder.

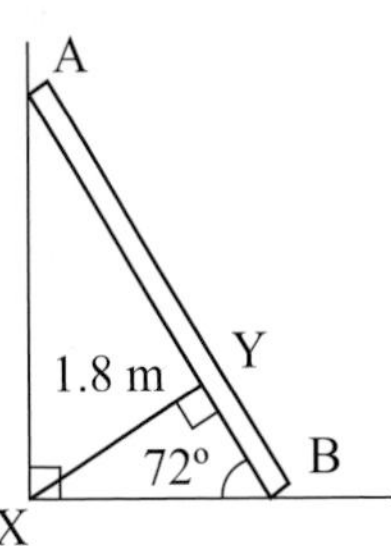

7 The two spinners shown are spun at the same time. One possible outcome is a '2' and a 'Red' (2, R).
(a) List all the possible outcomes.
(b) Find the probability of spinning a '4' and a 'White'.

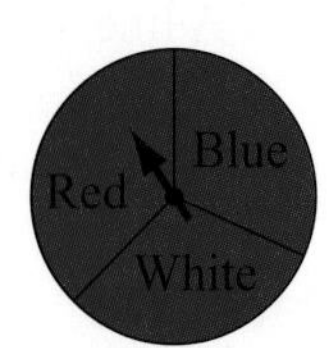

8 Find the range of values of x which satisfy the inequalities.

(a) $3x - 1 < 14$ (b) $\frac{x}{3} + 4 > 8$

(c) $9x + 10 \geq 12$ (d) $3(x - 2) \leq 4$

9 In Guy Fawkes' time matches were expensive and not very reliable. Guy had just five matches of which only one could work. As the alarm was sounded he only had enough time to strike 2 matches.
What is the probability that he chose the match that would work?

10 Here are the equations of several straight lines.

A $y = 8 - x$ B $2y = x + 4$ C $4x + 12y = 5$

D $x + 3y = 10$ E $y = x + 3$ F $y = 8 - 5x$

G $5x + y = 12$ H $y = 7 - 2x$ I $y = 2x + 5$

(a) Find **two** pairs of lines which are parallel.

(b) Find **two** pairs of lines which are perpendicular.

(c) Find **one** line which is neither parallel nor perpendicular to any of the other lines.

11 Find the side or angle marked with a letter. All lengths are in cm.

(a)
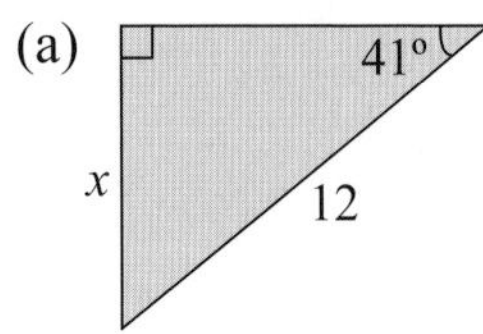

(b)

(c)
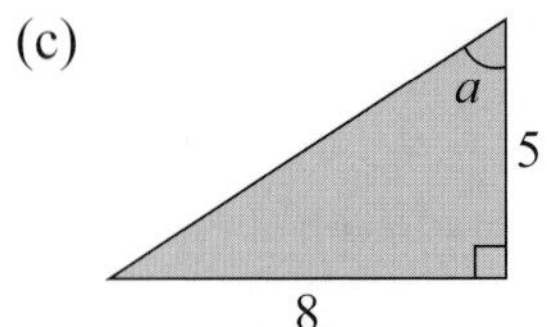

(d)
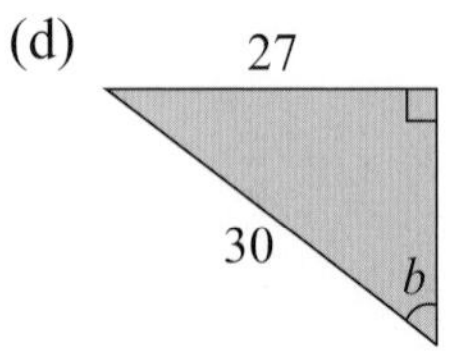

(e)
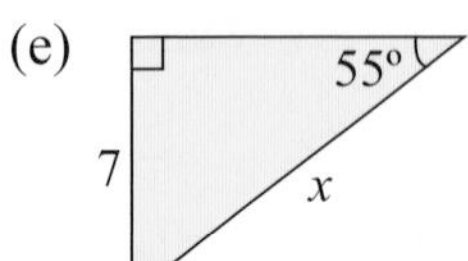

(f)
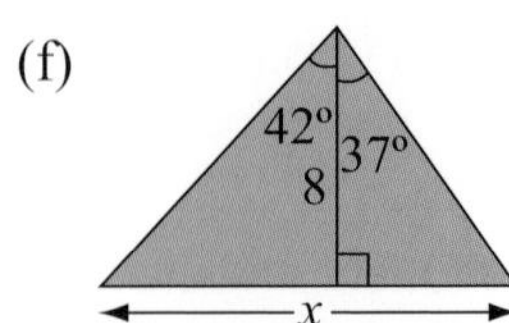

12 The square shown has four lines of symmetry. One line of symmetry is shown by the broken line.

(a) Write down the equation for each line of symmetry.

(b) The pink shaded region is defined by three inequalities of which one is $y \geq 0$.

Write down the other two inequalities.

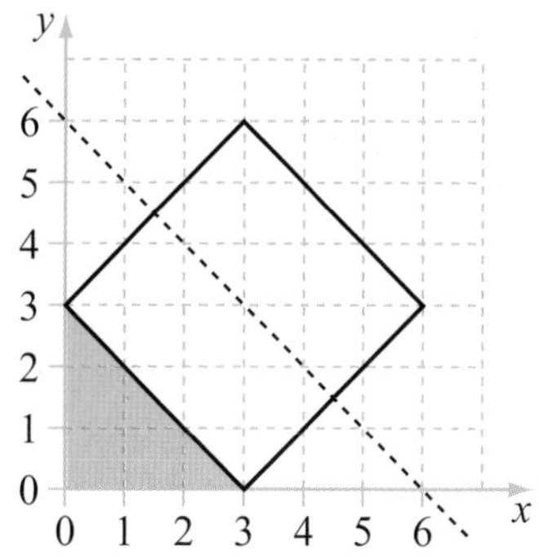

13 The fractions $\frac{1}{6}$, a, b, $\frac{1}{4}$ are in increasing order of size. The differences between successive fractions are all the same.

Find the values of a and b.

14 The chains connecting the chairs to the roundabout ride at a funfair are 6.5 m long. The central diameter of the roundabout is 8 m and when the ride is at full speed the chairs trace out a circular path of radius 9.8 m. What angle, to the nearest degree, do the chains make with the vertical?

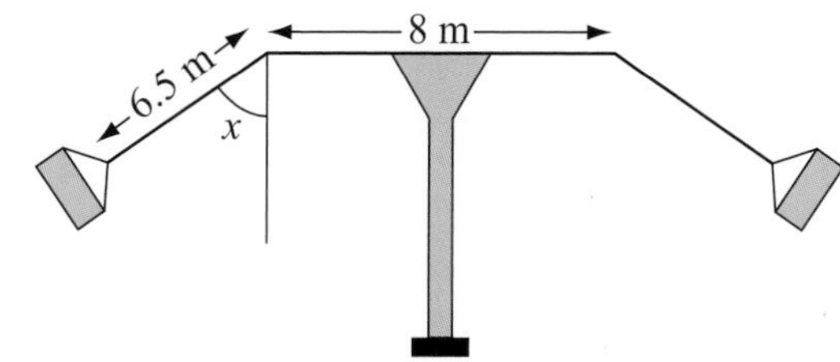

Puzzles and Problems 5

Cross numbers

Make three copies of the pattern below and complete the puzzles using the clues given. To avoid confusion it is better not to write the small reference numbers 1, 2…18 on your patterns. Write any decimal points on the lines between squares.

1		2		3			4
				5			
	6		7			8	
9					10		
		11					12
				13	14		
15	16				17		
			18				

Part A

Across

1. $(0.5 \div \frac{1}{2}) \times 253$
3. 0.003 kg written in mg
5. Next in the sequence 1, 3, 7, 15, 31
6. (1 across) × 4 + 500
8. Number of cm in 6 inches (nearest cm)
9. A third of $(9.9 \div 0.1)$
10. $(1 + 2 + 3 + 4)^2 - 1$
11. Total number of heads and legs of 75 ducks and 75 sheep.
13. 3008 – 2986 [No calculator!]
15. $15^2 + 10^4 - 10^3$
17. (2 down) – 2.97
18. A quarter share of a third share of a half share of £6000.

Down

1. Digit sum of 9873
2. Mid-way between 3 and 3.1
4. $\left(\frac{1}{20}\right)^2 \times 100$ as a decimal
7. 10% of £1304.31 to the nearest pound.
8. Area of a square of side 14 units
9. $(5 \text{ across})^2$
11. (12 down) ÷ 12 – (7 down)
12. Number of hours in a leap year.
14. 720 km/h in m/s
16. $(1.47 \times 10^4) \div (7 \times 10^2)$

Part B

Across

1. Tenth term of the sequence 169, 171, 175, 181,….
3. $10^2 + 2^{10}$
5. (1 down) – (8 across)
6. $1127 \times 7 \times 17 \div 23$ [no calculator!]
8. The value of $2x^2 - x$, when $x = -2$
9. (11 across) – (3 down) [You must find 3 down]
10. Middle two digits of $(19 \div \frac{1}{2})^2$
11. $(3 \times 10^{-2}) \div (2 \times 10^{-4})$
13. $1\frac{2}{5} \div 1\frac{1}{6}$
15. Find n if $\sqrt[3]{n - 117} = 19$
17. $\frac{3}{7}$ of 11% of 2.6^4, (2 d.p.)
18. [Number of letters in the word 'cubed']^3

Down

1. Work out $(a + b - c)^2$ when $a = -2$, $b = 3$, $c = -4$
2. $31.6^2 - \left[\frac{1}{6} + \frac{1}{3} + \frac{3}{50}\right]$
4. $(1 \text{ down} - 5)^2$
7. North-west as a bearing
8. $\dfrac{6.9 - 0.71^2}{2.3^2 - \frac{1.4}{1.7}}$, correct to 2 d.p.
9. $(20^2 - 5^2 - 1^2) \times 3^2$
11. Next in the sequence $5.\dot{4}$, $16.\dot{3}$, 49,…
12. The hypotenuse in a triangle in which the other two sides are 3330 and 7992
14. Angle in degrees between the hands of a clock at 2.15
16. Interior angle of a regular quadrilateral.

Part C (Harder)

Across

1. $\frac{13}{104}$ as a percentage
3. 4 more than a cube number
5. (A square number) + 10
6. $(8 \times 10^3) + (50 \div 0.1) + 2^5$
8. $10^{-2} \div 10^{-3}$
9. Find the value of x if, $3 - 5\%$ of $x = 1.35$
10. Surface area, in cm^2, of a cube of side 2 cm
11. $\sqrt{\dfrac{1.3}{1.23^2}} + \sqrt{\dfrac{1.515}{0.3 - 0.261}}$, to 2 d.p.
13. Next in the sequence 23, 25, 32, 45, 65
15. $346\frac{1}{2} \times$ (1% of 10 across)
17. Area of a triangle with sides 30, 40, 50
18. Longest diagonal in a cuboid measuring $4 \times 6 \times 13$ units

Down

1. $(4\frac{1}{3})^2$ to the nearest whole number
2. Change 189 km/h into m/s
3. $(\frac{1}{3} + \frac{1}{4}) \div \frac{1}{5}$, correct to 2 d.p.
4. Number of seconds taken to travel 500 m at a speed of 10 km/h
6. Solve the equation $\dfrac{3}{4} - \dfrac{21}{x + 1} = \dfrac{1}{2}$
7. Square number
8. Next in the sequence 1.2, 2.4, 7.2, 28.8,…
9. $3^3 + 4^4 + 5^5$
11. Smallest integer solution of $9x - 1 > 6666$
12. Surface area, in cm^2, of a cuboid measuring 5 cm × 10 cm × 40 cm
14. Smallest angle in a 3, 4, 5 triangle (to 1 d.p.)
16. Angle in degrees between the hands of a clock at 3.10.

A long time ago! 5

The Golden Ratio

The Fibonacci sequence is formed by adding each pair of successive numbers to make the next number.
1, 1, 2, 3, 5, 8, 13, 21, 34, 55, 89, …..

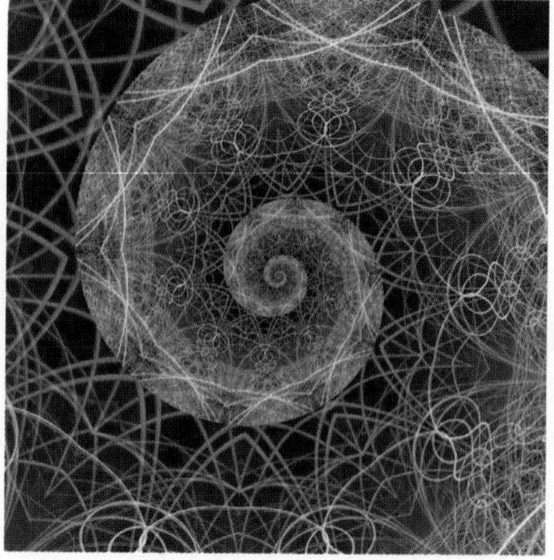

1 Investigate what happens when you keep dividing successive pairs of numbers, for example $\frac{55}{34}$ then $\frac{89}{55}$. Extend the Fibonacci sequence and divide more numbers. You may find it helpful to use a spreadsheet.

2

$$\longleftarrow x \longrightarrow\!\!\!\!\longleftarrow 1 \longrightarrow$$

In the line above the ratio of the whole line to the larger part x is equal to the ratio of the larger part x to the smaller part 1.

$$\frac{x+1}{x} = \frac{x}{1}$$

$$\text{so } x = \frac{x+1}{x}$$

Get a calculator.

Type [3] [=] [(] [ANS] [+] [1] [)] [÷] [ANS] [=]

Now press the [=] button about 20 times. Compare this calculator number to the answers you were finding in task 1.

This number is very significant. It is known as the 'golden ratio' and is referred to by the greek letter ϕ (phi). It is a number which never stops like π (pi). The digits never repeat.

$$\phi = 1.6180339887....$$

By rearranging the ratio equation into the form $x^2 - x - 1 = 0$, we can get the 'exact' value

$$\phi = \frac{1+\sqrt{5}}{2}$$

ϕ appears in geometry, art, architecture and other areas.

3 'Golden rectangles' have sides in the golden ratio. A perfect snail shell fits within golden rectangles. Draw the golden rectangles shown below. In each golden rectangle use compasses to join the diagonal corners with an arc. Colour as you wish to make a snail shell design.

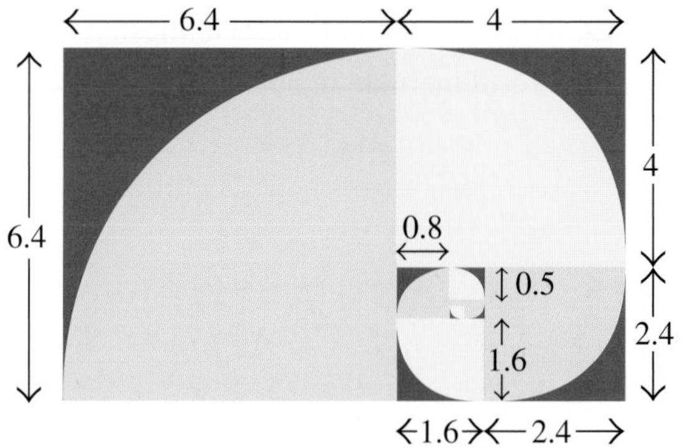

All lengths are in cm. The lengths had to be rounded off so the final small rectangles will not work perfectly.

4 **RESEARCH:**

(a) Find a way to construct a perfect golden rectangle using ruler and compasses only.

(b) Find and describe other situations in which the golden ratio is evident.

General knowledge quiz

The answer to each question is a number.

Quiz A

1. Hills of Rome.
2. Faces on a Dodecahedron.
3. James Bond.
4. Links in a Chain.
5. Birdie.
6. British standard voltage.
7. Sextant.
8. Greenwich meridian.
9. Tchaikovsky overture.
10. Trafalgar.
11. Green bottles.
12. Octave.
13. Major planets.
14. Trilogy.
15. Pleiades.
16. Visually handicapped rodents
17. Novel by George Orwell.
18. Marathon.
19. Unlucky.
20. Four score and ten.

Quiz B (Harder)

1. Tethera.
2. Googol.
3. Lunar months in year.
4. Proud walkers.
5. a′ (Concert pitch).
6. Going to St. Ives.
7. Yorkshire Ridings.
8. Barleycorns in an Inch.
9. Tetralogy.
10. Albatross.
11. Mercurial year (In Earth days).
12. Sides on an Undecagon.
13. Diptich.
14. Pillars of Wisdom.
15. For joy.
16. Preludes and Fugues.
17. This year had only 354 days.
18. Kilobyte.
19. Dewey index of mathematics.
20. Tardi merulae in 355/113.

UNIT 6

6.1 Drawing and using graphs

In this section you will:

- Practise drawing accurate straight line graphs
- Learn to draw curved graphs
- Learn to solve difficult equations approximately using graphs

Straight lines

Draw the graph of $y = 2x - 2$ for x from -2 to 3.

Method 1. Draw a flow chart.

$x \rightarrow \boxed{\times 2} \rightarrow \boxed{-2} \rightarrow y$

x	-2	-1	0	1	2	3
y	-6	-4	-2	0	2	4

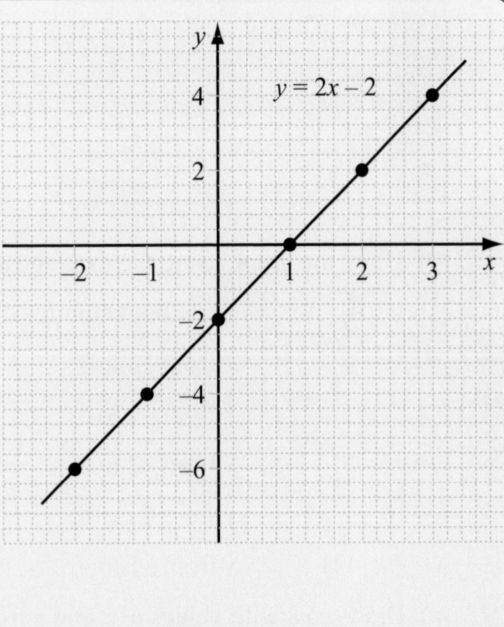

Method 2. Make a table of values.

x	-2	-1	0	1	2	3	
$2x$	-4	-2	0	2	4	6	add these numbers
-2	-2	-2	-2	-2	-2	-2	
y	-6	-4	-2	0	2	4	

Many people use method 2 because we use that method for curved graphs. (see next page)

Exercise 1M

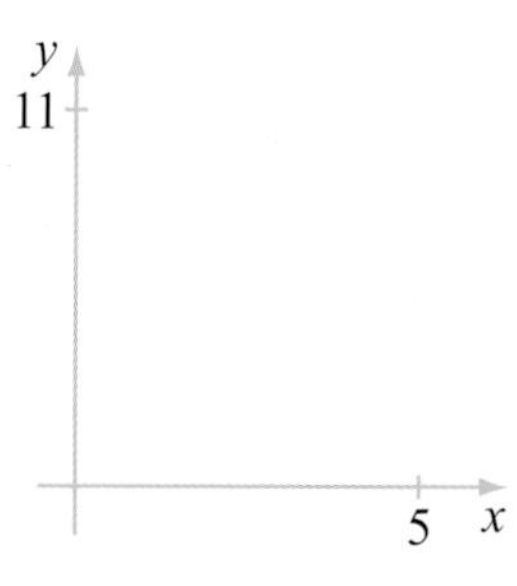

1 (a) Copy and complete the table for $y = 2x + 1$.

x	0	1	2	3	4	5
$2x$	0	2	4	6		
$+1$	1	1	1			
y	1	3				

(b) Draw the graph using the axes shown.

2 (a) Make a table similar to the one above for the graph of $y = 2x - 3$. Take x from 0 to 5.

(b) Draw the graph of $y = 2x - 3$.

(c) Write down the coordinates of the point where the line cuts the x axis.

3 (a) Copy and complete the table for $y = 3x - 2$.

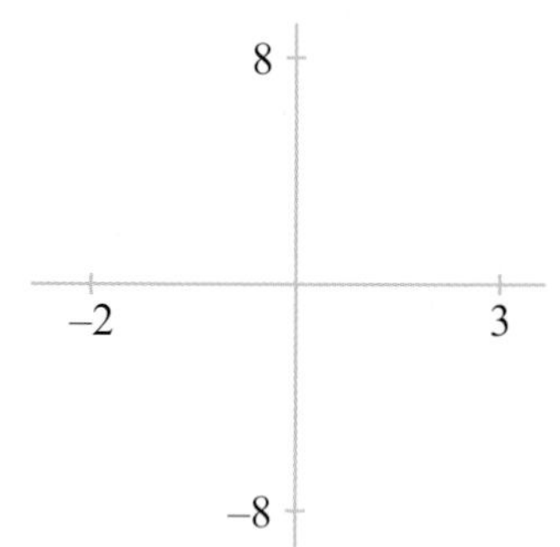

x	–2	–1	0	1	2	3
$3x$	–6	–3				
-2	–2	–2			–2	
y	–8					

(b) Draw the graph using the axes shown.

In questions 4 to 8 draw the graph for the values of x given.

4 $y = 3x + 1$; x from –3 to 3.

5 $y = 2x + 5$; x from –1 to 5.

6 $y = 4x - 7$; x from –2 to 3.

7 $y = 10 - x$; x from 0 to 10.

8 $y = 2(x - 3)$; x from –1 to 4.

9 (a) Draw axes with values of x and y from 0 to 9.

(b) Draw the lines $y = 2x$, $y = 9 - x$ and $y = \frac{1}{2}x$.

(c) Work out the area of the triangle enclosed by the three lines above. Give your answer in square units.

Curved graphs

Draw the graph of $y = x^2 - 2x - 3$, taking values of x from -2 to 4.

Here is a table of values

x	−2	−1	0	1	2	3	4
x^2	4	1	0	1	4	9	16
$-2x$	4	2	0	−2	−4	−6	−8
−3	−3	−3	−3	−3	−3	−3	−3
y	5	0	−3	−4	−3	0	5

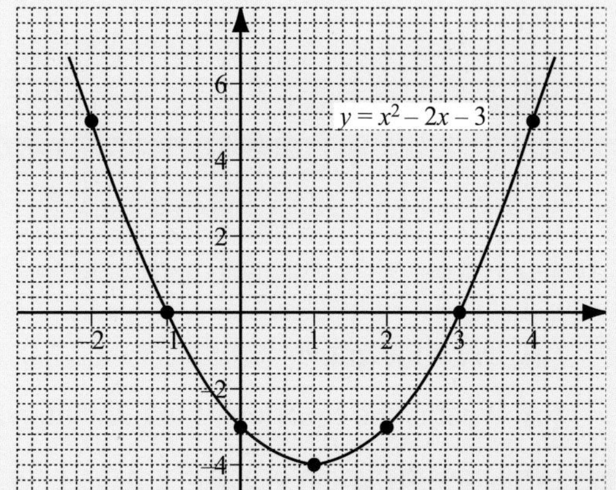

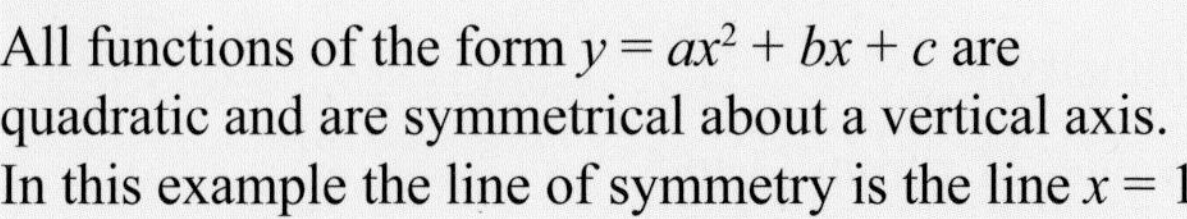

All functions of the form $y = ax^2 + bx + c$ are quadratic and are symmetrical about a vertical axis. In this example the line of symmetry is the line $x = 1$.

Exercise 2M

1 (a) Copy and complete the table for $y = x^2 + 2$.

x	−3	−2	−1	0	1	2	3
x^2	9	4					
+2	2	2	2				
y	11						

(b) Draw the graph using the axes shown.

2 (a) Copy and complete the table for $y = x^2 + 2x$.

x	−4	−3	−2	−1	0	1	2
x^2	16						4
$2x$	−8	−6					4
y	8						8

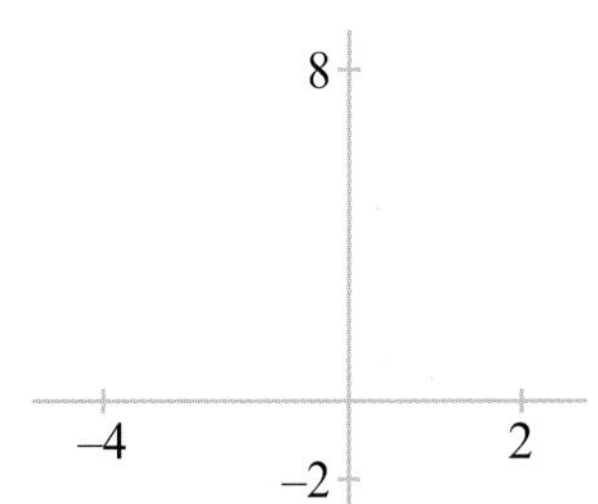

(b) Draw the graph using the axes shown.

3 (a) Make a table like the one above for the curve $y = x^2 - 3$, for x from -3 to 3.

(b) Draw the curve and write down the coordinates of the two points where the curve cuts the x axis.

4 (a) Copy and complete the table for $y = x^2 + 2x - 5$.

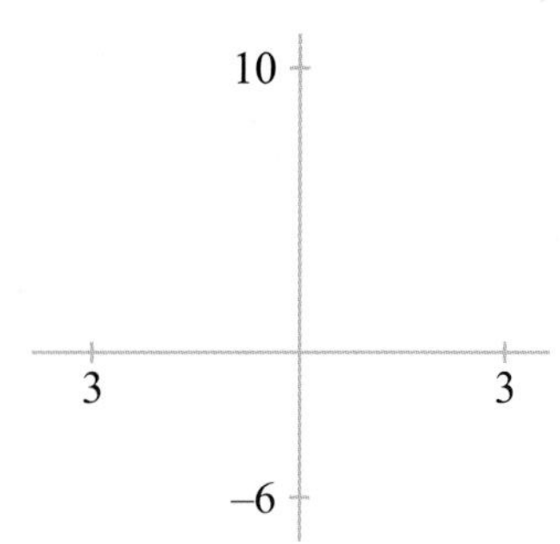

x	–3	–2	–1	0	1	2	3
x^2	9			0			
$2x$	–6			0			
–5	–5	–5	–5	–5			
y	–2			–5			

(b) Draw the graph.

(c) What is the equation of the line of symmetry?

5 (a) Draw the graph of $y = x^2 - 3x + 1$ for values of x from –2 to 5.

(b) What is the equation of the line of symmetry?

6 (a) Draw the graph of $y = x^2 - 4x - 3$ for values of x from –1 to 5.

(b) Write down the coordinates of the lowest point on the curve.

Exercise 2E

In questions 1 to 6 draw the graph for the values of x given.

Remember: $2x^2 = 2(x^2)$

1 $y = 2x^2 - 5$; x from –3 to 3.

2 $y = 2x^2 + x$; x from –3 to 2.

3 $y = x^3$; x from –3 to 3.

4 $y = x^3 - 4x$; x from –3 to 3.

5 $y = \frac{12}{x}$; x from 1 to 12.

6 $y = \frac{20}{x}$; x from 1 to 20.

7 (a) Copy and complete the table for $y = 2^x$.

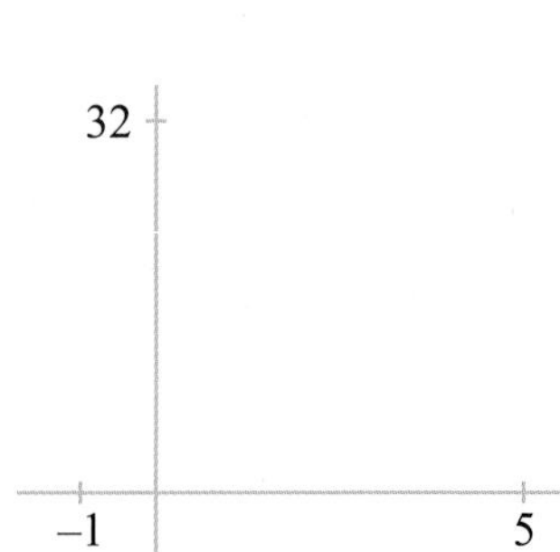

x	–1	0	1	2	3	4	5
y	0.5	1	2				

(b) Draw the curve using the axes shown.

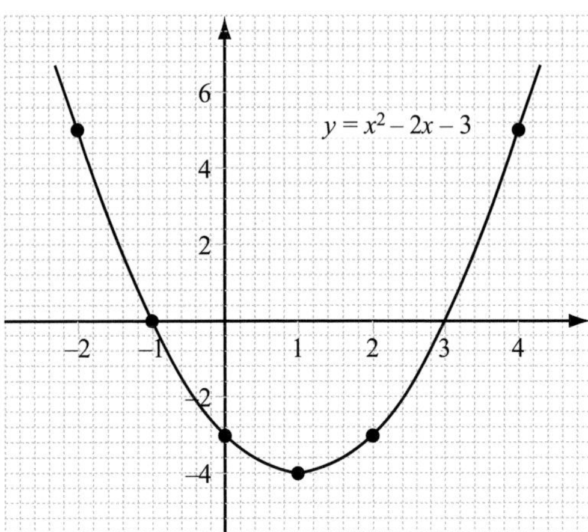

8 (a) Copy the graph of $y = x^2 - 2x - 3$.

(b) Draw the graph of $y = x - 1$.

(c) Write down the coordinates of the two points of intersection.

9 (a) Draw the graph of $y = \frac{8}{x}$ for x from 0 to 8.

(b) Draw the graph of $y = \frac{x + 4}{2}$ for the same values of x.

(c) Write down the coordinates of the point of intersection.

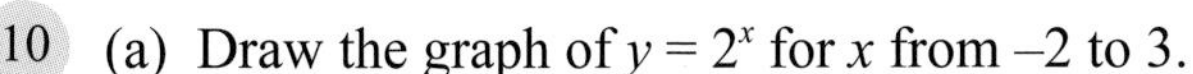

10 (a) Draw the graph of $y = 2^x$ for x from –2 to 3.

(b) Draw the graph of $y = 4 - x$ for x from –1 to 3

(c) Use your graph to find approximate solutions to the equations

(i) $2^x = 1.5$

(ii) $2^x = 4 - x$

6.2 Compound measures

In this section you will:

- Solve problems involving speed, distance and time.
- Learn how to solve problems involving density, rates of exchange and various compound measures.

Speed

Speed is an example of a compound measure. When a horse runs at a constant speed of 16 metres per second, it means that it moves a distance of 16 metres in 1 second.

Remember: distance = speed × time .. ①

We obtain two other formulas from ①:

Divide both sides by time: $\frac{\text{distance}}{\text{time}} = \text{speed}$ .. ②

Divide both sides by speed: $\frac{\text{distance}}{\text{speed}} = \text{time}$ .. ③

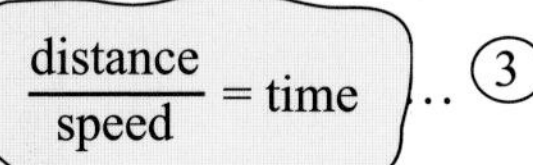

These three important formulas can be remembered using a triangle as shown. [D is at the top]

To find S: cover S, and you have $\frac{D}{T}$

To find T: cover T, and you have $\frac{D}{S}$

To find D: cover D, and you have $S \times T$

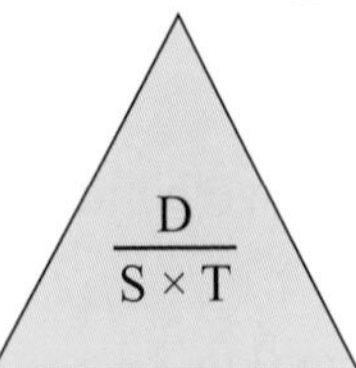

Note: The above formulas can only be used for objects moving at a constant speed.

The units used for speed, distance and time in a question must be compatible.

- If the speed is in miles per hour, the distance must be in miles and the time must be in hours.
- If the speed is in metres per second, the distance must be in metres and the time must be in seconds.

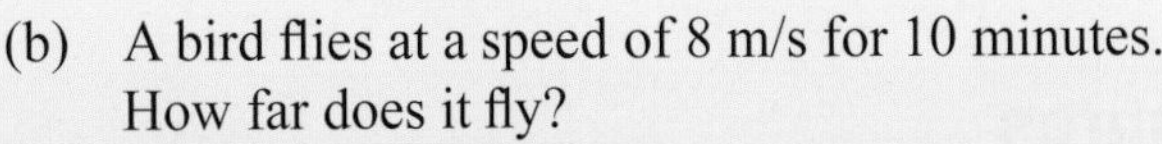

(a) A plane is flying at a steady speed of 500 m/s. How long does it take to fly 200 m ?

$$\text{time taken} = \frac{\text{distance}}{\text{speed}}$$

$$= \frac{200}{500} = 0.4 \text{ seconds}$$

(b) A bird flies at a speed of 8 m/s for 10 minutes. How far does it fly?

Change 10 minutes into 600 seconds.

$$\text{Distance} = \text{speed} \times \text{time}$$

$$= 8 \times 600$$

The bird flies 4800 m.

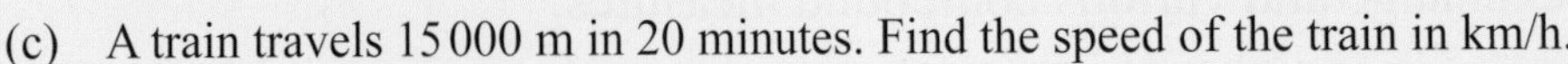

(c) A train travels 15 000 m in 20 minutes. Find the speed of the train in km/h.

Change 15 000 m into 15 km.

Change 20 minutes into $\frac{1}{3}$ hour.

$$\text{Speed of train} = \frac{\text{distance}}{\text{time}}$$

$$= \frac{15}{1/3}$$

$$= 45 \text{ km/h}$$

Exercise 1M

1 A bike has a top speed of 150 km/h. How long will it take to travel 200 km? Give your answer in hours and minutes.

2 An athlete runs at a speed of 6.5 m/s. How far will she run in 4 seconds?

3 An arctic tern flies a distance of 245 km in 9 hours. How fast does it fly?

4 A steamroller takes 180 seconds to travel 60 m. What is its speed, in m/s?

5 A bus travels 200 m at a speed of 25 m/s. How long does it take?

6 How long does it take a coach to travel 270 km at a constant speed of 90 km/h?

7 An aircraft flies at a speed of 680 km/h. How far does it fly in 1 hour 30 minutes?

8 A swallow flies 8 miles in 15 minutes. What is its speed in miles per hour (m.p.h.)?

9 A lorry travels 32 km in 20 minutes. How far does it go in one hour at the same speed?

10 A donkey walks for half an hour at a speed of 2 m/s. How far does it walk?

Exercise 1E

1 Eurostar goes 420 km from London to Paris in just 2 hours 15 minutes.
Find the average speed of the train.

2 A balloon rises 15000 feet in 5 minutes. Find its speed of ascent in feet per second.

3 Find the distance travelled:
(a) 65 m.p.h for 2 hours
(b) 8 cm/day for 5 days
(c) 5 m/s for 1 minute [units!]

4 In the 1996 Olympics Donovan Bailey won the 100 m in 9.81 seconds and Michael Johnson won the 200 m in 19.37 seconds. Who ran at the faster average speed?

5 A bullet from a rifle goes 520 metres in 0.2 seconds. Find its speed.

6 Find the time taken:
(a) 260 km at 20 km/h
(b) 2 km at 10 m/s
(c) 4 miles at 8 m.p.h.

7 A T.G.V. travels 567 km from Bordeaux to Paris at an average speed of 252 km/h.
Find the arrival time in Paris, if it leaves Bordeaux at 1410.

8 A boat sails at a speed of 13 knots for 2 days. How far does it travel?
[1 knot = 1 nautical mile per hour].

9 In a grand prix, the winning car passed the chequered flag 0.3 seconds ahead of the next car. Both cars were travelling at 84 m/s. What was the distance between the two cars?

10 (a) Sam drives from Liverpool to York at an average speed of 30 m.p.h. How long will it take in hours and minutes?

(b) Mike takes $2\frac{1}{2}$ h to drive from Hull to Newcastle. What was his average speed?

(c) Nikki drives from Preston to Newcastle at an average speed of 42 m.p.h. and the journey takes 2 h 40 min. What is the distance from Preston to Newcastle?

	Hull	Liverpool	Newcastle	Preston
Liverpool	126			
Newcastle	122	170		
Preston	121	29		
York	38	100	84	83

11 A train leaves London at 0815 and arrives in York, 193 miles away, at 1100. Find the average speed of the train.

12 Convert a speed of 1000 m.p.h. into furlongs per fortnight.

Other compound measures

Exercise 2M

In questions 1 to 5 use the formulas shown.

Density = $\frac{\text{Mass}}{\text{Volume}}$ or

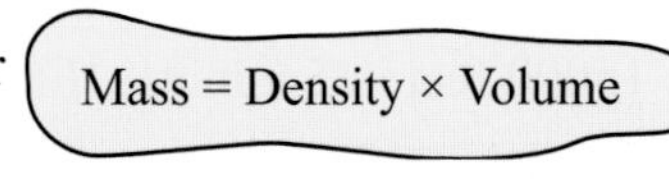

1 Find the density of a metal if 100 cm³ weighs 800 grams.

2 The density of copper is 9 g/cm³. Find the mass of a copper bar of volume 20 cm³.

3 A silver ring has a volume of 3 cm³ and a mass of 36 grams. Find the density of the silver.

4 A liquid weighs 400 g and has a density of 2.5 g/cm³. Find the volume of the liquid.

5 Which has the greater mass: 40 cm³ of iron with density 7.5 g/cm³ or 25 cm³ of nickel with density 9.1 g/cm³.

In questions 6 to 11 use the exchange rates for foreign currency shown.

Country	Rate of exchange
Spain (euro)	£1 = €1.20
USA (dollar)	£1 = $1.65
Turkey (lira)	£1 = L2.42
South Africa (rand)	£1 = 12 rand

6 Change the pounds into the currency stated

(a) £150 (euros) (b) £5520 (rand) (c) £1 million (lira)

(d) £0.60 (rand) (e) £220 million (dollar) (f) £1.25 (euros)

7 A holiday near 'The Mexican Hat' (in Utah) cost £1650 in Britain and €2310 in Italy. In which country was the holiday more expensive?

8 A helicopter trip around 'The Mexican Hat' cost \$300. How much is that in euros?

9 (a) Change 420 rand into pounds.

(b) Change 1 Turkish lira into pounds, to the nearest penny.

10 A car driver is fined \$360 in America for speeding. Can he pay the fine if he has £200?

11 Work out the total value of these banknotes in dollars.

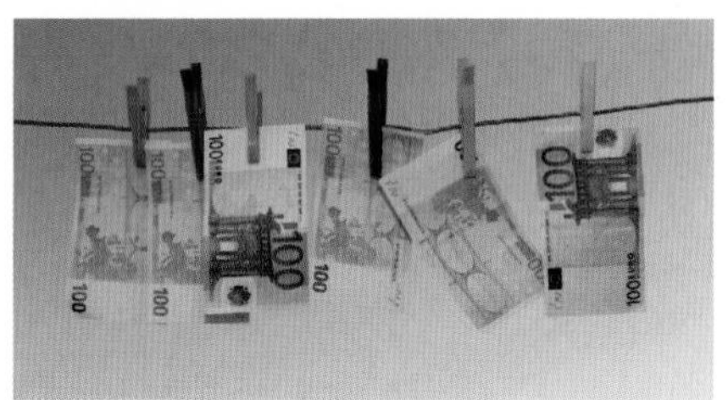

Exercise 2E

1 Heavy duty cable costs £1.50 per m. Find the cost of laying 3000 m of this cable.

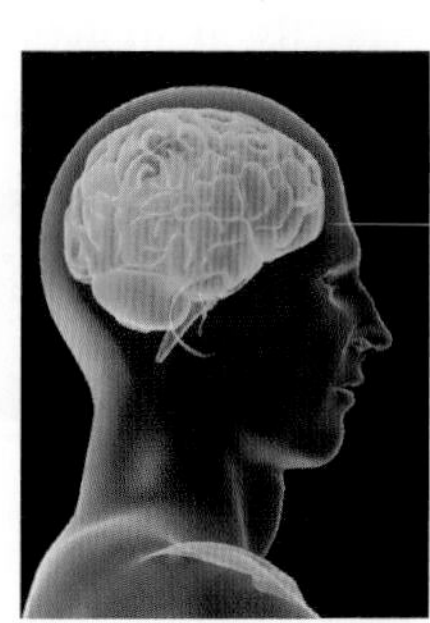

2 A powerful brain scanner can be hired at £4.90 per minute. How much will it cost to hire the scanner for $9\frac{1}{2}$ hours?

3 Silver plating costs £4.50 per cm^2.

(a) How much will it cost, in pounds, to plate a cube of side 10 cm?

(b) How much will it cost in Turkish lira?

4 A gambler lost \$3.2 million in one year. On average how much did the gambler lose per day? Give your answer to the nearest thousand dollars.

5 Good farmland is sold at £4000 per hectare (1 hectare = 10 000 m^2). Bacon farm has a rectangular field measuring 300 m by 80 m. Find the cost of the field.

6 The open box shown is made from metal weighing 5 g/cm^2. Find the weight of the box.

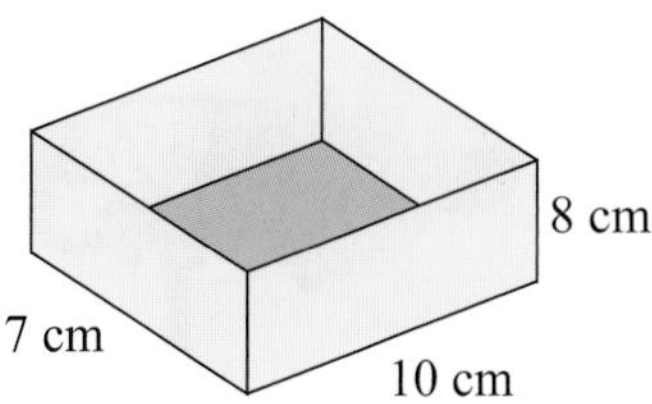

7 The table shows the land area and population for four countries.

Country	Area in km^2	Population
Italy	301 000	58.3 million
Portugal	91 600	10.7 million
Ireland	68 900	3.4 million
Brazil	8 510 000	122.6 million

(a) Work out the number of people per km^2 for Ireland.

(b) Which country has the *most* people per km^2?

(c) Suppose all the people in Portugal had an equal area of land. How much would each person have in m^2? [1 km^2 = 1 000 000 m^2].

8

A one euro coin has diameter 2.2 cm and thickness 2 mm. It is made of metal with density 7.8 g/cm^3. How much will 500 coins weigh?

9 Two birds start from the north pole and fly in opposite directions to the south pole. They each fly at an average speed of 8.2 km/h and the radius of the earth is 6400 km. How long will it be before they next meet?

10 Thick marine rope is used to encircle a shrine to the birthplace of Peter Gibson, the radius of the circle being 2400 m (his age at the time). Fifty metres of the rope weighs 34 kg. A van can carry a maximum load of 1.2 tonnes. How many vans are needed to transport the holy rope?

11 Paint has a density of 600 kg/m^3. Convert this density into g/cm^3.

12

The winner of an office chair race travelled 50 metres in 8 seconds.

Work out his average speed in m/s.

13 The population of France is about 60 million and the land area is about 480 000 km^2.

Work out the population density of France [number of people/km^2]

14 This solid cuboid is made of wood with density 7 g/cm^3.

Calculate the mass of the cuboid, giving your answer in kg.

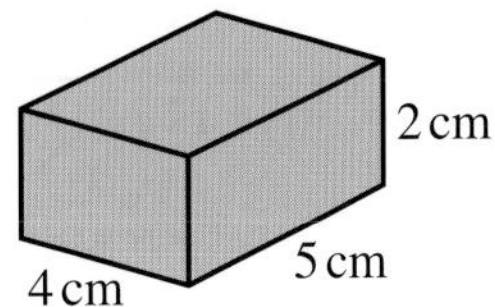

15 Change the units of the following speeds as required.

(a) 40 m/s into cm/s.

(b) 8000 cm/s into m/s.

(c) 72 km/h into m/s.

16 A statue is made of metal of density 8 g/cm^3.

Calculate the mass of the statue if its volume is 42.5 cm^3.

17 A 1.5 kg box of grass seed covers 30 m^2 of lawn. How much seed is needed for a field of area 6 hectares?
[1 hectare = 10 000 m^2]

6.3 Locus

In this section you will:

- Learn how to show the locus of a point
- Use geometric construction to show the locus of a point
- Answer a range of questions, including some involving three dimensions

Locus

A locus is the set of points which fit a certain description. Sometimes a locus can be described in words, sometimes it is better to draw a diagram. The plural of locus is loci.

(a) Jack walks so that he is always 1 km from point P. He walks in a circle and this circle is the locus of Jack.

(b) In this diagram the shaded region shows the locus of points inside a room which are within 1 m of a wall.

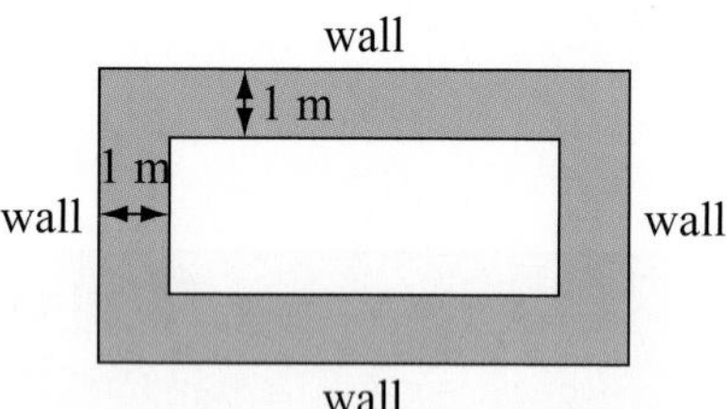

(c) Find the locus of points which are an equal distance from the points A and B. (we say 'equidistant' from A and B).

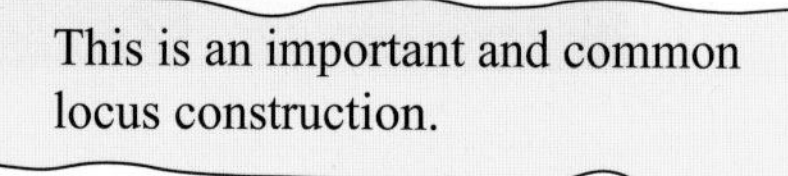

Take a pair of compasses and set the radius at more than half the length AB. With centre A draw two arcs. With the same radius and centre B draw two more arcs. Draw a straight line through the points where the arcs cut. This is the locus of points equidistant from A and B. (shown with a broken line).

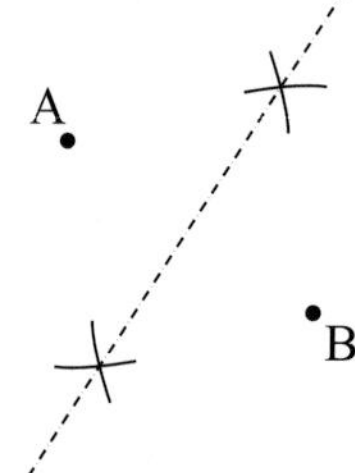

Exercise 1M

1 Draw the locus of a point P which moves so that it is always 4 cm from a fixed point A.

A

2 Draw points B and C 6 cm apart. Draw the locus of a point P which moves so that it is equidistant from B and C.

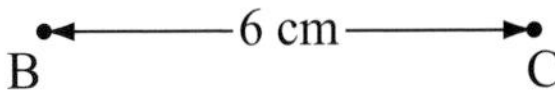

3 Television reception is good within 100 km of a transmitter T. Draw a diagram to show the locus of points where reception is good.

4 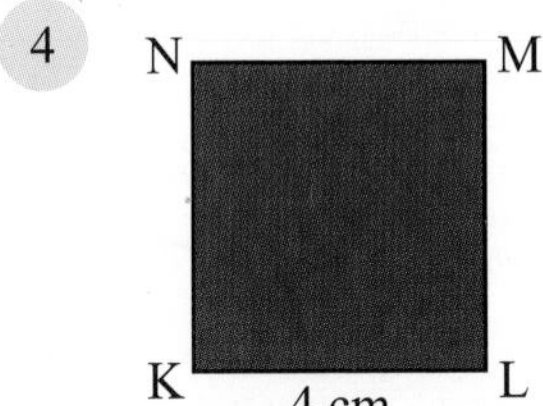

Draw the square KLMN. A tiny spider wanders around inside the square so that it is always nearer to corner K than to corner L. Shade the region to show the locus of the spider.

5 Draw the locus of a point X which is always 1 cm from the line segment PQ.

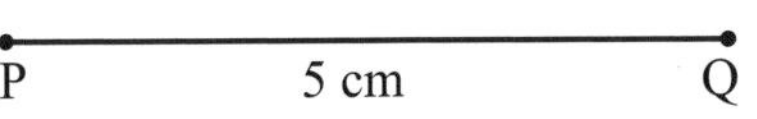

6 A newt crawls across a rectangular garden so that it is always at an equal distance from the two stone walls. Draw a sketch to show the locus of the newt.

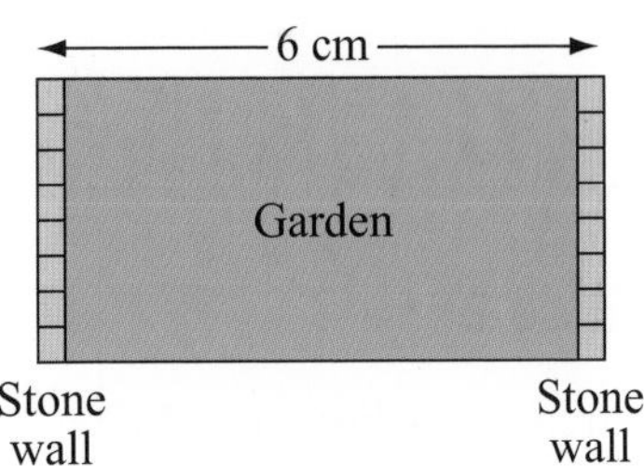

7 

Sketch the locus of a bumble bee as it moves around a garden.

8 (a) Describe in words the locus of M, the tip of the minute hand, as the time changes from 3 o'clock to 4 o'clock.

(b) Sketch the locus of H, the tip of the hour hand, as the time changes from 3 o'clock to 6 o'clock.

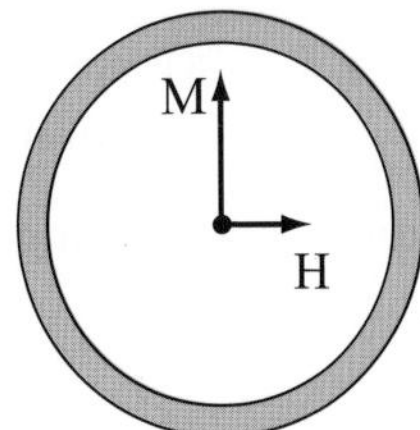

9 The diagram shows a rectangular room ABCD. Draw three diagrams with a scale of 1 cm to 1 m to illustrate the following loci:

D C E 4 m A 6 m B

(a) Points in the room up to 3 m from A
(b) Points in the room up to 2 m from E, the centre of the room.
(c) Points in the room equidistant from A and B.

10 A snake's cage is built against a wall, as shown. The public are not allowed to be within one metre of the cage.

Sketch the cage and show the locus of points where the public are not allowed.

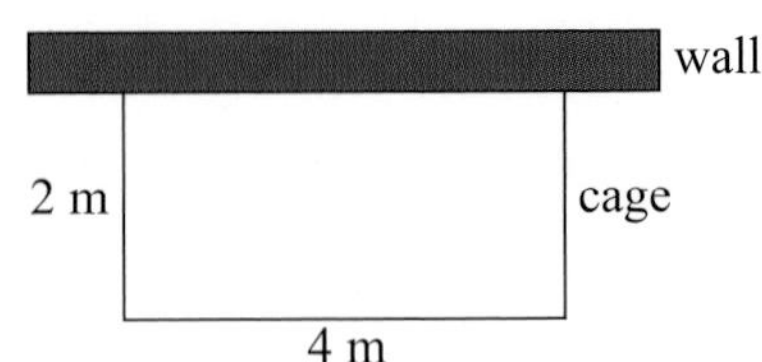

A submarine is known to be within 26 km of port P. The submarine is also known to be within 15 km of port Q. Show the region where the submarine must be.

(a) Draw an arc of radius 2.6 cm with centre P.

(b) Draw an arc of radius 1.5 cm with centre Q.

(c) The submarine must lie inside both arcs so it lies in the region shaded red.

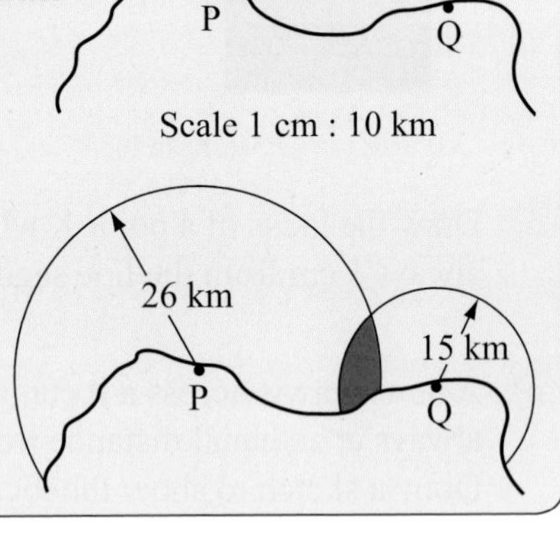

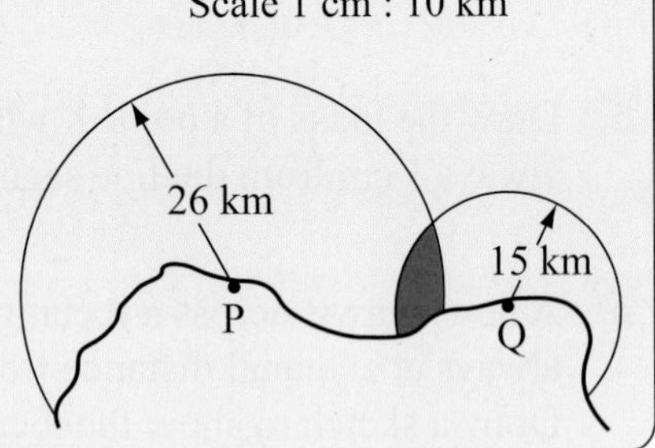

Exercise 2E

1 A treasure is buried in the rectangular garden shown. The treasure is: (a) within 4 m of A and (b) more than 3 m from the line AD.

Draw a plan of the garden and shade the points where the treasure could be.

D C 4 m A 6 m B

2 Inspector Clouseau has put a radio transmitter on a suspect's car, which is parked somewhere in Paris. From the strength of the signals received at points R and P, Clouseau knows that the car is

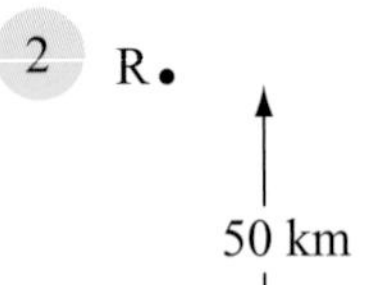

(a) not more than 40 km from R, and
(b) not more than 20 km from P.

Make a scale drawing [1 cm = 10 km] and show the possible positions of the suspect's car.

3 Draw four copies of square KLMN and show the locus of points *inside the square* which are:
(a) within 3 cm of the mid point of KL,
(b) equidistant from K and M,
(c) nearer to M than to K,
(d) more than 5 cm from N.

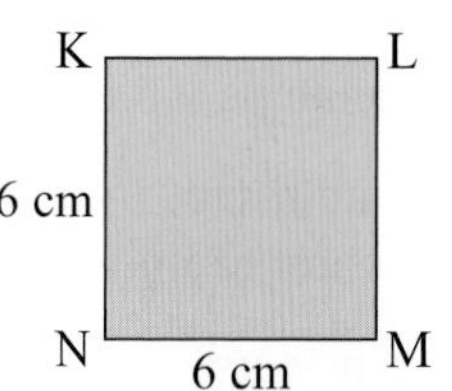

4 A goat is tied to one corner on the outside of a barn.

The diagram shows a plan view. Sketch a plan view of the barn and show the locus of points where the goat can graze if the rope is 4 m long.

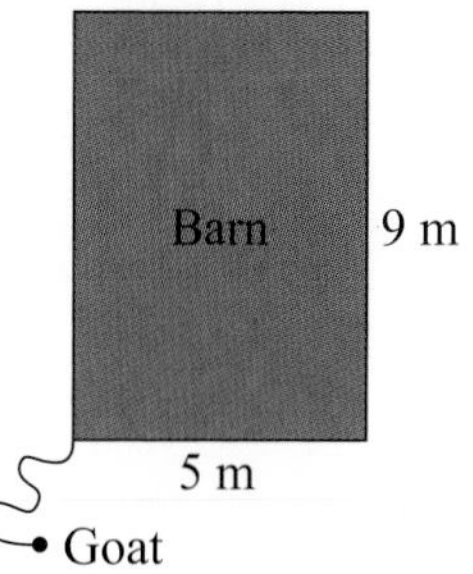

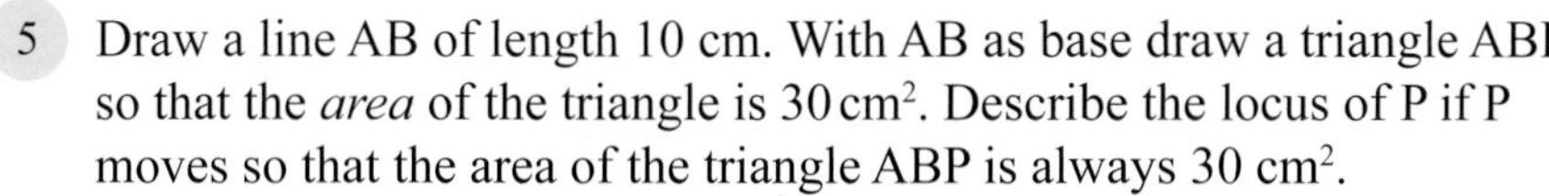

5 Draw a line AB of length 10 cm. With AB as base draw a triangle ABP so that the *area* of the triangle is $30\,cm^2$. Describe the locus of P if P moves so that the area of the triangle ABP is always $30\,cm^2$.

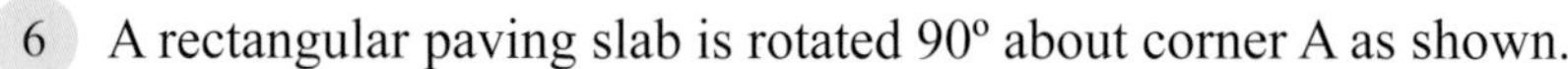

6 A rectangular paving slab is rotated 90º about corner A as shown.

(a) Copy the diagram and use a pair of compasses to draw the locus of X during the first rotation.

(b) The slab is then rotated a further 90º clockwise, this time about the corner B. Draw the new position of the slab. Use compasses to draw the path of X during this second rotation.

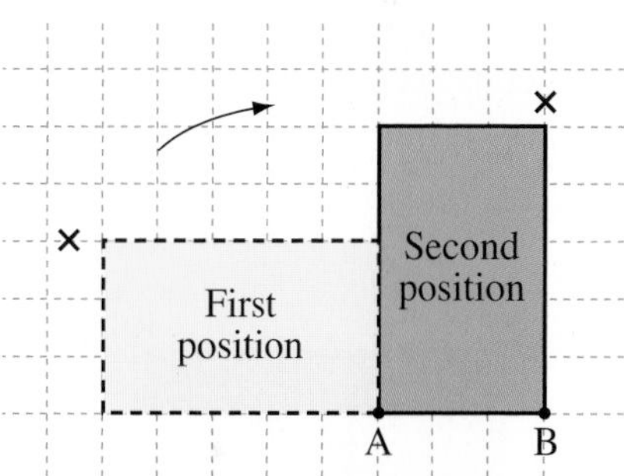

7 Bungee jumping has been introduced as an option in PE lessons.

Sketch the locus of one of the jumpers.

8 A conker is hanging motionless on a string. I move a finger so that its tip is always 20 cm from the conker. Describe the locus of my finger tip.

In a rectangle ABCD, AB = 4 cm and BC = 3 cm. Find the points inside the rectangle which are:

(a) equidistant from lines AB and AD,
(b) nearer to line AD than to line AB.

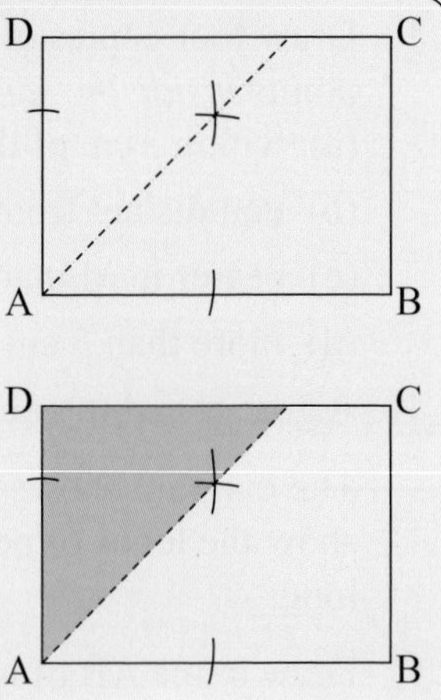

Answers

(a) Construct the line which bisects angle BAD. The broken line is the required locus.

(b) Use the line drawn above and shade the points above the broken line. Points on the line are *not* included in the locus as the question asks for points *nearer* to AD than to AB.

Exercise 3E

1 Draw two triangles ABC as shown. In each triangle construct the locus of points which are equidistant from lines AB and AC.

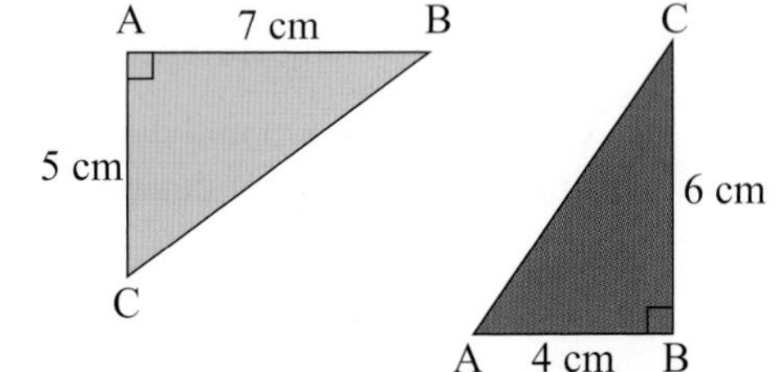

2 Draw full size the rectangle PQRS.

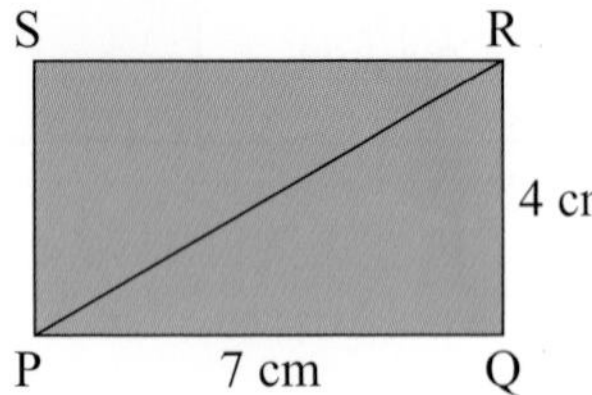

(a) Construct the locus of points which are equidistant from lines SP and SR.
(b) Construct the locus of points which are equidistant from lines RP and RQ.

3 Draw one copy of triangle PQR and show on it:

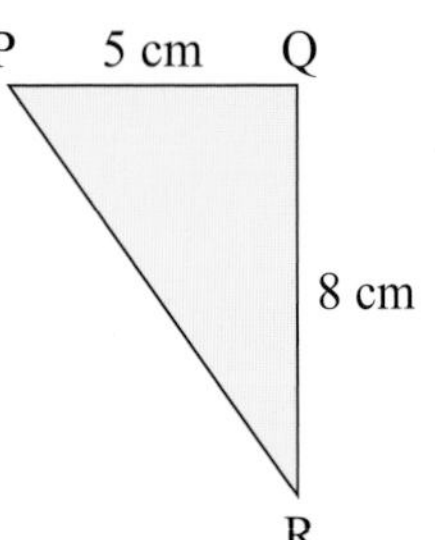

(a) the locus of points equidistant from P and Q,
(b) the locus of points equidistant from lines PQ and PR,
(c) the locus of points nearer to PR than to PQ.

4 Draw a circle with centre O and radius 3 cm.
Indicate by shading, points which are between 3 cm and 2 cm from O.

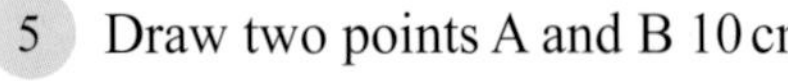

5 Draw two points A and B 10 cm apart.

Place the corner of a piece of paper (or a set square) so that the edges of the paper pass through A and B. Mark the position of corner C. Slide the paper around so the edges still pass through A and B and mark the new position of C. Repeat several times and describe the locus of the point C which moves so that angle ACB is always 90°.

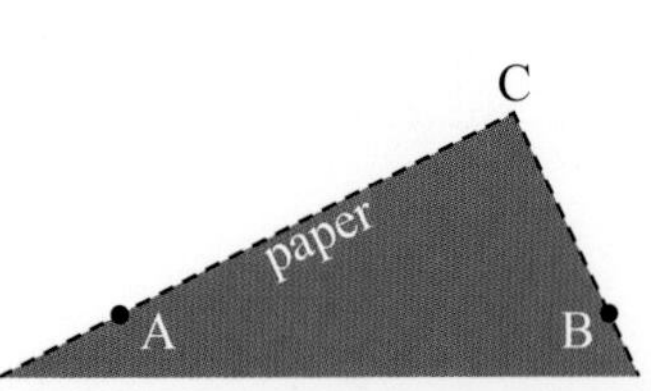

6 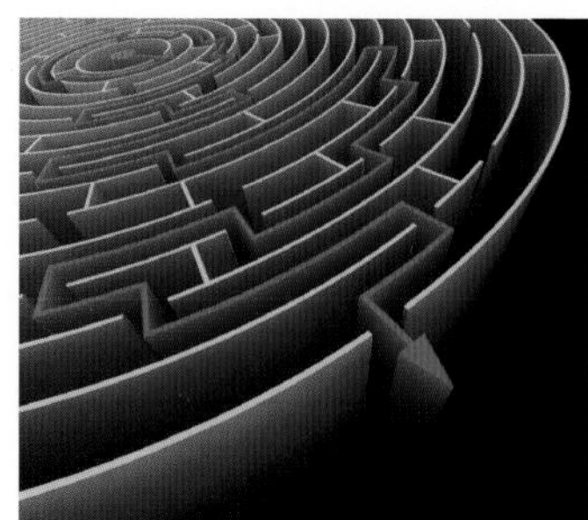

Design a maze, either square or circular, and show the locus of a route around the maze. Make your maze fairly difficult!

6.4 Changing the subject of a formula

In this section you will:

- Learn how to change the subject of a formula

The method for changing the subject of a formula is generally the same as the method for solving an equation. The examples below are written side by side to make comparison easy.

(a) Solve the equation		(b) Make x the subject of the formula
$3(x-1)=5$		$a(x-b)=t$
$3x-3=5$	[Multiply out the brackets]	$ax-ab=t$
$3x=5+3$	[Get the x term on its own]	$ax=t+ab$
$x=8/3$	[Divide by the coefficient of x]	$x=\dfrac{t+ab}{a}$

A formula for the distance moved by an accelerating swimmer is $s=ut+\frac{1}{2}at^2$.
Rearrange the formula to make a the subject

$s=ut+\frac{1}{2}at^2$	
$s-ut=\frac{1}{2}at^2$	[Subtract ut from both sides.]
$2(s-ut)=at^2$	[Multiply both sides by 2.]
$\dfrac{2(s-ut)}{t^2}=a$	[Divide both sides by t^2.]

This formula can now be used to calculate the value of a if we know the values of s, u and t.

Exercise 1M

In questions 1 to 12 make x the subject.

1. $x - a = e$
2. $x + t = h$
3. $a + b = x - g$
4. $v + x = m^2$
5. $h + x = 2h + n$
6. $s - t = t + x$
7. $x - y^2 = y$
8. $x - pq = m$
9. $n = x - mn$
10. $ax = c$
11. $mx + c = y$
12. $bx = a + c$

In questions 13 to 24 make y the subject.

13. $my - c = n$
14. $5b = ay + b$
15. $a + c = ky - c$
16. $e + d = b + cy$
17. $t^2 + ty = p^2$
18. $ay - z = z$
19. $-m = fy$
20. $pqy = \pi r^2$
21. $aby = m + n$
22. $c^2 + d^2y = a^2$
23. $mty + c = d$
24. $xyz - p^2 = q^2$

Exercise 1E

In questions 1 to 12 make the letter in brackets the subject.

1. $a + tb = e$ $[t]$
2. $ab + kn = a^2$ $[k]$
3. $n + mw = 2n$ $[w]$
4. $s(y + a) = b$ $[y]$
5. $p(a + x) = b$ $[x]$
6. $z(c + d) = e$ $[z]$
7. $m(r + s) = t$ $[m]$
8. $b = a(m + n)$ $[n]$
9. $b^2 = w(y - a)$ $[y]$
10. $s = (u + v)t$ $[u]$
11. $m^2 (a + e) = n^2$ $[e]$
12. $ab(a + x) = c$ $[x]$

13. A formula for the cost, c, of refurbishing a clock of age n years and diameter d is $c = n\,(155 + 3d)$. Make d the subject.

14. Using the formula $t^2 = z(a + c + d)$,
    (a) Make c the subject
    (b) Make z the subject.
15. Using the formula $(y + z)m = c + d$
    (a) Make m the subject
    (b) Make y the subject.

Formulae involving fractions

(a) Make x the subject.

(i) $\frac{m}{x} = e$

$m = ex$ [Multiply both sides by x.]

$\frac{m}{e} = x$ [Divide both sides by e.]

(ii) $\frac{x}{t} = a + b$

$x = t(a + b)$ [Multiply both sides by t.]

(b) Make p the subject

$\frac{h}{p - t} = a$

$h = a(p - t)$

$h = ap - at$

$h + at = ap$

$\frac{h + at}{a} = p$

Exercise 2M

Make x the subject.

1 $a(m + 2n - b) = \frac{x}{t}$

2 $\frac{x}{(a + b + c)} = n^2$

3 $\frac{x}{m} = n$

4 $a = \frac{x}{t}$

5 $\frac{x}{c} = a + b$

6 $a = \frac{x}{m + n}$

7 $\frac{x}{2} = ab$

8 $c = \frac{x}{c}$

9 $\frac{a}{x} = d$

10 $\frac{y}{x} = t$

11 $a + b = \frac{c}{x}$

12 $(a + b) = \frac{(c + d)}{x}$

13 $\frac{e + f}{x} = a^2 + b$

14 $\frac{x}{m} = \frac{a}{b}$

15 $\frac{x}{t} = \frac{m}{n}$

16 $\frac{ax}{p} = \frac{s}{t}$

17 $\frac{b}{a} = \frac{ax}{b}$

Exercise 2E

Make a the subject.

1 $\frac{h}{a} = p^2$

2 $h = \frac{w + z}{a}$

3 $c - d = \frac{d + b}{a}$

4 $\frac{t^2}{r} = \frac{mn}{a}$

5 $\frac{\pi}{h} = \frac{a}{e - f}$

6 $\frac{a(e + k)}{b} = b$

7 $\frac{m}{a + b} = c$

8 $\frac{p}{a - c} = d$

9 $\frac{h}{x + a} = y$

10 $p = \frac{d}{a - e}$

11 $t + w = \frac{m^2}{a}$

12 $\frac{f}{g} = \frac{e}{a - b}$

13 $\frac{z}{a(p + q)} = t$

14 $\frac{y}{a} = \sin 20°$

15 $\tan 48° = \frac{x}{a}$

Formulae with negative x terms

Make x the subject of the formulae.

(a) $m - tx = c$

$m = c + tx$ … [A]

$m - c = tx$

$\frac{m - c}{t} = x$

(b) $a(a - x) = t$

$a^2 - ax = t$

$a^2 - t = ax$ … [A]

$\frac{a^2 - t}{a} = x$

Notice that in line [A], in both examples, the x term is taken to the other side of the equation to make it positive. Most people find it easier to work with a positive x term.

Exercise 3M

In questions 1 to 12 make x the subject.

1 $b - x = e$

2 $t^2 = h - x$

3 $z^2 - x = n^2$

4 $a + b = c - x$

5 $4q - x = 2q$

6 $d = a + m - x$

7 $t - ax = b$

8 $e = u - gx$

9 $w^2 = u^2 - ux$

10 $p = h^3 - tx$

11 $a + c - x = ac$

12 $3b - a^2 x = b$

In questions 13 to 21 remove the brackets and then make x the subject.

13 $c(m - x) = n$

14 $h(a - x) = g$

15 $k = a(a - x)$

16 $t^2 = p(q - x)$

17 $a = p(p + q - x)$

18 $w = m(n - mx)$

19 $v(u + t - x) = w$

20 $t(t^2 - p^2x) = a$

21 $ab(a - x) = d$

Formulae involving squares and square roots

(a) (i) Solve the equation

$x^2 + 5 = 9$

$x^2 = 9 - 5$ [Get the x^2 term on its own.]

$x = \pm 2$ [Take the square root of both sides. The answer can be positive or negative.]

(ii) Make x the subject

$x^2 - b = t$

$x^2 = t + b$

$x = \pm \sqrt{t + b}$

(b) (i) Solve the equation

$\sqrt{x + 2} = 7$

$x + 2 = 7^2$ [Square both sides.]

$x = 49 - 2$ [Get x on its own.]

$= 47$

(ii) Make x the subject

$\sqrt{x - c} = m$

$x - c = m^2$

$x = m^2 + c$

Exercise 3E

In questions 1 to 12 make x the subject.

1 $\sqrt{x} = c$

2 $\sqrt{x + a} = t$

3 $m = \sqrt{x - c}$

4 $a\sqrt{x} = k$

5 $a + b = m\sqrt{x}$

6 $\sqrt{ax} = c$

7 $p = \sqrt{\frac{x}{m}}$

8 $\sqrt{\frac{x}{a}} = c$

9 $\sqrt{x} = \frac{a}{b}$

10 $\sqrt{\frac{d}{x}} = k$

11 $q = \sqrt{\frac{e}{x}}$

12 $\sqrt{\frac{x}{n}} = \frac{a}{b}$

In questions 13 to 24 make a the subject.

13 $a^2 + b = c$

14 $ma^2 = e$

15 $a^2 + f = g$

16 $(a + d)^2 = m$

17 $(a - y)^2 = h$

18 $ta^2 - n = c$

19 $h = \frac{(a - z)^2}{t}$

20 $\frac{ea^2}{m} = t$

21 $\frac{za^2}{n} + p = q$

22 $(ma - c)^2 = y$

23 $(t + ab)^2 = w$

24 $m - a^2 = n$

Exercise 4E

1 To convert from Fahrenheit to Celsius we can use the formula

$C = \frac{5}{9}(F - 32)$

(a) Convert the following temperatures to Celsius
(i) 77ºF, (ii) 50ºF

(b) Make F the subject of the formula.

(c) Convert the following temperatures to Fahrenheit
(i) 100ºC (ii) 60ºC

2 Area of a trapezium, $A = \frac{1}{2}h(a + b)$

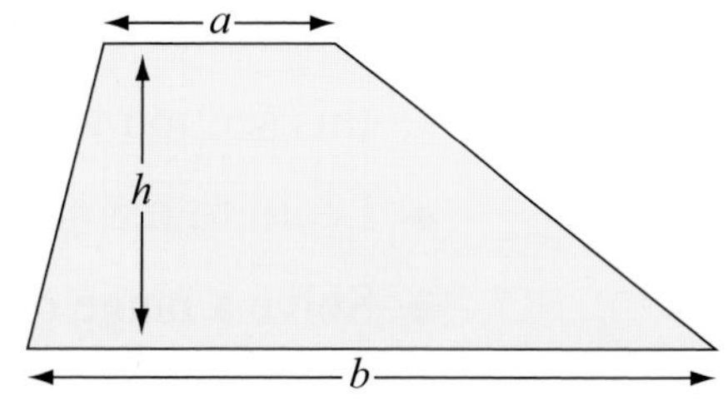

(a) Rearrange the formula to make h the subject.

(b) Find h if $A = 340$ cm^2, $a = 7$ cm, $b = 10$ cm.

(c) Rearrange the formula to make b the subject.

(d) Find b if $A = 136$ cm^2, $a = 12$ cm, $h = 8$ cm.

3 A challenge! Here is part of a famous formula in mathematics

$$x = \frac{-b + \sqrt{b^2 - 4ac}}{2a}.$$

Rearrange the formula to make c the subject.

'Make your Million' board game

Rules: You are given £10 at the start of the game. The object is to earn as much money as possible by substituting your dice score into the expression on your new square. The person with the biggest balance *when landing on the finish square* wins.

Example. Throwing a 5, then a 1.

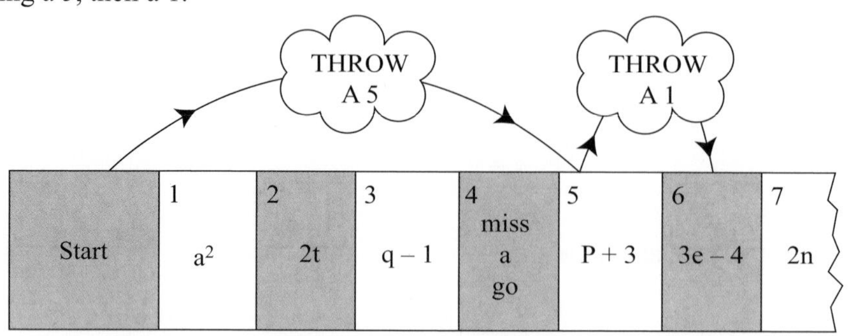

Score on dice	Expression on square	Value of expression using dice score	Balance £
—	—	—	10
5	P + 3	5 + 3 = 8	10 + 8 = 18
1	3e – 4	(3 × 1) – 4 = 3 – 4 = –1	18 – 1 = 17
•	•	•	•
•	•	•	•
•	•	•	•

Note:

(i) Landing on 'miss a go' means that your balance remains the same.

(ii) Landing on 'back to start' means that your balance becomes *zero*.

(iii) Teachers: The board for 'Make your Million' can be photocopied from the Book 9H answer book.

6.5 Similar shapes

In this section you will:

- Learn to recognise similar shapes
- Solve a range of problems involving similar shapes

In everyday use the word 'similar' merely describes things which are 'alike', 'of the same kind' or 'resembling one another'. For example the taste of an orange is similar to the taste of a tangerine.

In mathematics objects *are* described as *similar* only if they are exactly the same shape. When two shapes are similar one is an enlargement of the other. Corresponding angles are equal and corresponding lengths are in the same proportion.

The shapes A and B *are* similar. All the corresponding angles are the same and all the sides in shape B are twice as long as the corresponding sides in shape A.

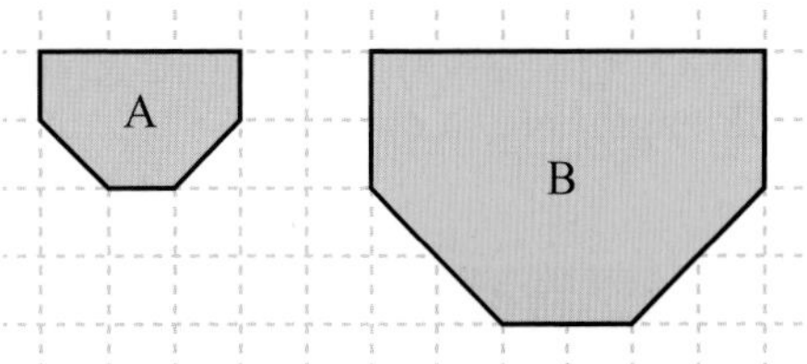

The shapes P and Q are not similar. The ratio $\frac{4}{2}$ does not equal the ratio $\frac{5}{3}$.

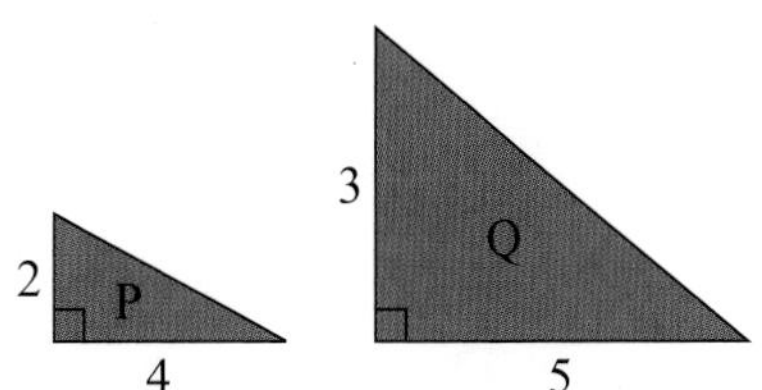

Picture A is enlarged to fit frame B.

Find the length x.

Method 1. The two rectangles are similar.

$$\therefore \frac{x}{10} = \frac{11.2}{7}$$

$$x = \frac{11.2}{7} \times 10 = 16$$

Method 2. The scale factor of the enlargement is $\frac{10}{7}$.

$$x = \frac{10}{7} \times 11.2$$

$$= 16$$

Exercise 1M

1 Which of the rectangles A, B, C, D, E, F, G, H are similar to rectangle R?

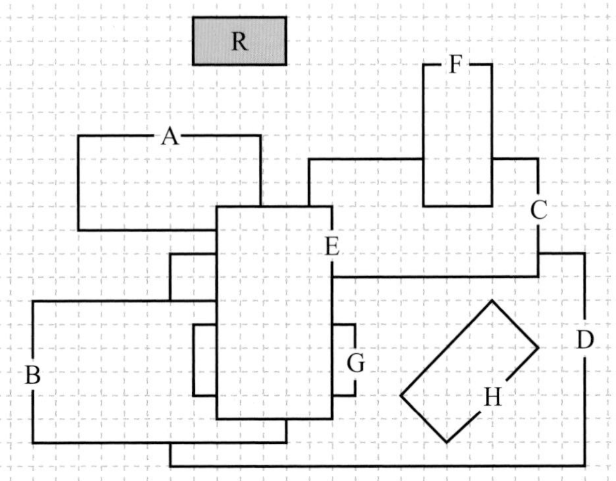

In questions 2 to 7 you are given two similar shapes. Find the lengths marked with letters. All lengths are in cm.

2

3
1
5
4
y

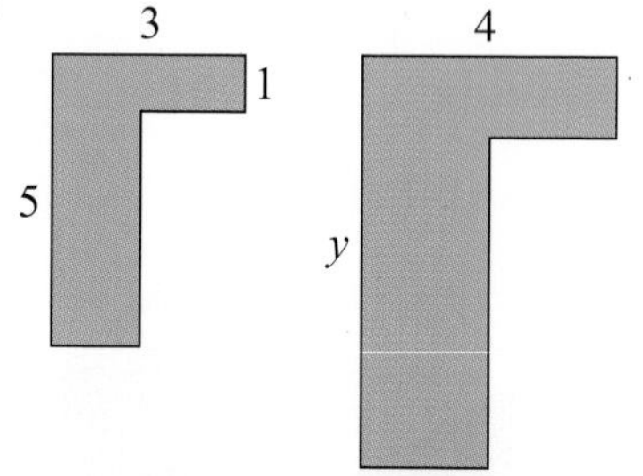

3

12
7
15
x

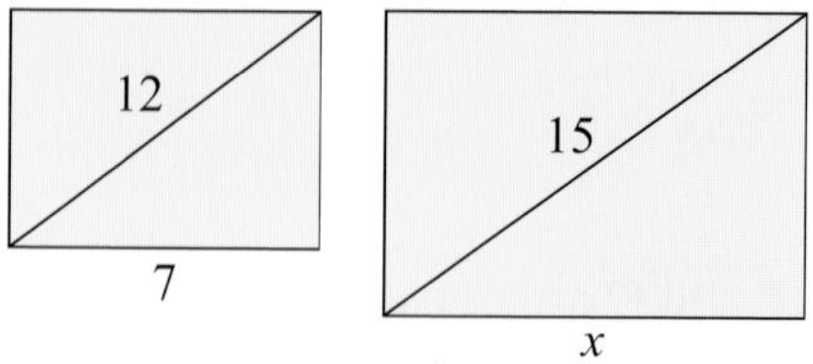

4

x
3
10
7.5

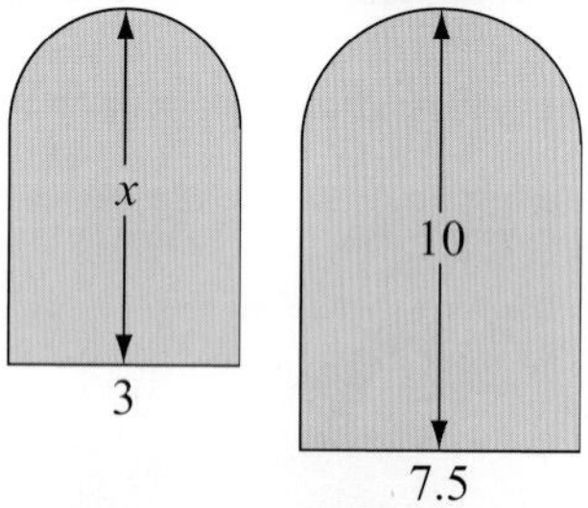

5

6
3
4.2
5
x

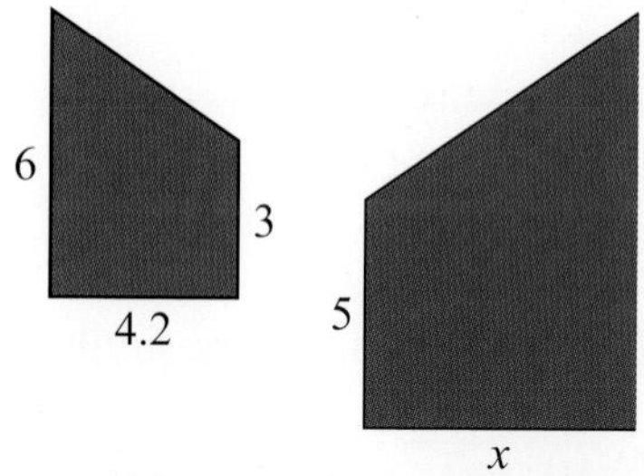

6

3.2
2
4.8
x

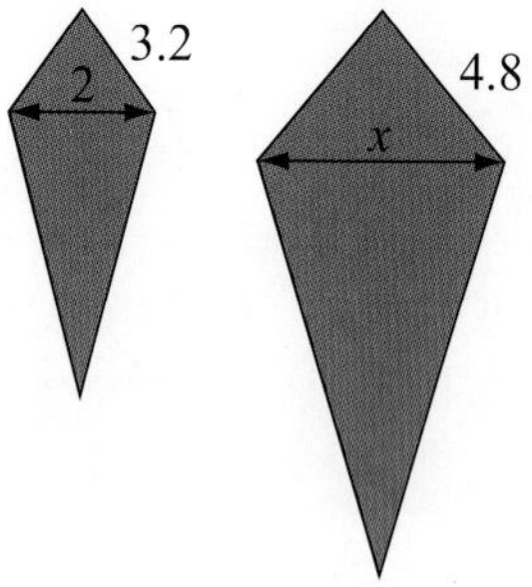

7

2
5
x
3.2

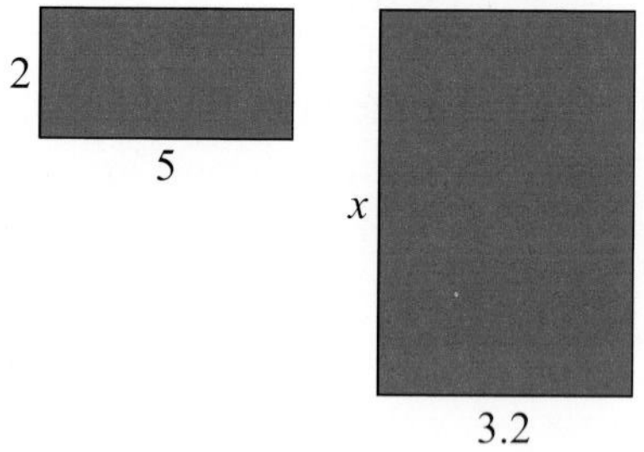

8 The photo in frame Q is either reduced or enlarged to fit exactly into frames P, R and S. Find the lengths x, y and z.

P
x
2
5.4
3
R
9
y
S
z
8

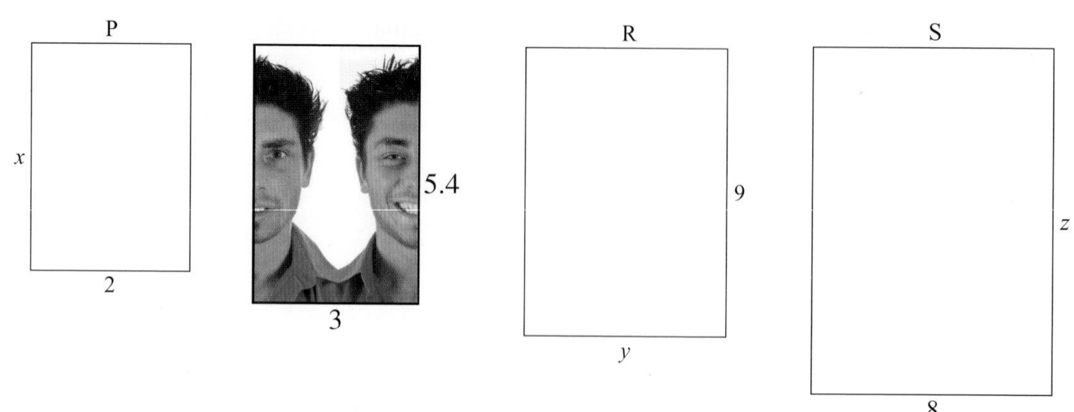

9 The diagram shows 3 similar rectangles. Find the lengths marked m and n.

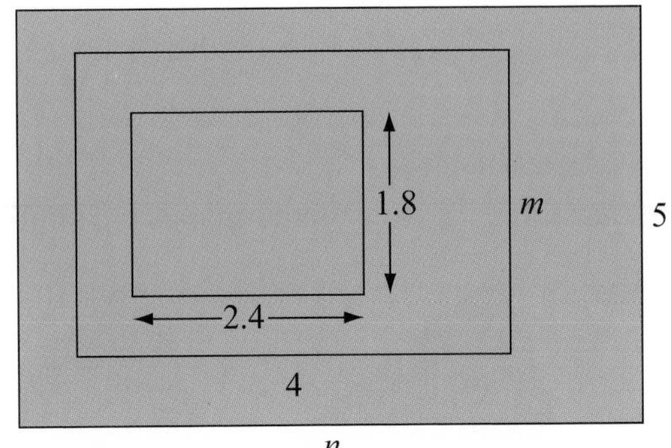

10 Decide which of the following are *always* similar. Write 'yes' or 'no'.

(a) Any two squares

(b) Any two circles

(c) Any two right-angled triangles

(d) Any two semicircles

(e) Any two rectangles

(f) Any two isosceles triangles.

Triangles

Two triangles are similar if they have the same angles.

Triangles ABC and PQR have two angles the same, as shown.

Since the angles in a triangle add up to 180°, the triangles must have the same three angles and are similar.

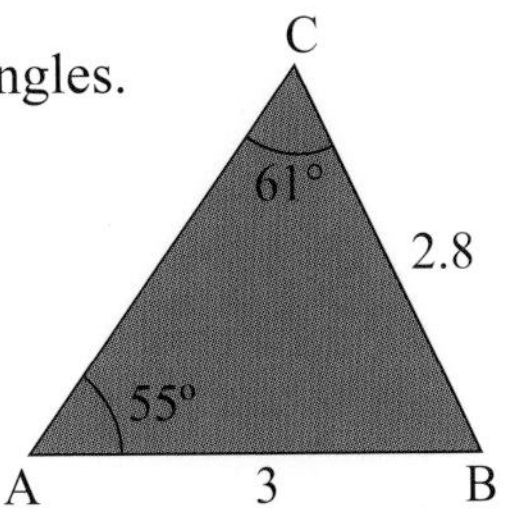

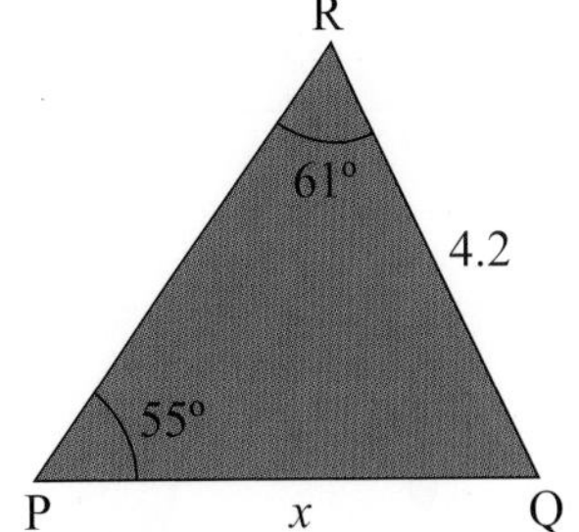

To find the length x, use corresponding ratios.

[x and 3 are opposite the 61° angles.]

$$\nearrow \frac{x}{3} = \frac{4.2}{2.8} \nwarrow$$

[4.2 and 2.8 are opposite the 55° angles.]

$$x = 4.5$$

Exercise 2M

1 Decide whether or not the pair of triangles are similar. Write 'yes' or 'no' for each pair.

(a)

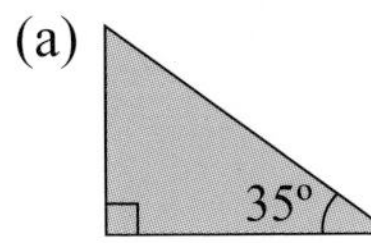

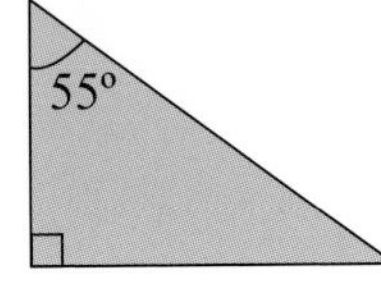

(b)

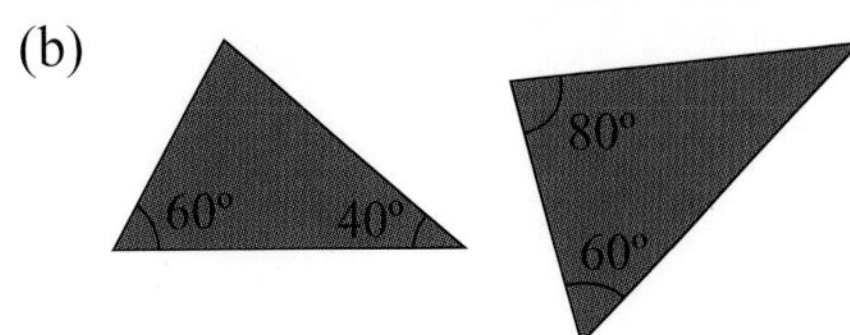

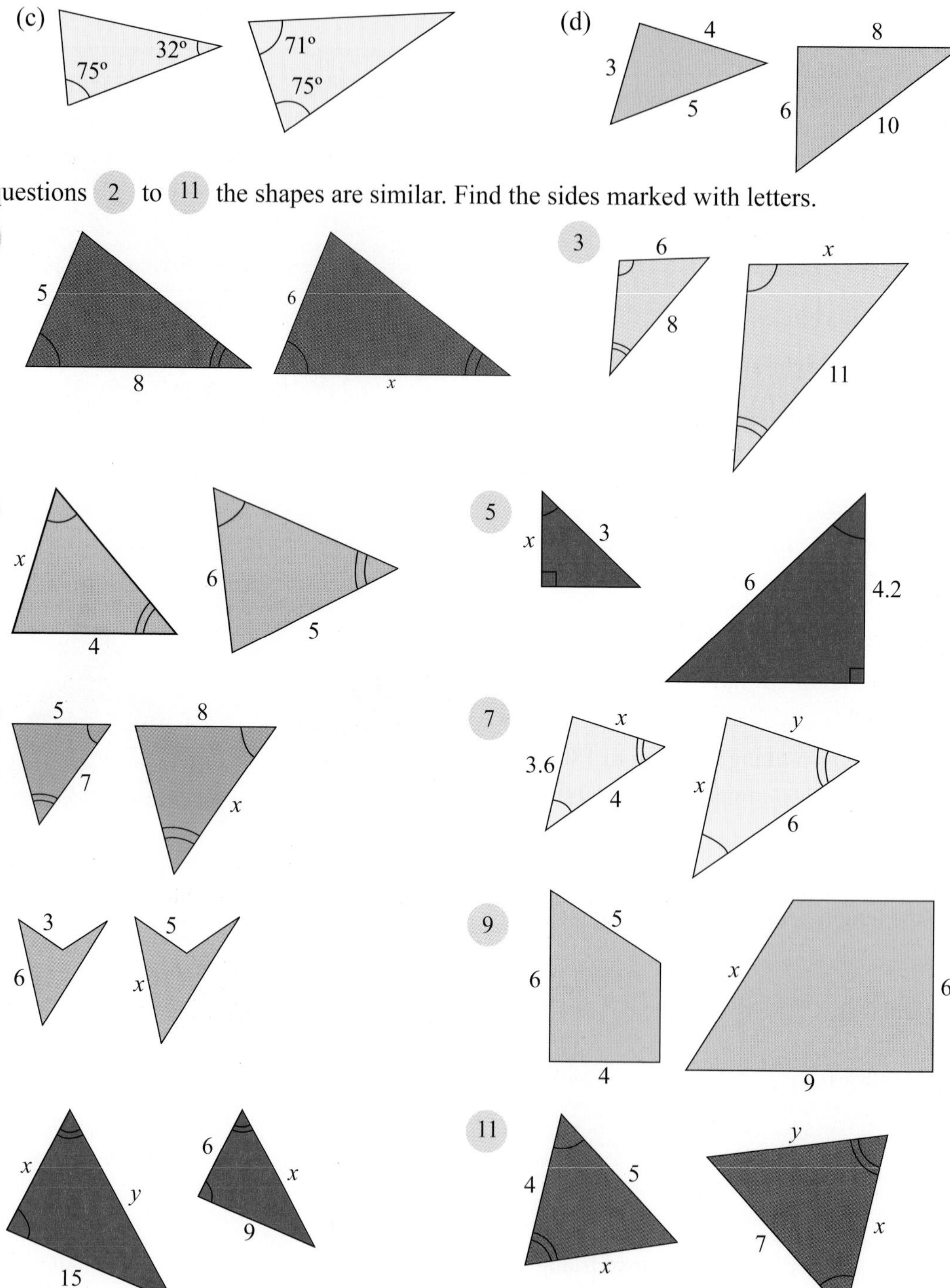

In questions 2 to 11 the shapes are similar. Find the sides marked with letters.

12 Sabina is 140 cm tall and her shadow is 120 cm long. The tree next to her has a shadow length 28 metres. How tall is the tree?

In the diagram XY is parallel to BC. Find the length XY.

Triangles ABC and XYZ are similar (same angles)

$$\frac{AX}{AB} = \frac{XY}{BC}$$

$$\frac{4}{6} = \frac{XY}{8}$$

$$XY = \frac{4 \times 8}{6} = 5\tfrac{1}{3} \text{ cm.}$$

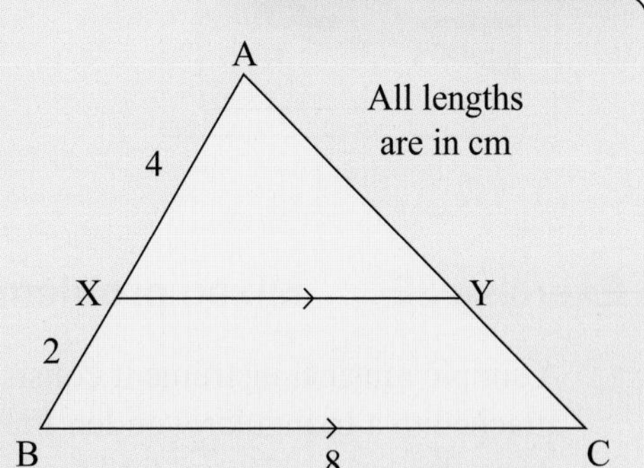

Exercise 2E

1 Triangles ADE and ABC are similar
Copy and complete:

$$\frac{DE}{BC} = \frac{AE}{AC}$$

$$\frac{x}{4} = \frac{3}{\square}$$

$$x = \square$$

In questions 2 to 7 use similar triangles to find the lengths marked with letters.

2

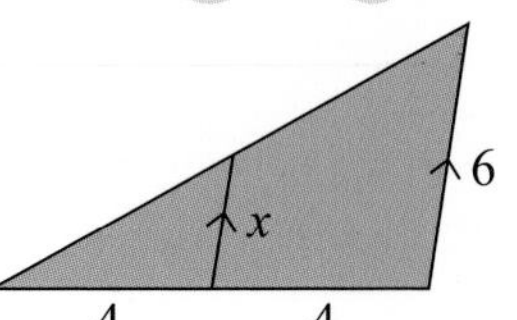

3

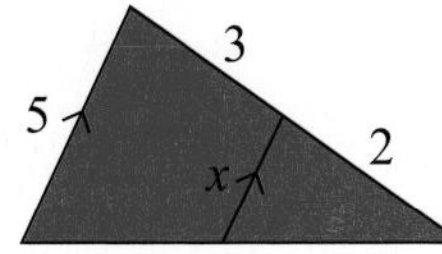

4

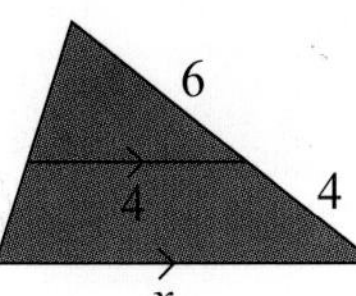

5

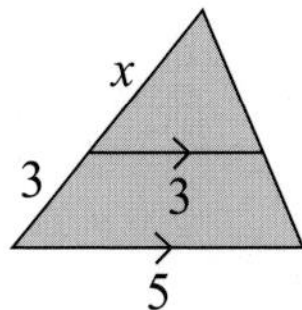

6

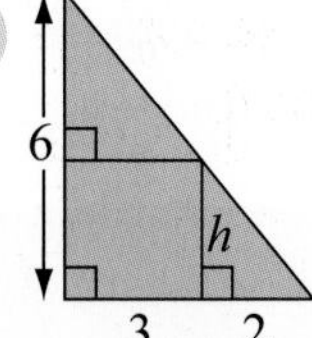

7

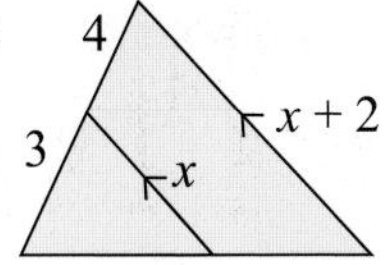

8 The two sides of a step ladder are each 2 metres long. A cross strut 1 metre long is attached 70 cm from the foot of each side. How far apart are the feet of the ladder?

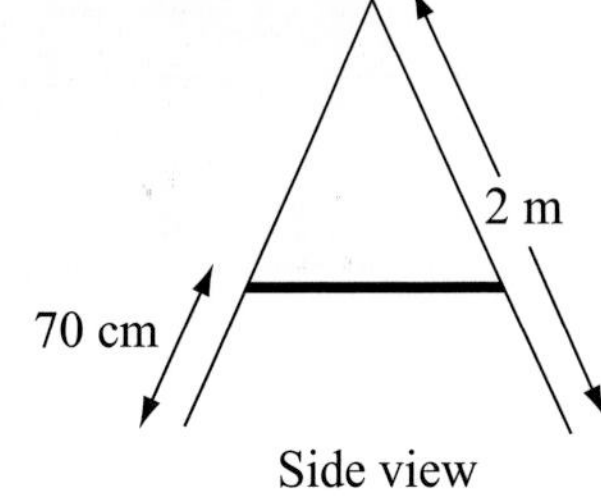

9 

A photo measuring 8 cm by 12 cm is mounted on white card with margins 3 cm wide at the sides and 4.5 cm wide top and bottom. Are the two rectangles similar? Explain your answer.

Exercise 3E Mixed problems

1 A simple musical instrument consists of 4 strings attached to a triangular wooden frame. If the shortest string P measures 10 cm, find the lengths of the other three strings.

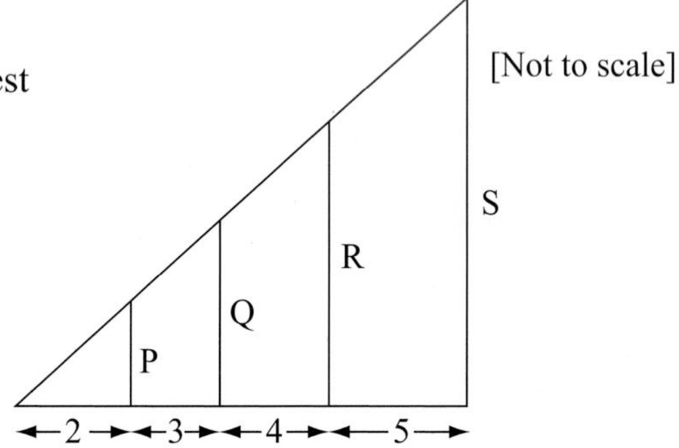

2 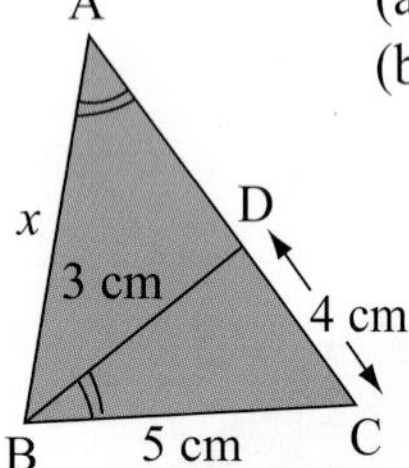

(a) Name two similar triangles.
(b) Calculate the length x.

3 Photo B is an enlargement of photo A with scale factor 3.
If the area of photo A is 20 cm², find the area of photo B.

A 
not to scale

 B

4 The sides of triangle ABC are each increased by 1 cm to form triangle DEF.

Are triangles ABC and DEF similar?

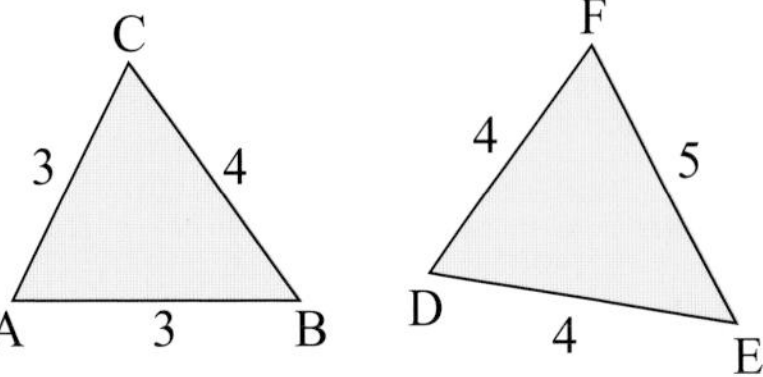

5 In the diagram $A\hat{B}E = A\hat{D}C$.

Find the length x.

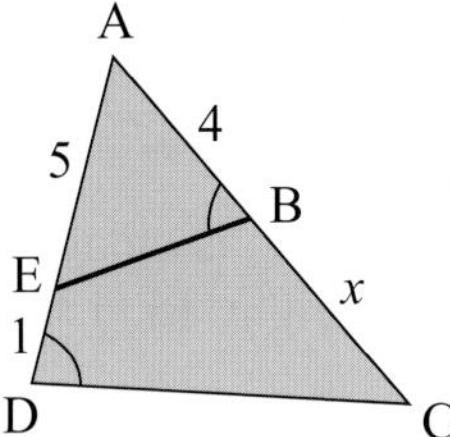

6 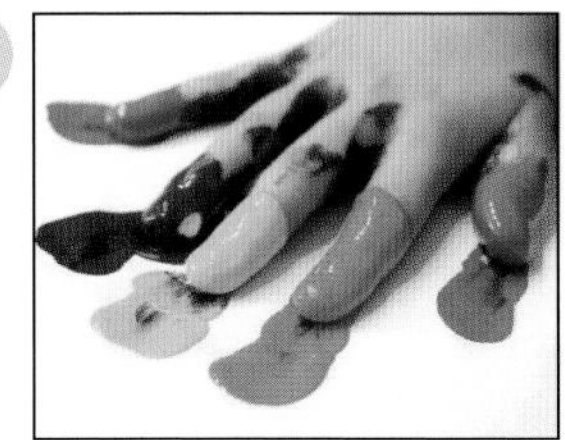

The photo shown is similar to a photo 3 cm by x cm. Find the two possible values of x.

7 When the large rectangle is folded in half along PQ, each of the smaller rectangles is similar to the large rectangle.

Form an equation and use trial and improvement to find x, correct to 1 d.p.

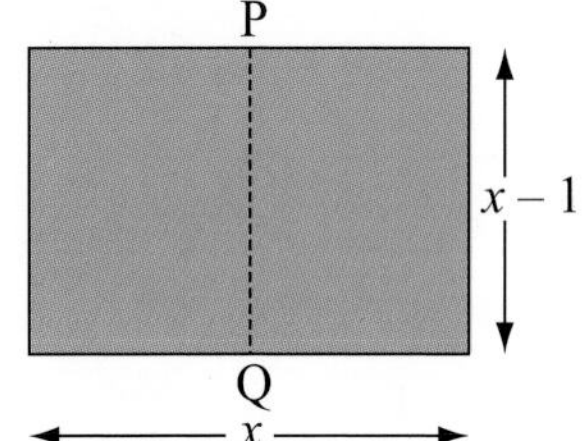

CHECK YOURSELF ON SECTIONS 6.3, 6.4 and 6.5

1. Locus problems

(a) Draw the rectangle ABCD and then construct the following:

(i) the locus of points equidistant from points B and C

(ii) the locus of points equidistant from lines AB and AD

(iii) the locus of points inside ABCD which are 3 cm from C

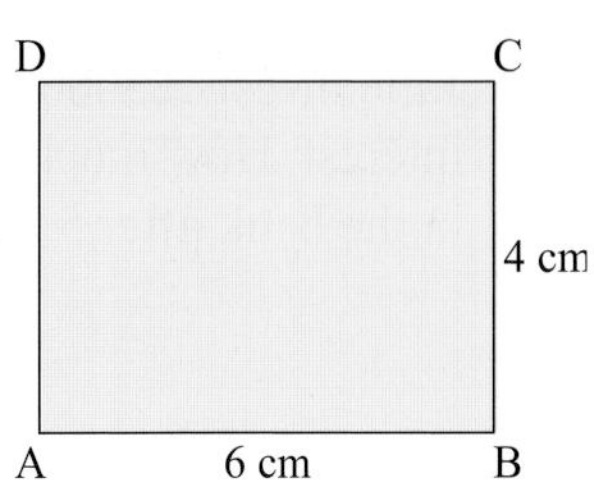

2. Changing the subject of a formula

(a) Make n the subject.

(i) $an = c - d$ (ii) $a^2 + pn = c^2$ (iii) $\frac{u}{n} = a$

(iv) $h - n = a + b$ (v) $a(l - n) = b$ (vi) $p\sqrt{n} = x$

3. Similar shapes

(a) 

2.6 cm

3.8 cm

This photo is enlarged to fit a frame 5.7 cm across and x cm height. Find x.

(b) Use similar triangles to find x.

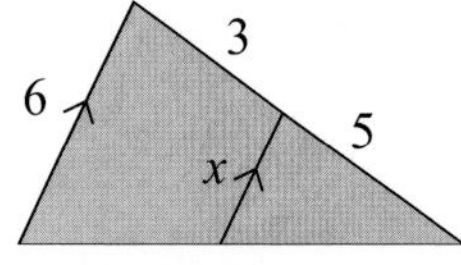

(not to scale)

6.6 Simple interest

If I invest £1000 at 5% *simple interest*, I work out the interest for one year and then multiply by the number of years.

Interest = 5% of £1000 = £50

Total interest for 3 years = £50 × 3 = £150

Total money after 3 years = £1000 + £150 = £1150

Exercise 1M/E

1 Steve invests £600 in a bank at 3% simple interest. How much money will he have in the bank after two years?

2 Julie invests £3000 in a bank at 4% simple interest. How much money will she have in the bank after 5 years?

3 A bank pays 6% per annum simple interest.
How much will the following people have in the bank after the number of years stated?

(a) Pete: £400 after 2 years (b) Annie: £650 after 3 years (c) Wendy: £6500 after 4 years

4 A bank in France pays 5% simple interest.
How much will these people have in the bank after the number of years stated?

(a) Micheline: €800 after 5 years

(b) Antoine: €12 000 after 9 years.

5 Sharon invests £5000 in a bank at 10% simple interest.
After how many years will she have £10 000 in the bank?

6 £45 000 is invested at 3.5% simple interest. How much money will there be after 6 months?

7 The rate of inflation shows how much more expensive things are in shops.
If the rate of inflation is 4% and a TV costs £240 in 2015, how much will it cost in 2016?

8 The rate of house price inflation in 2015 was 6.2%.
A house was valued at £320 000 in 2015. At what price would it be valued one year later?

UNIT 6 MIXED REVIEW

Part one

Country	Rate of exchange
France (euro)	£1 = €1.18
USA (dollar)	£1 = $1.60
Turkey (lira)	£1 = L2.62
South Africa (rand)	£1 = 10 rand

1 The exchange rates for several countries are shown.

(a) Change €354 into pounds.

(b) Change £2 million into dollars.

(c) Change 60 pence into rand.

2 Using the table in question 1 work out the cost in rand of a TV priced at $400.

3 (a) Draw axes with values of x and y from 0 to 9.

(b) Draw the lines $y = 9 - x$ and $y = \frac{1}{2}x$

(c) Write down the coordinates of the point of intersection of the lines in part (b).

4 (a) Construct the triangle ABC.

(b) Construct the locus of points which are equidistant from the points A and B.

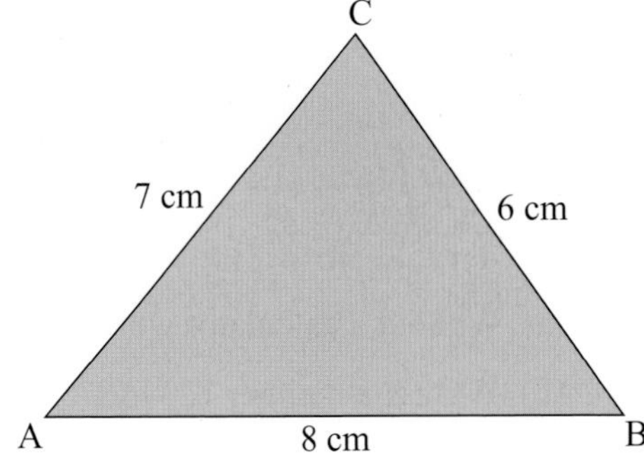

5 Make n the subject of the formulae below

(a) $sn + a = c$

(b) $nt - t = x^2$

(c) $\frac{n}{x} = y$

6 Find whole numbers m and n such that $m^2 + 4 = n^3$

7 On a calculator the figure four (4) has four bars.
Which other numbers have the same number of bars as the number itself?

8 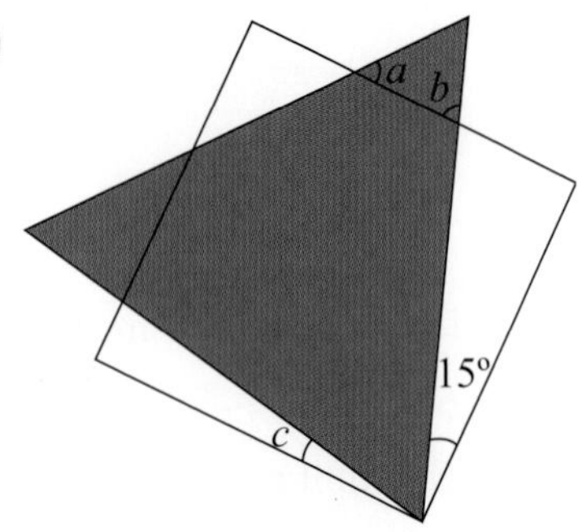

The diagram consists of a square and an equilateral triangle. Find the angles a, b and c.

9 In a sale all products were sold at 25% off. Imran bought a laptop for £315. How much did he save?

10 A car takes 5 minutes to travel 6 miles. Find the speed of the car in m.p.h.

11 On January 1st I changed £1560 into euros at €1.20 euros per pound. By July 1st the exchange rate had changed so that I got 20% fewer euros per pound. How much would I get if I changed the euros I got on January 1st back into pounds?

12 Make x the subject.

(a) $a(x - b) = c$

(b) $\sqrt{nx} = m$

(c) $\frac{e}{x} = h$

13 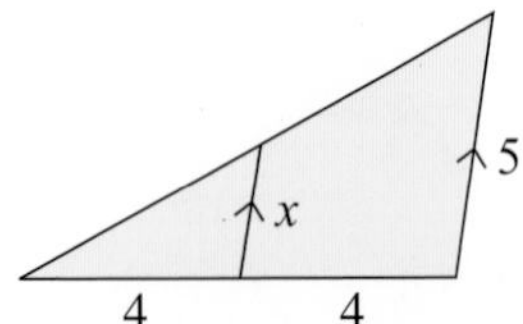

Use similar triangles to find x.

14 (a) Without a calculator work out $12345678 \div 9$

(b) Write the number 12345678 in terms of its prime factors.

Part two

1 The diagonal of a square is 8 cm. What is the area of the square?

2 In the number 275 the middle digit is equal to the sum of the other two digits. How many numbers between 300 and 600 have this property?

3 

The cost of a holiday in Italy is €1771 or £1540. What is the rate of exchange between pounds and euros?

4 (a) Draw a pair of axes with x from -4 to 3 and y from -1 to 8.

(b) Draw the graphs of the lines
$$y = x + 4$$
$$y = 3x$$
$$y = 0$$

(c) Find the area of the region enclosed by these three lines.
Give your answer in 'square units'.

5 The shaded region is bounded by the line $y = 3$ and the curve $y = x^2$.

Which two inequalities from the list below, fully describe the shaded region?

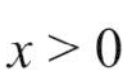

$x > 0$	$y > 0$	$y \geqslant x^2$
$y \leqslant x^2$	$y \leqslant 3$	$y < x$

y $y = 3$ $y = x^2$ x

6 Make c the subject of the formulae below.

(a) $\frac{h}{c} = n^2$

(b) $c \tan 20° = b - x$

(c) $t = a - cb$

7 (a) Draw the graph of $y = x^2 - 2x - 5$ for values of x from -2 to 4.

(b) On the same graph draw the line $y = x - 1$.

(c) Write down the coordinates of the two points where the line cuts the curve.

8 The wood of an oak tree has density 3.2 g/cm^3.

The trunk of the tree is roughly a cylinder of diameter 1.45 m and height 26.4 m.

Calculate the approximate mass of the trunk.

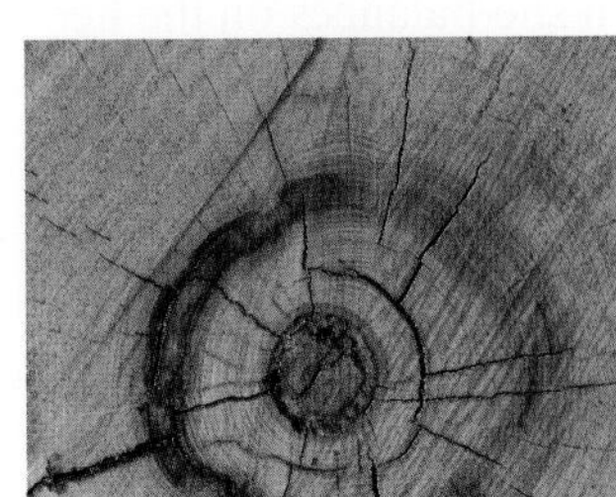

9 One sunny afternoon when Jane, who is 150 cm tall, is in Paris she notices her shadow measures 125 cm. She estimates that the shadow thrown by the Eiffel Tower is approximately 250 metres long. Roughly how high is the Eiffel Tower?

10 A cubical box of negligible weight has sides of length 0.72 m. The box holds half a tonne of wet sand. Find the density of the sand.

11 When the number $1^2 \times 2^3 \times 3^4 \times 4^5 \times 5^6$ is written, how many zeros are there at the end of the number?

12 In this question angular speed is measured in degrees per minute. What is the angular speed of

(a) the seconds hand of a clock,

(b) the minutes hand of a clock?

13 AB = BD = 3 cm
BC = 5 cm
CE = 2.4 cm

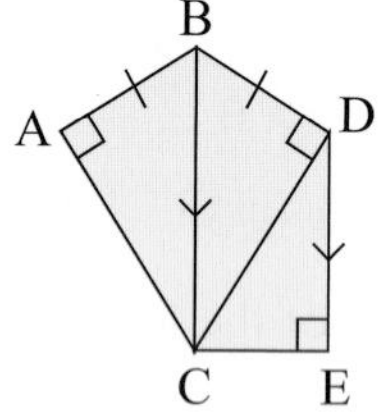

(a) Name a triangle that is congruent to ABC.

(b) Name a triangle that is similar to ABC.

(c) Find the length DE.

14 In this question pressure is measured in kg/cm^2.

A lady weighs 58 kg and the total area of the soles of her bare feet is 400 cm^2. The area of the tip of the heel on her boot is 0.8 cm^2.

Find the pressure she exerts on the floor:

(a) when she stands on her two bare feet,

(b) when she balances on the heel of one boot.

15 (a) Draw the graph of $y = 10 - x$ for x from 0 to 10.

(b) Draw the curve $y = \frac{12}{x}$ for x from 1 to 12.

(c) Write down the x coordinates of the two points where the line cuts the curve. Give your answers correct to 1 decimal place.

16

Spel cheker

At larst sumwun of ad the sence to publish a dikshunery ware you can find eloosive wurds witch are dificult to spel, like seperate, definately and recieve. Bloomsbury realy shud be complemented on thare inishytive.

Rite a fu sentenses taking inspirashun from the newspapa articul.

Answers to 'check yourself sections'

Page 22 ***Sections 1.1 and 1.2***

1. (a) (i) 0.96 (ii) 4.17 (iii) 9.18 (iv) 56 (v) 2 (vi) 9999
(b) (i) £34, £51 (ii) $2^2 \times 3 \times 7$

2. (a) (i) 9.9 (ii) 11.6 (iii) $10\frac{6}{25}$ (or 10.24)
(b) (i) -11 (ii) 15 (iii) -14 (iv) -4 (v) 2.1

3. (a) (i) $9n + 2$ (ii) $16n - 9$ (iii) $3n^2 + 6n$
(b) (i) 2.5 (ii) 1.25 (iii) $\frac{4}{7}$

Page 33 ***Sections 1.3 and 1.4***

1. (a) 8 cm (c) bisector using compasses

2. (a) $a = 58°$, $b = 83°$ (b) $c = 104°$ (c) $d = 117.5°$ (d) 20

Page 48 ***Sections 1.5 and 1.6***

1. (a) 0.8 kg (b) 162.3 cm **2.** (a) (i) $n^2 + 12n + 20$ (ii) $a^2 - 2a + 1$
(iii) $3x^2 + 8x - 16$ (b) $\frac{1}{2}$ (c) 12

Page 77 ***Sections 2.1, 2.2 and 2.3***

1. (a) (i) $\frac{3}{28}$ (ii) $6\frac{2}{3}$ (iii) $11\frac{1}{9}$
(b) 540 litres

2. (a) (i) 5^{-4} (ii) 3^8 (iii) n^{13}
(b) (i) 3 (ii) -2 (iii) 0
(c) 3.8×10^8

3. (a) (i) 5.6×10^4 (ii) 2×10^{-6} (iii) 2.5×10^8
(b) (i) 2.795×10^{17} (ii) 1.8×10^{-4} (iii) 9.6×10^{-11}
(c) (i) 200 (ii) 4000.05 (iii) 6.4×10^{10} (iv) 400

Page 95 ***Sections 2.5 and 2.6***

1. (a) negative (b) no correlation (c) strong positive
(a) (ii) positive correlation, the higher the cost the higher the rating
(c) (i) about £236 (ii) correlation is not very strong

2. (c) (i) 11.6 (or -8.6) (ii) 6.5 (or -14.5)
(b) (i) $(x + 3)$ cm (ii) $x(x + 3) = 80$ (iii) 7.6

Page 122 ***Sections 3.1 and 3.2***

1. (a) 15.3 cm^2

(b) (i) reflection: $x = 1$ (ii) translation: $\begin{pmatrix} 10 \\ 5 \end{pmatrix}$ (iii) rotation: 180°, centre (0, 0)

(iv) enlargement: scale factor 2, centre $(-8, 6)$

(v) rotation: 90° clockwise, centre $(-2, 1)$ (vi) reflection: $y = -2$

2. (a) (i) $2n + 5$ (ii) $10n + 1$ (iii) $8n - 7$ (iv) $\dfrac{n}{n+1}$ (v) $(n + 1)^2$

(b) (i) 48, 46, 44, 42 (ii) 3, 9, 27, 81 (iii) 4, 10, 18, 28

Page 137 ***Sections 3.3 and 3.4***

1. (a) (i) 0.52 (ii) 11700 (iii) 2.3 (b) (i) £800 → 900 (ii) 120 − 140

(c) (i) 211.5 cm (ii) 2.75 kg

2. 6 cubes

Page 146 ***Section 3.5***

(a) 55% (b) £19.20 (c) £252 000

Page 182 ***Section 4.1***

1. (a) (i) reflection in $y = -1$ (ii) enlargement scale factor 2, centre (0, 0)

(iii) rotation 90° clockwise, centre (0, 0) (iv) translation $\begin{pmatrix} -4 \\ 3 \end{pmatrix}$

(c) $\begin{pmatrix} 6 \\ 10 \end{pmatrix}$ (d) $\begin{pmatrix} -1 \\ 2 \end{pmatrix}$ (e) $\begin{pmatrix} 1 \\ -2 \end{pmatrix}, \begin{pmatrix} -1 \\ 2 \end{pmatrix}, \ldots$

Page 204 ***Sections 4.3 and 4.4***

1. (a) 3300 cm^2 (b) 48 cm (c) 17·8 cm

2. (a) Question 1 may produce a large number of answers which would be difficult to analyse. Question 2 is easier to analyse.

(b) Add further options and possibly add a question where people can say what they do not like about living there.

Page 269 ***Sections 5.1 and 5.2***

1. (a) 63.0°, 60·3° (b) 5.31 cm (c) 7.99 cm (d) $25.0\,\text{cm}^2$

2. (a) (i) $x > 5$ (ii) $x \leqslant 7$ (b) 2

(c) region between $y = 1$ and $y = 7$ with unbroken lines (d) 4, 5, 6

Page 292 ***Sections 5.3 and 5.4***

1. (a) (i) $\frac{1}{8}$ (ii) $\frac{1}{2}$ (b) $\frac{y}{x+y}$ (c) 0.95

2. (a) (i) $4, -\frac{5}{3}, -\frac{1}{4}$ (ii) yes (b) (i) grad. −2, int. 3

(ii) grad. 3, int. 2 (c) (i) grad. = 1, int. = 2 (ii) grad. = 2, int. = $-\frac{3}{2}$

Page 331 ***Sections 6.3, 6.4 and 6.5***

1. (i) perpendicular bisector of BC (ii) bisector of angle DAB

(iii) arc center C, radius 3 cm

2. (a) (i) $n = \frac{c-d}{a}$ (ii) $n = \frac{c^2 - a^2}{p}$ (iii) $n = \frac{u}{a}$ (iv) $n = h - a - b$

(v) $n = \frac{a-b}{a}$ (vi) $n = \left(\frac{x}{p}\right)^2$

3. (a) 3.9 cm (b) 3.75 cm

INDEX

Algebra, basic 12
Algebraic fractions 62
Angles, finding 106
Area 171, 183
Applying mathematics 78, 205
Arithmetic check up 1
Arithmetic progression 115, 221
Averages 34

Bar charts 164
Bearings 108
Bias 202
Bisector of a line 314, 318
Bisector of an angle 318
Brackets 13, 44
Bounds of accuracy 129

Calculator words 8
Changing the subject 319
Circle 187
Compound measures 307
Cone 190
Congruence 23
Conjectures 203
Connect the transformations 287
Construction 23
Correlation 85
Crossnumbers 102
Cumulative frequency 42
Cylinder 183

Data collection 198
Decimals (fractions and percentages) 11
Density 310
Diamonds and triangles 286
Drawing 3D shapes 132

Equations, linear 18, 46, 63
Errors in measurement 129
Estimation 123
Exclusive events 277
Exponential graphs 70, 170
Exterior angles, polygon 31

Factors 4, 21
Find the letters 10
Finding a rule, formula 115
Foreign currency 310
Fractions 56
Frequency distribution 36
Frequency polygon 38

Games 324
Geometric sequences 223
Geometrical reasoning 26, 106
Gradient 280
Graphs, drawing 303
Graphs, interpreting 166

H.C.F. and L.C.M. 176
Hidden words 153

Indices 64
Inequalities 263
In search of pi 288
Interpreting charts and graphs 164
Intercept on y-axis 281
Inverse proportion 7, 226, 229
Isometric drawing 132

Line of best fit 86
Listing possible outcomes 275
Locus 314
Long multiply and divide 11

Mathematical reasoning 285–292
Mean 34, 37
Möbius strip 104
Multiples 4

Negative numbers 9

OR rule, probability 278

Parallel and perpendicular lines 284
Pascal's triangle 245
Percentage change 138
Percentage, reverse 142
Pie charts 164
Plane of symmetry 136
Polygons 29
Prime numbers 4
Prisms 183
Probability 179, 270
Proof 288
Proportion 6, 224
Puzzles 53, 102, 152, 243, 298
Pyramid 190
Pythagoras 109

Quadratic sequences 120
Quadrilaterals 26
Questionnaire design 198
Quiz 302

Radius, finding the 187
Range 34
Ratio 6, 325
Reciprocal graphs 172
Recurring decimals 60
Relative frequency 270
Reverse percentages 142
Rounding 123

Scatter graphs 85
Sequences, finding a rule 115, 221
Sets 174
Significant figures 124
Similar shapes 324, 327
Simple interest 332
Simultaneous equations 212
Speed 307
Sphere 190
Standard form 71
Statistical problems 187
Stem and leaf diagrams 35
Surds 238

Transformations 111, 158
Translation 158
Travel graphs 169
Trial and improvement 89
Trigonometry 247–262

Vector 158
Venn diagrams 174, 179
Volume 50, 183, 190
$y = mx + c$ 280, 282